GEOGRAPHY
IN THE TWENTIETH CENTURY

GEOGRAPHY IN THE

A Study of Growth, Fields,

Edited by

WITH CHAPTERS BY

CANADA

KENNETH HARE, DONALD F. PUTNAM, GEORGE
TATHAM, GRIFFITH TAYLOR, J. WREFORD WATSON,
A. L. WASHBURN

CZECHOSLOVAKIA

JIŘÍ KRÁL

POLAND

JERZY KONDRACKI

NEW YORK:

LONDON:

TWENTIETH CENTURY

Techniques, Aims and Trends

GRIFFITH TAYLOR

THE FOLLOWING AUTHORS

UNITED STATES

ISAIAH BOWMAN, ELLSWORTH HUNTINGTON, KARL PELZER, J. K. ROSE, SAMUEL VAN VALKENBURG, STEPHEN VISHER, JOHN K. WRIGHT

ENGLAND

HARRISON CHURCH, CHARLES FAWCETT, E. W. GILBERT, DUDLEY STAMP, S. W. WOOLDRIDGE

PHILOSOPHICAL LIBRARY

METHUEN

PUBLISHED, 1951, IN THE U.S.A. BY THE
PHILOSOPHICAL LIBRARY, INC., 15 EAST
40TH STREET, N.Y.

AND IN GREAT BRITAIN BY METHUEN & CO. LTD.,
36 ESSEX ST., LONDON, W.C.2

CATALOGUE NO. 5264/U (METHUEN)

PRINTED IN GREAT BRITAIN

PREFACE

SO far as I am aware no book in English has yet been published which covers the ground exploited in the present volume. There are, of course, several on allied topics; notably the history of our discipline by Dickinson and Howarth, the review of Social Studies by Isaiah Bowman, and Hartshorne's *Nature of Geography*.

The Philosophical Library of New York is issuing a series of volumes discussing philosophical aspects of the various disciplines in the arts and sciences. The editor, responsible for two of these volumes, approached me with a view to producing a study of the growth, fields, techniques, aims and trends of geography. Characteristics of its evolution during the period since 1900 were specially to be described. After consulting some of the leading American geographers, and obtaining their support, I agreed to attempt the production of such a work. I am much pleased that Methuen's are publishing an English edition simultaneously.

As a result twenty geographers have busied themselves with the twenty-six chapters of the book; and with two exceptions they all belong to the Anglo-Saxon world. Seven of the authors are American, five are English, six are Canadian, and two are of Slav nationality. The editor may be described as somewhat cosmopolitan, since he has been associated for many years with universities in Australia, England, U.S.A., and Canada respectively.

GRIFFITH TAYLOR

UNIVERSITY OF TORONTO

v

CONTENTS

PART I

EVOLUTION OF GEOGRAPHY AND ITS PHILOSOPHICAL BASIS

PART II

THE ENVIRONMENT AS A FACTOR

PART III

SPECIAL FIELDS OF GEOGRAPHY

ILLUSTRATIONS

PART I

EVOLUTION OF GEOGRAPHY AND ITS PHILOSOPHICAL BASIS

The frontier where science and philosophy meet, and where the conclusions of one are handed across to be the premises of the other, should be taken as the vital centre in the wide realm of thought.

LORD SAMUEL

CHAPTER I

INTRODUCTION: THE SCOPE OF THE VOLUME

GRIFFITH TAYLOR

Griffith Taylor, born at Walthamstow, London, England, was educated at the Universities of Sydney and Cambridge. He was Senior Geologist in the British Antarctic Expedition of 1910–13; Head of the Department of Geography at Sydney 1920–8 ; Professor of Geography at the University of Chicago 1928–35; Head of the Department of Geography at Toronto University since 1935. He has written a score of books on geography, geology, meteorology, and anthropology.

PART I. THE IMPORTANCE OF THE ENVIRONMENT

THIS volume by twenty American, British, and European geographers is an attempt to answer questions which are engaging the attention of all geographers. What are the salient features of our modern geography? What are we trying to accomplish? How have our ideas as to what are the important fields of our discipline changed during the last fifty years? How do our studies touch the fields of allied disciplines? Have America, Britain, France, Germany, and the Slav nations and even Canada produced special contributions, determined in part by the somewhat different problems which engage the attention of workers in these distinct national fields? Broadly speaking, are there different schools of geographic thought which cut across national boundaries to some degree?

The introduction to such a composite study as is here outlined would seem to fall into two parts. Firstly it is necessary to give a brief survey of the development of geography in the last fifty years—though this will be covered in greater detail in many of the later chapters; and secondly it will be helpful to explain how the choice of the varied topics discussed in the score of chapters was arrived at. Needless to say no final answers can be given to all the questions posed above; but it is hoped that the authors involved will cover most of the fields in question, and their personal views will be advanced in their chapters. It is natural that the authors will take opposite sides in certain problems; as for instance in the broad question of Possibilism versus Environmentalism. The reader himself must be the judge as to which attitude in such cases seems to be the most rational. Certainly the editor has not tried to modify the conclusions of any writer; and indeed he is himself quite willing to be classed as one of those geographers who is to some extent tarred with the determinist brush.

It is often useful to adopt the heuristic approach in discussing a somewhat complex problem, i.e. we may examine the path followed by the pioneers in geography. In Fig. 1 a much generalized diagram illustrates the evolution of the various ramifications of geography in the early days of the subject; and some brief reference is made to those eminent workers who have done so much to advance our study. We may rapidly pass over the studies of classical and medieval times when many essays and books

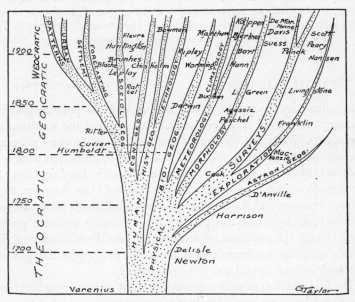

FIG. 1.—The Ramifications of Modern Geography since 1700. Note the shift from exploration to urban patterns

appeared in which the question 'How do the people live?' was answered more or less adequately, so that the study was almost purely descriptive. In the sixteenth century or thereabouts the development of cartography was so far advanced that a fair answer could be given to the question, 'Where do the people live?' It was not however till about 1770 that the invention of the chronometer by Harrison enabled this localization of places to be carried out with any accuracy. Accurate world-maps appeared for the first time after longitude could be ascertained with some exactitude as in the famous maps of Delisle and D'Anville.

Great navigators such as Cook and La Perouse added some of the last coastlines to the continents during the latter years of the eighteenth century. Franklin and Livingstone were two of the many who penetrated the unknown interior lands in the earlier years of the nineteenth century, and it is in this period of our history that modern geography had its beginnings. In the diagram (Fig. 1) I have suggested, by the thinning of the 'branch' concerned, that the essential principles of '*astronomical* geography' were known by about 1800. This is not to say that much work has not been done since that date, but it is not so new or fundamental as before 1800. So also the next branch '*exploration*' is shown to be dwindling in importance, since today—apart from the heart of Antarctica—there is no large area of the lands which is not charted in some detail.

We may I think agree to call Humboldt 'the father of modern geography'. He travelled through Central and South America from 1799 to 1804, while in 1829 he traversed Russia and Siberia. He described his travels and discoveries in some forty scientific volumes. He was the first to plot world isotherms, and to demonstrate man's dependence on his environment. He thus developed what I have been accustomed to call a '*Geocratic*' type of geography, which suggests that the earth (i.e. Nature) itself plays a great part in determining the type of life which develops in a particular area. No biologist would deny this, but many modern geographers seem disposed to deprive Nature of almost all claims as a factor in such matters.

Of course during the Middle Ages there was a strong tendency towards a teleological slant in all sciences, as was expounded by Roy and Butler (1736). In their opinion, an all-wise providence arranged matters with a view to the well-being of that privileged biped, *homo sapiens*. This point of view we may term the '*Theocratic*' aspect; and it was by no means wholly displaced by the disciples of Humboldt. Thus we find the historian Ritter (about 1820) using Humboldt's data in many of his books, which however had this theocratic slant. Guyot of Princeton advanced similar ideas as lately as 1873! It is perhaps not going too far to say that even today, when Nature and the environment in general is receiving such a drubbing at the hands of the 'Possibilists', who stress what one may term '*We-ocratic*' control, the theocratic approach is not altogether a thing of the past.

The second half of the nineteenth century was marked by the intense interest in evolution in plant, animal (and human) life. Darwin and many of the early biologists of his time placed the greatest emphasis on environment and environmental changes. It would be surprising if the young geographic science was not strongly affected. Accordingly we find Ratzel (1844–1904) developing the 'geocratic' or environmental approach

very strongly in Germany. This emphasis on causes was very characteristic of this period, and it was now possible to answer with some degree of
accuracy the question 'Why do people live as and where they do?'

The term 'geography' has been in use since the early days of the
Greeks. At first it naturally included all aspects dealing with description of
the earth and its parts. But gradually daughter disciplines branched off
from the parent stem. (For instance the term 'geology' was used about
1690 by Erasmus Warren in a book dealing with the Earth before the
Deluge.) As our diagram suggests it is possible to separate the physical and
human aspects of the subject to some extent, and most of the purely
physical aspects are moving further and further away from what is now
accepted as the 'core of geography'. Accurate surveys are so elaborate
today that they are taken over by specially trained surveyors and engineers.
Meteorology, with its close affiliation with dynamics and other branches of
physics, is still close to the borderland of geography; but was definitely
included in geography with its sister climatology a few decades ago. So also
geomorphology has a liaison position, some claiming it as essentially geology,
others as geography. The new science of geophysics seems to have little
liaison with geography, but to lie halfway between geology and physics.

Perhaps we may date the rise of a definite Human Geography towards
the close of the nineteenth century. Ratzel published his Anthropogeography
in the decade 1882–91; but in spite of the title, he gave little power to the
human factor in his relation of nature and man, and was most definitely a
determinist. Meanwhile the purely human aspects were being very closely
studied by the early sociologist Leplay about 1855, and we see here another
science (sociology) branching from the common geographical trunk. It
was natural that sociologists and anthropologists (who perhaps may be
dated from Prichard in 1843) should object strongly to the small part
played by man in the world scene as discussed by Ratzel. Especially would
economists and economic geographers object to any belittlement of man's
work on the earth. The latter school became prominent about 1862, when
Andrée's Geographie des Welthandels was first published.

At the beginning of the twentieth century geography was on a firm
footing in Germany and France, for Ritter held a chair at Berlin before
1870, while by 1886 there were twelve professors in Germany and about
the same number in France. At Oxford the first University teacher was
appointed in 1887 and at Cambridge in 1888. The United States lagged
behind somewhat, and the first Professor of Geography was appointed in
1900. The present writer occupied the first independent chair in Australia
in 1920, and the first in Canada in 1935.

Fundamentals of Geography

In a later chapter Dr. Tatham deals with the rise of a determinist outlook in geography. The conclusions of the early unscientific determinists —such as Buckle—were erroneous because they had no accurate data as to the environment, i.e. the climate, structure, geology, soils, &c. Moreover they dealt with the effect of environment on intangibles such as character and temperament. Even today such relations are quite uncertain. Very different is the picture now with regard to *material progress*.

The modern scientific determinist has an entirely different technique, and he knows his environment. Thirty years ago I predicted the future settlement-pattern in Australia (Fig. 55). At Canberra (in 1948) it was very gratifying to be assured by the various members of the scientific research groups there, that my deductions (based purely on the environment) were completely justified. This aspect of geography is *Scientific Determinism*.

In every branch of science we find specific differences developing as organisms spread into different environments. This is true in regard to the outlooks of exponents of geography in different parts of the world. Thus geographers in France, Germany, and England were dealing with areas for the most part fairly completely occupied by man. They were blessed with adequate detailed maps long before this was the case in such lands as the United States, Australia, or Canada. As a consequence there developed about the turn of the century a somewhat different feeling as to the main purposes of geographic research in the two contrasted areas, the Old Lands and the New Lands.

Vidal de la Blache taught in Paris from 1877 to 1918, and he developed the concept that the environment contains a number of *possibilities*, and their utilization is dependent almost entirely on human selection. This concept gave rise to the school of *Possibilists*. He realized the necessity for detailed synthetic studies in geography; and through his inspiration a number of regional monographs were published in the last decade of the last century. It is very important to understand that la Blache was dealing with the land of France—which some geographers are willing to accept as the best environment for all-round human development to be found on earth. What was the natural result of this environment, and of the plenitude of detailed maps of all parts of the country? Surely enthusiasm for the detailed study in the minutest particulars of all aspects of the human habitat, and the growth of a firm belief that man played the chief part in the development of the region.

Another somewhat psychological factor comes into play here too.

2

Although the emphasis on regional studies was soon stressed in Germany, yet the latter had been the birthplace of Ratzel's determinism. It is probable that there was a slight tendency of French geographers to swing to the other extreme and support very strongly the new 'regionalism'. To sum up we may say that a somewhat determinist approach fostered by the great advances made in the knowledge of evolution, was the characteristic of the latter part of the nineteenth century; but that in Europe in the next half-century the popular point of view, following Vidal de la Blache, Brunhes (and in Germany Hettner and Passarge) was the regional and possibilist outlook on geography.

What was the state of affairs in the first of the New Lands to develop a geographic outlook? Here in U.S.A. the population in 1900 was just half of what it is today, and the law of diminishing returns had hardly begun to operate. The greatest names in fields allied to those of geography were geologists such as Gilbert, Powell, Agassiz, and later William Morris Davis. It has been pointed out that early publications of the American geographers around 1900 consisted largely of morphological research, and regional studies were almost unknown. In those happy days the geographer discussed the structure and climate of a country, and then proceeded to show how man had spread through the land in response to these major environmental factors. Ratzel was honoured and Ellen Semple was his prophetess.

However, a younger generation of geographers was soon occupying the chairs of the main teaching institutions. As ever, as new ideas appealed to many of them, and accurate maps accumulated and detailed research was possible, the disciples of the possibilist and regional school became more and more numerous. The concept of the 'cultural landscape' rapidly spread throughout the United States. Some leaders went so far as to state that 'an *uninhabited* region can only be considered geographically in regard to its potential value to man'. They stated that the landscape as a whole is greater than its parts, and in this landscape the emphasis is to be laid on the changes due to man rather than on the original environment. Thus the regional complex must include both the natural and the cultural landscape; though to the writer the emphasis should be laid on the former.

Most geographers accept regional geography as the core of our discipline, and this aspect is discussed in later chapters. Sauer in his *Morphology of Landscape* (Berkeley, 1925) discussed the relations of systematic and regional geography much as in the following summary by L. S. Wilson.[1]

[1] 'Geographic Training for the Postwar World', *Geographical Review*, October 1948.

The Agent (culture) working on the Medium (natural landscape) through Time yields the Forms (habitation by type and group, population, land use and workshop, communication, population, density and mobility) of the Cultural Landscape. The cultural landscape is moulded from the natural landscape by the cultural group. The group is the active force, the natural area the medium in which the group works, and the cultural landscape is the final result.

In the same article Wilson makes a plea for a closer liaison between geography and allied sciences such as physics, geology, and botany. This aspect of geographic philosophy is pursued further in a final chapter in this volume dealing with Geopacifics. It seems to the editor that far more geographers have written voluminously about the *need* for liaison than have written texts to *illustrate* the virtues of such a pooling of results! May I venture to refer them to my tetralogy on Race, Nation, City, and Civilization. These volumes definitely attempt such interrelations.

The writer has no objection to most of what is implied in the preceding paragraphs emphasizing the landscape. He agrees that a vast amount of useful research has been done by the 'landscape gardeners' of geography, especially in those memoirs which emphasize the changing cultural pattern. Here Whittlesey has introduced the useful phrase 'sequent occupation' as an important feature of the cultural landscape. But I am of the opinion that we shall see a swing away from this 'micro-geography' to a broader point of view in the next decade or so. After all geography is the science of the *world*; and it is the understanding of the whole world that concerns us mainly. Those micro-geographers who oppose the older environmentalism are doing useful work in the unusually endowed regions where most of them work; in France, Germany, and the eastern United States. Let them however leave the less attractive portions of the world to the 'macro-geographer', who believes that the old controls of structure and climate are all-important in our efforts to make the most of our varied habitats.

I find that some geographers use the term *environment* to include *every cultural factor* which affects man. To use an extreme example, they would call the tobacco and chocolate—donated to us by kindly manufacturers in the Antarctic expedition with which I was connected—part of the explorers' environment. The American pioneer moving to the far west carried with him—as pointed out in a private letter recently—a hundred technological inventions due to man's intelligence in the last million years. These minor cultural accretions have little relevance, in my opinion, in a discussion of the importance of environmental control. Their field of study is *sociological* rather than geographical.

Geocratic versus 'We-ocratic'

Let us examine this idea of the difference between the habitats of the micro-geographers (who to some extent are possibilists) and macro-geographers (who are nearer environmentalists) somewhat more closely. One of the best studies of the broad capabilities of the world is the well-known memoir by O. E. Baker (*Geographical Review*, 1923) dealing with the arable lands of the earth. He assumed there were about 52 million square miles of land surface, for at that time the extent of Antarctica (some $5\frac{1}{2}$ million square miles) was not known. He estimated that only 10 million square miles are arable, leaving 47 million square miles as not likely to be of great importance for man's close settlement.

The writer has had extensive experience in three large areas of the world. Some of his earliest geographical publications dealt with the $5\frac{1}{2}$ million square miles of Antarctica. Is this to be completely ignored by the geographer, because in the phrase quoted above, its potential value to man is at present zero? Quite otherwise. It is an outstanding example of the fact that a very small knowledge of structure and climate is enough to demonstrate that the environment is all-powerful here, and that man has practically no say in the development of this huge region.

Let us turn to Australia—a land of 3 million square miles. For twenty years the writer was vilified because he stoutly maintained that the environment precluded any important settlement in 55 per cent of the continent. What is the use of talking of 'possibilism' in a region such as the arid centre of Australia? I quote from the writings of one of the leading American geographers—'Deserts may be transformed into garden spots by irrigation.' Such remarks, made without qualification, to my mind do far more harm than good. Applying them to Australia we find there that there is an area of $1\frac{1}{2}$ million square miles which needs more water. The total amount irrigated is less than 1,500 square miles, and I am unable to see how more than 3,000 square miles can ever be irrigated. We may conclude that irrigation may make a garden-spot of *one part in 500* of the desert, but this statement does not seem to support the opponent of environmental control very satisfactorily.

Finally let us glance at the Dominion of Canada for a moment. Here is an area of $3\frac{1}{2}$ million square miles, which the writer has divided into two divisions; firstly 800,000 square miles with a population of more than about one to the square mile; and secondly the remainder, some 2,700,000 square miles, which is practically empty. It is to be remembered that the whole of Canada was sufficiently known for us to estimate its major possibilities fifty years ago. Is the macro-geographer to cease to try to discover the best way to develop empty Canada—which in his opinion is along the lines of structure, climate, and soil—i.e. environmental control? In fine he is unwilling to agree that the possibilist approach is superior in the 80 per cent of the lands of the world of poor quality, for they are better understood by the older (in part) determinist approach.

I have been accustomed to refer to the ideas of the possibilists as the 'We-ocratic' approach, as opposed to the geocratic and theocratic systems mentioned earlier. I often wonder why there is so much opposition by many geographers to the concept of environmental control. One would think little of a doctor who spent ten years studying medicine, and threw his learning overboard, and practised according to the tenets of Mary Eddy Baker! Or of a lawyer who summed up his studies in the words of Bumble the Beadle, and loudly proclaimed that the 'Law is an Ass'! It is our special duty to study geology, structure, climate, soils, &c. and their effects on man. It is not our special duty to study all the ramifications of *man's* interests. We share this duty with the sociologist, economist, historian, medico, parson, &c. &c. Does not this suggest that it is the natural landscape— rather than the cultural landscape which is the prime factor! Far be it from me to belittle the cultural landscape, which has ever been one of the chief features of the writer's work; but he does hope that the present generation of young geographers will swing away from the 'we-ocratic' ideology towards the older 'geocratic' attitude; which is, in this writer's opinion, the one which most closely characterizes our discipline.

I have often used a familiar scene to illustrate the relation of nature to man in world geography. In any large city we see traffic moving along established routes, i.e. the main roads. The directions are completely established, but what is the function of the police officer at the crossing-places? He can block all traffic, he can accelerate the movement, or decelerate it at his wish, but he does not turn it out of the established routes. In nine-tenths of the world (and I am willing to agree the analogy is not so close in highly-endowed areas) man is like the traffic controller. Nature says, 'This land is too dry, or too cold, or too wet, or too rugged; there is very little choice as to what can be done with it.' Man can ignore the region, as in the case of Antarctica, or he can struggle along in a sparse pastoral occupation as in half of Australia, &c. He definitely has very little choice; and the extreme possibilists encourage those ignorant boosters, who are a menace to the scientific utilization of the almost empty—and very widespread—areas of the world. It is absurd to say that man can choose which he pleases among many possible directions. It is safer to adopt the concept which I have suggested above, which may be called 'Stop-and-Go Determinism'. We must learn the path clearly indicated by Nature. (The views of the Possibilist are given by Dr. Tatham on p. 128.)

Historical and Technocratic Aspects

The attitude of the younger progressive historians to environmental control has been expressed in an interesting fashion by J. H. Dales in the recent volume *Engineering and Society* (Toronto, 1946).

Individuals are not always masters of their own destinies. His way of life, his fortunes, and his happiness are to a large extent governed by 'forces' working in the society in which he lives. These forces may be of many varieties, geographical, technological, religious, or social. They all have one similar characteristic, however, namely, that they are of such magnitude and nature that they are commonly beyond the control of individuals. They thus work 'on' him.

The whole history of learning has been an attempt by man to change things so that forces, which formerly worked 'on' him, will now work 'for' him. To control, one must first learn. '*In order to master Nature*', said Francis Bacon, '*we must first obey her*' . . . The past, which history studies, yields many more facts than its students can handle. The historian therefore has to decide which facts to study. Early historians usually picked on a range of facts which they considered to be the most important—facts about kings, treaties, wars, church leaders, and military heroes. Because theories grow out of the facts which are studied, these early historians came to the conclusion that great men, their wars, and their diplomacy, were the forces which shaped history. Only in the last half-century (with some notable exceptions such as Karl Marx and Thomas Buckle, who wrote in the eighteen-fifties) have historians suspected that other less spectacular but more pervasive forces have been at work in society, and gone to the records to study another range of facts. They wanted to know what he did for a living, what his social habits were, and how these changed over time. A revolution in the study of history has taken place . . . and modern scholars draw our attention to the influences of such things as *geography, mechanical invention*, and *type of business enterprise* on the fortunes of society and 'the common man'.

Much of history may be looked upon as consisting of a series of strata one above the other in the time scale. Each stratum represents the product of the interaction of the whole environment upon the people at that particular time. Until relatively recent times this way of looking at history was little studied, for the obvious reason that very little was known of the environments of the past. An illustration of this sort of approach to history is afforded by the book *An Historical Geography of England*,[1] which seems

---

[1] Edited by H. C. Darby; Cambridge, 1936.

to be as fairly classed a history as a geography. The book is a symposium—in which each chapter is written by a specialist on the interpretation of a special period. The dozen authors are all geographers rather than historians.

In the volume *Engineering and Society* Dean Young of Toronto quotes with approval the opinion of the technocrat (in this case C. E. Inglis) on this same problem of environmental control. We learn that 'The commercial greatness of nations . . . depends entirely upon engineering enterprise.' The engineer who has spent his life in the study of technological improvements may perhaps be pardoned for this sweeping statement. But the geographer who takes a view of the world *as a whole* realizes that only 10 million square miles out of nearly 60 million square miles of the lands are capable of close settlement. He does not see the engineer making much impression on the 'greatness' of regions which nature has decreed shall remain almost empty. In Australia, as mentioned earlier, $1\frac{1}{2}$ million square miles need more water. The layman immediately thinks that the irrigation engineer will remedy this. So far irrigation has not ameliorated one-thousandth of the arid area, and it is difficult to see how the engineer can make any material alteration in the future.

It must however be admitted that many capable geographers belittle the importance of environmental control. A recent publication by my former colleague Robert S. Platt [1] expresses very definitely his attitude to this problem as follows: 'Environmentalism . . . appears to have outlived its usefulness, and to require extermination as an obstacle to better understanding.' I can only repeat that the difference between our views depends largely on the 'facts which we have decided to study' to quote Dales. I have spent a large part of my life studying the conditions affecting man in the immense areas of Empty Canada, the Sahara, Empty Australia, and Empty Antarctica. No geographer who has this experience could ignore the paramount control exercised by the environment. Granted that all these areas are in a primitive state of civilization where Bacon (unlike some of our geographers) realized 'that we must obey Nature', my point is that they will remain in much the same stage of development for many a decade to come, if not for ever. A sense of proportion should teach us that the geographer (who should surely study the world as a *whole* in his major conclusions) will err very considerably if he bases his philosophy on conditions which obtain in such progressive but restricted areas of the world as Western Europe and much of the United States, and ignores the real, *simple* and *direct* control by Nature in the larger part of the earth.

[1] 'Environmentalism versus Geography', *American Journal of Sociology*, Vol. LIII, No. 5, March 1948.

Stage and Environment

While the writer believes that Nature in large measure determines the plan, it is of course obvious that man is the agent whereby civilization progresses. He is of great importance, and as his technology improves he develops a region farther along the lines of the obvious plan. Thus the concept of *stage* in the plan must be kept in mind. This may be illustrated by an example which I discuss in my recent book *Urban Geography* (1948).

Every geographer will admit that there is a close similarity between the environments in eastern Algeria, western Spain, and the southern littoral of Australia. In Fig. 2 I have charted the relation of population-

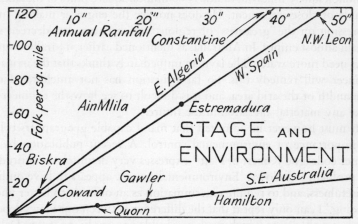

FIG. 2.—The diagram (based on the relation of Rainfall to Population) illustrates three stages in the logical development of the Mediterranean environment.

density to rainfall in these three allied regions. To my mind they suggest to some degree different stages in man's development of Nature's 'plan' for an arid 'Mediterranean' environment. Let us confine our attention at first to Biskra and Coward Springs. The Algerian town is about 150 miles from the Mediterranean, while the South Australian settlement is 450 miles inland.

Both lie on the edge of the desert in artesian basins, and have a winter rainfall of four inches. The covering of sparse but regular vegetation in each case is similar in pattern, though not in genera. Both have railways which have been running for many years, in the case of Coward Springs since 1890. When I visited Coward Springs in 1919 it was the chief settlement on the railway for fifty miles in either direction; yet there were only four houses, two of which were empty. (Given an excellent environment, such as at Chicago, a settlement might add a million to its population in the same period.)

Let us now see what has happened in the Sahara with a far lower standard of living and a far greater population-pressure. In spite of equally unfavourable environments, Biskra is an apparently flourishing town with about 10,000 inhabitants, of whom 2,000 are French. It is supported primarily by the date oases, but also by the French military station, and to a lesser degree it acts as a caravan terminus, and, in winter, as a tourist resort.

How does Biskra fit into our determinist-possibilist debate? When we think of the enormous length of the northern border of the desert, which extends about 2,500 miles from the Wadi Draa to Suez, it is clear that only a few districts are as favoured as Biskra. There is only *one* bygone 'Igharghar River' (i.e. that south of Biskra) with river gravels still carrying a little water; and probably no comparable artesian basin to that found at Biskra. Hence I should make use of our Biskra example as follows.

Given desert conditions such as obtain in the Sahara, there are only a very few sites where the ameliorating factors have justified modern enterprise as the French have developed Biskra. Even the military site was strictly determined by the water and the traffic conditions. The possibilist, it seems to me, puts the cart before the horse. He would say, 'Ah! but the vital trade in dates owes much to the artesian bores and to the desert railway, and surely these are due to human energy.' The determinist replies, 'Man can put down bores and build railways anywhere in the Sahara; but in the vast majority of cases he takes very good care to do so only where Nature has provided the conditions to make such expenditure worthwhile. In such exploitation Nature determines the route of development, while man determines the rate and the stage.'

To return to the parallel with Coward Springs in Australia, I see no sign of man utilizing this southern region yet. But when population-pressure has increased to something like that present in Algeria, then we shall find man in Australia developing the environment along much the same lines as Nature led him to do in Biskra. In the graph (Fig. 2) the relation is expressed approximately by a straight line for each of these regions. Spain and Algeria exhibit very similar conditions; and to the writer this indicates that the population-pressure is about the same in each. Southern Australia shows a much lower density of population for the same rainfall. (The natural result is that the standards of living are far higher in Australia.) But it is entirely possible that population-pressure in Australia will increase considerably as time goes on. Later on, the graph line for Australia will climb to a position much closer to those for Spain and Algeria, and man will follow *along much the same plan* determined by the common environment. The difference is not really due to human choice, but to the immature character of Australian settlement. Nature's plan is the same, the stages are different.

A further example may make clear what I mean by scientific (or Stop-and-Go) determinism. Demangeon has stated (p. 82) as an argument against determinism, that Australia has been changed out of all recognition, as the result of British settlement there. I cannot follow his argument here. The scientist can determine pretty closely *today* what may happen, for instance, to the half million square miles or more of desert Australia. At present·a few hundred miserable aborigines live there by precarious hunting. In the next stage of development Nature may allow ranchers to graze a few thousand stock there during specially good seasons. The third stage would be for an exceedingly wealthy rancher to dig waterholes ('tanks'), and so somewhat increase the usefulness of the area. (This has happened at Mutooroo.)

Nature's plan is obvious, and only the stage of development depends on man. Surely it is the character of the environment which should interest the geographer, so that he can best follow the plan 'determined' by Nature. Moreover, whatever man does in such a region, it will make little difference to the nation as a whole; since in better-endowed districts the stages of development will still keep far ahead of what he is doing in the 'deserts'. It is my firm belief that centuries hence the deserts of the world will still be deserts; and man will have shown that he has had the good sense to use the better areas, which Nature has determined shall be worth his attention. Much the same argument applies to the vast areas of semi-desert and precarious croplands of the world. Only as applied to such fortunate regions as Europe and Eastern U.S.A. (where most of my opponents live) are the arguments of the 'possibilist' at all convincing. These two paragraphs summarize what I mean by 'scientific determinism'.

Geography and Education

So far I have been dealing largely with the philosophic aspects of our discipline. But there is another side to geography which should not be neglected, and that is its great value as an educational subject. Most folk learn history, not because they are going to be professional historians, but because of its great value to them in understanding their place in life. Geography should play a still greater part in their education, for in a sense it is the 'history of today'. It is concerned with many of those factors which dominate the actions of *living* folk. It is the topmost and most interesting of those 'life strata' which in the aggregate make up the history of a country. I venture to repeat some remarks which I made in an address at Cambridge in 1938 on this aspect of geography.

If we look back at the relation of education to the four major divisions of knowledge, the Physical, Biological, Social Sciences, and the Humanities—we see a most interesting evolution. First of all in the fourteenth century the protagonists of the new 'Humanism' waged a bitter fight against the Church and the Schoolmen. In the end the modernistic views of the humanists won, and we call this period the Renaissance. Next, around 1600, the physical sciences were damned by the leaders of reaction, only to emerge triumphant in their turn. Some eighty years ago the biological sciences, in the persons of Darwin and Huxley, advanced truths which were anathema to the orthodox. Few educated folk attempt to oppose these truths now. But today the social sciences are challenged by the forces of reaction. I will only instance the perverted use of anthropology and sociology to advance the views of some of the totalitarian nations; and though they have been defeated we shall find the same dogmas flourishing among fascist-minded folk for a long time to come. We geographers can do yeoman service—as I see it—to clarify some of these issues, if we teach tolerantly and scientifically what is becoming known as Cultural Geography.

This liaison aspect of geography is best brought out by a diagram which I first used twenty years ago (Fig. 3). It suggests that the field of geography (the large circle) contains eight subdivisions, which in turn are linked with eight major disciplines. Thus geography links the four 'environmental sciences' of geology, physics, astronomy, and botany with the four 'human sciences' of history, anthropology, sociology, and economics. There are vast uncharted areas on the borders of regional geography which merge into the eight subjects specified. In the centre of the large circle is charted a map of the world, with the continent of North America placed in the centre. This may be taken to indicate that our research should be directed towards the problems of our own folk primarily. It also suggests that the geography of regions is our prime objective, but that the liaison with the other sciences must not be lost sight of.

Among professional geographers the great majority will always carry on the vital work in the central fields; but we may hope for Raleighs, Drakes, Hawkins, and Dampiers, who will explore far afield and extend our realms. They will perchance trespass on other empires, and doubtless some competitive historians and anthropologists will call them buccaneers and pirates. Dropping metaphor, I firmly believe that by applying techniques learnt in the realms of geography, biology, and geology—and carried across to anthropology, history, and sociology—such pioneers will ultimately earn the respect of the leaders in the 'purer' social sciences. But

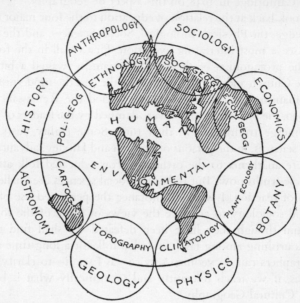

FIG. 3.—Geography correlates the specified branches of the four 'Environmental' Sciences with the four 'Human' Sciences. (*Partly after Fenneman.*)

I must caution any piratical young geographer who cruises in strange waters that his reward, if any, will probably be a posthumous one.

In conclusion I cannot do better than quote the opinion of the British publicist Lord Samuel which is somewhat as follows:

Science in modern times can be trusted to look after material things, but philosophy and religion are still in the melting pot. The frontier where science and philosophy meet, and where the conclusions of one are handed across to be the premises of the other, should be taken as the vital centre in the wide realm of thought.

This is surely somewhat the position of the 'liaison subject', geography.

REFERENCES CONNECTED WITH THE INTRODUCTORY CHAPTER

1. E. C. Semple, *Influences of Geographic Environment*, New York, 1911. Based essentially on Ratzel's teaching.
2. Jean Brunhes, *Human Geography*, Chicago, 1920. Stresses the possibilist approach to geographic philosophy.
3. P. Vidal de la Blache, *Human Geography*, New York, 1926.

3a. W. M. Davis, 'Progress of Geography', *Ann. Assoc. Amer. Geog.*, Lancaster, Pa., 1924.

4. Lucien Febvre, *Geographic Introduction to History*, New York, 1925. Devoid of maps, and not very objective.

5. Isaiah Bowman, *Geography and the Social Sciences*, New York, 1934. Indispensable in the present study.

6. Dickinson and Howarth, *Making of Geography*, Oxford, 1933. Short but useful volume, mostly concerned with data before 1800.

7. Richard Hartshorne, 'Nature of Geography', *Ann. Assoc. Amer. Geog.*, Lancaster, Pa., 1939. Two large volumes with philosophical treatment.

8. Roderick Peattie, *Geography in Human Destiny*, New York, 1940. Interesting. 'The author dare not claim to be an environmental determinist, but cannot entirely exclude such a philosophy' (p. 52).

9. Various authors, *Education for Citizen Responsibilities*, Princeton, 1942. Hartshorne and Taylor discuss geographic matters.

10. Griffith Taylor, his four volumes dealing with *Race* (1937), *Nation* (1936), *Cities* (1949), and *Civilization* (1946); and the two volumes on *Australia* (1940) and *Canada* (1947) stress the paramount importance of environment especially in pioneer and empty lands. See also the Presidential Address, *Annals of American Geographers*, March, 1942.

PART II. SCOPE OF THE PRESENT VOLUME

When I was asked to edit a volume bringing together the ideas of geographers regarding the philosophical aspects of their discipline, considerable thought was expended in deciding the topics to be discussed and the authors responsible for the same. I consulted a few of the older generation of geographers—and I found that they agreed that such a book was likely to be of considerable value, and that they were willing to write sections dealing with the subjects in which they were authorities. Thus Isaiah Bowman agreed to discuss Pioneer Settlement, and Ellsworth Huntington some aspect of the borderland geography to which he has contributed so much. They in turn made a few suggestions as to writers to be invited to join in the symposium.

The contents seem to fall into three sections: The first is mainly historical, and the editor succeeded in obtaining authoritative chapters discussing the rise of geography as a whole—and of the special schools in England, France, and Germany. I had hoped to have studies from three or four Slav countries—but my friends who tried to make contact with Russian and Jugo-Slav scientists received no replies to their queries. The reports from Czechoslovakia and Poland should be all the more welcome.

The second part of the book discusses general environmental topics such as topography, climate, and soil. A discussion follows of characteristic regions in the varied world pattern, such as Pioneer Lands, especially in polar and tropical regions. Two chapters describe geographical factors in a closely-settled area like Great Britain.

The third part is concerned with more general topics of world-wide application, such as aviation, fieldwork, and political, social, and racial problems. Sections dealing with the great importance of government and private institutions, and with the hope that geopacifics may promote world peace, close the volume.

Before commencing the study of progress in geography during the twentieth century, it seemed advisable to devote one chapter to the evolution of geography before that period. Professor Tatham has been lecturing on this field for a number of years. He devotes some pages to geography as practised by the Greeks and by the writers in medieval times. Then he summarizes the volumes by Cluverius and Varenius which appeared around 1650. New discoveries in science led to the remarkable progress in Germany which began about 1750. The two Forsters were worthy pioneers, basing their work on extensive travels. Of all the philosophers Kant has had most influence on geographic thought. Ritter and Humboldt however laid the foundations of German geography; and Dr. Tatham gives a number of illuminating quotations from their works, and contrasts their viewpoints. A period of confusion was followed by the outstanding contributions of Frederick Ratzel. The chapter closes with a brief reference to pioneers in France, U.S.A., and Britain.

The research of distinguished French teachers has been studied for a number of years by Mr. Harrison Church, who has had the advantage of some years of work at the Sorbonne. He points out that the early French research was of a 'gazetteer' type, but this was changed with the advent of Vidal de la Blache. Regional geography is perhaps the most characteristic field in French geography. Human geography owes more to de la Blache and Jean Brunhes than to any other pioneers, and the French school has had worthy successors to these forerunners.

Church points out that the French have been much less interested in political and economic geography. Physical geography, however, owes much to de Martonne for his text of 1909, and to many of his publications of later date. It is of interest that during the recent Nazi occupation of France many studies in this somewhat non-controversial field have been published in France.

The later progress of German geography is covered in the chapter by Samuel van Valkenburg. He studies the period since 1900 in various divisions, giving the name of the Golden Age to the decade of 1905 to 1915. Albrecht Penck was the leader at this time, and William Morris

Davis was also teaching in Germany. Hence physical geography received most attention. In the World War period we see a number of books akin to Naumann's *Mittel Europa* appearing, and Kjellen (a Swede) began to teach geopolitics. After the First War the Germans devoted much attention to political geography, and the *Zeitschrift für Geopolitik* appeared. Van Valkenburg shows that the geographers of the day were not so much pro-Nazi as lukewarm during this early phase. In the period from 1925 to 1933 there were many expeditions and investigators in all parts of the world; and often they were supported by party funds. After Hitler came into power there was a rapid deterioration, and a great deal of attention was given to the concept of 'Raum', in which the right of Germany to dominate the 'Space' available was stressed. During the last Great War those in authority gave much less attention to geographic research than did the United States, though the *Forschungsstaffel* changed this in the closing years.

Two short accounts of the growth of Slav Geography come next in our volume. Professor Král of Prague describes the work of geographers in Czechoslovakia, a country of special historical and geographical importance. The order in which the various branches of our discipline were developed will interest western readers, who have laboured under less strenuous conditions. Czechoslovakia is at the 'cross-roads' of Europe, but as Dr. Král points out, it has interchanged ideas with Poland and Jugo-Slavia, though its geography is mainly based on the work of western teachers.

Dr. Král kindly interested Dr. Kondracki of Warsaw in the present volume. The latter has recently published a valuable atlas of Poland. His account brings home to the western world the disorganization of scientific research due to repeated invasions by enemy forces. Nevertheless a large body of valuable work has been accomplished by Polish geographers since 1900.

One of the chief sections of the book deals with the opposition between those who believe strongly in environmental control, and those who minimize its importance. Dr. Tatham in Chapter VI describes the work of early writers such as Montesquieu and Ritter—who explained the character and temperaments of nations in terms of climate, &c. Humboldt held much more judicious views on these problems. Buckle however dashed in where scientists, today, fear to tread; and his views are now generally discredited. The ideas of Demolins and Ellen Semple are explained at length. Dr. Tatham then points out many weaknesses in this early determinism, and describes the rise of possibilism in France. The views of Brunhes and Bowman are discussed, and some attention is paid to Taylor's belief in 'Stop-and-Go' Determinism.

In the second part of the book I have collected those chapters which show in some detail how environment affects human interests. The three major factors are perhaps topography, climate, and soil. Professor Wooldridge's book[1] on geomorphology is very well known.

In Chapter VII Professor Wooldridge discusses progress in geomorphology, and gives much credit to the work of early American students. The views of Davis and Baulig on the erosion of valleys are described, and some space is given to Walther Penck's contribution to this study. The later views of Kirk Bryan and D. W. Johnson are referred to. One interesting section deals with the dating of the peneplains, and much recent work in England is concerned with this topic. The arid cycle and the work of Passarge and of Kirk Bryan on deserts is described; as also is that of Steers and Lewis on coastlines. The chapter closes with some reference to the liaison between geology and geography as demonstrated in the south of England.

Turning now to climate—the second of the environmental elements —there are two distinct branches of the subject, meteorology and climatology. The former of these is rather moving away from geography into the realm of physics, but the liaison is quite close still. Professor Hare is one of the younger geographers whose knowledge was utilized in the recent war, and he has contributed an interesting chapter. The shift from isobaric maps to air-mass maps is described. The new weapons of research, radio-sonde and radar, have greatly improved our knowledge of meteorology; while he has much of interest to tell us about the evaporation factor, and the possibilities of rain-making.

Few American geographers of today have contributed as much to climatology as Professor Visher. In this volume he discusses climatic influences on man from various points of view. He then takes up the climatic elements—temperature, humidity, wind, rain, floods, clouds, &c. and shows how increased knowledge enables us to cope with these aspects of the environment. His own detailed study of the climate of Indiana is called upon in illustration of this section. He concludes by some reference to new methods of graphing climate by researchers such as Koeppen, Huntington, and Thornthwaite.

The importance of pedology (soil-science) is only just being realized in many geographical schools. Its origin in Russia rather than in the West partly accounts for this. Professor Putnam's work on the soil surveys of Canada is well known, and he has given us a valuable summary of the work of Dokuchaev and other Russian scientists before Hilgard, Whitney, and Marbut began their classic studies in U.S.A. Putnam discusses also the

[1] Wooldridge and Morgan, *Physical Basis of Geography*, London, 1937.

progress in soil-classification and soil conservation. He emphasizes the new trends towards the study of soil series and land-types.

The world pattern is very complex, and certain types merit special study. The research on Pioneer Regions by Isaiah Bowman has produced several notable volumes, and in his chapter he describes a number of features of interest to all geographers. He commences by discussing the apparent 'closing of the frontier' in the United States, and then passes to the important series of pioneer studies in Canada which he initiated in 1928. In Australia also the views of Abbott and Taylor are quoted at length. The role of the native is illustrated in Rhodesian and Brazilian settlement.

Many other factors of note are described, such as the role of government in pioneer problems, especially as regards defence and emigration. The conditions of pioneer life have changed in each generation, as Bowman points out in some very illuminating paragraphs. He concludes his important chapter with a section warning the geographer against loosely-compiled maps of pioneer lands. Charts showing density of population are probably not so useful in pioneer studies as those which distinguish different systems of production.

Two special areas in the world-pattern surround the Poles. Dr. Washburn as head of the Arctic Institute has had a long experience in high latitudes. He gives us a comprehensive account of the chief features of Arctic life in the New World. Climate, topography, and techniques of travel are all discussed. Especially interesting is his description of the shift from sledges to tractors, and from sailing ships to ice-breakers and aeroplanes. The recent expansion of research stations in Canada and their contributions to meteorology, magnetism, and other sciences complete a very informative study.

The Antarctic regions have a unique position in geography, since they have been the major field of exploration since 1900. Accordingly the editor has contributed a chapter on exploration in which the exploits of Scott, Shackleton, Mawson, Byrd, and others are narrated briefly. Here as in the North there has been a great change in the technique of exploration; but more emphasis is laid on the growth of our knowledge of Antarctic structure and glaciology due to the work of David, Gould, Priestley, Wright, and others.

Passing to the other extreme of the world-pattern the book would not be complete without a study of tropical settlement. We owe this to the pen of Karl Pelzer—well known for his research in the East Indies. He discusses the rise of nationalism in the so-called subject colonies, and the plans of various nations (such as Britain in Africa) for improving the

3

living conditions of under-privileged native communities. He contrasts slave-labour and modern plantation labour, and describes the migrations of labourers to seek work in much of Africa. His opinions as to true 'white' settlement—by European families in the humid tropics—are of special value. The latter part of his chapter deals with modern attempts to wipe out tropical diseases.

In the more densely settled areas of the world geographical research is found indispensable in a number of fields. Two well-known geographers contribute chapters on Regionalism and Land Utilisation. Mr. Gilbert surveys the development of practical regional divisions in France, Germany, Spain, United States, and especially in Britain. He suggests fifteen of these regions, and discusses where the regional capitals are likely to develop. Various maps illustrate his descriptions.

Dr. Stamp shows how the need for a planned economy after the First Great War, led to the development of the remarkable land-use maps for which he was so largely responsible. The immense amount of work done by volunteer geographers is very inspiring to research folk in lands not yet blessed with a series of vital base-maps. Within a year or two land-use maps were available to the public—and County Reports accompanying the maps were even more valuable.

The technique of classifying the various types of land is described at some length, and the major principles by which the maps are interpreted are discussed. It was decided that good croplands should be conserved for food production, and Dr. Stamp explains how these categories were arrived at. His general conclusions with regard to Optimum Use and Multiple Use will be read with interest by all students of Economic Geography.

In the third section of the book a number of topics of a general nature are considered. Ellsworth Huntington discusses the effect of aviation as a geographic factor. He concludes that it will tend to bring about one general type of civilization—but will lead to increasing contrasts between various parts of the world. Free trade must be more widely adapted in an air age, but accidents are likely to be more frequent in travel. He does not agree with the general belief that travel across polar areas will increase greatly. His speculations as to the sources of future power-alcohol suggest new uses for the tropical grasslands. He closes with a warning that widespread aviation may lead to a considerable diffusion of dangerous diseases.

In Chapter XVII Dr. Putnam points out that geography is preeminently a practical subject. He discusses the value of field-work in rural and urban areas, and describes a number of techniques which he has found to be most useful. Field-record codes are to be commended, while facility in sketching should be encouraged. In the laboratory the various types of maps to be studied are mentioned, and the need for drawing block diagrams in the study of geomorphology is emphasized. Notes are given as to the culture-patterns to be investigated. The chapter closes with advice as to the use of isopleth maps and of aerial photographs.

Few British geographers have given more attention to Political Geography than Professor Fawcett. His chapter deals with Geography and the Empire, and he traces the concept of empire from medieval days to the present time. He shows that a great empire must be based on a nuclear area of sufficient population and resources. Spain, France, and Britain are considered at length from this point of view.

The rivalry of France and England is discussed in terms of their power resources, and the importance of the Industrial Revolution and of technological improvements are emphasized. His chapter closes with a brief study of the 'Giant States' of U.S.A. and U.S.S.R.; and he explains his belief that Western Europe is still the key region in world politics.

Man has spread over the earth in various major stages. Far back in prehistoric times human groups were tribal, and it is likely that the biological classes which we call races were fairly distinct. Later with the development of civilization much smaller societies developed. Today the urban group is characteristic of our Occidental way of life.

The distribution of races is still a vital factor in world affairs, as witness such terms as the Yellow Peril, White Australia, Non-Aryan, &c. &c. Unfortunately few geographers and fewer laymen understand the criteria which determine race, or the conditions which have led to their distribution. In Chapter XIX Griffith Taylor summarizes the growth of Racial Geography, and demonstrates how the use of isopleths of racial distribution has almost completely altered former ideas of racial relationships. Racial mixing akin to that occurring between 'white' and 'yellow' races has been taking place in Europe throughout our whole history without evil consequences. Race prejudice is found to be in general due to complete ethnological ignorance.

The importance of social aspects of geography is stressed by Professor Watson. As research is devoted more and more to the purely *physical* side it can be handled competently by the geologist or exponent of natural sciences. He discusses at length the differing implications of human, functional, and natural regions; using the research of LePlay, Geddes, Mumford, and others in support of his arguments. The geographer differs from the sociologist since he stresses patterns rather than processes. A brief study of the social geography of Hamilton (Ontario) illustrates his field of study.

In Chapter XXI Griffith Taylor discusses the evolution of cities, from hamlets, through villages and towns, to the largest type which Mumford calls the Megalopolis. After a brief historical introduction, the early work of Geddes, Jefferson, Haverfield, and others is discussed. Using his Zones and Strata technique he shows that we can deduce the evolution of early urban types by studying conditions far from the centre of culture today. He describes a Cycle of City Growth comparable to the Cycle of Normal Erosion put forth by William Morris Davis. To the geographer the site factor is one of the most significant, and this is described with a number of examples. Certain characteristic features of mining, tourist and shrine centres are also briefly discussed.

Progressive national governments have always included many workers in geographical fields in the civil services. In time of war the number increases rapidly. John K. Rose has been engaged in geographical research at Washington for a dozen years. He traces the growth of research from 1894, when there were only two geographers at the capital, to 1945 when there were 500 on the Federal payroll. The activities of private institutions near the capital are described, and the opportunities for employment offered to young geographers are set forth in various economic, carto-graphic, and regional fields.

John K. Wright, Director of the American Geographic Society, con-tributes a valuable study of the nine leading geographic societies of Britain and the United States. He describes the growth of such institutions in a historical summary. Geographical societies may be essentially constituted of laymen or professionals. Their fields are concerned chiefly with research or with education. But in addition to publishing journals and books they exercise much influence by conferring honours, and in some cases by assisting professional geographers to obtain positions. Exploration and cartography have been greatly promoted by some of these famous societies. Dr. Wright also discusses political aspects of the research carried out by the various types of society.

In the last chapter Griffith Taylor discusses the rise of Geopolitics, at first on the continent due to the writings of Kjellen, Haushofer, and others. In England Mackinder was the chief exponent, and in U.S.A. Weigert, Dorpalen, Whittlesey, and others. In the two latter countries this branch of geography is of course not studied as a means to military conquest.

The youngest branch on the geographic 'tree' is Geopacifics. This term means the study of all types of geography with a view to promoting World Peace—and is based on the recent volume by the editor (*Our Evolving Civilization*). Geographers could do more than other teachers to prevent war, if they would extend the education of students in the field of cultural geography. We learn by 'patterns'; and geography is emphatically the discipline which can instruct mankind objectively and visually as to the problems of our troubled world.

A glossary of seven hundred geographic terms will, it is hoped, be found convenient by many students of geographic literature.

CHAPTER II

GEOGRAPHY IN THE NINETEENTH CENTURY

GEORGE TATHAM

George Tatham—Associate Professor, Department of Geography, Toronto. Graduated B. A. Liverpool University 1929, M.A. 1932. Lecturer in the Department of Geography, University College, London, 1930–2. Commonwealth Fellow, Clark University, 1932–4; Ph.D. (Clark) 1934. University of Toronto, 1939.

Classical Geography

SCIENTIFIC GEOGRAPHY as we know it today is the product of the nineteenth century, or more precisely of the hundred and fifty years beginning about 1750. It was during that period that the great formulators (Kant, Humboldt, Ritter, Peschel, Ratzel) defined the scope and content of the subject and elaborated the method of collecting, organizing, and presenting its material. But the science is very much older; its roots extend far back into antiquity. The earliest records of man's interest in the nature of the physical world around him contain observations and speculations of geographical type. No science can claim a longer genealogy than geography.

In the ancient world geography grew out of three closely related activities: exploration, which led to the accumulation of facts about the earth's surface; charting and mapping of the areas known; and speculation about the material collected. All the early civilizations of the Near East were interested to a greater or lesser degree in the first two, but speculation was almost a monopoly of the Greeks and consequently it is them that we look upon as the first geographers.

All the main branches of geography were established by the Greeks. Mathematical Geography developed by Thales (*c.* 580 B.C.), Anaximander (611–547 B.C.), and Aristotle (384–322 B.C.), reached its zenith with Eratosthenes (Alexandria 276–194 B.C.). The sphericity of the earth was proved, its size computed from surprisingly accurate measurements. The latitude and longitude of many places were calculated and the practice of plotting world maps on a grid was begun.

Physical Geography progressed less rapidly. Various writers speculated about the phenomena of weather, tides, and vulcanism. A correct explanation of the Nile floods was advanced, the formation of deltas was studied, and Polybius (210–128 B.C.) even pointed out how streams slowly

28

eroded their valleys. Posidonius (135–50 B.C.), the most outstanding physical geographer, investigated tides at Gades, measured the depth of the sea off Sardinia, and sought to discover the origin of the Crau gravels.

Theophrastus (born c. 370 B.C.), a pupil of Aristotle, wrote a history of plants. He examined the relationship of plants to climate, and compared the vegetation of the Macedonian lowland with that of the adjacent mountains and that of the island of Crete. This was the beginning of Plant Geography. The human aspects of geography, with the exception of historical geography, were not studied so systematically. Still, many interesting observations were recorded. Agarthacides (170–100 B.C.) classified the Ethiopian tribes according to their diet, and Posidonius gave an accurate description of the mountain folk of Galicia and Asturias.

Herodotus included much valuable geographical material in his history, though he rarely handled it scientifically. Polybius on the other hand is remarkable for his scientific use of geographical facts in historical writing. He argued that 'what man wants to know is not so much the fact that a thing took place, as the way in which it happened', and with this aim constantly in mind he always endeavoured, for example, to relate strategy to the build of the country. In his works are many excellent descriptions of town sites. Finally in the work of Hecataeus of Miletus (520 B.C.) who wrote a general survey of the inhabited world on a regional basis, we have the beginning of Regional Geography.

This promising start ended almost abruptly with the decline of Greek political power. The Romans lacked the scientific mind, they were more practical than philosophical in outlook. They were primarily concerned with commercial and administrative problems and plans for military conquest. Military campaigns and extension of trade routes particularly into Asia, produced much new data but little attempt was made to organize it scientifically. Most of the writers were concerned with itineraries, or topographical dictionaries. Two workers are however outstanding, and both of these it is interesting to note wrote in Greek.

Strabo (63 B.C.–A.D. 36), the first of these, summarized the geographical knowledge of his time in seventeen volumes. He recognized the intrinsic value of geography. For him it was not merely an aid in the task of government, it had individual importance because it 'acquaints us with the occupants of land and ocean and vegetation, fruits and peculiarities of the various quarters of the earth and marks him who cultivates it as a man earnest in the great problem of life and happiness'. Strabo was a regional geographer. Ptolemy (Claudius Ptolemius of Alexandria, 150 A.D.), the other important figure, was concerned primarily with Mathematical Geography. His great work *Geographike Syntaxis* dealt with projections, gave tables of latitude and longitude and calculations of the varying length of day at various distances from the equator.

The well known *Historia Naturalis* of Pliny and *De Chorographia* of Pomponius Mela, were of little scientific value compared with the above-mentioned works. However, since they were written in Latin they had considerable importance in early medieval times. With the spread of anarchy that accompanied the collapse of Roman authority in the West, the geographical knowledge of classical times gradually faded from the mind of European man. The medieval period was on the whole, one of retrogression.

Trade, always a stimulus to geographical thought, continued it is true, but it clung to the old routes, and deprived of the protection of a central authority gradually dwindled. The missionary who carried the gospel into Abyssinia, China (Nestorian), and the remoter parts of north-west and northern Europe, replaced the trader and explorer and pushed back the boundaries of the known area, but geography benefited little. The prevailing cast of mind was indifferent to the scientific investigation of nature. Pilgrims visiting holy shrines, or making the long trip to the Holy Land, travelled 'reverently prepared for further wonders' (Beazley), and it was the wonders seen with the eye of faith that they reported on their return.

Early Medieval Geography

Much the same attitude is evident in the works of Fabulist writers like Solinus (third century A.D.) whose aim was to 'astound and amuse rather than instruct' (Beazley). A few such as the Ravennese geographer (mid-seventh century A.D.) concerned themselves with statistics and strove to give facts and figures about every country, enlivened by strange stories and fables. It is the work of the Cosmographers, however, which shows most clearly how much ground had been lost. These scholars (e.g. Cosmas Indicopleustes) tried to give pictorial form to their conception of the universe, but in doing so worked exclusively from a basis of faith not reason. Their outlook was purely theological; the statements of Job in their eyes were far more valid than the views of the classical, heathen writers. Their world maps, though extremely decorative, bore no relation at all to actual facts.

The Carolingian Renaissance marks the end of this recession and a return to more scholarly research. Starting in the eighth century the renewed study of Greek revived much of the forgotten learning. But the classical spirit of inquiry was not revived. The Renaissance remained a religious movement, more concerned with preserving the knowledge of the past than expanding it through scientific investigation. Compared with this decay in Christendom developments in the Moslem world, though in themselves not very considerable, stand out in sharp relief. Many factors conspired to stimulate Moslem interest in geography.

First there was the immensity of the Arabic Empire which stretched over so many different areas from the Atlantic to the borders of China; then the excellent system of roads, a legacy of Rome, and the desert routes which encouraged movement and facilitated the pilgrimages to Mecca demanded by the faith. Trade which arose naturally out of the diversity within the Empire was further stimulated by the high rank of the trader in Moslem society, a result of the promise of Mahomet, himself a trader, that in the Day of Judgement the honest Moslem trader would stand alongside the martyrs of the faith. This too had influence on geographical study. Most important of all, however, was the conquest of Syria, Persia, and Bactria, where Greek culture, sprung from the seeds scattered by Alexander, still flourished and gave to the Moslem the rich fruit of Greek learning.

Moslem Geography, significantly enough, did not develop until after the founding of the Abbasid Dynasty (A.D. 766), when the Caliphate was transferred from Damascus to Bagdad and Persian culture with its strong Greek imprint, triumphed over Arabic. Greek science was the starting-point. The works of Aristotle and Ptolemy were most assiduously studied. It is not surprising therefore that Mathematical Geography received the most attention. The very clear atmosphere of the desert and semi-desert region, by favouring astronomical observations, may share some of the responsibility for this bias.

Accurate calculations of latitude and longitude were made, and there were several attempts to ascertain the size of the earth. Surprisingly such calculations did not bring about any marked improvement in cartography. Sea charts based on a cylindrical projection seem to have had merit (Vasco da Gama spoke highly of them), but land maps were distorted by the love of ornamentation. Descriptive geography on the other hand flourished. Under the patronage of the Caliph excellent regional descriptions of India and Arabia were published, and the works of Idrisi (the most voluminous writer) are still remarkable for the scientific handling of a wealth of regional detail.

On the whole, however, Beazley considers that the development of a real science among the Arabs was hampered by the over-refined state of the language, and the love of story-telling which caused the mingling of oriental fancy to be interwoven with geographical and historical fact. Nevertheless the Arabs did keep Greek learning alive, and it was from their hands that Europe received it as the Dark Ages drew to a close.

The transition from medieval to modern geography was not accomplished early in the Renaissance nor was it achieved quickly. Much preliminary work had to be done so that the new outlook only gradually entered into geography. From the middle of the fifteenth century explorers had pushed back the limits of the medieval world. Columbus, Vasco da Gama, and their successors brought back a bewildering mass of new facts, which was quickly made accessible through the compilations of Hakluyt, Ramusio, and de Bry. These new facts had to be charted. Efforts to do this with the greatest possible accuracy initiated a development in cartography that attained its zenith in the maps of Gerhard Kremer (Mercator, 1512–94) and Abraham Ortelius (1527–98).

Cluverius and Varenius

Simultaneously attempts were made to rewrite the old geographies. The first efforts were mainly compilations of old and new data, but gradually a new style appeared which found expression in the early seventeenth century in two formative works which are generally considered to mark the end of the transition from the medieval and the beginning of the modern period. The first, an *Introduction to Universal Geography* by Cluverius, a German writer, was published posthumously about 1626. It starts with a brief and inadequate account of Mathematical Geography, and then passes on to a regional description of the countries of the world which occupy four-fifths of the whole. It is these excellent descriptions which Cluverius wrote as an aid to the study of history that give the work its importance. They set a standard in regional geography that for long was unsurpassed.

More influential however in the development of geographic thought was the work of Varenius. His *Geographia Generalis* published in 1650 was the first geography to include the new theory of the universe. So deeply had the mathematical work of Copernicus, Kepler, and Galileo impressed Varenius that he defined geography as a branch of mixed mathematics and rebuked those who would limit it to a description of the various countries. To Human Geography he grudgingly conceded a place in 'Special Geography', the second of his two major divisions of the subject, but apologized for doing so, and explained its inclusion as a concession to custom.

General or Universal Geography, his first major subdivision, was the only one with which he dealt.[1]

This he divided into three parts:

Absolute—the terrestrial part, in which the earth as a whole, its form, size, &c. were discussed.

Relative or planetary part—concerned with the earth's relation to other stars.

Comparative part—giving a general description of the earth, the relative location of places on the surface and the principles of navigation.

His early death (aged twenty-eight) prevented the completion of the work. All we have of his Special Geography is the definitions and its subdivision into:

Celestial properties—including climate.

Terrestrial properties—description of the relief, vegetation, and animal life of the different countries.

Human properties—a description of the inhabitants, trade and government of the countries.

Geography in the Eighteenth Century

The century after Varenius witnessed no advance in scientific geography itself. Interest was focused on the natural sciences. This was the period when the prodigious mass of empirical knowledge, accumulated to a large extent under the guidance of the Scientific Academies, was organized on systematic lines. The work of such investigators as Dampier (1723), Halley, and Hadley, supported by the increasing mass of temperature and rainfall records from all parts of the world, established meteorology as a separate science. In 1780 the Mannheim Academy of Meteorology was founded. A parallel development connected with the names of Stené (1667), Woodward (1665-1728), Strachey (who published the first geological cross-section in 1719), James Hutton (1726-97), and William Smith laid the basis of geology.

Appreciation of the beauty of the Alps had been aroused by the writings of Rousseau, and this led to a revival of scientific interest in mountains. Before the end of the eighteenth century studies of mountain

---

[1] *Geographia Generalis* (the most remarkable work that appeared before the time of Ritter) was translated into many languages. Newton arranged for an English edition for the use of his students, and it remained a standard work for over a century.

structure and origin (Pallas, 1777, de Saussure, 1740–99), of their climatic and vegetation belts (Wildenow 1792) and of the characteristics of glaciers had all been published. Physiographic research of this type was facilitated by improved methods of representing relief on maps. Hachures came into use in 1676, contours in 1728. Similarly, improvements in the compound microscope (1650) opened new fields of inquiry in the biological sciences.

Systematic study of botany began with John Ray (1627–1705). In 1735 Linnaeus published his famous empirical classification of plants. Corresponding, though somewhat later, developments in zoology were marked by the appearance of Buffon's (1707–88) *Natural History of Animals*. Anthropology lagged behind the natural sciences. Nevertheless significant advances were made particularly in physical anthropology (Camper and Blumenbach), and comparative philology. Of more immediate importance to geography was the work of Achenwall (1748) and Süssmilch (1747) in the statistical study of population, and of Montesquieu and Herder who focused attention on the effect of nature on man.

Such unprecedented expansion of knowledge paved the way for a new advance in geography. The light thrown on the nature of the physical and biological phenomena by the natural sciences made it possible by the middle of the eighteenth century to give a more scientific description of the earth's surface than ever before; and at that very moment the problem of man's place in nature, as to whether or not the earth was a stage purposefully created for the development of man and his culture, made such a description urgently necessary.

Equally important was the growing desire for some synthesis of the data produced by the systematic science. 'The Natural Sciences had once again reached a point where scattered detail work craved a living conception of nature as a whole' (Windelband). These circumstances revived interest in geography and at the same time gave it a higher status.

Previously a utilitarian attitude had prevailed. Geography was only of value for the light it could cast on historical events or for its aid in the science of government. Even as late as 1807 Pinkerton, the English geographer, whose writings had a great vogue both at home and on the continent, could categorically state 'Geography like Chronology only aspires to illustrate History'. Now faced with new tasks and a rapidly increasing mass of subject material the restricting bond with history was snapped. Geography took its rightful place as an independent science and 'from being the servant of history rose to be its teacher, indeed endowed with prophetic vision it had the power to foretell the future' (Peschel, *Geschichte der Erdkunde*, p. 805).

The securing of this independence we owe to German scholarship. Hitherto Germans had contributed little. 'The best that German geographers could offer was reflected light, information derived from British and French research,' writes Peschel in his discussion of the period before the eighteenth century; 1754, the year when Büsching's *Neue Erdbeschreibung* was published, marks the end of this inferiority and the opening of a new era. For the next 150 years geography was almost a purely German science, indeed right up to the opening of the present century all the most significant developments were the work of German scholars.

The first new geographies for which Büsching provided a pattern were purely descriptive. 'My aim', wrote Büsching, 'is to produce a description of the known surface of the earth.' Almost no attempt was made to explain facts, or seek for causal relationships, the sole aim was to make the description as accurate as possible.

Political units were chosen as the basis for regional description, a procedure encouraged by the extensive use of the statistical material provided by Achenwall and Süssmilch, and later by the great national censuses. The work was therefore no different from that of the old masters such as Strabo; Büsching's only contribution lay in his insistence on the critical handling of all source material and the setting up of a high standard of accuracy.

Geographers of this so called 'political-statistical school' (e.g. Mentelle) developed the art of regional descriptions as far as was possible within the rigid, artificial, statistical framework Büsching had used. But the political fragmentations of the eighteenth-century Germany made it very clear that a healthy development could not be expected until geographers discarded the strait-jacket of state boundaries.

Leyser, among others, had pointed this out as early as 1726, and advocated the use of natural boundaries. Such criticisms had no practical results, however, until it was reinforced by the teaching of Buache (1700–73) on the framework of the globe (*Charpente de Globe*). According to Buache the skeleton of the earth was simply a number of basins separated by a continuous line of mountains and submarine ridges. This theory had been elaborated a century before by Athanasius Kircher but ignored. Now it was revived and given a certain graphical expression in the accurate contoured relief maps such as the one Buache constructed for his study of the English Channel (1737). Geographers were quick to respond. This continuous mountain line seemed to offer a stable natural alternative to the man-made shifting frontiers of political units. Gatterer (*Abriss der Geographie*, 1775) used the new boundary to divide the world up into natural divisions. It is in his work we encounter for the first time such expressions as the Pyrenean Peninsula, Baltic Lands, Carpathian Lands, West, South, and North Alpine Regions. Gatterer did not make a clean break with the politico-statistical geographers. The natural classification of regions (Vol. 2) was followed by a description of political units (Vol. 3) after the fashion of Büsching, though in a much abridged form. Nevertheless his work started the trend towards Pure Geography (*Reine Geographie*).

Hommeyer carried the concept to its logical conclusion. He abandoned political boundaries altogether, and divided his areas into 'terrains', natural regions which were in most cases river basins. He claimed that his *Reine Geographie von Europa* (1810) justified the attribute 'reine' since it explained nothing; 'it simply furnishes a view [*Ansicht*] of the present form [*Gestalt*] of the earth's surface and its parts, and a picture of the size, position and connection of the natural regions' (*Zusammenhang der natürlichen Länder*).

Zeune (Gäa, *Versuch einer wissenschaftlichen Erdbeschreibung*) worked on much the same lines. He rigorously separated historical material from the geographical; where regional description called for historical data he summarized it in a preliminary section. River basins were his natural units too, but he drew attention to the tendency for plants, animals, and even men within such basins to acquire special features, so that mountain ridges besides being water divides were natural boundaries for plants, animals, and human types. Following this line of thought, he sought to discover the inter-relationships of plants, animals, and men and to define his subdivisions of the earth's surface by reference to several factors (climate, vegetation, &c.), not just relief.

J. R. and J. G. Forster

Quite apart from these two schools of geographical thought (Politico-statistical and 'Reine' Geography) was the brilliant contribution of the two Forsters. Johann Rheinhold (the father), accompanied by his eleven-year-old son (Johann George), visited the Volga steppe in 1765 at the invitation of the Russian Government to investigate the problem of settlement. Seven years later they both accompanied Cook on his second voyage to the South Seas (1772–5). Johann Rheinhold's observations on this voyage were published in England in 1778.

Forster approached geography from a practical standpoint. His interest arose solely from his direct contact with a variety of natures in various parts of the earth, and his contribution is the method he adopted in the treatment of the data he collected. Endowed with keen powers of observation and a scientific attitude of mind he collected facts, compared and classified them, drew from this classification generalizations for which he then sought a causal explanation. His systematic treatment of material is well shown by the classification of his observations in the South Seas. These were published under six headings, Earth and Land, Water and Ocean, Atmosphere, Variations of the Globe, Organic Bodies (Animals and Plants), and Mankind.

Over and above this careful scientific method Forster's work is remarkable for its contribution to human geography. He recognized the close tie between man and his environment, and though not the first to do so, he was one of the first to attempt to explain it, seeking a solution of a mechanistic type. In particular he drew attention to the mobility of peoples and the frequent necessity of seeking the explanations of their physical and cultural characteristics by reference to an earlier environment. His descriptions of the South Sea Islands contain analysis of settlement, of the density of population, and the relation between the density and the resources of the environment which commanded the respect of geographers even as late as Ratzel.

Writers in methodology have all paid tribute to the quality of Forster's work. Plewe[1] calls him 'the first great German Methodological geographer in the modern sense'. Peschel describes him 'as the first traveller, who gave a physical survey of the section of the world he had seen and who was the first to perform the highest function of a geographer, namely, that of scientific comparison' (p. 494).

Johann George, the son, though highly gifted, has less importance as an innovator. Yet during his lifetime he was more honoured than his father. This was partly due to a more congenial personality, and partly to his outstanding literary ability, added to the fact that he was often given credit for the excellence of his father's *Observations* which he translated into German (1783). A further reason was his relation with Humboldt. Humboldt met him at Göttingen in 1789 and the acquaintance ripened into a lifelong friendship which had a profound effect on Humboldt's development. In many places Humboldt has expressed the debt he owed 'to the distinguished teacher and friend whose name I can never mention without a feeling of heartfelt gratitude' (*Cosmos*, Vol. I, p. 327).[2]

In contrast to this repeated eulogy of Johann George, Humboldt rarely mentions Johann Rheinhold with whose work he was of course familiar and with whom he corresponded. This undoubtedly had some

---

[1] E. Plewe, 'Untersuchungen Über den Begriff der "Vergleichenden" Erdkunde', *G. F. Erdkunde*, Berlin, 1932.

[2] See also letter to Heinrich König, July 28, 1858, p. 92 : Bruhns and Lassell.

bearing on the greater contemporary fame of the son. It is, however, only in comparison with his father that George Forster's fame seems exaggerated. His own contribution was notable quite apart from the publicity he gave to his father's research.

He was the 'first writer who awakened the love and feeling for the beauty of scenery' (Peschel, p. 493), and his sensitive descriptive style set the standard for Humboldt. By his own work such as the regional account of the Lower Rhine area (*Ansichten von Niederrhein*) 'he founded more securely his father's method and prepared the way for a systematic development of regional geography' (Plewe).

Kant's Contribution

The last important figure in eighteenth-century geography was the great philosopher Emmanuel Kant. Kant lectured on Physical Geography in the University of Königsberg from 1756 to 1796, during which period he gave the course forty-eight times. In contrast to J. R. Forster, Kant was an armchair geographer. His interest in Physical Geography was not stimulated by actual experience of the variety of nature in different parts of the earth, it arose through his philosophical investigation of the whole field of empirical knowledge.

For this reason Kant's contribution was more philosophical than Forster's, since it consisted of his definition of the nature of geography and its relationship to the natural sciences. This definition given in the introduction to his lectures describes so completely the scope of geography that it has affected directly or indirectly all succeeding methodological discussion. One can go further and say that confusion about the aim and content of geography has almost always only appeared when Kant's analysis has been ignored.

In recent times, particularly through the work of Hettner in Germany and Hartshorne in the United States, Kant's views have been given fresh currency, and from them has been derived the most generally accepted concept of geography. The following summary of Kant's introduction has therefore more than historical interest.[1]

Knowledge, his argument begins, is obtained either by the exercise of Pure Reason, or through the senses. Sense perceptions are of two kinds, those perceived by the inner and those by the outer senses, and together they furnish the whole of man's empirical knowledge of the world. The world, as perceived by the inner senses, is Soul (*Seele*), or Man (*Mensch*)

[1] The discussion is based on D. F. T. Rink's version of Kant's *Physische Geographie*, 1802. Kant's *Werke*, Band IX, Berlin and Leipzig, 1923.

(i.e. the Self); as perceived by the outer senses is Nature. Anthropology (Kant uses Anthropology in the modern sense of Psychology) studies the Soul or Man; Physical Geography (*Physische Geographie oder Erdbeschreibung*) studies Nature. Physical Geography is thus the first part of knowledge of the World (*Weltkenntnis*), indeed it is the essential preliminary (*Propaedeutic*) for understanding our perceptions of the world.

It is necessary that our experiences should not be merely an aggregate but that they should be organized into a systematic whole. Just as before building a house one must have a concept (*Idee*) of the whole from which the various parts can later be derived, so it is necessary before studying the World to have a concept of the whole, an architectonic frame from which the manifold details can be derived. Physical Geography provides such a framework for the study of Nature.

Knowledge of the world requires more than just seeing the world. He who wishes to draw what is useful from his travels must previously have planned his travel, not just observed the world with the external senses (p. 157). . . . If we are prepared beforehand through education—then we have already a whole—a frame of knowledge [*Inbegriff von Kentnissen*] that teaches us to know man. Only then are we in the position to assign each experience to its place in the whole. Through travel one expands one's knowledge of the outer world, but this is of little use if one has not been prepared by education (p. 158).

Since every person's experience is limited both in time and space, each one must supplement his personal experience with that of others, always taking care to examine thoroughly the reliability of what is borrowed. Such borrowed indirect experiences are of two kinds; they are either a narrative (*Erzählung*) or a description (*Beschreibung*). The first is a history (*eine Geschichte*), the second a geography (*eine Geographie*).

Empirical knowledge, furthermore, can be classified in two ways, according to a concept (*Begriff*) or according to distribution in time and space. Classification according to concepts is a system of nature (*Systema Naturae*) such as that of Linnaeus; that according to time and space is a physical classification and gives us a geographical description of nature.

In classifying cattle to put them first among quadrupeds and then in the subdivision of this general group, those with cloven hooves, is to classify them according to a system one has made in one's head; it is a logical classification, a *Systema Naturae*. 'The *Systema Naturae* is, moreover, a register of the whole where I place all things each in its appropriate class, even though on the earth they are to be found in different, widely separated places.'

In contrast to this method of rational classification stands the physical classification, the geographical description of nature, which considers

4

things according to the place in which they occur on the earth. Thus the crocodile and the lizard, which are basically the same animal, differing only in size, would in a System of Nature be classified together. Yet they are found in very different parts of the earth, the crocodile in the Nile, the lizard on land and over a wide range of latitude. In a geographical classification this difference would be recognized for 'above all we consider here the scene of nature, the earth itself and the regions where things are actually found', not as in a system of nature, similarity of form.

History as well as geography may be called a description, but history is the record of events which follow one another (*nacheinander*) in time, geography is a report of phenomena that occur next to each other (*nebeneinander*) in space. Together they comprise the whole of our perceptions (i.e. Empirical Knowledge).

History, since it should record all that has happened in different periods, is nothing more than a continuous geography, hence it is a great imperfection in history if one does not know in what place something happened, and what quality (*Beschaffenheit*) it has thereby acquired.

Then follows an argument to prove that a true Natural History (*Naturgeschichte*) is impossible, all one can have is a Natural Description (*Naturbeschreibung*), since a complete Natural History would have to record the full account of the development of things through all time since the beginning of the world, for which data are not available.

Next Kant poses the question, Which was in existence first, history or geography? and decides geography has existed at all periods and is the substructure of history, for events must always have occurred in a certain setting. As the changes recorded by history took place, however, they brought into being a new geography; thus if there is an Ancient History, so there must also be an Ancient Geography, which helps to make clear the events of history.

Of these many geographies that of the present is the one we know best and it serves many purposes. For example, common sense is related to experience, but experience cannot be extended to any considerable degree without a knowledge of geography. Many people are indifferent to newspaper reports of current events because they have no overall picture of land and sea and the total surface of the earth, and so do not know how to use such information.

Peruvians are in a way simple since they put everything that is offered to them into their mouths. This they do because they do not understand how they could use it more suitably. Those people who do not understand how to use information given in newspaper reports because they have no place for it, are like these poor Peruvians, if not in the same at least in a similar condition.

Physical Geography is, then, a general outline of nature (*ein allgemeiner Abriss der Natur*) and constitutes not only the basis of history but also of all other possible geographies.

These other geographies Kant defines as:

1. Mathematical Geography—which treats of the form, size, and movement of the earth, and of its position in the solar system.

2. Moral Geography—which discusses the different customs and characters of men, e.g. examines the contrast of Oriental civilizations where parricide is a most fearful crime, with customs in Lappland where a father, if wounded, while hunting, expects his son to kill him.

3. Political Geography—the study of the relationships between political units and their physical background. For example, in ancient Persia two states existed whose mutual independence arose from, and was assured, by the Kerman desert which divided them.

4. Commercial Geography—which examines the reasons why certain countries have a superfluity of one commodity while others have a deficiency, a condition that gives rise to international trade.

5. Theological Geography—which studies the changes theological principles undergo in different environments (*Boden*). For example, one would make a comparison of the form of Christianity in the Far East with that in Europe, and of the variation of Christian beliefs in different parts of Europe.

Finally Kant concludes with the statement, 'The need for this study is very extensive. It provides a purposeful arrangement of our perceptions, gives us pleasure and provides much material for friendly discussion.'

Compared with the introduction, Kant's lectures have little importance. Though entitled Physical Geography they include, in conformity with current usage, the distribution of plants, animals, and man. The treatment of animals is particularly detailed and not very geographic, the discussion being divided into sections headed, 'those with hooves', 'those with cloven hooves', 'those with webbed feet', 'quadrupeds that lay eggs', &c.

He refers to the interaction of man and environment but does not expand the theme. Likewise he points out the necessity of studying the variations of nature that give each land individuality, but makes no attempt to do so in the regional section (Part 3). These descriptions are extremely slight and in fact contain nothing more than one could expect from the title: *A summarized consideration of the most important natural curiosities, of all lands arranged geographically*. Certainly they betray no signs of being influenced by Forster's work and they make no contribution to the development of regional geography.

Viewed as a whole the work of the late eighteenth-century geographers is very notable. Academic controversy between Politico-statistical and Pure Geographers levelled the barriers of traditional thought and opened the way for fresh, unimpeded advance. The Forsters demonstrated a method of research and a literary style, while Kant clearly defined the field. The foundations were thus securely laid, on which during the next fifty years the edifice of scientific geography arose. This great task of formulation is associated with two men, Alexander von Humboldt and Karl Ritter, and the period during which they worked is justly looked upon as the Classical Period in the evolution of Geographical Thought.

Karl Ritter

Karl Ritter was born in 1779. He received his early training in a school in Schnepfenthal near Gotha, where the teaching was based on the principles of Rousseau and Pestalozzi. It was there his interest in geography was awakened. One of the aims of Pestalozzi's system was to arouse enthusiasm for nature, and pupils were trained to make accurate observations during long country walks.

Space relations were also emphasized. Scholars were taught to observe the relationships of things in their immediate vicinity; the school, then the school yard, then the home region, the boundaries of the area surveyed being gradually expanded until they embraced the whole world. Interest in foreign lands so aroused was further sharpened as in the case of Humboldt,[1] by the drawing of maps. A schooling of this type was almost ideal for a geographer.

At seventeen he entered the university of Halle. There he studied mathematics and philosophy, and later history and natural science. His college days over, he accepted the post of tutor to the family of a rich Frankfort banker, and remained in that employment for twenty years. His first publication, Europe, a Geographical, Historical and Statistical Painting,[2] appeared in 1804. Two years later he published six maps of Europe, followed by a number of papers in Methodology.

[1] The reedy shores of the Caspian Sea as I viewed them from the delta formed by the mouths of the Volga, are certainly not picturesque, yet the first sight of this vast inland sea of Asia yielded me great delight from the fact that in my youthful days I had drawn its outline on a map. The tastes first awakened by the impressions of childhood and moulded by circumstances of after life, often become when imbued with the deep earnestness of later years, the incentive to scientific labour or to great enterprises (Humboldt, Ansichten der Natur, 418 (Bohn. ed.)).

[2] Europa, Ein Geographisch-Historisch-Statistisches Gemäldes. für Freunde und Lehrer der Geographie, Vol. I, 1804; Vol. II, 1807.

In 1817, while in Göttingen where the elder of his pupils was attending university, he published the first volume of the *Erdkunde*.[1] This dealt with Africa. Volume II on Asia appeared a year later.

These works made a great stir. He was appointed Professor of History and Geography in 1819 at the Gymnasium of Frankfort, but at the end of twelve months he resigned to become the first Professor of Geography at the newly founded University of Berlin.

There he spent the rest of his life teaching, writing, and directing the affairs of the young *Gesellschaft für Erdkunde* (founded 1828), which he served as President with very few breaks until his death in 1859.

In 1827 Humboldt, whom Ritter had met twenty years before, returned from Paris and settled in Berlin. The two men became firm friends and from their professional intercourse derived mutual stimulus to which both have paid tribute.

A clear exposition of Ritter's approach to geography is difficult because his voluminous writings often lack clarity and precision of expression. His early works state an unequivocal position, but as his ideas developed 'the clear basic principles become cloudy', his methodological statements become more complicated and at times seem almost at variance with the practice adopted in the *Erdkunde*. For this reason Ritter has frequently been misunderstood, and later scholars have attributed to him varied and often conflicting opinions.

It is now generally agreed that Ritter's position cannot be established by reference to any particular methodological paper, nor even by reference to his methodological writings as a whole, but only by a survey of his entire work. This opinion seems well founded in the light of the fact that Ritter's ideas were continually evolving, and there is every indication that he himself never considered that they had been given their final shape.

Ritter rejected Gatterer's and Hommeyer's idea of Pure Geography. His concept, somewhat akin to that of Zeune though much broader and logically more consistent, was formed early, as the preface to his first publication (*Europa*) shows. There he states his objective to be

to present a living picture of the whole land, its natural and cultivated products, its natural and human features [*derMenschenwelt und Naturwelt*], and to present all these as a coherent whole in such a way that the most significant inferences about man and nature will be self evident, especially when they are compared side by side.[2]

---

[1] *Die Erdkunde im Verhältnis zur Natur und zur Geschichte des Menschen oder allgemeine vergleichende Geographie*. The second edition was published in nineteen volumes, 1822–59.

[2] Quoted by Plewe, p. 30.

Later he remarks, 'The earth and its inhabitants stand in the closest reciprocal relations, and one cannot be truly presented in all its relationships without the other. Hence History and Geography must always remain inseparable. Land affects the inhabitants and the inhabitants the land.'[1]

When one compares these extracts with Hommeyer's definition of Pure Geography (given six years later) as 'nothing other than a general description of terrain', or with his statement quoted above (p. 36), one can see the gulf between Ritter and his contemporaries.

Contemporary ideas he discussed in a paper in 1806, and condemned them on the ground that geography must do more than merely describe, 'its aim is to acquaint man with the scene of his activity, therefore it is a description of this scene not in itself but in its relation to man.'[2]

Geographers' preoccupation with description Ritter attributed to the unfortunate appellation 'Erdbeschreibung' (geography). 'Erdkunde', he suggested, was a more fitting name for scientific geography. This he used in the title of his major work, and in defining it wrote 'Erdkunde should strive to embrace the most complete and the most cosmical view of the earth, to sum up and organize into a beautiful unit, all that we know of the globe', and to show the 'connection of this unified whole with man and his creator'.[3]

These excerpts make it clear that for Ritter geography was centred on man; its aim was to study the earth's surface from an anthropocentric standpoint; to seek to relate man and nature and to see the connexion between man and his history and the ground on which he lived. Thus a dynamic element entered his teaching, 'he saw he must not just describe the earth's surface and subdivide it into natural regions, but he must understand it as the fundamental cause of events' (Ursache von Geschehnissen).[4]

As regards method, Ritter followed Forster's lead and strove to develop geography as an empirical science. Careful accumulation of observations was the first essential. 'The fundamental rule which should assure truth to the whole work is to proceed from observation to observation, not from opinion or hypothesis to observation.'[5]

[1] Quoted by Plewe, p. 30.   [2] Ibid., p. 32.
[3] Dickinson and Howarth, p. 152.
[4] A. Penck, Neue Geographie Sunderband der Zeitschrift der Gesellschaft für Erdkunde zu Berlin, 1928, p. 31.
[5] Erdkunde, Vol. I; quoted Hartshorne, p. 54.
The Nature of Geography—A Critical Survey of Current Thought in the Light of the Past, R. Hartshorne (First Edition, 1939; Second Edition, 1948).
This is one of the most scholarly geographical books ever published in English. In

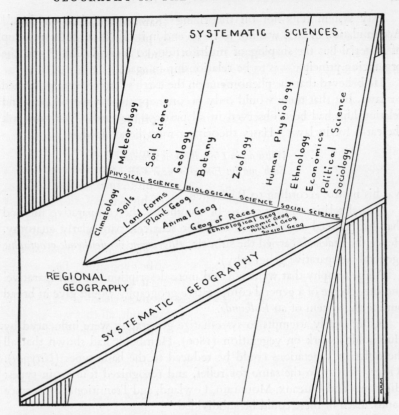

FIG. 4.—A diagram suggesting the special character of geography as an integrating science cutting a cross-section through the systematic sciences, rather than bordering on them. (*After Hettner, on page 323 of Hartshorne's* Nature of Geography.)

this chapter frequent reference is made to the early sections which summarize the development of geography in the nineteenth century. Readers interested in studying further the trends of geographic thought in the twentieth century will find stimulating discussion of most of the problems involved in Hartshorne's book along with a comprehensive bibliography. The following list of chapter headings indicates the scope of his book.

    I Introduction
   II The Nature of Geography According to its Historical Development
  III Deviations from the Course of Historical Development
  IV The Justification for the Historical Concept of Geography as a Chorographic Science
   V 'Landschaft' and 'Landscape'

(*Footnote continued on next page.*)

'My system rests not on theorizing [*Räsonnement*] but on facts.'[1] Accumulation of facts was not to be an end in itself, 'Not the heaping up of material but the shaping of multiformity to individuality',[2] and the organizing principle was to be relationship in space.

He believed that the phenomena on the earth's surface were governed by laws, but that these would only become apparent when all facts and relationships had been observed in all parts of the earth. 'We must ask the earth for its laws.'[3] Hasty theorizing must be avoided,

> *Willst du in Unendlichkeit schreiten*
> *Such' nur im Endlichen nach allen seiten*

was his motto, according to Richtofen.

Causal relationships were to be sought by the comparative method that had proved so successful in other sciences, particularly anatomy. Hence the *Erdkunde* carried the subtitle, *Allgemeine vergleichende geographie* (general comparative geography).

All geography that went beyond mere description was 'comparative' and the scheme of a general comparative geography would give in broad outline the system of an *Erdkunde*.

Ritter's early attempts to systematize geography were influenced by Humboldt's work on vegetation (1806). Humboldt had shown that all the different vegetations could be reduced to the basic types (*Urtypen*). Ritter tried to do the same for relief, and recognized four main types: Highlands and Plateaux, Mountain, Lowland, and Transitional or Terrace Lands. Each of these could be subdivided.[4]

Although not very satisfactory he used this classification in his regional studies. Later this comparative method of seeking causal relations was chiefly applied in the study of regions in the attempt to distinguish natural units, area that would possess individuality.[5]

VI   The Relation of History to Geography
VII   The Limitation of the Phenomena of Geography to Things Perceived by the Senses
VIII A Logical Basis for the Selection of Data in Geography
IX   The Concept of the Region as a Concrete Unit Object
X   Methods of Organizing the World into Regions
XI   What Kind of a Science is Geography?
XII   Conclusion: The Nature of Geography

[1] Letter quoted by Plewe, p. 35.
[2]   ditto
[3] *Erdkunde*, Vol. I, p. 4; Hartshorne, p. 55.
[4] See Dickinson and Howarth, p. 156.
[5] In this regard note Hartshorne, p. 57, where Ritter's definition of geography as the study of '*Der irdisch erfüllten Räume der Erdoberfläche*' is expanded into 'the

The concept of regional individuality, a development from the ideas of Zeune and Forster, combined with the concept of a *ganzheit* or whole derived from Kant, became one of the motifs of the *Erdkunde*. Individual 'wholes' could be of various dimensions. Each continent contained numerous *ganzheiten*, yet was itself a 'whole'. So too the entire earth was a cosmic 'whole' with an individual organization (*ens sui generis*). To inquire into, and present the individuality of the earth was the highest task of geographical science.

Writers before Ritter (Forster, Zeune) who had conceived the idea of 'wholes' had never clearly distinguished them from a mere aggregate of parts. Ritter was the first to try to bring all the various elements together and present them as a distinctive totality. In the first volume of the *Erdkunde*, for example, he divided Africa into four parts. Each of these were further subdivided,[1] but after this detailed treatment all the parts were reassembled and presented again as an entire continent, or individual whole which was something more than the sum of its parts.

As in the Idealism of Fichte, Schelling, and Hegel, the concept of 'wholes' was linked with a teleological view of the universe. Schelling, for example, held that nature was not just a living unity it was developing towards some end. ' "Nature is the ego or self in the process of becoming", this is the theme of Schelling's philosophy of nature,' says Windelband.[2] This teleological view was accepted by Ritter, and reinforced by his Pietistic sympathies (another link with Kant), led him to search for the inner relationship which bound the separate parts together in a 'whole', and from which some indication of the purpose of that 'whole' might be derived. The earth in its totality must be purposeful, and the purpose it served Ritter seemed to be that of the training ground or nursery (*das Erziehungshaus*) of man. The configuration of the continents was thus not fortuitous, it was determined by law. Each had been given a form and position that would enable it to play its appointed role in the development of mankind.

Later writers in the nineteenth century criticized this teleology as though it impaired the quality of Ritter's work, making it somehow unscientific. There is, of course, no basis for such criticism. Contemporary developments in science have shown that a teleological philosophy can

areas of the earth are not to be studied in themselves, as mere division of the earth's surface, but neither are the objects that are found on the earth's surface to be studied in themselves, in geography, but rather the areas of the earth's surface are to be studied in terms of the particular character resulting from phenomena, interrelated to each other and to the earth which fill the areas'.

[1] For a brief outline see Dickinson and Howarth, p. 158.
[2] Windelband, *A History of Philosophy*, p. 597.

be combined with most rigid scientific accuracy in research, and there is every indication that in Ritter it was so combined.

Although as stated earlier it is difficult to summarize Ritter's concepts adequately, there is no problem in assessing his importance in the development of geographic thought. He was the great formulator. He took the uncoordinated viewpoints of the eighteenth-century geographers, revised them, and forged them into a concept of geography that is still valid. He demonstrated the importance of empirical and comparative methods of research. He pointed the way to the analysis of the relation of man to his environment while avoiding rash generalizations. His *Länderkunde* stressed the importance of natural as opposed to political divisions of the earth's surface, and established the framework of Regional Geography. Even the teleological point of view was instructive in that it emphasized the significance of considering not 'just the present but the future', not just the 'is' but the 'becoming'. In short, to use the words of Penck, 'he gave to geography its systematic frame' (*ihren systematischen Ausbau*).[1]

Alexander von Humboldt

Alexander von Humboldt (1769–1859) is the other great figure in Classical Geography. A man of great and versatile genius, he contributed to so many branches of science that his work is almost as difficult to summarize as Ritter's. At various times he did research in botany, geology, physics, chemistry, anatomy, physiology, history, and all aspects of geography. Industry so varied and comprehensive brought frequent criticism. On several occasions Humboldt had to defend himself against the change of being too versatile.

His training was very different from Ritter's. Born of wealthy parents he was educated privately till the age of eighteen, when he entered the University of Frankfurt-on-the-Oder. There he stayed a bare six months. A year later he resumed his studies at the University of Göttingen whither his brother Wilhelm had preceded him. His interest in botany had already been awakened, and under the stimulus of his friendship with Wildenow, whom he met in 1788, it developed into a lifelong enthusiasm.[2]

At Göttingen geology attracted his attention. Although he previously had had no training in either mineralogy or geology, he published a short monograph and several papers on the Rhineland Basalts, which he had examined during a short 'scientific tour' in the autumn of 1789. In these

[1] p. 31, Sonderband, der *Gesellschaft für Erdkunde*, 1928.

[2] His first paper published anonymously in 1789 was entitled *Sur le Bohun Upas*, par un jeune gentilhomme de Berlin.

papers he upheld with ingenious arguments the current theory of the aqueous origin of basaltic rock.

The longing for travel which he had entertained from childhood was now sharpened by his meeting with George Forster. In his company Humboldt made his first foreign tour through Holland, Belgium, central and southern England, and northern France, an account of which Forster has given in his *Sketches of the Lower Rhine*. Forster's interest in geography, his method of careful observation and critical treatment of facts, and above all his talent for artistic though scientific description of landscape made an indelible impression on his young companion. After a short period studying in Hamburg, Humboldt entered the School of Mines at Freiburg (Saxony) at that time (1791) under the direction of the famous geologist Werner.

Eight months later he left Freiburg to take an official position in the Prussian Department of Mines. His official position gave him a welcomed opportunity to travel back and forward through southern Germany, and to carry on an extensive investigation in botany, geology, and meteorology. Visits to his brother Wilhelm, then living in Jena, brought Humboldt into contact with Goethe and Schiller, which strengthened both his aesthetic appreciation of nature and his philosophical approach to nature. After his mother's death he left the Government service in order to travel. Several plans were made and discarded before he finally secured permission of the Spanish Government to visit their colonies in the New World. He sailed from Corunna in 1799.

He landed at Cumana, in what is now Venezuela, and from there set out on the long itinerary that lasted five years and extended over 40,000 miles. First he explored the Orinoco and established the truth of its connexion with the Amazon. Then after an excursion to Cuba, he went south up the Magdalena Valley and along the Cordillera, through Quito to Lima and Callao, where he hoped to join a French expedition on its way around the globe. Disappointed in these hopes he returned by sea to Acapulco and spent the next twelve months in Mexico. He returned home via Havana, Philadelphia, with a detour to Washington in order to meet President Jefferson, and landed at Bordeaux in April 1804.

The following twenty years were spent mainly in Paris preparing the results of his expedition for publication. The incomparable vigour and brilliance of intellectual life in Paris at that time was a great stimulus to Humboldt. Gay-Lussac, Laplace, Lamarck, Cuvier, Arago, Jussieu, De Candolle, Pictet, and many other eminent scientists were his friends and collaborators. Richtofen attributes much of Humboldt's intellectual eminence to this grafting of French culture on to his basic German training. He returned to Berlin in 1827. In 1829 at the request of the Russian Government he made a nine months' tour through the metalliferous regions of the Urals, and across the western part of Asiatic Russia as far as the Altai Mountains.

The remaining years of his life were spent in Berlin, deeply involved in the daily routine of court duties which his post of Chamberlain to the King imposed on him. Despite these heavy drains on his energies he yet found it possible to fulfil a long-held desire and complete, in the five volumes of *Cosmos*, that comprehensive survey of the Universe which he had first sketched in lectures given in Berlin during the winter of 1827.

Humboldt's renown sprang originally from his achievements as a scientific traveller, and it is probably that achievement for which posterity will give him most honour. He developed the technique of the Forsters to the peak of perfection and his method served both as a model and a spur to later explorers. On all his travels, however short, he made multitudinous observations. Temperatures of air and ground, pressure, winds, latitude and longitude, elevation above sea level, magnetic variation, nature of rocks, types of plants and their relation to climate and altitude, human features, all were accurately recorded. Nothing escaped his eye, and no aspect of nature failed to arouse his scientific curiosity.

The diary he kept during his visit to England with George Forster shows how early he had acquired the habit of careful observation.

Poole's Hole—560 yards in length—it lies to the Southwest of Buxton towards the limestone mountain of Axe Edge, on the banks of the little river Wye. As the cave is narrow, more beautiful stalactites are formed in it than in the Peak Cavern. A small stream issues from the cavern. On the road from Buxton to the Cave I found some quantity of Saxifraga granulata and S. tridactylites. At the entrance of the Cave I noticed Vida montana, Alchemilla vulgar and Polypod vulg. In the neighbourhood of Poole's Cavern are several lime kilns in the open air, for in England lime is burnt in the open air and tiles in conical furnaces, exactly the reverse of the custom in Germany.[1]

Scientific details overflow the limits of his note-books into his letters. A postscript of a letter from Cumana runs as follows:

During our stay in this province we have dried more than 1,600 plants and described about 600 new varieties, including some unknown cryptogamia; we have also collected the most beautiful shell-fish and insects. I have made more than 60 drawings of plants, besides illustrating the comparative anatomy of various shell-fish. We took Berthoud's chronometer and Ramsden's and Troughton's sextants with us, across the Guarapichi. I determined the latitude and longitude

---

[1] Appendix—*Life of Humboldt*, Bruhns and Lassell, pp. 393–4.

of more than fifteen places—observations which may be of use at some future time in affording fixed points for the construction of a map of the interior. By means of the barometer, I measured the height of the Cordilleras. The loftiest peak is limestone, and does not exceed in elevation 6,405 feet. Farther west, towards Avila, there are mountains nearly 10,500 feet in height, which connect these Cordilleras with those of Santa Martha and Quito.

The oppressive and almost unbearable heat did not prevent me from observing the solar eclipse of the 28th of October. On the same day I took altitudes of the sun with Bird's quadrant ; I give the results below, and I should be glad if you will kindly look them through and correct them. . . . In making these observations, my face was so severely burnt that I was obliged to keep my bed for two days and apply medicinal remedies. The reflection from the white limestone is distressing to the eyes and liable to injure the sight. The metal of an instrument exposed to the power of the sun's rays is heated to a temperature of 124°.

If you have looked into my last work on 'Subterranean Meteorology', you will have seen that the temperature of the interior of the earth is a problem of the highest interest. Here, under 10° of latitude, the temperature at the depth of 371 fathoms is 66°. My meteorological instruments have been compared with those of the National Observatory at Paris, and corrected according to that standard. At the sea level the thermometer in the shade, even during the hottest part of the year, does not rise above 91°; the temperature keeps very regular, rarely varying more than from 75° to 82°. Early in the afternoon, when the heat is at its maximum, a thunderstorm comes on, and is succeeded by a display of lightning, which lasts for nine hours. Truly a volcanic climate!

On the 4th of November we experienced a severe shock of earthquake; no serious damage, fortunately, occurred. I was surprised to notice that during the earthquake the dip of the magnetic needle was reduced by the amount of 1·1°. The earthquake was followed by a succession of slighter shocks, and on the 12th of November we had a regular display of fireworks. From two o'clock till five in the morning large fire-balls passed without intermission across the sky, and kept discharging sprays of fire two degrees in diameter. The eastern portion of the province of New Andalusia is covered with numerous small volcanoes, emitting warm water, sulphur, sulphuretted hydrogen, and petroleum.[1]

Attempts to co-ordinate all these observations of natural phenomena led Humboldt into geography; yet notwithstanding this practical approach and his very different background, Humboldt's concept of geography was basically the same as Ritter's. In an early work (*Flora Fribergensis*) he briefly touched upon the limits of the various sciences and distinguished between '*Physiographia*' (the systematic natural sciences), '*Naturgeschichte*' (natural history) where the emphasis was on the development of things in time, and '*Geognosie*' or '*Weltbeschreibung*', which discussed spatial distribution.[2]

[1] Bruhns and Lassell, pp. 270–1.   [2] See also Hartshorne, p. 77.

These terms were later changed, but the distinction between them
he maintained throughout his writing. In the first volume of *Cosmos* he
enlarges on this theme. His argument runs as follows:

The catalogues of organized beings to which was formerly given the pompous
title of 'Systems of Nature', presents us with an admirably connected arrangement
by analogies of structure. . . . But these pretended systems of nature, however
ingenious their mode of classification may be, do not show us organic beings,
as they are distributed in groups throughout our planet according to their different
relations of latitude and elevation above the level of the sea and to climatic
influences which are owing to general and often very remote causes. . . .
   The distinction which must necessarily be made between descriptive botany
(morphology of vegetables) and the geography of plants, is that in the physical
history of the globe, the innumerable multitude of organized bodies which
embellish creation are considered rather according to 'zones of habitation' or
'stations' and to differently inflected 'isothermal bands', than with reference to
the principle of gradation in the development of the internal organism.[1]

The science of spatial distribution thus established was not limited to
the earth's surface, it was not an *Erdbeschreibung* but a *Weltbeschreibung*,
a description not of the earth but of the world, i.e. a science of the Cosmos.

The uncommon but definite expression of the science of the Cosmos recalls
to the mind of the inhabitant of the earth that we are treating of a more widely
extended horizon; of the assemblage of all things with which space is filled, from
the remotest nebulae to the climatic distribution of those delicate tissues of vegetable matter which spreads a variegated covering over the surface of our rocks.[2]
   . . . If scientific terms had not long been diverted from their true verbal
signification, the present work ought rather to have borne the title 'Cosmography'
divided into 'Uranography' and 'Geography'.[3]

'Uranography' which had the task of describing the celestial part of
the cosmos may be translated as 'descriptive astronomy'. Geography, or
Physical Geography (the terms are synonymous for Humboldt) described
the terrestrial part. Its ultimate aim was 'to recognize unity in the vast
diversity of phenomena; and by the exercise of thought and the combination of observations, to discern the constancy of phenomena in the midst
of apparent changes'.[4]
   Humboldt also differentiates between physical history and physical
geography of the world [5] very much along the lines of Kant's discussion of
Naturgeschichte (see above, page 40).
   To what extent is Humboldt's thought derived from Kant? The

---

[1] *Cosmos*, Vol. 1, pp. 42–3. Bohn's edition.   [2] Ibid., p. 50.
[3] Ibid., p. 53.   [4] Ibid., p. 43.   [5] Ibid., p. 43.

question naturally arises. *Flora Fribergensis* was published nine years before Kant's lectures on geography, but Humboldt was so thoroughly acquainted with Kant's philosophy and scientific opinions from the age of sixteen onwards [1] that it is highly probable he had some notion of Kant's concept of geography before he wrote the *Flora*. There is however no conclusive evidence. Whatever the actual facts may be it was the Kantian concept of geography that Humboldt held and that he expounded in *Cosmos*.

The preceding quotations further indicate that Humboldt shared with Ritter the concept of the unity of nature and agreed that the task of physical geography was to demonstrate that unity. Here both men were reflecting the philosophical outlook of their time. The idea of the living unity of nature as propounded by Spinoza had been revived by the idealists. It was an essential part of the thought of Fichte, Schelling, and Hegel, and found magnificent expression in the poetry of Goethe and Schiller.

Nature [wrote Humboldt in the Introduction to *Cosmos*], considered rationally, that is to say submitted to the process of thought, is a unity in diversity of phenomena, a harmony blending together all created things, however dissimilar in form and attributes, one great whole animated by the breath of life. The most important result of a rational inquiry into nature is therefore, to establish the unity and harmony of this stupendous mass of force, and matter, to determine with impartial justice what is due to the discoveries of the past and to those of the present, and to analyse the individual parts of the natural phenomena without succumbing beneath the weight of the whole.[2]

To establish this unity the relationships of organic life (including man) to the inorganic surface of the earth must be investigated. 'My attention will ever be directed to observing the harmony among the forces of nature, to remarking the influence exerted by inanimate creation upon the animal and vegetable kingdom.'[3]

The investigation of the relationship was the task of geography.

[1] In this regard the following notes and extracts from Humboldt's biography by Bruhns and Lassell are suggestive.

'In 1785 Humboldt attended lectures by Marcus Herz, an ardent disciple of Kant, on Kant's physics and philosophy' (p. 40).

'Humboldt had been educated in the liberal school rendered so popular by Mendelssohn and Engel side by side with the severe rules of thought and perception inculcated by Kant' (J. Lowenberg) (Bruhns and Lassell, p. 200). While at Göttingen (1789) Humboldt wrote about his brother, 'He is killing himself with study and has already read the whole of Kant's works, and lives and moves in his system' (p. 59).

[2] *Cosmos*, Vol. 1, pp. 2–3.   [3] Bruhns and Lassell, p. 247.

It must, however, be remembered, that the inorganic crust of the Earth contains within it the same elements that enter into the structure of animal and vegetable organs. A physical cosmography would therefore be incomplete, if it were to omit a consideration of these forces, and of the substances which enter into solid and fluid combinations in organic tissues, under conditions which, from our ignorance of their actual nature, we designate by the vague term of 'vital forces', and group into various systems, in accordance with more or less perfectly conceived analogies. The natural tendency of the human mind involuntarily prompts us to follow the physical phenomena of the Earth, through all their varied series, until we reach the final stage of the morphological evolution of vegetable forms, and the self-determining powers of motion in animal organisms. And it is by these links that the geography of organic beings—of plants and animals—is connected with the delineation of the inorganic phenomena of our terrestrial globe.[1]

The general picture of nature which I have endeavoured to delineate, would be incomplete if I did not venture to trace a few of the most marked features of the human race, considered with reference to physical gradations—to the geographical distribution of contemporaneous types—to the influence exercised upon man by the forces of nature, and the reciprocal, although weaker, action which he in his turn exercises on these natural forces. Dependent, although in a lesser degree than plants and animals, on the soil, and on the meteorological processes of the atmosphere with which he is surrounded—escaping more readily from the control of natural forces, by activity of mind and the advance of intellectual cultivation, no less than by his wonderful capacity of adapting himself to all climates—man everywhere becomes most essentially associated with terrestrial life.[2]

With Ritter, Humboldt also emphasized, though much more strongly, the importance of the empirical method of research.

I limit myself to the domain of empirical ideas. Facts remain ever the same when the hastily erected edifice of theory has long fallen into ruins. I have always kept my facts distinct from my conjectures. This method of dealing with the phenomena of nature appears to me to be the one best grounded and most likely to succeed.[3]

An attempt to comprehend the plan of the universe—the order of nature—must begin with a generalization of particular facts, and a knowledge of the conditions under which physical changes regularly and periodically manifest themselves; and must conduct to the thoughtful consideration of the results yielded by empirical observation, but not to 'a contemplation of the universe based on speculative deductions and development of thought alone, or to a theory of absolute unity independent of experience'. We are, I here repeat, far distant from the period when it was thought possible to concentrate all sensuous perceptions into the unity of one sole idea of nature. The true path was indicated upwards of a century before Lord Bacon's time, by Leonardo da Vinci, in

[1] *Cosmos*, Vol. i, p. 349.   [2] Ibid, pp. 360–1.
[3] Letter to Blumenbach, 1795—quoted Bruhns and Lassell, p. 197.

these few words: 'Comminciare dall' experienza e per mezzo di questa scoprirne la ragione.' 'Commence by experience, and by means of this discover the reason.' In many groups of phenomena we must still content ourselves with the recognition of empirical laws; but the highest and more rarely attained aim of all natural inquiry must ever be the discovery of their *causal connexion*.[1]

In the handling of his multitudinous observations Humboldt demonstrated far more clearly than Ritter the value of the comparative method, so much so that Ritter attributes the idea of comparative geography to him. The essay on 'Steppes and Deserts' in *Views of Nature*, as Plewe points out,[2] is full of comparisons,[3] comparison of steppes and ocean, of all the steppes of the world, the heaths of Central Europe, Llanos, Pampas, North American prairies, African desert, Central Asiatic steppes—all are compared so as to bring out the peculiar character or physiognomy of each as determined by diversity of soil, climate, and elevation above the sea. His letters show how almost every new observation he made was immediately compared with previous observations of similar kind, and the similarities or differences recorded.

One instance has become celebrated. During his Russian journey he wrote to a member of the Russian Government: 'The Ural Mountains are a true El Dorado, and I am confident from the analogy they present to the geological conformation of Brazil . . . that diamonds will be discovered in the gold and platinum washings of the Ural Mountains.' A few days later diamonds were found in the gold and platinum washings:[4]

An equally important characteristic of Humboldt's method was the graphical representation of data. While in the service of the Department of Mines at the age of twenty-three he investigated the salt springs at Reichenhall. In a letter to his geologist friend, Freisleben, he reported on his findings as follows:

I wish to complete my chart showing the connexion between all the salt springs of Germany. . . . This map originated from an essay appended to my report: 'On the method of boring for brine.' The leading ideas are that the mountains of Franconia, Suabia and Thuringia have one main position of strata, that they are connected by a valley extending from twenty to thirty miles between Eisenach in the mountains of the Thuringian Forest and Osterode among the isolated Hartz Mountains, that all the brine in Franconia and Suabia flows in the

[1] *Cosmos*, Vol. 3, p. 7.
[2] Plewe, p. 51.   [3] See *Views of Nature*, pp. 1–21.
[4] Dr. Charles T. Jackson in the Report of the Centennial Anniversary of Humboldt's birth published by the Boston Society of Natural History records a similar successful prediction of the discovery of diamonds and platinum in the U.S.A. (p. 84).

upper gypsum, that all the salt springs in Germany lie in one given direction, that it is possible to draw lines upon the map, by following which salt springs may be found mile after mile, that these salt streams follow the general slope of the land, which throughout Germany is from the south-west to the north-east, and flow round the primitive rocks wherever these project above the surface.[1]

Here is clear evidence of his cartographic technique at the very start of his career. Later he invented isotherms to facilitate his studies of comparative climate. He drew sections across the Andes based on 1,500 of his own measurements, and started the practice of using these profiles to show the altitudinal belts of vegetation, an idea conceived during his visit to Teneriffe (1799). He also used them to show geological structure and, though not the first to do so, he demonstrated their value and geological cross-section so successfully that their invention is frequently attributed to him.[2]

He was also the first to divide the regions he explored into botanical provinces, maps of which were published in his *Atlas Géographique et Physique du Nouveau Continent* (published 1814–19). It is to Humboldt in fact that modern geographers are indebted for most of the graphical methods that make their work practicable.

In all these ways Humboldt was fundamentally at one with Ritter. The two differed however in their philosophical approach to nature. As shown earlier Humboldt believed in the unity of nature. He also accepted the idea of inherent causality. 'I have endeavoured in my delineation of the earth to arrange natural phenomena in such a way as to indicate their causal connexion'[3] (cf. Ritter's statement, p. 46). 'In many groups of phenomena we must still content ourselves with the recognition of empirical laws; but the highest and more rarely attained aim of all natural inquiry must ever be the discovery of their causal connexion.'[4]

But in Humboldt's concept of unity and causality there is nothing of Ritter's anthropocentric attitude nor of his teleological views. Humboldt could not go as far with the Idealist philosophers as Ritter. He was antipathetic to Hegel. His idea of unity was far more aesthetic than theological, and was more akin to Goethe's concept than to Ritter's. This link with Weimar Humboldt himself recognized. In a letter to Frau Caroline von Wolzogen, he wrote:

The vast mountain ranges and an immeasurable ocean, and the aspects of nature, if possible more impressive and sublime, have intervened between these

---

[1] Bruhns and Lassell, p. 130.
[2] See address by L. Agassiz, Humboldt Centennial, Boston Society of Natural History, p. 25.
[3] *Cosmos*, Vol. 3, p. 2.   [4] Ibid., p. 7.

days and the present—though a thousand wondrous forms have since passed before my mind yet 'the new has always been interwoven with the old', the unfamiliar has been assimilated with the associations of bygone days; and I have been constrained to admit, while ranging the forests of the Amazon, or scaling the heights of the Andes, that there is but One Spirit animating the whole of Nature from pole to pole—but One Life infused into stones, plants, and animals, and even into man himself. In all my wanderings I was impressed with the conviction of the powerful influence that had been exerted upon me by the society I enjoyed at Jena, of how, through association with Goethe, my views of nature had been elevated, and I had, as it were, become endowed with new perceptive faculties.[1]

> *Wie alles sich zum ganzen webt,*
> *Eins in dem Andern wirkt und lebt.*[2]

This was what Humboldt sought in nature. He apparently felt no need to see this unity ordained by God for the development of man. His attitude, though he never gave it formal expression, was so pantheistic that even before his death he was charged with being an atheist, and Humanism to this day honours him as one of its founders.

Such a judgement, however, seems far from true. Louis Agassiz, who knew him, in the address given in Boston on the Centennial Anniversary of Humboldt's birth, refutes the charge and draws attention to Humboldt's description of the universe as 'Gottes erhabenes Reich'. In the same pamphlet T. S. Fay reports Humboldt's indignation on one occasion when charged with disbelief in God.[3]

Humboldt and Ritter further differed in their sphere of work. Systematic studies were Humboldt's domain, Regional Geography (*Länderkunde*) that of Ritter. This difference however can be easily overstressed. Ritter in his lectures emphasized the importance of systematic studies as the basis of *Länderkunde*, and his plan of the '*Erdkunde*' included a final volume on Systematic Geography. Humboldt on the other hand, published several regional studies, models of their kind.[4] More than that he not only recognized the existence of the region but he seemed to accept the idea of geographical individuality which figured so prominently in Ritter's thought.

The division of mountains into chains separates the earth's surface into different basins, which are often narrow and walled in, forming cauldron-like valleys, and

---

[1] Bruhns and Lassell, Vol. I, p. 359.   [2] *Faust*, Part I, p. 447.

[3] Centennial Anniversary of the Birth of Alex von Humboldt, Boston Society of Natural History, 1869.

[4] See 'Plateau of Coxamana' in *Views of Nature* and Essays on Cuba (published separately) and Mexico in reports on his *Journey in the Equinoctial Regions of the New World*.

(as in Greece and in part of Asia Minor) constitute an individual local climate with respect to heat, moisture, transparency of atmosphere, and frequency of winds and storms. These circumstances have, at all times, exercised a powerful influence on the character and cultivation of natural products, and on the manners and institutions of neighbouring nations, and even on the feelings with which they regard one another. This character of geographical individuality attains its maximum, if we may be allowed so to speak, in countries where the differences in the configuration of the soil are the greatest possible, either in a vertical or horizontal direction, both in relief and in the articulation of the continent.[1]

Humboldt, however, did not develop this theme. He was not primarily concerned with *Länderkunde* and made no pronouncement as to its position in geographical work.

Ritter and Humboldt, although their work overlapped, were really complementary. Humboldt gave method and form to Systematic Geography (climatology and plant geography). Ritter founded regional study. Together they provided an almost complete and modern programme for geography.

It was, therefore, unfortunate that Ritter, through his university teaching and his many papers on methodology, should have had so much more influence on the succeeding generation than Humboldt, whose writings, scattered through so many journals, were less well known, at least among geographers. His (Humboldt's) influence at first was far greater in the development of the systematic sciences, and when a decade later it began to affect geographers they saw his work not as complementary to, but as opposed to Ritter's and used it to strengthen the dualism between Regional and Physical Geography that persisted till the end of the century.

Ritter and Humboldt both died in 1859. In the same year Darwin's *Origin of Species* was published. Their deaths thus mark not only the end of a period in geographic development but the beginning of a crisis in scientific and philosophic thought.

Idealism in various forms for half a century had held the field, now it succumbed before the attack of materialism. In science materialism led to a greater emphasis on natural law and causality. However, it was almost a decade before materialistic influences clearly affected geographical thought. The interval was one of confusion.

Ritter and Humboldt, although together their work covered the whole field of geography, had not left a clear and unmistakable framework for the subject; in fact the complementary character of their work was not immediately recognized. Moreover their successors, failing to realize how strongly their outlook was moulded by Kantian Idealism,

[1] *Cosmos,* Vol. I, p. 334.

sought to deduce a philosophy from the study of their writings, in particular those of Ritter. First one aspect, then another was seized upon and advanced as the essential core of geography, each proponent claiming the authority of the master for his particular interpretation.

Ritter's concept of *Ganzheit*, or Whole, so completely out of accord with materialistic thinking, was for the most part discarded, and with it seemed to go the recognition of the need for a science to study the relationship of phenomena in space. Deprived of this all-important unifying factor, a coherent system for geography was impossible.

Ritter's terminology, not a very happy one, increased this perplexity. Just as earlier geographers had tried to deduce the scope of their subject from its name *Erdbeschreibung* and limited themselves to description, so now definitions were derived from *Erdkunde* and *Vergleichende Geographie*, and the idea spread that geography was really a comparative knowledge of the earth.

Fröbel and Peschel

The correct interpretation of 'comparative' produced much methodological controversy. Fröbel (1831–6) during Ritter's lifetime had criticized the use of this term and asked for a definition. Ritter's reply indicated that it had no very clear meaning, it was just a convenient term for distinguishing geography of the nineteenth century from that of the eighteenth. But Fröbel seemed never to understand fully.

He argued that to compare one region of the earth's surface with another was equivalent to comparing a leg anatomically with an arm. Comparative earth science could only be justified as a title if used to designate a comparison of the earth with other celestial bodies. Geography, as the study of the earth's surface, he continued, could only employ comparison in the treatment of detail, i.e. in comparing a single mountain (or a river, &c.) with another, and since such comparison was already implied by the accepted terms, steppe rivers, high plains, nomad folk, '*Vergleichend*' as qualifications of geography was superfluous.

Fröbel also rejected Ritter's teleology. 'Geography can no more look upon the earth as the mere dwelling place of humanity than the botanist can entertain the view that grass exists only to serve as fodder to cattle.'[1] What followed if a botanist could consider grass in this way was not explained.

Geography he claimed was a natural science, concerned with the

[1] As quoted by Leighly, 'Methodological Controversy in the Nineteenth-Century German Geography', *Annals of the A.A.G.*, Vol. 28.

earth's surface studied in a systematic way, i.e. taking in turn relief, climate, vegetation, animals, and man, attempting throughout to make clear the interrelation of the various factors. Hence there was no place in geography for Ritter's *Länderkunde*, nor for the method of synthesis such studies required. Geographers should use only analysis. This he argued from the example of anatomy, where the anatomist first encounters the whole body and proceeds to dissect it into subordinate parts for study. Geographers, he asserted, first meet the complete region; this must then be analysed into its separate parts, relief, climate, vegetation, &c., for study. At this point Fröbel failed to realize that Ritter's synthesis in *Länderkunde* was preceded by the very analysis he proposed.

Later Fröbel in elaborating his views confined geography to systematic physical geography, including ethnography. Alongside this there could be a Philosophic-Historical Geography concerned with a systematic study of the earth as the home of man, but the two could never be combined into one science.[1]

Less critical disciples of Ritter were equally uncertain of the essential meaning of *Vergleichend* and put forward many definitions.

The most logical development of Ritter's work was probably that of the geographers who studied the interrelation of the various phenomena, relief, climate, vegetation, animal and man in a particular area. Lüdde was one of these. He pointed out (1841–50), for example, that there were three types of comparison in geography.

1. The comparison of one element with another in a given region, i.e. vegetation with climate and soils.
2. The comparison of the present conditions of a region with those of the same region at an earlier stage of development.
3. The comparison of one region with another, each being considered as a whole.

All these were essential, no single one by itself could claim the title 'Comparative Geography', indeed it was only when one studied the physical and biological features of a region along with man, his history and culture (including the ethical, religious, and aesthetic forms), that one could really claim to be doing *Vergleichende Geographie* in the Ritterian sense.

Wappäus (1885) gives much the same definition in his Physical Geography, when he says, '*Vergleichende Erdkunde* is geography when in considering the earth's surface it does not separate the physical and

[1] See Hartshorne, p. 104.

historical viewpoint, but presents in every unit the physical and ethical [*ethischen*] relations in their mutual dependence and interaction.'[1]

Others impressed by Ritter's anthropocentric viewpoint limited *Vergleichende Erdkunde* to the study of man in his relation to the physical environment, some even pushing this interpretation so far that they left geography to become historians. A few in their desire to justify the adjective *comparative*, compared everything, geometric shapes of countries, length and breadth, heights of all the mountains, &c., carrying it to absurd lengths.

A measure of order was restored and a new lead given when Oscar Peschel (considered by Kirchoff to be with Humboldt and Ritter one of the three *Hauptlehrer der neuerer Erdkunde*), 1826–75, published *Das Wesen und die Aufgaben der Vergleichende Erdkunde* (1867) and *Neue Probleme der Vergleichende Erdkunde als Versuch einer Morphologie der Erdoberfläche* (1870). Imbued with the materialistic philosophy of his age Peschel broke through the Idealistic framework which Kant, Humboldt, and Ritter had constructed.

Geography was to be a systematic, empirical science; its method, observation, drawing induction from these observations, and correcting these by still new observations. His enormous respect for natural law led him to attempt causal classification, of the relief features of the earth's surface. In this study he employed the term '*Vergleichend*' to designate the method of investigation which compared all forms of one particular relief type (i.e. fiords) with one another, so that by recognizing intermediate stages one could arrive at an understanding of their mode of formation. The causality Peschel sought was purely mechanical, it had nothing to do with purpose; Ritter's teleological views were quite unacceptable.

Peschel's criticism of Ritter's philosophy and of his use of '*Vergleichend*' aroused heated discussion, but produced nothing of permanent value since it was based on a misinterpretation of Ritter's position.

On the other hand Peschel's morphological research produced a revolution in Physical Geography. Interest was deflected from Länderkunde and focused on systematic studies in a manner reminiscent of Humboldt, though there was no revival of Humboldt's broad interest in all aspects of Physical Geography nor of his idealistic stressing of the unity of nature. Systematic studies in their new guise were highly specialized, and prosecuted by scientists who tended to be geomorphologists and climatologists first and geographers only secondly.

[1] *Handbuch der Geographie und Statistik*, Stein und Hörchelmann, 7th edition, Vol. I, J. E. Wappäus.

Peschel's genetic classification of relief types provided the concept from which the formulation of geomorphology could and did proceed. It started the development that culminated in the work of W. M. Davis and the recognition of the Cycle of Erosion. This achievement was so remarkable and the possibilities of investigation it opened up so attractive that for a time the study of land-forms became the dominant part of geography, indeed it is possible to point to Universities where that is still the situation today.

Systematic studies in Climatology (Buchan, Loomis, Hahn, Köppen), Plant Geography (Von Sachs, Haberlandt, Grisebach, Wärming) confirmed this concentration on Physical Geography (in its modern sense) introducing a new form of dualism into the subject. Previously there had been a double division, one between Physical and Historico-Political Geography (see Fröbel), the other between systematic studies and *Länderkunde*. Now this was resolved into a division between a systematic physical and a human regional geography, of which the former was considered to be by far the more important.

An extreme example of this type of attitude is provided by Gerland (1887). Accepting *Erdkunde* as the correct designation for geography, he argued that this meant the 'science of the earth', and therefore the earth itself (not just the surface) was the proper object of geographical investigation.

The earth is an assemblage of matter undergoing development. . . . The task of the geographer is to investigate the interaction of the forces operating on the material of this earth, and the results of the operation of this force in the shaping and modification of that material.[1]

Geography, as so defined, must be an exact physical science, i.e. one with fixed and exact laws. Man therefore must be excluded, partly because he cannot be treated by exact laws, and partly because such studies as anthropology, ethnology, historical geography, which are concerned with man, teach us nothing about the earth itself, and in them geography merely serves as an aid in elucidating their data.

This argument was carried so far that not only was the study of man's relation to environment excluded from geography, but Gerland actually asserted that the destiny of peoples was determined not by their geographic environment but by their character and historical 'background'.[2] Gerland's geography thus was a combination of geophysics and descriptive

[1] Quoted by Leighly, 'Methodology and Controversy in Nineteenth-Century German Geography', *Annals of the A.A.G.*, Vol. 28, p. 250.

[2] Leighly, op. cit., p. 252.

physical geography, including strangely enough, plant and animal geography. These views had little effect on the main course of geographical thought. Geographers as a whole, though not very certain as to the proper place of man in their field of study, were not prepared to exclude him altogether; in fact, as was quickly pointed out, Gerland's thesis itself was illogical in excluding man while retaining plants and animals.

Friedrich Ratzel

Uncertainty was ended and the place of man firmly and finally secured in geography by the work of Friedrich Ratzel and his followers. Ratzel's *Anthropogeographie*, the first volume of which appeared in 1882 just before the Gerland controversy, did for Human Geography what Peschel's work had done for geomorphology, i.e. it established the study of all those features of the earth's surface related to man on systematic lines. Ratzel had approached geography very much as Humboldt did 'by travel, by direct contact with realities'.[1] In his own words 'I travelled, I sketched, I described. Thus I was led to *Naturschilderung*.' His interests were wide and his training thorough. He did research in Physical Geography on fiords, and the snow cover in the German mountains, and edited the *Bibliothek Geographischer Handbücher*, a series in which Heim's '*Gletscherkunde*', Hann's '*Klimatologie*', and Penck's '*Morphologie*' appeared.

It is important to recall this interest in Physical Geography because it helps to explain why, when Ratzel turned to the complex human phenomena, he never lost sight of environmental forces.

He possessed to a very high degree the sense of terrestrial reality [writes Brunhes]. He perceived the human facts on the earth no longer as a philosopher or historian or as a simple ethnographer, or as an economist, but as a geographer. He distinguished their manifold, complex, variable connexions with the facts of the physical order, altitude, topography, climate, vegetation. He observed men peopling the globe, working on its surface, seeking their livelihood, and making history on the earth; he observed them with the eyes of a true naturalist.[2]

Volume I of the *Anthropogeographie* attempted to show how the distribution of man on the earth had been more or less controlled by natural forces. Volume II, published 1891, described the existing distribution. The first volume was a reworking of the theme developed by Ritter in his *Erdkunde*, and Ratzel, himself, stressed the fact that he was developing the ideas of Ritter in conformity with the newly established scientific method.

---

[1] Brunhes, *Human Geography*, p. 33. (English translation.) [2] Ibid., p. 33.

In his last great work *Die Erde und das Leben. Eine Vergleichende Erd-kunde* (1901–2) he wrote, 'This book bears the subtitle *"Vergleichende Erdkunde"* because it presents the interrelation of the phenomena of the earth's surface in the sense of Karl Ritter.' He, like Ritter, sought to comprehend 'the earth as an integral whole, an interacting unity'. But Ratzel's work differed in two important respects from Ritter's. It treated Human Geography (1) systematically not regionally, and (2) from a Darwinian point of view.

Ratzel saw man as the end product of evolution, an evolution in which the mainspring was the natural selection of types according to their capacity to adjust themselves to the physical environment. Thus whereas Ritter wrote of the reciprocal relation of man and nature, a relationship which was part of an harmonious whole serving the creative purpose of God, Ratzel tended to see man as the product of his environment, moulded by the physical forces that surrounded him, and succeeding only in so far as he made the correct adjustment to their demands; the ultimate purpose of these adjustments, if any, lay outside the core of his inquiry. A deterministic tint thus colours most of his writing.

In 1897 Ratzel made yet another major contribution in his *Political Geography*. This reshaped the old topic along lines conformable with the principles he had enunciated in his *Anthropogeographie*. In the introduction, Ratzel pointed out that since Ritter had demonstrated the importance of geographers studying the influence of environment in historical development, his successors had brought 'regional description, compilation of statistics, and political and historical maps to a state of perfection never previously attained'; yet

the development of political geography is still behind that of all other branches of our subject, and Political Science shows scarcely a trace of geographical influence other than that geography has placed at its disposal increasingly better maps, regional studies, and areal and population statistics.

What was necessary he argued was to 'organize the great volume of subject matter into a clear classification' and bring into research a comparative method and evolutionary viewpoint (*eine vergleichende und auf die Entwickelung ausgehende Durchforschung*). In other words 'what still remains to be done, in order to give political geography a higher status, can only be achieved by a comparative investigation of the relations between the state and the earth's surface'.

The influence of evolutionary biology led Ratzel to adopt the organic theory of state and society, i.e. the concept of the state as an organism, a piece of humanity and a piece of earth (*Ein Stuck Menscheit und ein Stuck Boden*).

In this book [he wrote] the states are considered at all stages of their evolution as organisms, of which the geographical aspect lies in their necessary relation with the ground. On this ground they evolve, as history and ethnography show, whilst they draw ever deeper on its resources. So they appear as areally limited, areally located [*räumlich begrenzt und räumlich gelagerte*] forms in the circle of phenomena which geography can scientifically describe, measure, map or compare.

Ratzel, though he used this concept, was alive to its inadequacy, for him it was only a convenient framework. Semple, in her magnificent exposition of Ratzel's method, was able to eliminate it without destroying anything of the real value of his work.

The organic theory of society and state permeates the *Anthropogeographie*, because Ratzel formulated his principles at a time when Herbert Spencer exercised a wide influence upon European thought. This theory, now generally abandoned by sociologists, had to be eliminated from any restatement of Ratzel's system, though it was applied in the original often in great detail, it stood there nevertheless rather as a scaffolding around the finished edifice; and the stability of the structure after this scaffolding is removed shows how extraneous to the whole it was. The theory performed, however, a great service in impressing Ratzel's mind with the life-giving connexion between land and people.[1]

More recently, unfortunately, geographers lacking Semple's wisdom revived the concept and in a very rigid form made it a basic principle in geopolitics. The development of the organic theory of the state forms only part of the *Political Geography*. In the rest of the book relations between the growth and character of political units and their positions on the earth's surface, their size, boundaries, relation to the sea, &c. are all systematically and critically investigated.

These ideas, so commonplace today, had never before been so scientifically expounded; and it is only after comparing Ratzel's treatment of Political Geography with the dull, statistical compilation of his immediate predecessors that one gets any idea of the revolutionary quality of his work.

Ratzel's contributions to geography were great, and not the least of these was his coining of the word *Anthropogeographie* which could be used for the new group of systematic studies, but it is as 'an originator of ideas that his greatness lies, not in the development of a methodical discipline' (Brunhes). Semple's judgement agrees with this.

The very fecundity of his ideas often left him no time to test the validity of his principles. He enunciates one brilliant generalization after another. Sometimes

_____

[1] E. C. Semple, *Influences of Geographic Environment*, 1911, p. v.

he reveals the mind of a seer or poet throwing out conclusions which are highly suggestive, on the face of them convincing, but which on examination prove untenable, or at the best must be set down as needing further qualification. But these were just the slag from the great furnace of his mind, slag not always worthless. Brilliant and far-reaching as were his conclusions, he did not execute a well-ordered plan. Rather he grew with his work, and his work and its problems grew with him. He took a mountain top view of things, kept his eyes always on the far horizon, and in the splendid sweep of his scientific conceptions sometimes overlooked the details near at hand. Herein lies his greatness and his limitations.[1]

Whatever the final verdict on Ratzel's work may be (and Brunhes ranks him with Ritter) it was of major importance in that it corrected the prevailing tendency to overstress the physical aspects of geography and establish a more balanced viewpoint.

The gaps in his work were filled by the many younger workers he inspired. Just as Peschel's work had caused geomorphology to dominate geography for a time, so too Ratzel's led to an overemphasis of Human Geography. This was particularly true in England and America where largely, because of the interest in Anthropogeography roused by Semple, geography began to be defined as the study of the relation of man to his environment. This development, however, belongs to the story of the twentieth century and lies outside the scope of this chapter.

Ratzel had rescued the study of man from its previous subordinate position as part of *Länderkunde* but he had not thereby affected the dualism in geography. Indeed his work served to fix interest still more firmly on systematic studies, and regional geography continued to receive scant attention.

Nevertheless the importance of regional studies was never lost sight of. Marthe (1877) was one who stressed their importance. Geography he defined 'as the science of distribution', or more briefly, as the 'Where of Things', and *Vergleichende Geographie* as the search for causal relationships. In such a search the starting point, he argued, was the study of a restricted area; the recognition of causal relationships in small localities was the essential preliminary to their recognition in larger regions or over the world as a whole. For the studies of small areas he reintroduced the Greek terms 'chorography', 'chorology'.[2] This point of view was restated in stronger terms by Richtofen in his inaugural address at Leipzig, 1883.

Though primarily interested in geomorphology Richtofen recognized that the areal principle was indispensable to geography. The heterogeneous nature of the phenomena on the earth's surface, he argued, made system-

[1] E. C. Semple, *Influences of Geographic Environment*, 1911, p. v.
[2] Hartshorne, pp. 91–2.

atic studies necessary, and these he divided into three; studies of the physical features, of the plant and animal life, and of man and his works. But they were only a preliminary to the main task of geography, 'the understanding of causal relation in areas' (Hartshorne). Richtofen thus offered a compromise between the regional and systematic studies, a compromise that recalled the point of view of Ritter and Humboldt.

The last decade of the century saw this compromise forged into a stable system. Again changes in philosophical thought prepared the way. Extreme materialism, however attractive to scientists, is rarely acceptable to professional philosophers. As early as 1860 refutations of the materialistic thesis appeared, and attempts were made to combine the scientific viewpoint and Kantian Idealism in a single system. Neo-Kantianism, in recent times, has become far more acceptable to scientists than to professional philosophers. The change in the attitude of scientists is indicated by comparing Tyndal's speech at the British Association 1874, when he spoke of 'the purely natural and inevitable march of evolution from the atoms of the primeval nebula to the proceedings of the British Association of Science', and that of Sir James Jeans at the British Association of 1934, 'Little is left of the forbidding materialism of the Victorian scientists, modern physics is moving in the direction of philosophical idealism.'

The implications of this new philosophy for geography were worked out by Alfred Hettner, a geographer with a thorough training in philosophy. In his writings he has revived the Kantian definition of geography, and within this framework welded the systematic studies of Humboldt, Peschel, Ratzel, and the regional studies as defined by Ritter, Marthe, Richtofen into a coherent whole. It is mainly due to Hettner that dualism which so long hampered geography has been successfully overcome. The bulk of Hettner's work, however, was published after 1900, and therefore a more detailed examination of his contribution lies outside the limits of this chapter.

Geography outside Germany

One other important development accompanied the rise of Regionalism. This was the rapid spread of interest in scientific geography beyond the boundaries of Germany. During the last decades of the century rival schools were established in most European countries and in the U.S.A., and with their founding came an end to the German monopoly of geography that had persisted unchallenged since 1750.

In 1898 a report on the current situation given by Prof. C. R. Dryer of the Indiana State Normal School revealed that geography was being taught by 121 instructors in 92 institutions of higher learning. 'Germany headed the list with 32 instructors in 22 institutions, France had 22 instructors in 16, Russia 16 in 11, Austria 14 in 10, Italy 9 in 7, Great Britain 6 in 6, Switzerland 6 in 4 and the United States 3 in 3.' Almost all this development he recorded had taken place after 1850, and by far the greater part after 1880.

In the U.S.A. academic interest in geography was more widespread than the figures quoted suggest. The first Professor of Geography had been appointed at Princeton in 1854. This was Arnold Guyot, a pupil of Ritter and a friend of Humboldt, who had left his native Switzerland in 1848 and at the suggestion of Louis Agassiz had settled in America.

Between the date of his appointment and 1900, twelve universities had offered at one time or another courses in geography, though all of these had not made the subject a permanent part of their curriculum. Moreover Physical Geography was frequently taught in departments of geology by instructors who might not be listed as geographers in *Minerva* and from which Dryer had taken his data.

Certainly, however low the United States stood in regard to numbers of university departments of geography, it had the glory of one great teacher William Morris Davis, in stature equal to the greatest of the nineteenth-century geographers, and whose work had already influenced German scientific thought.

French interest in geography had been aroused by the voluminous writings of Élisée Reclus, one of Ritter's students. Reclus published *La Terre*, a physical geography, in 1866–7, and the *Nouvelle Géographie Universelle*, a regional survey of the world along the lines of Ritter's *Erdkunde*, in nineteen volumes (1875–94).

Research in Human Geography was encouraged by the sociologist Le Play (1806–82), by his emphasis on the close link between habitat and society. His teaching bore fruit in de Préville's *Les Sociétées Africaine* (1894) and Demolin's *Comment la route creé le type sociale* (1901–3).

The real founding of the French school, however, is generally assigned to the year 1898 when Paul Vidal de la Blache left his teaching post in the École Normale Supérieure to take the chair of geography at the Sorbonne.

For the next twenty years until his death in 1918 Vidal de la Blache through his writings and teaching moulded French geography. His *Tableau de la Géographie de la France* (1903) and the monographs on the French *pays* written by the men he inspired (Gallois, Demangeon, Levainville, &c.) are classics of regional geography, indeed in the development of the regional concept Vidal de la Blache played a major role.

University geography in Britain began in 1887 when the Royal

Geographical Society (founded 1831) offered Oxford and Cambridge grants towards the stipends of lecturers.

Halford Mackinder was appointed at Oxford in 1887 and Yule Oldham at Cambridge in 1893 (where the first two lecturers had resigned shortly after their appointment).

Twelve years later the Oxford School of Geography was founded and A. J. Herbertson became the assistant to Mackinder. With parallel developments taking place in Rumania, Austria, Italy, Switzerland, &c. scientific geography entered the twentieth century on a wave of expansion that has swept forward uncurbed to the present.

The work of these different national schools has vastly widened the field of research, and deepened and enriched the current of geographical thought, with interesting results, some of which are described in the following chapters.

Glancing back in final retrospect over the evolution of geography as sketched here, probably the most interesting aspect of the whole story is the sensitive way in which geographical ideas at all periods have reflected contemporary trends in philosophic thinking. And here many questions arise. What is the relationship between modern geography and present-day systems of philosophy? Is geography still so sensitive? If so, will the influence of thinkers like Bergson and Whitehead revive an interest in teleology reminiscent of that of Ritter, and for which Ritter has been so often criticized?

Here is a fascinating field for research and speculation.

CHAPTER III

THE FRENCH SCHOOL OF GEOGRAPHY

R. J. HARRISON CHURCH, B.SC. (ECON.), PH.D.

Dr. Church is Lecturer in Geography at the London School of Economics, University of London. French Government Post-Graduate British Fellow, at the Sorbonne, 1936–7. He studied at the Institut de Géographie, Paris, under Professors de Martonne, Demangeon, Cholley, and Gautier; and at the Collège de France under Professor André Siegfried.

Introduction

THERE is a saying that every man has two countries, his own and France. Any modern geographer interested in the philosophy and development of his subject must be conscious of a deep debt to the French School of Geography. That debt is immense in almost every branch, but particularly so in the fields of Regional and Human Geography. No country of comparable size, population, university and financial resources has produced such a galaxy of genius as is represented by the names of Vidal de la Blache, Gallois, Brunhes, Demangeon, de Martonne, Blanchard, Baulig, Siegfried, Cholley, Sorre, and many others. By reason of their cohesion and mutual collaboration they have made outstanding contributions, first to the status of the subject as an integrating link between the humanities—especially history, and the natural sciences; secondly, to its consequential acceptance in higher studies as an analytical subject and to the use of geographers in governmental work; thirdly, to the development of the inner framework of the subject by their work in Regional, Human, and Physical Geography.

The awakening of interest in geography among the general public in France dates from their losses in the Franco-Prussian War of 1870–1. Smarting under this defeat in Europe, France sought compensation in new lands in Africa and South-East Asia. The newly founded geographical societies in the provinces of France were the leaders in this movement in favour of colonial expansion.[1] Their action is discussed again later in this chapter, but here be it noted that it caused the general public to be more interested in the better kind of descriptive geography and that this was a valuable stage forward from 'gazetteer geography'.

There has been a chair of Geography at the Sorbonne, Paris, since

[1] See D. V. McKay, 'Colonialism in the French Geographical Movement, 1871–1881', *Geographical Review*, 1943, pp. 214–32.

1809 and another of Colonial Geography since 1892. A chair was created at Lille in 1893 for Professor Ardaillon who established there a separate Institute of Geography. There were also departments at Bordeaux, Lyons, Nancy, and Rennes by 1899. In the latter year de Martonne, then in his first university appointment, founded a special Laboratory of Geography at Rennes. In the University of Lyons, the teaching of geography has almost as long a history as at Paris; and at the end of the nineteenth century Professor Lespagnol had built up a noteworthy Institute and Museum. By 1900 we find Paul Vidal de la Blache in charge in Paris, de Martonne at Rennes, P. Camena d'Almeida at Bordeaux, Lespagnol at Lyons, and Augustin Bernard at Algiers, whilst Jean Brunhes was in charge of the department at Fribourg in Switzerland. Courses on Regional, Colonial, and Human Geography were prominent in the Faculties of Letters and Physical Geography in the Faculty of Science.

The beginning of the century is almost everywhere in France the watershed between the old and the new geography. Up to that time, the lectures were given either by historians, or were devised as subordinate to the teaching of history. In such circumstances, geography was considered as a mere description of real or supposed environmental influences upon historical development. At Besançon there was a chair of Modern Historical Geography, at Clermont Ferrand one of Ancient and Medieval Historical Geography, and at the Collège de France in Paris Research chairs of Historical Geography and of the Historical Geography of France. Yet in all but the latter, the real emphasis was on the history of geographical discovery, the study of the origin and evolution of place-names and of the history of frontiers. In French schools the geography taught was still of the 'gazetteer' type. Physical Geography if taught in the universities was in the province of geologists, and had the usual sub-surface emphasis normally given by pure geologists. Geological studies had made great progress in France in the nineteenth century, largely due to the work of Du Frénoy and Élie de Beaumont, but their work had not penetrated to such geographers as there were, since the latter had been trained first in history and had taught in conjunction with history courses. Thus most of them had neither the training nor the inclination to make geographical use of geological advances. Lastly, because of the strict and most unfortunate sharp division between the Faculties of Science and Letters, the geographers in the Faculty of Letters could not give courses on Physical Geography in that Faculty.

Elisée Reclus, who died in 1905, was the most famous representative of the best kind of descriptive geography. His influence was greater outside France than within, since his advanced political views caused him

6

to protest against the *coup d'état* of 1851, a protest which caused his banishment. He was later allowed to return, but in 1871 he took part in the Paris Commune. For this he was deported, a sentence later reduced to banishment after an international petition was sent to France on his behalf. His great work *Nouvelle Géographie Universelle—la Terre et les Hommes* was a synthesis of the results of geographical exploration. It was a mine of information, with considerable scientific detail elegantly described and with beautiful coloured maps. Reclus, although banished for so long from his beloved France, did a very great deal to induce a new interest in geography in France—albeit of a rather literary kind.

In 1898 M. Himly retired from the Chair of Geography at the Sorbonne which he had held for forty years, and was succeeded by Paul Vidal de la Blache. Himly represented the old school of historians who were interested merely in the geographical background to history, and he had published considerable works on the territorial formation of Europe. But he had taken no part in, nor was he interested in, the development of geography in contact with the natural sciences. The development of scientific regional, human, and geomorphological studies owed nothing to him.

Vidal de la Blache, in his Inaugural Lecture on 2 February 1899, immediately drew attention to the need for detailed regional studies to elucidate the influence of the rich variety of factors—physical, historical, political, and economic—which affect the present pattern of an area. He stated his aim as being

to bring into relief the geographical factor, not indeed as explaining history [he was too well informed and sagacious for that], but as a complex influence always to be kept in mind in the study of history. There can be no question of geographical determinism. Nevertheless, geography is the key that cannot be dispensed with.[1]

From detailed regional studies could be built up a synthesis of general and comparative studies, wherein the causes and consequences of the various factors would be clarified. This later led him to plan the great *Géographie Universelle*, the best complete study of the world on a regional basis available in any language. On comparative studies he asserted that

la Géographie comparée, l'idée surtout de toujours en revenir, même pour l'intelligence de l'histoire, à la connaissance du milieu physique, dans ce qu'il y a de complexe, mais aussi d'ordonné, parce que le monde physique est un enchaîne-ment de phénomènes qui réagissent les uns sur les autres. Ce qui revient à dire qu'expliquer les faits particuliers, c'est montrer leur dépendance par rapport aux lois générales, dépendance qui peut être complexe quand les causes qui agissent

[1] Quoted in Obituary notice in *Geographical Journal*, July 1918, p. 64.

sont nombreuses et variées, qui peut même échapper à tout déterminisme lorsque intervient l'activité humaine, mais qui s'exerce toujours par quelque côté, parce que l'homme ne peut se dégager entièrement de la tyrannie des forces naturelles. Les deux termes—nature et histoire sont toujours liés.[1]

Vidal de la Blache proceeded to direct geography away from a subsidiary and stultifying place in historical studies and, whilst keeping links with history, to direct attention to physical factors. He encouraged detailed field studies and their publication as substantial monographs or in the *Annales de Géographie*, which he founded. Under his vigorous leadership, the various university geography departments undertook field studies. As he once said, 'avec les livres on ne fait que de la géographie mediocre, avec les cartes on en fait de la meilleure, on ne la fait très bonne que sur le terrain.'

Reference has been made to the conceptions of Vidal de la Blache as set forth in his Inaugural Lecture and on other occasions. In an article entitled 'Des Caractères distinctifs de la Géographie' in the *Annales de Géographie* for 1913, p. 289, he set forth his ideas more fully. Starting with the assertion that geography must have a place among the natural sciences, as well as in human studies, he laid down six main principles. First, the unity of earth phenomena, by which he understood the interdependence and interconnexions of physical factors. Secondly, the variable combination and modification of phenomena, especially as seen in the study of world climates. Thirdly, that geography is concerned with all phenomena at the surface of the earth. Fourthly, the need to recognize the force of the environment in its various forms and types, such as the vegetational belts of the earth and man's adaptation within them. Fifthly, the need for a scientific method in defining and classifying phenomena; and sixthly, the recognition of the great part of man in modifying his basic environment. He concluded that geography was the scientific study of places and that

ce que la géographie, en échange du secours qu'elle reçoit des autres sciences, peut apporter au trésor commun, c'est l'aptitude à ne pas morceler ce que la nature rassemble, à comprendre la correspondance et le corrélation des faits, soit dans le milieu terrestre qui les enveloppe tous, soit dans les milieux régionnaux où ils se localisent.

Vidal de la Blache was truly the founder of modern scientific geography in France. By his death in 1918 France lost the *doyen* of the subject.

He was succeeded at the Sorbonne by Lucien Gallois, a kindred spirit. Like Vidal de la Blache he had been brought up in the historical tradition and for his doctorate produced a magnificent study of *Les géographes*

[1] Obituary notice in *Annales de Géographie*, 1918, p. 163.

allemands de la Renaissance (1890). Yet like his predecessor he saw the need for physical studies, and produced in 1908 his distinctive *Régions naturelles et noms de pays: Etude sur la région parisienne*, again following closely the interests of la Blache. He had collaborated with Vidal de la Blache in the direction of the *Annales de Géographie*, and after the death of the latter took over the organization of the *Géographie Universelle*. Again he combined, as do so many eminent French geographers, a sure knowledge of history with that of the physiography of a region. The American Geographical Society honoured him in 1926 with the Cullum Medal; and Douglas Johnson then said of him that he was 'one whose high erudition is graced by the charms of a delightful personality and then both the head and heart rejoice'. In every way he maintained the work and outlook of Vidal de la Blache.

By 1922 the French School of Geography had practically recovered from the losses and dislocations due to the First World War. Although the central figure in the scientific revolution in geography had died in 1918, the subject was well established at nearly all the sixteen French universities, at Algiers, and at four out of five of the free Catholic universities.[1] The heads of department were in every case either the pupils of Vidal de la Blache or pupils of his pupils. At Paris Gallois was in charge and lecturing on the political geography of post-war Eurasia; de Martonne was delivering his two-year course in Physical Geography and giving regional courses on the Alps and the Mediterranean peninsulas; Demangeon was responsible for Economic Geography and was discussing the localization of the world's textile industries besides giving regional courses on South-East Asia; Bernard was offering courses on the human geography of French North Africa and on problems of African geography, whilst Gentil was responsible for geomorphology. Brunhes at the Collège de France was occupied with the principles of regionalism, especially in France. At the École des Hautes Etudes Commerciales, Maurette and Vallaux were responsible for Economic Geography.

Bordeaux was fortunate in possessing Camena d'Almeida, the great authority on Russia, and Max Sorre. The former dealt with geomorphology, Human Geography, and the regional geography of Central Europe, whilst Sorre was responsible for Colonial Geography. Arbos was in charge at Clermont Ferrand, as he still is, and offered similar courses to those at Bordeaux, save that there were none on Colonial Geography. Blanchard,

---

[1] The French Universities are: Paris, Aix, Besançon, Bordeaux, Caen, Clermont Ferrand, Dijon, Grenoble, Lille, Lyons, Montpellier, Nancy, Poitiers, Rennes, Strasbourg, and Toulouse. The Catholic Universities are at Paris, Lille, Angers, Lyons, and Toulouse.

who had been at Grenoble nearly twenty years, had by 1922 created a world-famous department and Institute. He had organized excursions of outstanding merit and published much of his work and that of his students on the physical and human geography of the Alps in the journal he founded now called the *Revue de Géographie Alpine*. His department offered a very wide range of regional courses as well as those on Physical and Human Geography. At Lyons, another famous and well-equipped department, Zimmermann was in charge, having succeeded de Martonne who was here after leaving Rennes and before going to the Sorbonne.

Apart from the usual range of courses, Colonial Geography was particularly well developed especially in the comparative and economic fields. Sion was in charge at Montpellier, Musset at Rennes, and Baulig at Strasbourg, the last two specializing in Physical Geography and the study of France. Chabot, then lecturing on Europe, was also a member of the Strasbourg Faculty. At Algiers, Gautier was specializing on Colonial Geography, particularly of the French Empire, the physical geography of the Sahara and the historical geography of Algeria. The great geologist and physical geographer, Emmanuel de Margerie, who has had such a long and brilliant career, must also be noticed at this stage as the translator and annotator of Suess' *Das Anlitz der Erde*, and as the Director of the Geological Survey of liberated Alsace-Lorraine. Largely due to Vidal de la Blache, scientific geography was well established in French university life.[1]

Regional Geography

Vidal de la Blache, Gallois, and de Martonne have been the main inspirers in the production of a large number of regional monographs, particularly of French regions. These have a characteristic imprint very expressive of the French School in its evolution from subservience to history. The French have successfully merged the historical and geological schools and have achieved a regional synthesis unsurpassed elsewhere and for which they are justly renowned. It is this breadth of vision on the one hand, and a fine literary style on the other, that make French regional studies such a pleasure to read. Scientific analysis sustains their descriptions, and their expository art has survived. In France, geography has

---

[1] For details of courses at the various universities see *Annales de Géographie*, 1900, p. 82; 1901, p. 80; 1902, pp. 81 and 465; *Bulletin de la Société Royale Belge de Géographie*, 1906, p. 35; *La Géographie*, 1902, p. 433; 1920, p. 425; 1921, p. 555, and in succeeding volumes. See also *Geography in France*, Emm. de Martonne, American Geographical Society Research Series No. 4a, 1924, and 'Recent Geographical Work in Europe', W. L. G. Joerg, *Geographical Review*, 1922, p. 438.

become scientific, but has remained an art. Its literature is a thing of beauty, not a mass of technical jargon. It has become, on appropriate occasions, a light to history, rather than its dull servant. Demangeon's little book on Paris and his work on Rural Habitat are good examples of this latter point and no one can fail to appreciate the literary style of de Martonne or Siegfried.

It is manifestly impossible to describe the full magnitude of regional work in France, although this development is central to the French outlook. Demangeon's *Picardie*, which was his thesis published in 1905, was to serve as the model, soon joined by Blanchard's *La Flandre* published in 1906. Gallois' *Régions naturelles et noms de pays* already mentioned in this chapter, dealt with some of the problems of definition as illustrated in the Paris Basin.[1] A classic was Vidal de la Blache's *Tableau de la Géographie de la France* written for the first volume of Lavisse's *Histoire de France* and published thus in 1903. So successful was it that it was republished separately in 1908 with illustrations. The last book he published before his death, *La France de l'Est* (1917), was a return to the interests of his youth. Other outstanding studies have been: A. Vacher, *Le Berry* (1908); Passerat, *Le Poitou* (1909); M. Sorre, *Les Pyrénées méditerranéennes* (1913); R. Musset, *Le Bas Maine* (1917); P. Arbos, *La Vie Pastorale dans les Alpes françaises* (1922); A. Cholley, *Les Préalpes de Savoie* (1925); Emm. de Martonne, *Les Alpes* (1926); R. Blanchard, *Les Alpes françaises*; H. Baulig, *Le Plateau Central* (1928); and R. Dion, *Le Val de la Loire* (1934). This list is by no means comprehensive and includes only studies of French areas. Further references are made elsewhere in this chapter.

Regional studies in France have also been advanced by the university syllabuses which prescribe that students should prepare short but original pieces of work on small areas, or a relatively minor topic discussed over a wide area, for the *Diplôme d'études supérieures* and other certificates, the latter counting towards the *licence*.

Intensive as has been the study of the regions of France, the French have made an even greater contribution to geography by the *Géographie Universelle* series. Originally planned by Vidal de la Blache, who was succeeded on his death by Lucien Gallois, this series was greatly delayed by the First World War and the consequential obscurity of the world

---

[1] This treatise owed much to the 1 : 500,000 map of France published by the Dépôt des Fortifications under the direction of F. Prudent. This map, still of very great value in its oro-hydrography edition, shows the names of *pays*. Gallois was inspired by this map to write his book, and to urge upon the French Government on many occasions the need for better units than the departments. Vidal de la Blache made the same point in two articles entitled 'Les Régions Françaises', *Revue de Paris*, 1910, and 'La Renovation de la Vie Régionale', *Revue de Paris*, 1917.

picture. The first volumes to appear were those on the British Isles and the Low Countries, both by Demangeon and both published in 1927, representing thereby a great achievement by author and publisher alike. That on the British Isles was translated into Spanish, Czech, and English and is a standard work even for British students. It is invidious to pick out individual volumes in a large series which throughout maintains such a high order of scientific accuracy combined with broad vision and fine style in language and publishing, but mention might first be made of de Martonne's two volumes on Central Europe, published in 1930–1. They are particularly distinguished by his fine maps and photographs and the brilliant analysis of the physical geography. Yet equally profound is his discussion of national groups in which he shows his debt to the viewpoint of la Blache. Throughout, he has a philosophy—a key to the nature of central Europe. He regards it as the meeting-place of the Russian plain, of western Europe, northern Europe, and southern Europe. He works this out particularly in regard to the physique, climate, hydrography, vegetation, and the reaction of man. This philosophic key—a tool so necessary to understanding the essence of a large area, yet so frequently missing in non-French studies, where their literary logic is also missing—is summarized by de Martonne thus:

ainsi l'Europe centrale n'est pas un mot. Nous y reconnaissons une partie de notre continent, moins massive que l'Europe de l'Est, moins divisée que l'Europe péninsulaire et periphérique; moins précoce dans son développement que celle-ci, plus avancée incontestablement que celle-là; pays d'instabilité politique prolongée, répondant à une instabilité éthnique, lieu de rencontre d'influences qui se fondent plus harmonieusement dans l'Europe océanique, qui s'étalent plus largement dans l'Europe continentale de l'Est; région de contrastes violents de relief et de climat où les individualités locales basées sur la race et le milieu sont plus conscientes que dans l'Europe orientale, plus persistantes que dans l'Europe péninsulaire.[1]

The two volumes in this series on North America by Henri Baulig of Strasbourg have been described as constituting 'the best general regional geography of North America in any language'. For this work and that in geomorphology to be described later, Baulig was awarded the Charles P. Daly Medal for 1948 by the American Geographical Society.

The firm of Colin, founded by Armand Colin who died in 1900, has rendered a great service to geography by its publication of the *Géographie Universelle* and most of the large regional studies detailed above, as well as studies of non-French regions and of la Blache's *Principes de Géographie*

[1] Emm. de Martonne, *Europe Centrale*. *Géographie Universelle*, Tome IV, 1er partie, p. 3.

humaine, Max Sorre's *Les Fondements de la Géographie humaine*, de Martonne's *Traité de Géographie Physique*, and many geological studies by Haug, de Launay, and de Margerie's translation of Suess. They are the publishers of many smaller but brilliant geographical studies in the *Collection Armand Colin*.[1]

Since its inception in 1891 this firm has been responsible for the remarkable *Annales de Géographie*. Founded by Vidal de la Blache, assisted by Marcel Dubois, and later directed by L. Gallois, Emm de Martonne, A. Demangeon, and others, this journal is virtually unique in geographical literature in that it is not a journal of a learned society nor a journal of popular geography for the general public. It has had remarkable success inside France in the development of the subject, and outside France has been the main vehicle for spreading knowledge of the activities and ideas of French geographers. At first less than half its material was contributed by geographers. The articles were mainly on Europe and dealt with matters of Physical Geography. But by 1910, when scientific geography was being accorded an established place in higher studies in France, a change was noticeable, and the articles now became mainly the fruits of regional research by geographers. After the First World War even more attention was paid to Human Geography and to statistical notes.[2]

That great compilation the *Bibliographie Géographique Annuelle* originated in 1891 as part of the *Annales de Géographie*, and was compiled by A. Raveneau. During the war of 1914–18 it had to be abandoned for a time, but was revived by E. Colin and Emm. de Martonne when the latter founded the *Association de Géographes Français* in 1915. Since 1931 it has been known as the *Bibliographie Géographique Internationale* and is published by Armand Colin. It is the leading Geographic Bibliography.

Regional studies in France have been richly sustained by the very large number of geographical societies. The Paris Geographical Society, founded on 15 December 1821 with a membership of 217, is one of the oldest in the world. Local branches of this society have become independent societies. Thus there are or have been societies at Bordeaux,

---

[1] Famous titles are *Les Pyrénées*, M. Sorre; *Les Alpes françaises*, R. Blanchard; *Peuples et Nations des Balkans*, J. Ancel; *Les Alpes*, Emm. de Martonne; *Le Maroc*, J. Célérier; *La Crise Britannique au XXe siècle*, A. Siegfried; *L'Auvergne*, P. Arbos; *Fleuves et Rivières*, M. Pardé; *La France méditerranéenne*, J. Sion; *L'Afrique Centrale*, M. Robert; *L'Irelande*, A. Rivoallan; *L'Indochine française*, Charles Robequain; *La Tchécoslovaquie*, A. Tibal; *Extrême Orient et Pacifique*, R. Levy; *La Bretagne*, R. Musset; *La Turquie*, M. Clerget; *La Terre et l'Homme en Extrême Orient*, P. Gourou; *La Bourgogne*, G. Chabot.

[2] See Emm. de Martonne, 'Le Cinquantenaire des "*Annales de Géographie*"', *Annales de Géographie*, 1942, pp. 1–6.

Toulouse, Marseilles (founded 1876, with a quarterly journal from 1877), Toulon, Montpellier (founded 1878), Lyons (founded 1873, with a quarterly journal since 1875), Rochefort (founded 1878 and journal since 1879), Nantes, Lorient, Bourges, St. Nazaire, Poitiers, Le Mans, Dijon, Tours, Rouen (founded 1879), Le Havre, Dunkirk, Douai (founded 1880), Lille, St. Quentin, Laon, Valenciennes, and Nancy (founded 1879). There are similar societies at Algiers and Oran both dating from 1878, and one at Casablanca which was formed in 1922. Most of these societies have a house and library and publish papers and transactions. They have combined in frequent national congresses since 1878, and have encouraged detailed studies of local areas to a far greater extent than is true in other nations.[1]

Human Geography

The French have also excelled in the study and development of Human Geography. In this, as in Regional Geography, they have brought to their geographical work a fine literary style and a firm historical background which is particularly important in this aspect of geography. They have developed Human Geography as an entity, without undue subdivision into a multitude of doubtful sub-specialisms. Here again the work of Vidal de la Blache is pre-eminent. His *Principes de Géographie Humaine*, which was published posthumously in 1922 (through the efforts of Emm. de Martonne), is regarded by geographers as a classic. The historical evolution of each phenomenon in Human Geography is followed by a study of its present setting, localization, and correlations. In the Introduction he again analyses the principle of geographical unity, the significance of the environmental factor and of man's work in it. The first part of his book is devoted to studying the distribution, density, and movements of population in the world. Part 2 consists of an analysis of methods man has used to develop his environment and of his several civilizations, and Part 3 deals with transport and communications. The arguments are closely reasoned and the book has had great success in the English-speaking world through its English translation.

Another early writer in Human Geography was Jean Brunhes, a pupil of Vidal de la Blache. As early as 1901 Brunhes was lecturing in Paris at the Collège Libre des Sciences Sociales on the localization of settlement, rural house forms, the shape of villages and towns, and cognate matters. Brunhes published his *Géographie Humaine* in 1910, and it was revised and

---

[1] For fuller details of this matter consult D. V. McKay, 'Colonialism in the French Geographical Movement, 1871–1881', *Geographical Review*, 1943, pp. 214–32; and Emm. de Martonne, *Geography in France*, 1924, pp. 6–17.

enlarged in 1912, 1925, and 1934, the latter edition being revised after his death (in 1930) by his daughter Mme. Raymonde Brunhes-Delamarre. The book was published in America in 1920 as *Human Geography*, being translated and edited by I. Bowman, R. E. Dodge, and T. C. Le Compte. This book was the first large-scale attempt in France to examine fully the geographical facts in human economy. In the first volume he described and analysed the many patterns of man's occupancy of the earth as expressed in housing types; in village and town sites, their shapes and development; and in changing forms of communication. In the second section he discussed man's conquest and adaptation of the vegetable and animal kingdoms by his various agricultural techniques; and in the third section his study concerns man's destructive or robber economies of mineral extraction. All these matters were examined universally as a world picture and in a comparative manner. Volume 2 was devoted to regional examples and Volume 3 to photographs. The book had a great success in France and abroad, and is still justly described as a model study of the varying degrees of geographical influence upon man in his different stages of evolution.

Brunhes, by his training in history, the natural sciences, law, and finance—with his final specialization in Human Geography which he taught in Switzerland and France, was particularly well equipped to assess rightly the varying part that physical factors on the one hand, and social, economic, political, and historical factors on the other hand, have played on various human groups now and in the past. In France the book earned for him the creation of a special Chair in Human Geography at the Collège de France, whither he was called from Switzerland and where he remained thereafter as Research Professor.

Not only was Brunhes a great geographer, but he was an eminent littérateur and orator. His natural charm and ease of manner enabled him to collaborate easily with other geographers and historians, both in France and abroad. Thus in 1921, he published with C. Vallaux *Géographie de l'Histoire-Géographie de la Paix et de la Guerre sur terre et sur mer*. He also collaborated with G. Hanotaux to write for the latter's *Histoire de la Nation Française* two introductory volumes on General and Regional Geography of France, and on the Political and Economic Geography of France, the forms of which were in interesting contrast to the treatment by Vidal de la Blache in his introductory chapter to Lavisse's *Histoire de France*. Brunhes was a great admirer and friend of the American geographer Isaiah Bowman. The latter assisted in making available an American translation of Brunhes' book; and the latter translated Bowman's *New World* into French. Brunhes also collaborated with Deffontaines, Giradin, and his daughter. Outside his university work, Brunhes did much to improve the teaching of geography in French schools by the production of inspiring school text-books and wall maps. He had a wealth of social interests. At the end of his career he was a Director of a French Bank.[1] No one has ever been less of a narrow specialist than he, yet no one more profound in his specialism.

Demangeon, who had published his study of Picardy in 1905, was called from the University of Lille to the Sorbonne in 1911. Thereafter he became another outstanding human geographer of France and by the time of his death in 1940 he had become its most distinguished exponent. He set himself two aims, first to produce a manual of Human Geography which should be briefer and more didactic than that of Brunhes, and secondly to write an economic geography of France. Although not a year passed between 1905 and 1940 (save for two years in the First World War) without his publishing some major work or several articles, he never saw the publication of the two works which he had originally planned. He left copious notes for the first which, it is understood, is now being edited by his son-in-law Professor Aimé Perpillou. Demangeon's philosophy of human geography is contained in his posthumous *Problèmes de Géographie Humaine* published in 1942. His study of the economic geography of France was finally published in 1946–8 in the *Géographie Universelle* series. His great studies of the British Isles and the Low Countries for this series have already been mentioned.

One of Demangeon's greatest interests was rural settlement in France. He published articles in the *Annales de Géographie* and several books on these matters between 1920 and 1939.[2] He took the interior plan and agricultural function of houses as the basic differentiating factors. On the question of settlement, he regarded the degree of concentration or dispersion as the vital matter. His work attracted great attention at the International Geographical Congresses at Cairo, 1925; Cambridge, 1928; and Paris, 1931. In the later thirties he formulated questionnaires concerning rural habitat, agrarian structures and methods, and the part of foreigners in French farming. These inquiries were undertaken for the *Conseil Universitaire de la Recherche Sociale* and financed by the Rockefeller Foundation. The results were incorporated in articles in the *Annales*, in the *Atlas de*

---

[1] Pierre Denis, the great French geographical expert on South America, also turned to banking and other economic matters. He wrote the two volumes on South America in the *Géographie Universelle*; also books on Brazil (1911) and the Argentine (1922).

[2] There is a complete list of Demangeon's writings and an appreciation of him by his colleague and life friend de Martonne in A. Demangeon's posthumous volume *Problèmes de Géographie Humaine*, Colin, 1942.

France, and in his *Problèmes de Géographie Humaine*. Town studies were also his especial interest and that of Paris, published in 1933, is particularly noteworthy.

In the first essay of the *Problèmes de Géographie Humaine* Demangeon defined Human Geography as the study of human groups and societies in their relationships to the physical environment. He laid emphasis on the work of man in modifying his environment by means of communications, artesian wells, the control of rivers, and the evolution of new plants for human food. The study has four main aspects. First, the types of life in the large natural zones of the world—whether these be climatic, vegetational, or soil regions; secondly, the types of technique employed —collection, hunting, fishing, agriculture, stock-rearing, industry, or commerce; thirdly, the distribution, density, and limits of human settlement and the nature of human migrations; fourthly, the types of human settlement. Next he considered the principles behind the whole study. He rejected crude determinism. Thus, islanders are not necessarily seafaring, and the English first became so because of outside influences from northern Europe. Neither do rich soils necessarily cause rich agriculture, which depends upon man's energy and technique. By irrigation man may bring life to deserts, whilst by economic nationalism or necessity man may be led to grow crops beyond their economic margin, as was done by growing the vine in medieval Catholic England. A country may change out of all recognition if it is successfully settled in a short space of time by people of superior technique. Such has been the case with Australia and Palestine. (See, however, p. 16.)

Demangeon regarded it as of the essence of Human Geography that it should be based upon physical regional units. Whilst the sociologist studies the bearing upon settlements of religious, psychological, and social factors, the geographer is concerned with the physical influences or physical setting and pattern. The influence may be second-hand, as for example when a particular kind of region has been adapted to arable farming and this kind of farming leads to particular forms of farms and villages. Lastly, he emphasized the part of historical factors in settlement forms.

It should be noted that French geography has much to show in the way of studies of towns and cities. Apart from Demangeon's study of Paris and another by Gallois, there are other significant studies by J. Levainville on Rouen (Colin, 1913), and on Caen in *La Vie Urbaine* for 1923. Most work has been done by Blanchard, the versatile Professor of Geography at Grenoble, who in 1922 published in that same journal, a study of the methodology of urban geography. His book on Grenoble published in 1911 is a fine study of the general regional situation of the town, its detailed site, historical evolution, and modern status. He organized a regular school of urban geographers at Grenoble, which published detailed studies of Annecy, Albertville, Briançon, and Annonay. Blanchard has also published studies of Lille, Nancy, Lyons, Marseilles, Nice, and Bordeaux.[1] He has also been interested in rural house types in the Alps. Outside France, however, he is probably best known for his work on the physical geography of the French Alps; his great study *L'Est du Canada français-Quebec* (2 vols.), 1935; his *Asie Occidentale* in the *Géographie Universelle*, and his small *L'Amérique du Nord* (1933).

A further examination of the nature of Human Geography is given by P. Deffontaines, a collaborator of Brunhes, in the preface to G. Hardy's *Géographie et Colonisation*. He emphasizes that it is a young subject and since it is still in the exploratory stage, it proceeds by the sampling method. One aspect of the study is the struggle of man against his raw environment and the other aspect analyses the results achieved and classifies the types and limits. Thus on the one side are man's struggles against deserts, mountains, forests, seas, rivers, and on the other side the geography of settlement, transport, and colonization. Brunhes' study of irrigation belongs to the first aspect, and Demangeon's work to the second. Deffontaines differentiated two types of region of human occupancy; one in which there is an individual pattern of human economy and the other where through intensive and long contact present-day life is the result of many complicated influences.

Jean Gottmann, in an article in the *Annales de Géographie* for 1947, has made a revaluation of analytical method in Human Geography. He points out that Vidal de la Blache first elaborated the idea of the differential type of life or economy ('genre de vie'), but that this was still largely descriptive. The next step forward was the concept of the 'front of colonization' or 'pioneer fringe' of Bowman. By the use of this concept, regions were distinguished by the degree of occupancy and development. Gottman describes Demangeon's work, and proposes that more attention should now be given to the study of human mobility, communications, and to industrial location and density. It is doubtful, however, whether Gottmann's ideas fall so squarely within the realm of geography, as did those of la Blache, Brunhes, Demangeon, and Blanchard.

Until recently the study of the direct influence of the physical environment upon man's body and mind has been very neglected by European

[1] See for these town studies *Recueil des Travaux de l'Institut de Géographie Alpine*, Vols. 4 and 6; *Revue de Géographie Alpine*, Vols. 9 and 11; *La Géographie*, Vol. 30; *Revue de Géographie Commerciale*, Bordeaux, Vol. 43.

geographers. In France this field has been entered almost exclusively by Sorre, who in his *Fondements biologiques de la géographie humaine* (1943) has undertaken an ecological study of man with the help of agricultural, anthropological, biological, and medical data. He analyses the effect of the various climatic factors upon the human organism, then passes to crops, food, and diet, and in the last section deals with the stages of man's fight for existence. Sorre is the leader of a valuable new tendency in French geography which seeks closer contacts with the biological sciences.

French geographers have always regarded Historical, Political, Economic, and Colonial Geography as vital parts of the subject, but have sought to keep them within the mansion of Human Geography. This has retarded the growth of all but the last of these sub-specialisms, but the advantage has been the retention of the centrality of geographical studies and the universal recognition in France of geography as a true academic discipline. Outside France, some of these branches have advanced so far to the margins of geography, that historians, political scientists, economists, and anthropologists have claimed—often with justice—that geographers have invaded their fields without bringing in anything new or profound.

That the French have achieved relatively little in Historical Geography is surprising. It may be the natural reaction from the days when geography was entirely subservient to history. In the earlier years of this century it was largely due to initial confusion between the History of Geographical Discovery (which was the main aspect of geography taught in the old days) and real Historical Geography. But in view of the fact that almost all geography students in France study history it is still surprising that few specialized studies have been made in Historical Geography. By way of compensation it may be noted that most of the great treatises of French regions do treat very fully of the historical geography of settlement, crops, agrarian methods and structure, land drainage, and rural industries. Particularly good examples of this are found in Demangeon's book on Picardy and in J. Sion's *Les Paysans de la Normandie Orientale* (1909). Among general studies particular mention should be made of Camille Vallaux's *La Géographie de l'Histoire* (1921), which was written with Brunhes, and of Lucien Febvre's *La Terre et l'evolution humaine* (1922) which was translated into English as *A Geographical Introduction to History* (1925). Vallaux, it may be noted, believed very strongly in geography as an autonomous study whose branches have contributed notably to the natural and social sciences. This he dealt with in *Les sciences géographiques* (1925 and 1929).

Political Geography

Unlike American geographers, the French have achieved relatively little in Economic Geography. Certainly there is a wealth of material on particular industries, crops, and so forth; but little by way of discussion of principles or general surveys of continents or of the world. Economics in France is less well developed than in Britain or America and is still confined to the Faculties of Law. French geographers have had little or no contact with the general principles of economics and therefore they have produced particular rather than general works upon the subject.

In Political Geography, France has produced a few outstanding names, particularly A. Siegfried and J. Ancel—who died in Drancy Concentration Camp during the war. Siegfried has for long held a Research Chair in Political and Economic Geography at the Collège de France where he has undertaken work on the geographical factors in French political parties and elections. Some results of this may be seen in his *Tableau politique de la France de l'Ouest sous la Troisième Republique* and *Tableau des partis en France*. Siegfried has been most successful in securing recognition of the value of geography among economists and politicians inside France and in the Anglo-Saxon world. His lectures at the Institut des Sciences Politiques on the Political and Economic Geography of the Great Powers are regarded as outstanding in the French academic world. His books on England, the United States, Latin America, Canada, New Zealand, the Suez and Panama Canals and the Mediterranean have been highly successful among geographers and general readers in France and outside and have had many translations. Siegfried has indeed interpreted to the general reader the significance of the geographical factor, yet he has remained a great scholar of geography. He is highly respected in France and is the sole geographer ever to be a member of the *Academic Française*, to which he was elected in 1945.

Before his tragic death, Ancel had completed three volumes of his *Manuel Géographique de Politique européenne*. Tome 1, *L'Europe Centrale*, was published in 1936, part 1 of Tome 2, *L'Europe Germanique et ses Bornes*, in 1940, and part 2, *L'Allemagne* in 1945. Among many other studies, *Peuples et Pays des Balkans* (1930), *Géopolitique* (1936), and *Géographie des frontières* (1938) stand out. He was a staunch opponent of German 'geopolitics' as developed by Haushofer. Ancel denied that language was any sure guide to true national feelings. In the preface to *L'Europe Germanique et ses Bornes* he states 'enchevêtrement des paysages, opposition des genres de vie, traditions differentes dans le labeur—voilà à première vue les raisons d'être des contrastes que la géographie accuse mais que l'histoire amenuise'. In the second part he says 'nous chercherons à élucider les forces géographiques, specifiquement les pressions humaines, qui ont poussé les Allemagnes à s'unifier en Allemagne'.

Of all the sub-divisions of Human Geography, it is in Colonial Geography that the French have made their greatest contribution. In his article on 'Colonialism in the French Geographical Movement' in the *Geographical Review* for 1943, D. V. McKay details the part played by French geographical societies in popularizing the idea of French Colonial expansion, particularly in the decade 1871–81. Attention was directed mainly to Africa, particularly to North and West Africa. The first Chair of Colonial Geography was created in 1892 at Paris for Marcel Dubois who had been *Maître de Conférences* in the same subject back to 1885. It was he who with Vidal de la Blache established the *Annales de Géographie* in 1891 and from the first about 20 per cent of the articles in that journal have been devoted to colonial matters. In 1895 a *Bureau Scientifique d'Études Coloniales* was established at the Sorbonne, and similar provision was soon made at Lyons and Algiers. By 1902 we find Colonial Geography courses being given at Paris, Lyons, Aix-Marseilles, Bordeaux, Algiers, Caen, Toulouse, Lille, Clermont Ferrand, and Algiers. They were also provided at the École Coloniale (a staff college for colonial administrators founded in 1889) at the École (now Institut) des Sciences Politiques and in many other places, especially under the auspices of Chambers of Commerce.

In Paris, Dubois was succeeded in the chair by Augustin Bernard and the chair was then renamed that of North African Geography. A later holder was Professor Larnaude. In 1937 the original title was restored in a second chair which Professor Robequain holds. In 1946 three new chairs were created, one at Strasbourg held by Dresch, the second at Aix-en-Provence held by Isnard, and the third at Bordeaux held by Revert. At the colonial staff college (now called the École de la France d'Outre Mer) there are chairs of Colonial Regional Geography and of Tropical Geography. To this latter post Dresch was appointed in 1947. At the Collège de France there is a Research Chair of Tropical Geography held by Pierre Gourou, and at Algiers the chair of North African Geography has been held by Hardy, Bernard, and Gautier.

The French conception of Colonial Geography is best expressed by Demangeon in his little book *L'Empire Britannique* (1923, with English translation 1925 and German 1926). In the Introduction he explains that it is not merely a question of studying the regional geography of the colonies, for that is part of the normal work of the regional geographer. Rather it is a study of the geographical effects of the contact of two types of peoples associated by the fact of colonization.[1] Demangeon then proceeded to work out the implications of this in the British Empire, whilst G. Hardy in his *Géographie et Colonisation* (1933) has done the same for colonization in general. So great have been the detailed works on French colonies and general colonial matters that it must suffice to indicate a few merely by way of illustration. The *Atlas des Colonies Françaises* by G. Grandidier is an encyclopaedia in its text as well as being a superb atlas. Among outstanding authors we may cite A. Bernard, E. F. Gautier, Ch. Robequain, Y. Urvoy, J. Weulersse, P. Gourou, and Th. Monod, the latter being the Director of the *Institut Français d'Afrique Noire* which is doing such fine research work on Tropical Africa.[2]

Physical Geography

Since Analytical Geography first evolved in France from history, the whole emphasis of its trend has been with the humanities. The development of Physical Geography was slower and was effected either by geographers taking further training in geology or by geologists becoming interested in surface forms. As Professor Linton has pointed out, the genius of the French is for apt and vivid characterization of the essence of a region in words, illustrated by maps and diagrams. They have not restricted themselves to delimiting hard boundaries.[3]

It is Emm. de Martonne who was the first French geographer to concentrate on Physical Geography. He has produced one of the fundamental geographical texts for geographers the world over, namely, his *Traité de Géographie Physique* first published in 1909, when the author was

---

[1] The author of this present chapter has a fuller analysis of Colonial Geography in a paper published by the Institute of British Geographers in 1948.

[2] See the Memoirs of the *Comité d'Études Historiques et Scientifiques de l'Afrique Occidentale Française*, also *Memoirs* of the Institut Français d'Afrique Noire. Among many books by the above authors we may cite A. Bernard, *L'Evolution du nomadisme en Algérie* (1906); *L'Enquête sur l'habitation rurale des indigènes de l'Algérie* (1921); *Le Maroc* (many editions); *Atlas d'Algérie et de Tunisie* (1923); *Afrique Septentrionale et Occidentale* (*Géographie Universelle*, 1939). E. F. Gautier *Madagascar* (1902); *L'Afrique Noire Occidentale* (1935); *L'Afrique Blanche* (1939). Ch. Robequain, *L'Evolution économique de l'Indochine Française* (1939). Y. Urvoy, *Petit Atlas ethnodémographique du Soudan entre Sénégal et Tchad* (1942). J. Weulersse, *L'Afrique Noire* (1934); *Le Pays des Alaouites* (1941). P. Gourou, *L'Utilisation du sol en Indochine Française* (1940); *La Terre et l'Homme en Extrême-Orient* (1940); *Géographie des Pays Tropicaux* (1946). Th. Monod, *L'hippopotame et le philosophe* (1943).

[3] D. L. Linton, 'The delimitation of Morphological Regions', published in 1950 in *London Essays in Geography*. Edited by L. D. Stamp and S. W. Wooldridge.

7

in charge of the Department of Geography at the University of Lyons. This classic has had six editions, has been rearranged in a shorter edition *Abrégé de Géographie physique*, and has been translated in its various forms into many languages. When he succeeded Gallois as the Director of the *Institut de Géographie* at the Sorbonne he was able to secure the maximum possible recognition for his specialism. For some twenty years he was the senior professor in France, until succeeded in 1945 by Professor Cholley. During this period he brought a new viewpoint to the fore at Paris, where the previous heads—la Blache and Gallois—had both been rather more interested in Regional and Human Geography. The whole world is heavily indebted to de Martonne not only for his work on Physical Geography in general, Roumania, the Alps, Central Europe, and the physical geography of France,[1] but also for his outstanding work for the various International Geographical Congresses and the International Geographical Union, of which he was such an energetic and inspiring President.

De Martonne founded in 1905 the Annual Inter-University Geographical Excursion in France, which he has continued to organize ever since. It is based in turn on each of the French universities and is attended for one week by staff and senior students from each university department of geography. The present author, who was a member of the 1937 excursion based upon Bordeaux, looks back upon it as the most fruitful week in his geographical experience, since it enabled him not only to study an area then new to him, but to see it analysed by experts from all over France and to discuss methodology and viewpoints with staff and students from many different schools of geography.

With that equally eminent geologist Emm. de Margerie, de Martonne brought to completion in 1943 the magnificent *Atlas de France* which, in nearly 90 sheets and some 200 superbly coloured maps, covers every conceivable matter of France capable of cartographic representation. It has been truly said that 'a national atlas is an infallible test of the position attained by scientific geography in the country which produces it, as is also the reception accorded the atlas by the general public.[2]

The other two great physical geographers in France are Blanchard who, apart from studies in Human and Regional Geography to which reference has already been made, has done long work on the French

---

[1] See *La Valachie* (1902); 'Recherches sur l'évolution morphologique des alpes de Transylvanie' (*Revue de Géographie Annuelle*, 1906–7); *Les Alpes* (1926); *L'Europe Centrale* (*Géographie Universelle*, 1930–1); *La Géographie Physique de la France* (*Géographie Universelle*, 1942).

[2] *Bulletin de la Société Belge d'Études géographiques*, Jan. 1948, p. 1.

Alps; and Baulig who distinguished himself in analysing the Central Massif, particularly its several erosion and peneplain surfaces.[1]

Blanchard tries to work out the consequences of physical factors upon man's economy, whilst Baulig is very strictly geomorphological in his attitude. De Martonne occupies an intermediate position between Baulig and Blanchard. Many of the most important studies in Physical Geography are to be found in the *Revue de Géographie Annuelle*.

The Second World War had a serious effect upon French geography. Apart from the sad passing of Sion, Demangeon, Gallois, Albitreccia, Robert-Muller, and Camena d'Almeida by more or less natural causes; Lefebvre and Ancel died as the result of enemy action; and Musset, Baulig, and Elicio Colin suffered cruel imprisonment. Field work became impossible, except in the home district, and lack of access to statistics and the censorship prevented studies in Economic and Political Geography. French geographers did not have the chance to apply their specialized knowledge in governmental work as had the British, Americans, and Germans. Instead, they were forced back on elaborating their existing material and making it ready for publication. A surprising amount was published and it included many great works.[2] There was a very noticeable trend to Physical Geography, for the reason stated above. That tendency remains, due to the general uncertainty of post-war economic and political conditions. Since the Liberation, however, there is also a greater interest in Social Geography. Since French geographers were unable to travel, many re-examined their philosophic conceptions of the subject; and a short and concise view is to be found in A. Cholley's *Guide de l'Etudiant en Géographie*, published in 1942. Professor Cholley is now in charge at Paris and is the Dean of the Faculty of Letters.

A second chair of Geography has been created in the Universities of Bordeaux, Rennes, and Lille. Lyons and Strasbourg were so provided before the war. Paris now has six chairs. The new provision of chairs of Colonial Geography at three universities has already been mentioned. A new degree in geography has been established in France as also a separate *Agrégation*. It is in geography that the greatest increases in students have been noted in almost all French universities since the war.

As French geography moves forward towards completing a half-

[1] R. Blanchard, *Les Alpes Françaises* (several editions); *Les Alpes Occidentales* (in several volumes, 1938, 1941, 1943, 1945, &c.). H. Baulig, *Le Plateau Central* (1928). Both have also published works in the *Géographie Universelle*. See earlier references in this chapter to both men.

[2] See 'Geography and Geographical Studies in France during the War and the Occupation', A. Perpillon, *Geographical Journal*, Vol. CVII, pp. 50-7; and 'French Geography in Wartime', Jean Gottmann, *Geographical Review*, 1946, pp. 80-91.

century as a scientific study, the spirit of Vidal de la Blache is still evident
in the work now being done. The geography of his time has been enlarged
in scope and method by such men as de Martonne, Blanchard, Siegfried,
and Sorre. By their breadth of vision and fine literary style, originality
of approach, attention to detail—yet massive output, the French School
of Geography—although built up on such slender financial resources—
is the admiration of the world.

REFERENCES

The major studies by French geographers in each field, as also articles and com-
mentaries, have already been mentioned in the text and are not repeated here.
Other important references are:

Emm. de Martonne, 'Tendances et avenir de la Géographie moderne'. *Revue de
l'Université de Bruxelles,* 1914, pp. 453–79.
    'La Science Géographique' in *La Science Française,* Vol. 2, p. 375. Paris, 1915.
    Geography in France (American Geographical Society Research Series, No. 4a,
    1924).
W. L. G. Joerg, 'Recent Geographical Work in Europe', *Geographical Review,* 1922.
    For France see p. 438.
Emm. de Martonne, 'Le Cinquantenaire des *"Annales de Géographie"* ', *Annales de
Géographie,* 1942, pp. 1–6.

The volumes of the *Annales de Géographie* are a great source of information upon
the work, trends, and outlook of French Geography over the last fifty-seven years.

CHAPTER IV

THE GERMAN SCHOOL OF GEOGRAPHY

SAMUEL VAN VALKENBURG

Professor van Valkenburg was born at Leeuwarden, Netherlands. He attended the Universities of Utrecht, Zurich (Ph.D., 1918), Berlin, Lausanne, and Neuchatel. During 1921-6 he was Government Geographer in the East Indies. Thereafter he joined the staffs of Wayne and Clark Universities, becoming Director of the Graduate School of Geography at the latter in 1946. He has published several books on Europe, Political Geography, and Military Geography.

THIS personal evaluation of German geography and German geographers since the beginning of the century, does not purport to be an exhaustive study of German geographic thought, such as Richard Hartshorne made in his book, *The Nature of Geography*. Time available for the study did not permit careful reading of the huge volume of geographic material published in Germany during the period, while the space allotted allows only a rather brief general discussion. The author spent three semesters (1915–16) in the department of geography of Berlin University working under Albrecht Penck, and visited Germany many times afterwards while always trying to keep up with German publications.

Although he has great admiration for German geographic training and the scientific work done by German geographers, he cannot forget that German geographers, if not directly favouring German aggression and expansion, practically never protested against such policies. Their guilt lay not so much in what they did as in what they did not. Accordingly the study will, in spots, be rather adversely critical, and the way German geographers were involved in the events of the Hitler period and the collapse which followed will be emphasized. Nevertheless, he wishes to plead for the present German geographers, in their efforts to reoccupy their field, in teaching as well as in research; they need the understanding and co-operation of American and other geographers to restore geography to its proper role in the reconstruction of Germany as an asset to the world. The study is written in the hope that German geography will again take its place of prominence, such as it had in the days before two great wars had wrecked the German mind.

The chapter is divided into several units, each representing a period of development in German geography. They are generally limited by non-geographical events, such as war, recovery from inflation, and the rise of the Nazi doctrine and Nazi party. Such a course may impress the reader at first sight as illogical; however, for Germany no other divisions seemed possible.

The Turn of the Century (Period up to 1905)

At the dawn of this century German geography had already laid the solid foundation on which its house could be built. The decline which had followed the death of Alexander von Humboldt and of Karl Ritter (both in 1859), the two forerunners of modern German geography, had been overcome chiefly through the efforts of two other great men, Ferdinand von Richthofen and Friedrich Ratzel. Both men were still active when the present century started, but died soon afterwards: von Richthofen in 1904, Ratzel in 1905. Their influence was so deep and widespread, that no study of German geography, even of present conditions, would be complete without an evaluation of their role, brief as it must be.

Both came to geography by way of the physical sciences, von Richthofen by way of geology and Ratzel by way of a combination of geology, zoology, and comparative anatomy. Von Richthofen remained primarily a physiographer, although he did not neglect the human side. In his famous work on China, for instance, he stresses influence of the environment—which was his major concern—on the life of the people. Though Ratzel was the great anthropogeographer he never forgot his background and put a great deal of emphasis on the physical factors under which man lives.

Both were prominent teachers, von Richthofen at the Berlin University and Ratzel at Leipzig; both attracted many students, also from abroad. Of the two, Ratzel was the more popular and more than a hundred students wrote their dissertations under his direction. Von Richthofen appealed more to the mature geographers, even to those who had finished their academic study and still came to listen to his lectures. Ratzel was the prolific writer and some of his work, especially on anthropo- and political geography, is still regarded as essential reading for the geographer of today. Von Richthofen, in contrast, published personally only a part of his immense field material on eastern China.

It is understandable that the two masters were not the only noteworthy geographers of the period; others were prominent, although somewhat overshadowed. Otto Krümmel, the German oceanographer, whose handbook in that field is still used for reference, was professor at Kiel. George Gerland in Strasbourg worked in the border field between geography and geophysics; he was especially known for his knowledge of earthquakes. Alexander Supan, the publisher of *Petermann's Mitteilungen*, was especially known for his *Handbook of Physical Geography*. Julius Hann, at the University of Vienna, may not have regarded himself as a geographer, but his famous book on Climatology, which was published in 1897, had great effect on development of that field. Wilhelm Sievers at Giessen wrote a set of continental studies, which at that time were regarded as quite good. Theobald Fischer at Marburg was the expert on the Mediterranean, while Rudolf Credner at Griefswald covered the Baltic.

The rebirth of geographic interest attracted many young men, who were preparing themselves to take over leadership, when they matured. Extensive travels, field studies, and many important publications were indications of such preparations, and many of the so-called younger group already occupied university positions. Albrecht Penck, the author of *Morphology of the Earth's Surface*,[1] was at Vienna; Alfred Hettner, the methodologist, at Heidelberg; Alfred Philippson, who had published excellent studies on Greece, at Bern; and Karl Theodore Sapper, the expert on Latin America, at Tübingen; and Joseph Partsch, the author of a complete geographic study of Silesia, at Breslau.

Two new monthly magazines were added to the number of geographic periodicals, of which *Petermann's Mitteilungen* and the *Zeitschrift der Gesellschaft für Erdkunde zu Berlin* had previously been most prominent. One of the two, the *Geographische Anzeiger*, published by Justus Perthes, concerned itself chiefly with education, while the other, the *Geographische Zeitschrift* under editorship of Hettner, became one of the best geographic magazines published anywhere.

Educationally geography had become well recognized in Germany. In 1900 most of the more important German universities had a professorship in geography (see Fig. 5). Little difference can be made between Germany and Austria; nationality played only a minor part. It was, however, different for Switzerland, where at the Universities of Basel, Zurich, and Bern, the classes were given in German. The Swiss had—and still have—a strong sentiment for the home product, although Germans often had to be brought in because of lack of suitable Swiss candidates.

The rapidly increasing number of trained geographers made it possible to appoint *Privatdozenten*, who, after completing a special post-doctoral study, were allowed to give classes at universities; they could be compared

[1] Titles of publications are often translated because of the non-professional character of this book. The first name of the German geographers is only given the first time and not repeated, except in specific cases.

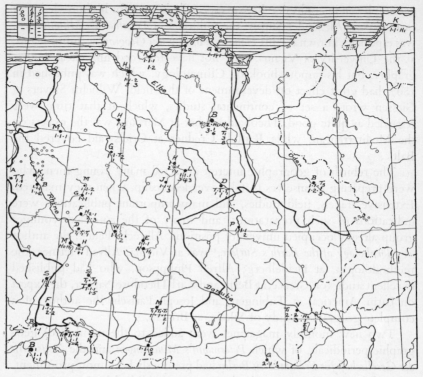

FIG. 5.—German geographers holding University lectureships.

The three vertical columns at each city represent the numbers of staff in 1900, 1914, 1935. *T* means Technical School; *H*, High School

to the American rank of instructor or even assistant-professor and it was from this group that new professors were usually selected.

Professional work, however, was still heavy. J. Russell Smith, who visited Germany during this period, gave the following example with regard to Professor Ratzel:[1]

Professor Ratzel regularly conducts a seminar, usually in some prescribed field, but the variety of work done in a term of years is as varied as his lecture courses. In the last eleven semesters (half-years) he has delivered the following twenty courses of lectures with only seven repetitions, a total of twenty-seven courses given.

Lectures by Professor Ratzel: The Extra European Countries Politically and Industrially Considered, 4 hrs. (per week); Biological Geography and Introduction to Anthropological Geography, 3 hrs.; Commercial Geography, 4 hrs.; Seas,

[1] *Journal of Geography*, 'Geography in Germany', p. 455.

Rivers, and Lakes, 2 hrs.; The Scientific Basis for the Judging of People, 1 hr.; General *Erdkunde*, Part I, Islands and Forms of Land, 4 hrs.; Contemporary Countries and Peoples of Europe with Especial Attention to Political and Industrial Conditions, 3 hrs.; Introduction to the Study and Teaching of Geography; Methods and History of the Newer *Erdkunde*, 4 hrs.; Germany and German Central Europe, 2 hrs.; General *Erdkunde*, Part II, Oceanography and Climatology, 4 hrs.; The Extra European Countries and Chief Centres of International Trade in Their Political and Industrial Relationship to Germany, 2 hrs.; The Basis of Landscapes (illustrated); General *Erdkunde*, 1st half, Introduction, Morphology, Hydrology with Illustrations, 4 hrs.; France, 3 hrs.; Basis of Political Ethnography, 1 hr.; the Mediterranean Sea and Mediterranean Lands, 2 hrs.; Landscapes and Cities of Middle Europe, 1 hr.; Anthropological Geography; The Alps and Related Mountains; England's World Power and World Policy.

The trend of geography during the period was well expressed by Alfred Hettner, first in his introduction to his magazine *Geographische Zeitschrift* (1895), then in his inaugural address, as professor of geography (1898), and later in many articles in his magazine which afterwards appeared in book form under the title *Die Geographie, ihre Geschichte, ihr Wesen and ihre Methoden* (1927). The following is an effort to summarize briefly his elaborate statements.

Geography, according to Hettner, is not a general earth science but the chorological science of the earth's surface. It is concerned chiefly with the interplay between nature and men, an evaluation of spatial (*Raum*) relations. Its aim is primarily to study areas or regions; such a study should contain descriptions as well as explanations derived either analytically or synthetically. The delimitation of regions is one of the major problems in geography, while observation in the field is the basis for geographic approach. He distinguishes between general geography (*Allgemeine Geographie*), which follows systematically the distribution of the various geographic phenomena over the earth's surface, and special or regional geography (*Länderkunde*), which elicits the concept of geographic regions. The doctrine sounds quite familiar to the modern geographer who still tries to define his own field; present emphasis on a third approach besides description and explanation, namely, the one of planning, is the only element missing.

The period was certainly one of geographic progress, academically as well as from the point of view of research. By 1905, when both von Richthofen and Ratzel had died, all signs pointed toward much wider development of German geography and the signs proved not misleading.

The Pre-World War I Period (1905–14)

The author would have liked to call this period the Golden Age of German Geography except for the fact that the physical side, especially physiography, was unduly emphasized. At the time of Ratzel's death, Hettner already deplored the lack of appreciation of the value of Ratzel's work. Physiography was overrated, due in large part to the influence of Albrecht Penck, who had been appointed successor to von Richthofen at the University of Berlin, Germany's highest geographic position. His imposing figure, actual as well as figurative, his tremendous research ability (*The Alps in the Ice Age*, written together with Edward Brückner, was published during the period), and the size and quality of his department, made him the most influential geographer in Germany. A magnet attracting young men not only from Germany but also from abroad, Penck was above all a physiographer. He did not wholly neglect the human side and in his famous field trips with his students used to point out many other phases of geography, but his chief interest was the study and explanation of the features of the land's surface.

Another reason for the emphasis on physiography came from America; namely, the lectures of William Morris Davis, Harvard geographer and exchange professor at the University of Berlin (1908–9). Davis's ideas, developed in class lectures as well as on excursions and sponsored in Germany by Penck, fascinated the younger geographers in Germany, and, in spite of sharp opposition by others, such as Passarge at Hamburg and also from Hettner, the Davis School of Physiography, as it was called, rose into prominence; and translations of his books, adjusted for German use by young German geographers, such as Gustav Braun, Karl Oestreich, and Alfred Rühl, dominated geographic thought.

Less spectacular, but perhaps of equal influence, was the work of Alfred Hettner through his articles in the *Geographische Zeitschrift*. Alone in Heidelberg—in contrast to the large staff around Penck in Berlin—his influence was less through the word than through the pen. His articles on what he called methodical rambles (*Methodologische Streifzüge*) and his discussions of climate and relief are still high spots in geographic knowledge and presentation.

The author ranks another man together with Penck and Hettner, namely, Alfred Philippson in Bonn. His field work in Asia Minor, the results of which were published in the period 1910–14, showed his quality as a research geographer, but the real reason for his top rating is his book on the Mediterranean (*Das Mittelmeergebiet*). This book will always remain a classical study in regional treatment: a beautiful interpretation of all factors which together make this area a homestead of man and culture.

Very important during the period was the increase of field work done abroad as well as at home (Fig. 6) Siegfried Passarge published the results of his work in South Africa especially on the Kalahari; Erich Obst was the leader of an East Africa expedition; Walter Behrmann made studies in German New Guinea; Leo Waibel and Fritz Jaeger were working in German South-west Africa when the war broke out; Gottfried Merzbacher and Fritz Machatschek published the results of their investigation in the Tien-Shan; Thorbecke worked in the Cameroons and Fritz Klute studied the Kilimanjaro; Karl Oestreich travelled the North-west Himalayas; Karl Sapper started his publications on Central America based on many travels; while Wilhelm Filchner led the second German South Polar Expedition. Nearer home, Roman Lucerna studied the glacial features of the Mont Blanc group; Hermann Lautensach, the Ticino; while Rudolf Marek made studies in the Austrian Alps, of which Norbert Krebs published in 1913 an excellent monograph. In 1914 Gustav Braun published his book on Germany showing clearly the hold of morphology on German geography.

The chief contribution to the rather neglected field of economic geography in that period was Andree's *Geographie des Welthandels* (1910) in which different parts of the world were treated by individual authors. Among the many authors some new names appear worth while mentioning because they became specialists in the areas they discussed. Erich Obst wrote on Great Britain, Walther Tuckermann on the Lowland Countries, Otto Quelle on Iberia, and Otto Maull on Greece. The author of the section of India was Hans Wehrli, Swiss geographer and professor at the University of Zürich. Wilhelm Volz treated Indonesia, and for China and Japan appears the name of Karl Haushofer who will be recorded as playing an important part in the latter part of this article. Incidentally, out of Sweden comes news of a new field, *Geopolitics*, sponsored by the Swede, Rudolf Kjellen; a reviewer of one of his books wrote that the idea was interesting but had little to do with geography.

Geography was greatly strengthened in the universities during this period. It was not only a case of further increase in the number of universities offering courses in geography, including Technical Universities and Commercial Universities, but in the strengthening of many individual departments. In 1914, for instance, the geography department of the Berlin University offered the following programme: Penck, the head of the department and also the director of the *Institut für Meerskunde*, gave General Morphology, supervised laboratory work, directed a seminar,

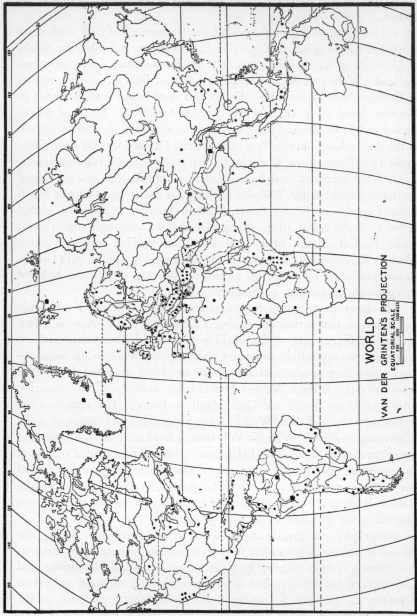

FIG. 6.—German expeditions (*square*) and individual geographers doing fieldwork abroad during the period 1935–?

and conducted excursions; Sieglin offered geography of the ancient world; Kretschmer, history of cartography; Merz, an Austrian, gave a class on lakes (*Seenkunde*) and oceanographic research; Rühl, economic geography as well as a seminar and research in that field; Spethmann lectured on Asia; Groll gave practical work in the field of cartography; and Herzfeld, geography of Mesopotamia; while Jaeger, the Africa expert, was on leave of absence. All were well-known geographers, carefully selected—an array of talent never reached before and scarcely surpassed anywhere since. Leipzig had a strong staff (Partsch, Friedrich, Scheu, and Lehmann) also Vienna (Oberhummer, Brückner, Müllner, Krebs, and Hanslick) and finally the Colonial Institute at Hamburg where Passarge was the leader. Practically every university presented a greater variety of courses, plus an increase in the staff. The training for students was excellent and dissertations were real contributions based on field observations. The yearly meetings of German geographers (*Geographentag*) showed the vigour of German geography and the excellence of the work done. At the last meeting before the war at Strasbourg, the attendance was 367; and excursions covered the crest of the Vosges where French and German armies would oppose each other a few months later.

This was indeed the golden age of German geography. German periodicals, especially *Petermann's Mitteilungen*, the *Geographische Zeitschrift* and *Zeitschrift der Gesellschaft für Erdkunde zu Berlin* presented a wealth of material, indispensable for all geographers, not only in Germany but over the whole world. German wall maps and atlases were without peer. German geographers were welcome guests wherever they went. Albrecht Penck, for instance, was exchange professor at the University of Columbia and lectured at Yale. Universities of other countries looked upon Germany as a model to strive for. The strong group of younger geographers being trained almost guaranteed a successful future, perhaps an even higher development. Then in 1914 came the war.

The World War I Period

Shortly after the war had started Hettner wrote an editorial in the *Geographische Zeitschrift* entitled 'Our Duty in the War'. In this article he tells the German geographers not to succumb to hatred but to remain geographically honest—although it would be difficult to be objective because it is impossible to forget how the enemies have been responsible for the war with the purpose to destroy Germany.

It can be said that German geographers, in general, followed this advice, and that the German geographical war publications of that period were more devoted to geographical description of the war zones and occupied area than to an evaluation of war aims. This lack of a geographic approach to a new Europe—the Germans up to the summer of 1918 were confident of winning the war—was perhaps due to the government policy to avoid discussion of war aims, but also to the fact that most of the German geographers were geomorphologists and not trained for political, or even for economic, geography.

There were, however, exceptions to this rule of geographic decency: Robert Sieger for instance discussing Britain's entrance into the war— which came as a great shock—explains it by saying that Britain's malicious impatience could not have moved its conspirators rapidly enough without entering the war itself. Hettner himself only once broke his own principle not to be swayed by emotions, namely, when Italy entered the war, which action he called the worst treason the world has ever known, and one can have some sympathy for that opinion, from the German point of view.

However, the many victories, especially along the east front, did not leave the mind untouched, and developed a feeling of German superiority; the German God seemed to have destined his chosen people to the great task of European and perhaps World leadership and control. Friedrich Naumann's idea of a German Central Europe (*Mittel Europa*) was well received. Articles stressed the former Germanic character of the border zone between France and Belgium and the ungeographical character of that frontier, with the tacit understanding that Germany would not permit the re-establishment of a free Belgium and sought control of the Dover Strait, while the Netherlands would be 'permitted' to join Germany after the war. Along the eastern front the founding of German satellite states was in full swing.

A typical example of the geographic line of thought of that period was the discussion in one of the seminars conducted by Penck at the Berlin University on the concept 'natural boundaries'. It was accepted by all present except two, both neutrals (one Swiss, Paul Vossler, now professor at Basel, and one Dutchman, the author), that 'natural boundaries are those which correspond to the economic needs [*Bedürfnisse*] of the nation'. The Geopolitics of Rudolf Kjellen grew well on such fertile soil. His book, *The Great Powers of Today*, appeared in German translation in 1914. The following quotation may explain its success. Speaking of the dangers, the American, the Russian, and the 'Yellow', which threaten Europe, he says:[1]

In such a situation Germany appears as the most natural leader, geographically as well as culturally. Such would mean for Germany that it, as administrator of

[1] Translations from the German are made literally in order to present the meaning accurately.

the right of primogeniture, should accept the position of world ruler and use to that purpose the immense source of power—which she seems to lack at present —namely, the faith in such a mission.

Is it surprising that the idea of that 'neutral' Swede fascinated the then victorious Germany?

Meanwhile geographic instruction continued at the universities without much curtailment although classes were depleted of men. Results of field research done before the war continued to be published, for instance, the excellent book of Ewald Banse on Turkey (1914) and Engelbrecht's agricultural atlases of India and Russia. It is possible to look through a volume of *Petermann's Mitteilungen* during the war period and scarcely find a hint of the war.

The *Geographische Zeitschrift* of Alfred Hettner, however, was put on a war basis and gave much of its space to articles on the areas of battle and the countries involved. Hettner himself, already the author of an excellent book on Russia (1905, rewritten in 1915) and a handbook on Europe (1907), published an evaluation of Britain's power (*England's Weltherrschaft und der Krieg*, 1915). Treated in the magazine were: the Polish front by Partsch, the Serbian front by Krebs, Roumania by Paul Lehmann, the Caucasus front by Fritz Frech, the Bosporus-Dardanelles campaign by Braun, the Turkish–Egyptian front by Valentine Schwöbel, the North Sea region by Ludwig Mecking, the Macedonian front by Krebs, the Roumanian front by Johann Solch, and the Albanian theatre of war by Hassert. There was also renewed interest in the economic aspects of the European nations, resulting in a number of articles, such as on Poland by Braun, Italy by George Greim, South-east Europe and the Near East by Richard Marek, Spain by Ernst Muller, and Bulgaria by Arthur Dix, one of the few political geographers of that period. The contrast between Flanders and Wallonia in Belgium received due attention.

Meanwhile German geographers were called upon to make studies of the occupied areas. The following is a quotation from the article of W. L. G. Joerg in the *Geographical Review*, 1922, entitled 'Recent Geographical Work in Europe':[1]

During the German occupation of Poland a Geographical Commission was appointed under the direction of Professor M. Friederichsen of the University of Konigsberg, later of Dr. E. Wunderlich, at present at the School of Technology in Stuttgart on leave of absence from the University of Berlin. After preliminary publications, which included a discussion of each aspect of Russian Poland's geography, culminating in its divisions into natural regions, a handbook was issued which constitutes a scientific regional geography of the area. This was followed by a series of separate monographs, a number of which, on the vegetation of Russian Poland, on the cities of Poland and Lithuania, on the geographical source material on Poland, &c., were published and others projected. Of none of the other areas occupied by the Germans was so systematic an investigation undertaken, partly because of the march of events, although Geographical Commissions were appointed in Roumania and Macedonia. Nevertheless good geographical work was carried out, as by Dr. W. Behrmann of Berlin in Roumania and Dr. Walther Penck, who for a time was professor of geography at the University of Constantinople, in the Bosporus region and Asia Minor.

The German collapse in the summer and fall of 1918 came to most Germans as a complete surprise and a terrible shock. The dream of German hegemony was suddenly shattered: instead of being the conquerors, Germany had lost the war and faced chaos. No wonder that the sudden shift affected German thought as well as that of the geographers.

The Post-War I Period (1918–24)

To present the German sentiment after the last war the author has again to use the opinion of Alfred Hettner, expressed in his periodical as an editorial statement ('Peace and Political Geography').[1] The following quotation is the first paragraph of his statement:

Peace is signed, a terrible peace, not one of reconciliation as Wilson had dangled before us, but a peace, based on force of the worst kind, in comparison to which the Peace of Brest–Litovsk and also the over-strung ideas of our worst chauvinists during the war were only childplay. The hatred of the French and the brutal egoism of the British, who covers himself with the Pharisee cloth of justice, have invented the worst they could do to the German nation; while the willingness of the Americans to please their allies together with their lack of knowledge of European affairs and fear for German competition in the world, has permitted all this to come about. The principles of Wilson, on which we had signed the armistice, have been shown to be only falsehood and deceit. Our work in the world is destroyed, our land is dismembered, our national wealth has been taken away from us, our economic life is burdened with numerous mortgages; and what is worst, the German nation, which had broken its back through the destitution of war and the insolent revolution, has signed a dishonourable peace.

All this sounds very bitter; one wonders if Hettner, if he had been still alive, would have spoken against the treatment Hitler forced on the nations he had conquered, often after violating their strict neutrality. The Treaty of Versailles was again child's play in comparison with what the

[1] *Geographische Zeitschrift*, 1919, p. 234.

Germans did later; while the author has always felt that the Versailles Treaty, but for a few blunders and mistakes, was primarily just and magnanimous.

The same feeling of bitterness and the will to restore Germany to its former glory, can be found in many books published after the war (Arthur Dix, *Political Geography*, published in 1922, is almost unreadable because of this attitude of hatred); and also in the action taken at the first post-war *Geographentag* at Leipzig to show on all atlases and wall maps the pre-war boundaries as well as the new ones. Understandable is the effort to defend the German point of view on the plebiscite areas (Schleswig, East Prussia, and Silesia), and the interest in German minorities in other countries, such as the new Poland and Roumania. Rudolf Kjellen's book, *The Great Powers of the World*, which had appeared—as has been stated— during the war had gone to nineteen editions, and was followed after the war by *The Great Powers and the World Crisis*, which continued to influence German political thought. Kjellen himself died in 1922 but his ideas had taken root.

In 1924 Karl Haushofer, the former general and political expert on East Asia, now professor at the University of Munchen, together with first-class geographers such as Obst and Lautensach, founded the *Zeitschrift für Geopolitik* which later became for a time the geographic bible of the Nazi party. Using ideas of Kjellen, Mahan, American expert on naval power, Fairgrieve, and Mackinder of Heartland fame, the magazine had as its objective, the restoration of German power. The ideas developed in Geopolitik were not new to the German mind. The seeds already had been laid in certain parts of Ratzel's *Political Geography* and especially in Supan's last book published in 1922 entitled *Guiding Principles of General Political Geography* (*Leitlinien der allgemeinen Geographie*), a typical example of post-war atmosphere. It is wrong to say that geopolitical thought was born abroad; it was strengthened by foreign ideas but was essentially German.

Haushofer himself was an interesting figure, who through his great personal charm and cleverness, was destined to become one of the outstanding leaders in the following period. It is therefore interesting what the old political geographer Sieger[1] wrote about him in a review on one of his books; also because it shows the scope of Geopolitik better than definitions are able to do.

In this expansion of geographic approach into the sphere of the finest political and social movements; in the bold lines of thought, which sometimes like

---

[1] *Geographische Zeitschrift*, 1925, p. 119.

geographic invasion reach into the unknown, in the use of the rich material of the past and the present, in the presentation of rules and law, sometimes based on exact interpretation sometimes based on surmises, lies the great inspiring, but sometimes also dangerous, charm of the work of Haushofer. His way of expression, full of illustrations, is crowded with ideas, sometimes subtle or difficult to grasp; straight logical is the approach to a definite goal, by the use of the results of real observations and of geographic and historical laws which are often proven, but sometimes only accepted as such.

That was Karl Haushofer, the friend of Hess, the man whose ideas influenced Hitler when he wrote *Mein Kampf*.

Meanwhile geographic life went on in Germany although under great financial handicaps. Gone was the time of world travel; only South America offered possibilities, as indicated by the work of Sapper (Central America), Maull (Brazil), and Fritz Klute (Patagonia), while the young geographer, Otto Schmieder, was called as professor to the University of Rosario in the Argentine. Hettner continued to publish studies in his periodical appearing in book form, such as *The Terrain Features of the Continents* and *The March of Culture Over the World*. His student, Heinrich Schmitthenner, did excellent morphological work on the explanation of the origin of escarpments of France and South-west Germany. Results of former field work on foreign areas continued to appear, such as on Turkestan by Arved Schultz and on Siberia by Richard Pohle. Philippson started on a handbook on General Geography, the first part appearing in 1921. Karl Dove wrote a text on General Economic Geography (1921) and Otto Schlüter studied settlements. Some of the old guard died during this period; among those were Supan, Sievers, and Theobald Fischer.

The definite time (1924) given to the end of this period is open to criticism, but the author bases his interpretation on the signs of new life in German geography, also shown at the *Geographentag* of the following year. Although less impressive than the one after the war, it indicated that geography trended strongly upgrade.

The *Geographentag* in Leipzig in 1921 renewed glorification of the pre-war and war periods. Walther Penck, son of Albrecht, defended his ideas on morphological analysis derived from field studies in the Puna de Atacama, stressing the interplay between tectonic movements and erosion and its influence on land forms, especially on valley slopes. His death, soon afterward, proved a great loss to the science of physiography. Alfred Wegener expounded his theory of the horizontal displacement of continental masses. Passarge described his ideas on general and regional studies (*Landschaftskunde*), as outlined in his ponderous publications. It was still essentially the old group, sitting among the ruins and talking of the past.

The new *Geographentag* (Breslau, 1925) was different—it faced facts. New studies adapted to the new conditions were presented. Stress was on the homeland and foreign area of German culture. Economic and political geography were well represented. The most encouraging sign, however, was the fact that the German Atlantic expedition under Merz (who died during the trip) was well under way; the first sign that Germany had survived its period of financial helplessness. German geography was again widening its horizons; the post-war period was coming to a close. It was difficult, however, to foresee at that time what direction the new development would take.

The Pre-Hitler Period (1925–33)

In 1925 a new period dawned in Germany. Inflation had been solved, and financial help by the *Notgemeinschaft* (National Emergency Board) made it possible to resume geographic research, of which the South Atlantic expedition was the first indication. The funds provided covered research done in Germany as well as abroad, and many were the geographers who gratefully accepted the opportunity to return to field work. Among those who went abroad and after return published the results were the following: Leo Waibel in southern Mexico, Hans Mortensen in Chili, Carl Troll in the Andes, Helmuth Kanter in Argentina; Kohl studied South Georgia and Alfred Wegener started the Greenland expedition in which he died. Schmieder continued his South American studies and spent some time at the University of California at Berkeley; Bruno-Dietrich was visiting professor at Clark and travelled widely in the United States. Much work was also done in Asia. Wilhelm Credner, who had done excellent work in Sweden, visited Siam and wrote the best study on that land, Mecking went to Japan, Schmitthenner to China, and Trinkler was the leader of a Thibetan expedition. Hermann Lautensach studied Portugal and his monograph on that country, published in the *Ergänzungshefte* of *Petermann's Mitteilungen* (1932), is of the greatest credit to the field of Regional Geography. The new edition of Seydlitz, *Geographic Handbook*, rewritten for its centennial celebration, combined the regional efforts of some of the very best of the German School of Geography.

However, the major emphasis during the period was on problems of geographic presentation in what Albrecht Penck called the 'New Geography', which almost became a revolt of the younger geographers against the old leaders. The chief attack came from Hans Spethmann, who advocated 'dynamic geography' in contrast to what he called the old static method. His book on Dynamic Geography, published in 1928, showed what he wanted to accomplish, stressing development and forecast as essential parts of a geographical analysis of regions. Carl Troll in his post-war article on German geography in the years 1933–45 states the controversy over the aim of geography in the following way:[1]

In 1933 German Geography had completed a period of very violent discussion over the aims and methods of research and presentation, especially over regional geography (Passarge), over so-called *seelische* (spiritual) geography, over dynamic geography (Spethmann), over the rhythm in areal geography as well as the entirety (Volz) of geography. Such a display of discussions on methods is in general not a sign of special power and prosperity of the geographic profession. However, they were the signs that important changes were made in the general interpretation of what is geography. The point of these discussions was the variety of geographic thoughts which had opposed each other from ancient times up to the present: namely, whether geography is a global science, a study of the complete earth surface or the science of the countries and continents. The question was also whether the major stress should be the analytical approach, taking the phenomena separately or the synthetic one based on all phenomena which are found within an area; the problem of the dualism of natural and cultural phenomena on the earth surface and accordingly the contrast between a physical and cultural approach: finally the more inductive empiric positive versus the deductive, speculative line of thought in geography.

Generally speaking, the dominance of the physical had been broken and the trend developed in the direction of regional studies stressing the human element and also emphasizing the totality of an area from all points of view.

Meanwhile Geopolitik had become an important factor in German geographic life, as indicated not only by the *Zeitschrift für Geopolitik* but also by the number of publications, partly by the master Haushofer himself (Geopolitik of the Pacific Ocean, Boundaries), and partly by his collaborators, such as Otto Maull, Erich Obst, Hermann Lautensach, Karl Sapper, Hugo Hassinger. The work of Kjellen was continued, first by *The World Powers Before and After the World War* (1930), then by *Beyond the Great Powers* (*Jenseits der Grossmächte*) (1932). Maull, Dix, and Hennig wrote text-books of Geopolitik. Efforts were made to define Geopolitik successfully; but the continuation of those efforts showed the difference of opinion. Haushofer himself described Geopolitik as the science

[1] *Erdkunde*, 1947, p. 23.

of the political life (*Lebensform*) in the natural environment, which tries to understand the political life in its close relation to the earth and its conditionality of historic movements. In *Bausteine zur Geopolitik* (*Cornerstones of Geopolitics*) geopolitics is defined as the 'study of the geographic foundation of political events'.

It is surprising that so many good geographers co-operated with Haushofer; they dropped out later, but during this period the geopolitical school could count on their support. Probably one of the reasons was the desire to free Germany from the restrictions of the Versailles peace treaty, and their conviction that geopolitics could strengthen such efforts. Troll also stresses the fact that many hoped through Haushofer to influence Hitler, and to prevent political disaster to German geography. The magazine became the geographical organ of the rapidly growing Nazi party; and already in 1931, a work unit for geopolitics was founded, which made geopolitics officially a basic principle and an inward state of mind, assimilating the result of geography, history, and biology.

It is possible to give an idea of the number of students majoring in geography in German universities. In 1925 Leopold Karl Goetz published in the *Petermann's Mitteilungen* a short résumé of students' statistics of Prussian Universities. His figures show a total of 144 advanced students in geography, of whom 109 were men and 35 were women. The accuracy of his figures was strongly attacked by Walter Behrmann who, with the co-operation of the geographic institutes, produced the following figures. In 42 German, Austrian, and Swiss universities, including eleven technical universities and two commercial universities, the total number of members of the geographic seminars was 2,219, out of a registration of 6,253. Of those 878 had geography as a major while the number of those working for the doctor's degree was 245. In total number of registrations Berlin came first (260) followed closely by München (250) and the Commercial University of Berlin (229). With regard to those working for the Ph.D. degree, Koln (Cologne) came first with twenty-one, followed by Vienna, twenty, and Stuttgart (Technical University), nineteen: Berlin had only nine, less than Frankfurt, Konigsberg, and Leipzig. Behrmann comes to the conclusion that most universities are undermanned, especially if taken in consideration that geography professors should frequently travel and accordingly be absent.

It is difficult to discover how the German geographers on the whole faced the political situation which in 1933 brought Hitler to power. Some of them, active in geopolitics, as has been mentioned, favoured the new régime; others seemed to be too much involved in theoretical discussion to worry how the new government would effect their lives and studies.

They could not have done much about it anyway; the emotional propaganda had done its harm; and Germany, including German geography, started a new era, hesitantly but not too much disturbed.

The Hitler Period (1933–9)

This is the dark period for German geography. It was one of government interference and regulations, of deterioration of the profession, and of unwillingness to rise in protest. It was also a period of mass production of books and articles dealing with practically all parts of the world (see Fig. 6). Only Soviet Russia was, since 1933, closed for German field work, while the work done in Africa also was chiefly concentrated in East Africa (after 1936 the Germans on Hitler's demand had again become colony-conscious) with disregard to most of the rest. Travelling and research was greatly helped through visiting professors and assistantships. The University of California in Berkeley employed five Germans as teachers and as assistants, while Clark had two German students who proved to be carefully selected for their political convictions. In South America it was also possible to get assignments paid for by the local authorities.

Nevertheless in a country such as Hitler's Germany, where everything is carefully planned, it is almost unavoidable to see in those many trips a definite scheme to compile material for later use. Also astonishing were the elaborate publications. The author, while writing this, has before him a book on North America (*Amerikanische Landschaften*), genesis and development in separate studies, treating the Ozarks, the Canadian Prairie, Florida, Jamaica, and Seattle; the articles are not bad but certainly not remarkable. The book is presented beautifully, on excellent paper; the numerous maps and fine cover show that cost was irrelevant. One wonders who paid for the book—sales certainly would not cover the cost. Was it perhaps part of the Nazi effort to simulate prosperity in contrast to the unemployment during the reign of the republic? Equally well illustrated are the volumes of the *Handbook of Geographic Science*, edited by Fritz Klute; but in spite of their elaborate appearance they geographically are not up to the level of the French *Géographie Universelle*.

One work which appeared during this period deserves special mention, namely, *The Geography of Switzerland* by Jacob Früh (1930–8). Früh, professor at the Federal Institute of Technology of Zürich, was the geographic expert of his own country, Switzerland. Wanting to write a perfect book, he delayed it so long that old age overtook him before he was able to finish it, and Swiss colleagues had to come in and finish the work, which however still stands as a monument of his brilliant mind.

Troll's list of references for this period totals 227 items; some authors appear several times and some items contain quite a number of separate publications. Due to the thorough training, especially before the Hitler period, the quality of the publication is generally good—only towards the end membership of the party became an important factor and the level dropped sharply. Studies of foreign countries moreover had the advantage of avoiding Nazi censorship, while the home studies reflected strongly the attitude of the government. The physical approach was no longer encouraged; economic geography was greatly hampered by the fact that vulnerability of the German household was not allowed to be mentioned, while anthropogeography received its death-blow through the racial doctrine which was unacceptable for any decent scientist. What remained were regional studies including land planning, and the continued battle of methods with special stress on the definition of the word (*Raum*) space.

From a geographic point of view *Raum* was interpreted as areal extension of a certain phenomenon, especially of ethnographic groups. Schmitthenner used the word in that sense in his book, *Living Space in the Battle of Cultures* (*Lebensräume im Kampf der Kulturen*, 1938), which was followed during the war by an effort to discuss space problems for the peoples of the world (*Lebensraumfragen der Völker*), on which many of the best geographers worked without finishing the project due to war interference. Typical of this is also the beautiful atlas, published by Norman Krebs, entitled *Atlas des deutschen Lebensraumes in Mittel Europa*, of which the first sheets appeared in 1937 but which also remained unfinished. On the other side was the Nazi interpretation of *Raum*, meaning space for them. A typical example of that was given in an article by Kurt Vohwinkel (*Zeitschrift für Geopolitik*, 1939) who distinguishes three kinds of German *Lebensraum*. The first kind is the real area occupied solidly by Germans; the second the area where besides Germans there are other people but the German cultural influence prevails; and the third is the one in which Germans are outnumbered by others but still because of their racial and cultural superiority have a right to dominate. Such would have been a pleasant world.

The regional studies within Germany, including such elements as protection against erosion, as well as planning, were probably still the best of this period; however, the Nazis also here introduced their own interpretation. Troll tells how development of what the French call *bocage* (fenced country) was attributed to the influence of the slavish East European, unable to understand how to develop the gifts of nature; and the English 'park landscape' was described as a decadent feature of former Germanic developments. Are not the Russians doing the same these days; claiming for themselves the introduction and invention of everything worth while? All this would have been ludicrous, if the Nazis had not been so deadly serious to influence German geography and reorganize it. Ageing Hettner, who had resigned as editor of the *Geographische Zeitschrift*, was accused of being a liberal positivist; Penck also, and especially Philippson of non-aryan background, were regarded as unable to understand the new era. Troll in his study tries to impress upon the foreign geographer that the new geography in Germany had its good sides by emphasizing functionalism, instead of causalism and historism, and instead of a static approach, but his arguments are not convincing.

During the whole period the German geographers, who for the greater part were not Nazis, fought a delayed retreat against the advance of government control. The School of Geography came entirely under Nazi supervision, and the periodical *Geographische Nachrichten* carried, next to the former publisher Hermann Haack, the name of Friedrich Knieriem with the title of *Reichssachbearbeiter für Erdkunde* in NSLB (National Socialist Teachers' Organization). The yearly meetings of school geographers, once the scene of often violent debates, were now examples of 'wonderful' discipline under the leadership of the *Gauleiter*.

The German atlases and wall maps also came in for criticism; and especially ethnographic maps were either forbidden or had to be presented according to the instruction of the party, varying according to the momentary point of view. Troll mentioned a case of the inhabitants of the South Tirol who were on different editions of an atlas regarded as Germans, Ladins, and Italians, according to the German foreign policy at those moments.

One might have thought that the *Zeitschrift für Geopolitik* would now reach its peak of influence. Such however was not the case. The tendentious character of its articles and lack of emphasis on a geographic background had forced most of the former geographic contributors to drop connexions. Material presented became more and more non-geographic and journalistic and of course orientated toward party politics. It was still interesting as an indication of Nazi foreign policy and even that side decreased in importance, when Haushofer himself gradually lost his influence on Hitler. The end was very tragic. Haushofer's son Albrecht was executed as party to the attack on Hitler's life in 1944; and the father, after efforts to clear himself of war guilt before the American occupation authorities, finally took his own life.

Some German geographers left the country during the period, either forced because of race or because of their own free will, but they were few. The great majority stayed and endured it. Many, forced to choose between membership in the party or dismissal from their position, elected to become members. There was no sign of willingness to fight to the bitter end against what they knew to be wrong, while the younger generations showed the impact of Nazi propaganda. There was no hope for the future and perhaps what happened, the complete collapse, was still the best way out.

The World War II Period

When the author visited Germany a few months after the armistice and contacted many of the German geographers, his major surprise was to discover that the Nazis had not called to any large extent on German geographers in the first years of the war; and, even after a change had come in their (Nazi) attitude after the débâcle of Stalingrad, used them to a much lesser degree than was done in the United States.

In the early years the German leaders were not interested in calling the geographic experts to work. They had, with a few exceptions, the reputation of being not entirely convinced of the blessings of the Nazi doctrine. We have already seen how the geographic societies and periodicals had tried to avoid too much government interference and control. The German war leaders thought they did not need the geographers in the war effort; that the armed forces would take care of that without the necessity of further geographical knowledge. After the war the geographers would undoubtedly be put to work, following the instructions of the authorities. The only exception was the Forschungsgruppe (research group) of Schulz-Kampfhenkel, later the so-called Forschungsstaffel. Schulz-Kampfhenkel was originally a botanical geographer who, through his Nazi sentiments and good connexions, had used his organizing ability to assemble a group of young men, of whom a part were geographers, to do research in any direction the Army considered worth while. Because of the practical significance of geographic work in wartime, the following quotation is taken from an article by Thomas R. Smith and Lloyd D. Black whose military task it was to investigate what was left of German geography and geographers during and directly after the collapse of German resistance.[1]

Its first assignment was to investigate the passability of the central Libyan Desert for troops moving from the south. The Forschungsstaffel, well equipped with planes, air-photo and survey equipment, and vehicles for ground reconnaissance, spent nine months in the area. The result was a three-volume manuscript atlas and accompanying text. The atlas includes 18 topographic sketch maps on the

[1] *Geographical Review*, July 1946, p. 401.

scale of 1 : 200,000, which make significant corrections to the pre-existing coverage
of the area and add many new data on geology, water supply, and passability.

After the completion of this work early in 1943, the Forschungsstaffel
broadened its activities. Projects related to the long-term administration of the
occupied areas were undertaken for the Speer ministry, the Todt Organization,
and the Commissariat for the Eastern Occupied Areas. Early in the summer of
1943 an office was established at Riga and work was begun on a vegetation
(*pflanzensociologische*) map of Lithuania, 1 : 1,000,000, and a vegetation and
ground-water survey of the oil-shale area in the Narva region. A group based at
Kiev worked on drainage problems along the Pripet, irrigation possibilities in the
southern Ukraine, and the general question of settlement of Germans in southern
Russia.

During this period the Forschungsstaffel continued to experiment with new
techniques of terrain evaluation and mapping. Consequently, when the pressure
of military events forced an abandonment of the long-term projects, it was able
to undertake numerous terrain studies for the OKW.[1] Additional regional offices
were established, from which teams were sent into the areas to be mapped. These
teams usually included one or more specialists in geography, geology, plant
ecology, hydrography, soil science, cartography, and photogrammetry, working
in co-operation. They developed the ability to recognize minor terrain irregularities and ground-water and soil conditions from air photographs and air reconnaissance without recourse to extended ground survey. The result was the rapid
compilation of maps showing these features in considerable detail for relatively
large areas. These terrain-evaluation maps (*Geländebeurteilungskarten*) were printed
in scales ranging from 1 : 50,000 to 1 : 500,000. Existing physical and topographic
maps are used as bases, and the terrain-evaluation material is overprinted in several
colours. Elaborate legends give both the natural description and the military
evaluation of the features shown. Some of the maps are extremely complicated,
but for the most part they are very readable, especially those designed for field
use by armoured or motorized units. A total of 36 sheets, published between
September 1943 and February 1945, have so far been identified. Scattered areas of
coverage range from northern Finland to the mouth of the Dnieper and from
north-western Germany to Greece.

After the débâcle of Stalingrad, geographers were called upon to help
in the war effort. Two military agencies were partly geographic, namely
the units of the Army and Navy concerned with the preparation of maps.
This work resembles similar work done in Washington by American
geographers. Maps and handbooks were prepared for the areas in which
the Nazis were interested; topographic sheets provided with geography
summaries on the reverse side and also such factors as trafficability were
stressed. The Navy units were concerned with coastal defence and
the danger of floods through the destruction of dikes. Finally, in

[1] Ober Kommando der Wehrmacht.

the later years of the war, geography was represented in the Reich's Research Council, first by Schulz-Kampfhenkel and later also by Georg Wust.

Among the relatively small number of publications, which were generally regional, based on pre-war field work, one general book needs mentioning, namely, the second volume of Fritz Machatschek on the *Relief of the World* (1940, the first volume had appeared in 1938), a work indispensable for those interested in world morphology but also a book at present very difficult to obtain.

Meanwhile at the end of 1941 the German Geographical Society was founded, which comprised all former organizations and accepted the *Zeitschrift der Gesellschaft für Erdkunde zu Berlin* as the official magazine. In March 1942 the contributors of the already mentioned handbook on *Space Problems of the Peoples of the Earth* were called together to Prague to be briefed. This book was the last effort of German geography; it had seventy contributors and two volumes were published—the one on Europe and on Colonial Areas of European Nations, while the other four were not completed. Penck wrote on potential world population, a theme in which he had been for a long time interested. The German Geographical Society called an international geographical meeting in 1942 at Würzburg; besides Germans eleven Italians, four Spaniards, one Bulgarian, and one Finnish geographer appeared; indeed not a triumph from the international point of view.

Racial purge also struck geography. The old Philippson was jailed in the concentration camp at Therresienstadt; he probably owes his life to the personal interference of Sven Hedin. F. Leyden, urban geographer who had left Germany for Holland, was arrested there and died in his prison camp. Individual geographers were given choice of either becoming party members or losing their positions: they generally selected the first solution. Germans do not seem to like being martyrs, even for a good cause: the defence of geographic decency.

In 1942 Alfred Hettner died, one of the greatest men of German geography; in the beginning of 1945 he was followed by Albrecht Penck. Both were spared the grief of the inglorious end of the Hitler state; but when Penck died German universities were already in ruins, and German geography, of which he had been the leader, was practically finished. When the news came to America, the author spoke to his class on the importance of Penck, a great geographer, who in spite of some German characteristics was never a Nazi. He quoted what Penck told him when he saw him last, an evening in 1937, when with the help of a bottle of French wine, a daring deed for a German at that time, they talked about

German geography. The *Geographentag* was then being held, and the author asked him why he was not there. The answer was: '*Aber mein Lieber, der Herr Kulturminister ist ja da: ich gehore nicht mehr dabei*' (But my dear friend, the Minister for Culture is there: I do not belong there any more).

The Post-World War II Period

This is not the place to evaluate the prospect for post-war geography in Germany; it has to start from scratch, with the sole difference that many of the geographers are still available, and some of them may have the energy to build again. It is almost a crusade, a wonderful mission if only the German geographers can free themselves from former inhibitions. The author is not too optimistic. He visited Germany directly after the war, and contacted many geographers. His major impression was that in many instances their desire was to clear themselves from the blame of Nazi contacts, or if they had been members of the Party to bring out the fact that the membership was made under pressure.

The older ones who still remember the pre-Hitler period are, however, not the ones who will build the new German School. They will advise, perhaps give certain directions, but the real work has to be done by the younger men who have been spending most of their productive years in a Nazi atmosphere, which must have infiltrated their minds as well as their lungs.

It is a strange environment in which to start rebuilding; destroyed structures and libraries, financial difficulties, and the unavoidable chaos of a period of transition, economic as well as mental. Carl Troll, together with Wilhelm Credner, one of the potential leaders, started the new magazine *Erdkunde* (all former magazines had ceased to appear) with an editorial from which the following quotations are taken.[1]

The step to found a new periodical for scientific geography was not done rashly. Among the ruins, which the past has handed to us, it was necessary to look around carefully in order to find material and mental material for reconstruction. Geography has undoubtedly an especially difficult task in the new organization and education of the German people. This task is to give with scientific tools, a true picture of the countries of the world, their natural background and structure, economic, social and cultural, and to prepare the results not only for the leaders of government, but by way of the school and by way of geographic organization also for the mass of population. It will be necessary to wipe out existing deceptions due to propagandic distortion, to indicate the relations between peoples, to cultivate political geographical knowledge of the best kind, and to be of service to bring world understanding.

[1] p. 1.

The task will be difficult, but if the impression prevails the German geographers have freed themselves of former misconceptions, if they are willing to surrender themselves wholeheartedly to complete reorientation, they deserve our full co-operation. It may be done through exchange of professors and students, and through effort to make books and magazines available to them, probably at the beginning, without payment. One last thought: shortly after the end of the war leading geographers met at the bedside of the old Philippson, who had been released from imprisonment; what thoughts may have gone through the mind of that old man, the only master left from the time when von Richthofen and Ratzel founded the modern German School of Geography!

BIBLIOGRAPHY

Bowman, Isaiah, 'Geography vs. Geopolitics', *Compass of the North*, a symposium edited by Hans W. Weigert and Vilhjalmur Stefansson, Macmillan, 1944.

Fischer, E., 'German Geographical Literature, 1940–45', *The Geographical Review*, Vol. 36, 1946.

Hartshorne, R., 'The Nature of Geography, a critical survey of current thought in the light of the past', *Annals of the Association of American Geographers*, Vol. XXIX, 1939.

Hettner, A., *Die Geographie, Ihre Geschichte, ihr Wesen und ihre Methoden*, Ferdinand Hirt, Breslau, 1927.

Joerg, W. L. G., 'Recent Geographical Work in Europe', *The Geographical Review*, Vol. 12, 1922.

Smith, J. Russell, 'Geography in Germany', *Journal of Geography*, Vol. I, 1902.

Smith, T. R., and Black, L. D., 'German Geography: War Work and Present', *The Geographical Review*, Vol. 36, 1946.

Troll, C., *Die Geographische Wisennschaft in Deutschland in den Jahren, 1933 bis 1945, Eine Kritik und Rechtfertigung*, Erdkunde, Band I, 1947.

Walsh, Edmund A., 'Geopolitics and International Moral', *Compass of the North*, a symposium edited by Hans W. Weigert and Vilhjalmur Stefansson, Macmillan, 1944.

CHAPTER V

THE WEST SLAV GEOGRAPHERS

PART I.—CZECHOSLOVAK GEOGRAPHY IN THE TWENTIETH CENTURY

DR. JIŘÍ KRÁL

Jiří Král, since 1945, has been Director of the newly created Department of Geography of the Slavonic Countries at the Charles University, Praha. Formerly he was Professor of Anthropogeography in Bratislava. He has published several books on human geography and on the Slavonic countries.

TWO different circumstances have combined to make the first half of this century a period of great importance in the history and development of geography in Czechoslovakia: the universal progress of geography during this period gave from the very opening of the century a new impetus to geography also in Czechoslovakia. This impetus was immeasurably strengthened by the restoration of national independence in 1918 and by the rise of the free and independent Republic of Czechoslovakia. New tasks were set them, new responsibilities, new opportunities came crowding in upon them, new spheres of work opened up to Czechoslovak geographers.

As in all countries so in Czechoslovakia the history of geography is a combination of outward, historical circumstances and the teaching of geography and research at the University level, which again means the scholarly history of the individual geographers. It will therefore be necessary to pass in review the work of some of the men who have contributed most to the development of Czechoslovak geography. But before this is done, it must be emphasized that though the initiative and leading scientific ideas come from the universities, these would be lost without that large number of workers in geography, do they belong to the school-world or to other branches of the state service, without whom the universities would perish for lack of recruits, for lack of seeing their work take effect in their own country. Unfortunately, this side of the history of geography falls outside the scope of the present article, but one cannot speak of Czechoslovak geography without drawing attention to it, for geography is keenly studied by many school teachers, and plays a large role in the interests of the community in general.

When in 1902 Professor *Václav Švambera* (1866–1939) became 'docent' (*professeur agrégé*) in geography, he became at the same time, through the retirement of Professor *Jan Palacký* (1830–1908) the one and only university teacher of geography for Czech students; the library and rooms at his disposal were commensurate with the size of the staff. He devoted his life to remedy all three conditions. At first, during Austrian rule, the progress made was relatively small and the obstacles many; this applies especially to the years 1914–18, when the indifference of the ruling power in the territory of Czechoslovakia to things Czech and Slovak turned to a badly hidden and active hostility. However, during the earlier period (1902–14) Švambera succeeded in 1907 in getting a lectureship of geomorphology established, whose first holder was *Jiří Daneš* (1880–1928).

Daneš is perhaps best known in the geographical world for his distinguished research on the Karst phenomenon. His importance for Czechoslovak geography lies, however, just as much, if not more, in the other of his two main interests: he was a confirmed traveller, who undertook long and sometimes arduous journeys in the interest of large-scale geomorphological field work in every zone of the globe. In his lectures he gave his students a synthesis of modern geomorphology, based on the work of Davis and De Martonne and largely on his own wide experience and research. These lectures, which meant so much to his students and therefore played an important part in the development of geography in Czechoslovakia, were to have been published, but his untimely death on a journey to the United States robbed the world of what would have been a great book of geomorphology. Some of Daneš's articles are published in English.

The other lectureship established in the Geography Department prior to 1918 was that of human geography whose first holder was *Viktor Dvorský* (b. 1882). Of Dvorský's brilliance as a geographer there cannot be any doubt, though a serious illness has now for many years prevented him from active work. It was Dvorský who introduced human geography into the Czech School of Geography. He himself was greatly influenced by the work of Vidal de la Blache and Jean Brunhes, as well as by the work of Jovan Cvijić of Belgrade. He was the first Czech human geographer to give a sociological interpretation of his subject, an interpretation which now has become so well-known through the work of American geographers. Dvorský was also vitally interested in regional geography, and made this subject contribute its utmost to his study of human geography, as is witnessed by his penetrating regional studies of Jugo-Slavia and Czechoslovakia.

Dvorský saw the precarious position of political geography in the Czech School of Geography, and he succeeded in placing this branch of geography on a solid foundation, and used its findings and methods in several works dealing with Czechoslovakia. As a professor in the Faculty of Commerce in Prague he gave the new branches of economic geography a firm place within the framework of Czech geography. His importance in the development of the Czechoslovak School of Geography may perhaps best be summed up by saying he did for human geography and its auxiliary subjects what Švambera had done for physical geography and its auxiliary subjects, and thus he rescued Czechoslovak geography from a one-sidedness which might otherwise have seriously threatened its healthy development. Though some of Dvorský's works have appeared in French and German, he has not so far published anything in English.

The restoration of the Czechoslovak State in 1918 made it possible to fill the long-felt need for a second Czech university, established at Brno, and for a Slovak university, established at Bratislava. Further, a Faculty of Commerce, with university rank, but not part of the Charles University, was established in Prague. Fortunately, a sufficient number of geographers had by then attained the experience and knowledge which made it possible to staff these new geographical departments. At the Charles University itself the lectureships were turned into professorships, and a number of new chairs and courses were established, such as cartography (Professor B. Šalamon), methodology, and pedagogy of geography (Dr. Fr. Machát). In 1919 Václav Dĕdina (b. 1870) became docent of geomorphology. To pursue the development of geomorphology: while Daneš within Czech geomorphology represents the outward-turned interest of Czech geographers, Professor V. Dĕdina represents the interest in the home-country. He has devoted most of his life to the exploration of regions within Czechoslovakia, and it is due to the research, initiative and steady enthusiasm that the great work Československá vlastivĕda (Czechoslovak Knowledge of the Home Country) was published 1930–3 in several volumes.

On the retirement of Dĕdina Josef Kunský (b. 1903) was appointed professor of geomorphology. Like Daneš one of the main fields of his studies is the Karst topography, and he has made several journeys of exploration in the Karst regions, and is an expert in speleology. Another student of the Karst is honorary Professor Karel Absolon (b. 1877), whose chief contribution to the knowledge of the subject is found in his studies of the Moravian Karst, although he is better known as a palaeo-anthropogeographer.

The main representative of physical geography today is Professor František Vitásek (b. 1890) of the Masaryk University of Brno. He has enriched the Czech geographical literature with a university text-book (in three volumes) of physical geography; and by further special works dealing with the former glaciation of the Czechoslovak mountains. He also directs the newly established Geographical Department in the Palachy's University in Olomouc (1948). Here we may also mention Professor V. J. Novak (b. 1882) of the Charles University, who in 1948 established a Pedagogical Faculty at Praha. He gives his attention chiefly to the geomorphology of the Bohemian-Moravian Uplands. Another member of the same group of teachers is Professor Jan Krejči (b. 1902).

In Slovakia Professor Ján Hromádka (b. 1886) at first studied physical geography and later human and regional geography. Based on his research in Slovakia he has published the first geography of Slovakia. A promising young Slovak physical geographer is Michal Lukniš (b. 1916).

Besides geography proper the auxiliary sciences have also had a considerable development. Among these are historical geography (B. Horák); statistics and demography (A. Boház, the late J. Auerhan, J. Korčák, and A. Malík); meteorology and climatology (St. Hanzlík, Zd. Sekera); geology (in connexion with geomorphology), the late C. Purkyně, and Radim Kettner, J. Kodym; ethnography (K. Chotek), &c.

The development of cartography and mathematical geography was the work of Professor Bedřich Šalamon (b. 1880) and his pupil Karel Kuchař (b. 1906). By their skilful handling of mathematical geography they made of it a school of geography whose strength lies in its regarding cartography as an applied science, and thus a most important auxiliary subject for all other branches of geography. Not content with this, however, they also built up a valuable collection of maps, the State Map Collection, of all types and of all parts of the globe. Their department of cartography and mathematical geography has also edited the Monumenta Cartographica Bohemiae (ancient maps of Bohemia), which have proved invaluable both for the historian and for those who for their work on Bohemia need evidence from the past.

Human geography, as is only natural at the present day, occupies, however, the pride of place within Czechoslovak geography. Today two distinct trends have developed within it. The first may be called the genetic one. True, this conception of human geography was first developed by German geographers, in the nineteenth century by men such as Ratzel, Gradmann, Meitzen; and it was later utilized for quite illegitimate and non-geographical purposes by the geographers of the Third Reich, who made it into one of the several Nazi pseudo-sciences. But for all that, the genetic approach contained much that was of value, and this has been taken up by some of the Czech geographers, notably by

9

Professor *František Koláček* (1881–1942) of the University of Brno, and Professor *František Řikovský* (1901-42), a pupil of Professor Koláček. (Both these geographers were murdered by the Nazis.) Another of the same school was B. *Horák* (b. 1881). Within the Charles University the genetic trend is represented by the work of Professor *Josef Pohl-Doberský* (b. 1888).

The second trend in human geography is represented by Professor Jiří Král (b. 1893). His approach to the subject has been influenced by the work of the French School of Geography (Jean Brunhes, A. Demangeon, Pierre Deffontaines); and also to some extent by the American School (I. Bowman, E. Huntington, W. Cushing); and by the outstanding work of the Jugo-Slav geographer Jovan Cvijić; as well as by the work of some Polish geographers such as L. Sawicki and S. Pawlowski.

Exceptionally wide field studies—especially in the Carpathian Mountains—form the background of Professor Král's work. His research has been published in a large text-book on human geography in which he emphasizes the activity of man as a geographical agent, and follows the development of man's growing influence on his environment from people of a primitive culture to peoples of highly developed culture. Starting from human geography Professor Král has devoted himself to the regional geography of Slavonic countries, and has done pioneer work on the geography of Carpathian Russia. Combining his knowledge of Western and Slav geographical work he has also published the first part of a geographical dictionary, drawing parallels between Czech and English geographical terms. (The French and Russian dictionaries are in preparation.)

Another representative of this trend in human geography is docent *Julie Moschelesová* (b. 1892). She began work as a physical geographer and geomorphologist, but her main work has been done within human geography, especially of Czechoslovakia on the one hand and the English-speaking countries on the other hand; her numerous works, especially those of a regional character, have played a large part in the development of Czech geography. Much of her work is written either in English or French.

Publishing Activities.—These follow two aims: to print the results of research and to spread geographical knowledge among the public. A popular geographic magazine is *Širým světem* and later *Zeměpisný Magazín*. Then there is the Journal (*Sborník*) of the Czechoslovak Geographical Society, founded in 1894, which includes most Czechoslovak geographers among its contributors. Specialized periodicals were since 1946–8 the *Zeměpisné aktuality* (the *Current Geographical Events*) published by Professor Král; and since 1945 the *Kartografický přehled* (the *Carto-graphical Survey*), published by Dr. K. Kuchař. Geographical libraries were the *Travaux géographiques tchèques* (1902–38), founded by Professor Švambera, the *Travaux géographiques* (1930–8), and the *Zeměpioné aktuality* (1947–), both founded by Professor Král; and Geographical Work of the Brno Branch of the Czechoslovak Geographical Society (Professors Koláček and Vitásek).

Geographical school atlases are published especially by the Carto-graphic Section of the publishers V. Neubert, and further by the State publishers in Prague. A special large statistic-geographical atlas entitled *Atlas Československé republiky* (*Atlas of the Czechoslovak Republic*), was published by the Czech Academy of Sciences and Arts in Prague in 1935, with the co-operation of some Czech geographers, statisticians, and other experts.

Detailed maps and plans, military, cadastral, technical, and others, are published on the one hand by the Army Geographical Institute, and on the other hand by the Geodetic Office in Prague.

Czechoslovak geographers have four opportunities to meet their fellow geographers. (1) As members of the Czechoslovak Geographical Society (*Československá společnost zeměpisná*, with branches at Brno and Bratislava) they receive its periodical, the *Sborník*; (2) The Congresses of Czechoslovak geographers have been arranged since 1930 (every third year) in one of the Czechoslovak cities. (3) The Congresses of the Slav geographers, the first of which was held in Praha in 1924, and the latest in 1936 in Bulgaria, aim at a closer co-operation in the programmes of Slav geographers. (4) Participation in the International Congresses of Geography. Contact with foreign geography is maintained through the geographical section of the National Research Council, and the Unesco.

From the above survey the special characteristics of the Czechoslovak School of Geography may perhaps be gathered. They may be summed up at first, as particularly close relationship between the various branches of geography and their auxiliary sciences; and second, an amalgamation (resulting in adaptation and change) of the work of both Western and Slav geographers. In the history of a nation (as in an individual with his own life to lead) it may be a handicap to be placed at the cross-roads of the world, where north meets south and east meets west. For the Czecho-slovak geographer it is a singularly fructifying position for the develop-ment of a broad outlook. The only handicap is that if one wishes one's work known and criticized in the Western parts of the world, one has to write in a foreign language; and then the question of terminology—in what is a newly developed science—presses hard on one.

PART II.—THE DEVELOPMENT OF GEOGRAPHY IN POLAND

JERZY KONDRACKI

Dr. Jerzy Kondracki, born in Warsaw in 1908, is lecturer in geography at the University of Warsaw. He is Secretary of the Polish Geographical Society, and of the (Polish) Geographical Review. He has specialized in cartography, geomorphology, and regional geography. Among his publications are studies of the Baltic Countries (1939), of Pomerania (1946), and of Poland (1947). He is responsible for the recent useful Little Atlas of Poland.

Geography in Poland has a very long tradition, for already Jan Dlugosz, a historian who lived in the fifteenth century, gave in the introduction to his work an excellent geographical description of Poland entitled *Chorographia Regni Poloniae*. In the sixteenth century the work of Miechovita, *Tractatus de duabus Sarmatiis et de contentis in eis*, printed for the first time in Cracow in 1517, was very well known and had many editions. From the same time dates the beginning of Polish cartography in which the first eminent results were the map of Poland by Bernard Wapowski printed in Cracow in 1526 and Waclaw Grodecki's maps printed in 1558. At the end of the eighteenth century there appeared detailed maps of the country in the scale *c.* 1 : 225,000.

The development of modern geography dates from the beginning of the nineteenth century. Stanislaw Staszic (1755–1826) was the precursor of the naturalist branch of geography and the first Polish geologist. He was the author of the geological map of Poland, printed nearly at the same time as the first geological map of England. At the same time there appeared also the first Polish handbook of physical geography by Jan Sniadecki, professor at the Wilno university.

In the middle of the nineteenth century two eminent geographers, Ludwik Zejszner (1805–71) and Wincenty Pol (1808–72), were working in Poland. The latter at the university of Cracow held one of the first chairs of geography in Europe (1849).

Joachim Lelewel, an excellent historian of geography who had emigrated from Poland after the revolution of 1830–1, lived and worked in Belgium. In the nineteenth century despite the fact that the Poles had no homeland of their own, their work in the field of geographical research is not insignificant; but the fruits of the research were gathered by foreign governments. It is sufficient to recall the names of Strzelecki, an eminent explorer in Australia, Dybowski, Czerski, Czekanowski, Grabczewski, Bochdanowicz, and many others, who explored Northern and Central Asia while living there as political exiles.

Scientific work was also developing at home, although it was hampered by the occupation governments. The Polish geographers could lecture only at the University of Cracow and Lwow; for instance, in Cracow F. Schwarzenberg-Czerny, and in Lwow A. Rehman. In Warsaw the new currents in geography were represented by an eminent 'private' scientist Waclaw Nalkowski (1852–1911). At that time, despite great difficulties, some capital research was published; as for instance the *Geological Atlas of Galicia*, edited by the Academy of Sciences in Cracow in about 103 sheets in the scale 1 : 75,000, and the *Geographical Dictionary of the Kingdom of Poland and other Slav lands* in sixteen volumes, elaborated in Warsaw.

In the years 1905–7 there arose the 'Polish Society for Advancing the Knowledge of the Country' (*Polskie Towarzystwo Krajoznawcze*), which, under the pretext of being a touring organization, propagated the knowledge of Poland and supported scientific researches.

However, only after the First Great War geography found in free Poland full possibilities for its development. All the five State Universities had chairs for geography; moreover, chairs for commercial geography existed also at four Commercial Academies at the School for Political Science in Warsaw and at the free University in Warsaw.

In 1917 the Polish Geographical Society (*Polskie Towarzystwo Geograficzne*) which afterwards opened branches in Cracow, Katovice, Łódź, and Wilno, was founded in Warsaw. Local geographical societies existed in Lwów and Poznań and, independent from them, the Association of Polish Geography Teachers exhibited a lively activity. Some geographical periodicals were founded such as *Przeglad Geograficzny* (*Geographical Review*), the chief scientific organ of the Polish Geographical Society; *Wiadomości Geograficzne* (*Geographical News*), informative publication of the Cracow branch of the Polish Geographical Society; then *Czasopismo Geograficzne* (*Geographical Journal*), edited by the Association of Polish Geography Teachers; *Wiadomości Służby Geograficznej* (*News of Geographical Survey*), edited by the Military Geographical Institute in Warsaw; and the *Polski Przeglad Kartograficzny* (*Cartographical Review of Poland*), edited until 1934 by Professor E. Romer in Lwów. Also geographical institutes of universities or connected with geography surveys have produced useful memoirs.

Two private editors have specialized in geography: Książnica-Atlas in Lwów, who edited chiefly school hand-books, atlases, and descriptions of journeys, and Trzaska, Evert i Michalski in Warsaw, editor of *Wielka Geografia Powszechna* (*Great Universal Geography*) in eighteen volumes, the publishing of which was unfortunately interrupted by the Second Great War. The most interesting volumes in the series are: *Polska*

(*Poland*), by Lencewicz; *Europa Wschodnia i Azja Północna* (*U.S.S.R.*), by Nowakowski; and *Geografia jako nauka* (*Geography as a branch of Science*), by Nowakowski.

Polish geography has developed under the influence of West European learning, although owing to political conditions, some branches could not develop adequately, and Polish thought remained a little behindhand. Thus there is no physical oceanography, and social geography has not found a wide echo. In the field of philosophy the trend of 'mechanical' determinism has prevailed until recently. Previous to World War I Waslaw Nalkowski and the outstanding sociologist Ludwig Krzywicki (1859–1941), who may also be considered to be one of the creators of Polish anthropogeography, represented the materialistic trend. The pure Marxist approach to geographical problems was represented by Stanislas Nowakowski (deceased in 1938), Professor of the Poznań University, and formerly lecturer in geography at Clark University at Worcester, Mass. He produced the most considerable work in the field of the philosophy of geography. Nowakowski rejected the encyclopaedical character of geography, and claimed that, to become an independent branch of knowledge, geography must be based on work by specialists, and that the representatives of 'one' geography (or *geosophy*) must disappear. Further research about geography as a science is due to Stanislaw Pawłowski, but his views were influenced by Alfred Hettner. Professor Pawłowski was the secretary of the International Congress at Warsaw in 1934. The Congress of 1934 was an important landmark in Polish geography, when a large circle of foreign geographers became acquainted with Poland.

The war period of 1939–45 shattered the edifice of Polish geography, and after the horrible terror of the German occupation the ranks of scientists were decimated. The list of Polish geographers who died as the result of the occupation contains sixty-six names.

A gradual reconstruction of ruined institutions began in the spring of 1945. The number of universities was increased to seven; and all the high schools were opened. The chairs of geography were taken up by new scientists. The Polish Geographical Society resumed its activities in May 1945, and at the first geographical meeting, which was held in Wrocław (previously Breslau), on the initiative of the Polish Geographical Society, all geographical societies existing before 1939 were united under the presidentship of Stanislaw Srokowski. The Polish Geographical Society is composed at present of 1,400 members grouped in ten local branches: Warsaw, Cracow, Lublin, Łódź, Wrocław, Poznań, Toruń, Szczecin, Częstochowa, and Gdańsk. The society edits two journals: *Przeglad Geograficzny* (*Geographical Review*), a scientific organ under the direction of E. Romer; and *Czasopismo Geograficzne* (*Geographical Journal*), devoted to school geography, with J. Czyszewski as director. Through its Department for Scientific Affairs the Society, under the direction of St. Leszczycki, supports new research and organizes conferences of specialists.

The publication of official maps is in the hands of two institutions: The Military Geographical Institute which chiefly prepares topographical maps, and the civil Chief Geodetic Survey, which (besides geodetical and photogrammetrical works) edits maps for economical, administrative, tourist, and other purposes. This institution is now preparing a great Atlas of Poland, and has already published under the direction of J. Kondracki an informative *Little Atlas of Poland*. Also the Central Office of Physical Planning has edited two atlases, that is *Studies for the National Plan* and an *Atlas of the Recovered Territories of Poland* under the direction of J. Zaremba. School cartography is represented, as before the war, chiefly by Professor Romer's maps and atlases.

We shall begin our review of the present situation of Polish geography with physical geography. Although its most eminent representatives, Professors Lencewicz, Pawłowski, and Smoleński, were killed by the Germans, we can mention many active explorers such as Czyżewski and Klimaszewski (Wrocław), Galon (Toruń), Różycki, Pietkiewicz, and Kondracki (Warsaw), Szaflarski (Cracow), Malicki, and Jahn (Lublin), Zierhoffer and Krygowski (Poznań). Among the best known climatologists are Professors Romer (Cracow) and Gorczyński (Toruń).

Most of the above-mentioned scientists are engaged in geomorphological research and, in connexion with the relief of the country, which to a great extent has arisen under the influence of the Scandinavian ice-cap, studies of the morphology of quaternary formations are the most frequent. Professor Lencewicz who at the Amsterdam Congress was entrusted with the general paper on the genesis of terminal moraines, was an outstanding specialist in that line. The concepts of W. M. Davis, whose warm propagator was Ludomir Sawicki, professor of the Cracow University (deceased in 1928 at an early age), have influenced Polish geomorphology to a great extent. The Cracow school of geography (particularly Professor Smoleński and his disciple Professor Klimaszewski) has developed the concepts of erosion surfaces in the mountainous areas of southern Poland. Studies in connexion with tertiary levellings and quaternary terraces are conducted by many scientists. Recently, the working out of a morphological map of Poland 1 : 300,000 has been undertaken. Hydrography and oceanography are less developed, though limnology has a very good record in Warsaw, Poznań, and Cracow.

Even before 1939 Professor Lencewicz worked out in Warsaw a catalogue of all Polish lakes with a surface larger than 1 ha., and this catalogue contained 6,659 cards. Now, under the direction of J. Kondracki, a new catalogue is in preparation. There are two limnological stations in Poland; in Wągrowiec (*voievodship* of Poznań) under the direction of J. Bajerlein, and in Giżycko (*voievodship* of Olsztyn).

In the field of human geography the most remarkable are the studies on rural habitation in which the following scientists engaged: Professor Leszczycki (Warsaw), Professor Kiełczewska-Zaleska (Toruń), and Professor Czekalski (Poznań). We should include here also an extensive paper by B. Zaborski (at present in London) on the shape of villages in Poland; and very interesting studies by Professor Dylk (Łódź) on prehistoric settlement and its connexions with natural conditions; and also the research, initiated by Professor Ludomir Sawicki on the shepherds' life in the Carpathians. Professor Kiełczewska-Zaleska in a book entitled *Geographical Bases of Poland* and Professor Leszczycki in the work *Geographical Bases of Contemporary Poland* gave an outline of the Poland of today. Formerly also Professors Romer, Srokowski, Wasowicz, and Zierhoffer dealt with problems of political geography. Nowadays researches in the field of geography are often connected with practical problems, especially those tied up with physical planning. The Polish Geographical Society has taken the initiative with a number of collective works among which the most important are the working out of a map of land utilization and researches in the sphere of the influence of cities and the division of Poland into anthropogeographical regions. The most eminent specialist in economic geography is Professor Stanislas Srokowski of Warsaw (president of the Polish Geographical Society); but we can mention here also Professor Jerzy Loth of the High Commercial School in Warsaw and Professor Florian Barciński of the Commercial High School in Poznań. After 1945 two handbooks of economic geography for high schools (one written by Professor Loth and the other by Professor Szaflarski) were published and a new edition of Sokowski's handbook is now in preparation. Economic geography suffered a great loss by the death of Dr. W. Ormicki (Cracow), who was murdered by the Germans. Professor Bolesław Olszewicz of Wrocław goes in for the history of geography.

Setting apart the great Polish explorers of the nineteenth century, the exploration of exotic lands was little developed. Before 1939 several expeditions of a scientific and alpine character were carried out; and the most important were directed to the arctic lands of Greenland and Spitsbergen. The leading Polish students of the polar regions are: A. B.

Dobrowolski, who was a member of the Belgica Antarctic Expedition, (1898), and author of the great monograph on *Natural History of Ice*; S. Z. Różycki, a member of the expedition to Spitsbergen (1934) and author of the *Geography of Arctica*; A. Kosiba, leader of the Polish Greenland expedition (1937) and author of a monograph on that land. Good scientific results were also attained by the expedition to the Caucasus (1935) in which the geomorphologist Edward Rühle took part.

Editor's Note.—I have to thank Professor L. Infeld and Dr. P. Sonnenfeld for revising the Slav names in this chapter.

REFERENCES

1. Buczek, K., *Rzut oka na dzieje kartografii polskiej* (*A short history of Polish cartography*), Warszawa, 1934.
2. Bujak, F., *Studia geograficzno-historyczne* (*Geographical and historical studies*), Warszawa, 1925.
3. Kondracki, J., 'Rozvoj zemepisu v Polsku' ('The development of geography in Poland'), *Zeměpisné Aktuality*, Praha, 1947.
4. Lencewicz, St., 'Polska' ('Poland'), *Wielka Geografia Powszechna*, Warszawa, 1937.
5. Nowakowski, St., 'Antropogeografia ogólna w Polsce' ('Human geography in Poland'), *Kosmos*, Lwów, 1927.
6. Nowakowski, St., 'Geografia jako nauka' ('Geography as a branch of Science'), *Wielka Geografia Powszechna*, Warszawa, 1936.
7. Olszewicz, B., *Polska kartografia wojskowa* (*Military cartography in Poland*), Warszawa, 1921.
8. Ormicki, W., 'Rozwoj polskiej myśli geograficzno-gospodarczej' ('The development of Polish economical geography'), *Przegl. Geogr.*, XII, 1932.
9. Pawłowski, St., Romer E., *Geografia i podróżnictwo* (*Geography and journeys*), *Polska w kulturze powszechnej*, t. II, Kraków, 1918.
10. Pawłowski, St., *Rzut oka na stan i rozwoj geografii w Polsce 1875–1925* (*A short history of geography in Poland 1875–1925*), Lwów, 1927.
11. Pawłowski, St., *Geografia jako nauka i przedmiot nauczania* (*Geography as a Science . . .*), Lwów-Warszawa, 1939.
12. Smoleński, J., *Rzut oka na stan ogólnej geografii fizycznej w Polsce* (*A short history of physical geography in Poland*), Lwów, 1927.

CHAPTER VI

ENVIRONMENTALISM AND POSSIBILISM

GEORGE TATHAM

Early Opinions

THE question as to how far the physical features of the earth affect man is an old one; it is also one to which no final answer has yet been given. Among the ancients, a people and their country were inseparable, and where unusual customs or strange physiognomies were found a cause was sought in one or other of the physical elements, climate, relief, or soil.

Hippocrates (*c.* 420 B.C.) in his discussion *On Airs, Waters and Places* contrasts the easy-going Asiatics living in a very favourable region with the penurious Europeans, who must seek through greater activity some amelioration of their poor environment. He also contrasts the tall, gentle, brave folk of the most windy mountain lands with the lean, sinewy, blond inhabitants of the dry lowlands. Similar observations are recorded by Aristotle in his *Politics*.

> The inhabitants of the colder countries of Europe are brave, but deficient in thought and technical skill, and as a consequence of this they remain free longer than others, but are wanting in political organization and unable to rule their neighbours. The peoples of Asia on the contrary are thoughtful and skilful but without spirit, whence their permanent condition is one of subjection and slavery.

Greeks however living in the intermediate region, he considered, combined the best qualities of both.

Strabo's geographical writings contain many comparable references. He attempts, for instance, to explain how shape, relief, climate, and space relations of Italy affected the rise and the strength of Rome. Such speculations as these are indeed common in the works of classical authors. Medieval writers on the other hand had little interest in them. Firm belief in the biblical account of creation did not encourage a study of why men differed physically from each other. Differences of climate, relief, and human form all were the work of God, and as such no fit subject for investigation.

Interest in the problem revived with the Renaissance and was heightened by the accounts given by explorers of hitherto unknown lands and peoples. Bodin,[1] writing in the second half of the sixteenth century, describes the peoples of northern lands as brutal, cruel, and enterprising; those of the south as vengeful, cunning, but gifted with the capacity for separating truth from falsehood. Inhabitants of temperate regions are more talented than those of the north, more energetic than those of the south, and they alone possess that prudence necessary for command. This analysis of character was made by Bodin to assist in his investigation into the form of the Republic. If the nature of men could be ascertained, he believed, the government could be adjusted to their idiosyncrasies.

Much the same spirit animated Montesquieu. Writing a century later he too sought to determine the effect of climate and soil on the character of people as a guide to the law-giver. Climate in his opinion was very potent. People in cold climates are stronger physically, more courageous, franker, less suspicious and less cunning than those of the south who are 'like old men, timorous, weak in body, indolent and passive', Northerners who go to live in the south quickly lose their vigour and acquire the passivity of those around them.[2]

Consequently the hot climate is the cause of the immutability of religion, manners, customs, and laws in the Eastern Countries.[3] Legislators must take cognizance of these physical facts; they are 'bad legislators who favour the vices of the climate and good legislators who oppose these vices'.[4] Soil, i.e. 'the goodness of the land', is less potent than climate, but nevertheless has great influence on the form of government. Monarchies are more frequently found in fruitful countries and republics in sterile ones. 'The barrenness of the Attic soil established there a democracy, and the fertility of that of Lacedaemonia an aristocratic constitution.'[5]

Island peoples are more jealous of their liberties than those of continents. Islands are commonly of small extent; one part of the people cannot be so easily employed to oppress the other; the sea separates them from great empires; tyranny cannot so well support itself within a small compass; conquerors are stopped by the sea, and the islanders being without the reach of their arms more easily preserve their own laws.[6]

These extracts, which may be taken as typical of the contemporary point of view, show that the aim of the writers, like that of their classical predecessors, was to understand the variation in the character of human types. They did not start from an interest in the earth; natural forces were mainly called in to supply reasons for human variations which other-

[1] J. Bodin, *Les Six Livres de la République*, Book V, Chap. 1.
[2] Montesquieu, *Spirit of Laws*, Book XIV, Chap. 2.
[3] Ibid., Book XIV, Chap. 4. [4] Ibid., Book XIV, Chap. 5.
[5] Ibid., Book XVIII, Chap. 1. [6] Ibid., Book XVIII, Chap. 5.

wise were inexplicable. 'On part de l'homme pour revenir par un detour a l'homme.'[1] Consequently there was no systematic approach; each writer drew conclusions from his own experience and contradictory conclusions were common.

Compare for example the German dictum quoted by Kirchoff 'Basalt is conducive to Piety'[2] with the quotation from Abbé Giraud Soulavié's *Histoire Nationale de la France Méridionale:* 'The inhabitants of basaltic regions are difficult to govern, prone to insurrection, and irreligious. Basalt appears to be an agent though hitherto unacknowledged in the rapid spread of the Reformation.' [3]

Historians and political scientists were more active than geographers at this time in the framing of such hypotheses. Geography was not yet anthropocentric; moreover it was still dominated by the conviction that its function was purely descriptive. Neither the politico-statistical geographers who followed Büsching, nor their critics, the 'pure (*reine*) geographers' like Hommeyer, were interested in the search for causal relations; Hommeyer in fact boasted that his geography explained nothing.

Man's relation to his environment was thus not looked upon as a proper subject for geographical research. Nevertheless many of the current hypotheses were incorporated in the geographical descriptions of different parts of the earth. Kant, for example, in the very short section on Human Geography, makes the following statements. Inhabitants on the coast of New Holland have half-closed eyes and cannot see to any distance without bending their heads back until they touch their backs. This is due to the innumerable flies which are always flying into their eyes. All inhabitants of hot lands are exceptionally lazy; they are also timid and the same two traits characterize also folk living in the far north. Timidity engenders superstition and in lands ruled by kings, leads to slavery. Ostoyaks, Samoyeds, Lapps, Greenlanders, &c. resemble people of hot lands in their timidity, laziness, superstition, and desire for strong drink, but lack the jealousy characteristic of the latter since their climate does not stimulate their passions so greatly.

Too little and also too much perspiration makes the blood thick and viscous, and great cold as well as great heat, by drying out the nerves and veins, makes the movements of animals stiff and unsupple. In mountain lands men are persevering, merry, brave, lovers of freedom and of their country. Animals and men which migrate to another country are gradually changed by their environment. Brown squirrels turn grey in

---

[1] Vidal de la Blache, *La Géographie Humaine*, p. 5.
[2] A. Kirchoff, *Man and the Earth*, 1907, translated A. Sonnenschein, p. 195.
[3] Vol. II, p. 455.

Siberia. The northern folk who moved southward into Spain have left a progeny neither so big nor so strong as they, and which is also dissimilar to Norwegians and Danes in temperament. There is nothing either fresh or particularly geographical in these remarks. They are almost identical in form and content with those of Montesquieu.

Zeune, however, in his attempt to define natural regions by their unique interrelation of all physical and biological phenomena was led, almost inevitably, to develop the thesis. Spaniards, he argued, must be lazy, languishing, sensual, inflammable, with all the burning passions natural to a hot climate. In like manner the speech of Peninsular Italy on account of the proximity of the sea has many sibilants and almost no gutturals, just as Low German because of the moist air of the north coastal lowlands is softer and more drawling than the harsher, quicker High German of the upland regions further south.[1]

Ritter and Humboldt

Here we see the seeds of environmentalism striking root in new soil. Ritter's anthropocentric viewpoint fostered their growth. But Ritter himself was much too cautious to indulge in facile generalizations; and furthermore, though he was interested in the effect of the earth on man, the reciprocal action of man on the earth was to him equally significant. In his first publication, 'Europa' ein Gemälde, each section dealing with a different country was subdivided into two parts, an historical introduction which showed what the land owed to man, and a second part showing the most important influences exerted by nature. The interaction of man and nature continued to figure prominently in all his later writings. He stressed the importance of the articulated coastline on European history, the influence of habitation on coastal peoples, and the significance of the islands of the Mediterranean as small nurseries where culture could evolve in safety.

An occasional rash statement escaped him, like the oft-quoted remark that the narrow eyes and swollen eyelids of the Turkoman peoples was an obvious effect of the desert upon the organism, but more usually his characteristic prudence kept him from such theories. Many among his disciples, however, lacked his scientific caution, and some even falsely attributed to him a concept of geography as the study of the relationship between the destiny of a people and the nature of their land. This concept

[1] Quoted Plewe, *Zeitschrift der Gesellschaft für Erdkunde zu Berlin*, Ergänzungschaft 4, 1937; pp. 21–2.

was carried into regional geography and led to descriptions such as the following by Reuter (1849).

Strength and persistence, sagacity and ingenuity, endurance and intelligence, arrogance and exclusiveness, hard mercenary mindedness, headstrong obstinacy, calculating indifference, and unyielding egotism, quiet thoughtfulness, and sincere love of order, unimaginative cast of thought, phlegmatic manner, great patriotism, and other individual traits characterize the Dutch. The soil won from the sea and rivers by toil and struggle, the cloudy rainy skies, the absence of varied relief, of romantic mountain valleys, the monotony of the level plain, and the landscape dissected by dykes and canals, the preoccupation with cattle raising, market gardening and agriculture on the one hand, with shipping and commerce on the other, engenders so many idiosyncrasies in the method, way of thought and behaviour of the people, in politics and intellectual development, that one would have no starting-point for their explanation if one did not seek it in the surrounding spaciousness and climatic conditions.[1]

Humboldt viewed the problem in a remarkably clear scientific manner. He realized that environment affected man but was not convinced that evidence was available to permit the formulation of an hypothesis. While a student at Göttingen he wrote:

I need scarcely fear to be misunderstood and be supposed to deny that the physical constitution of a country exerts an important influence upon the manners of a people. There can be no question that the inhabitants of a mountainous region differ very decidedly from the people dwelling in a plain; but to attempt to determine what particular influence upon the character is exerted by granite, porphyry, clay, slate, or basalt must be regarded as a wanton trespass beyond the boundaries of our knowledge.[2]

At the end of his life in *Cosmos* he displays the same judicious attitude. Discussing the effect of the configuration of the Mediterranean on the evolution of early civilization he writes:

The influence of the sea was speedily manifested in the growing power of the Phoenicians and subsequently in that of the Hellenic nations and in the rapid extension of the sphere of general ideas. . . . The active life of the Greeks, especially of the Ionians, and their early predilection for maritime expeditions found a rich field for its development in the remarkable configuration of the Mediterranean, and in its relative position to the oceans situated to the south and west.[3]

These very moderate statements contrast markedly with that of Reuter, though written about the same time. Even more revealing of Humboldt's careful scientific method is the following extract.

[1] *Prinzipien für die Begründung der Hauptaufgabe der Geographie*, Berlin, 1849; quoted by Plewe, op. cit., p. 63.
[2] *Life of Humboldt*, Bruhns and Lassell, Vol. I, p. 83.   [3] *Cosmos*, Vol. 2, p. 484.

Although the purity and rarely disturbed transparency of the sky of Arabia must have especially directed the attention of the people in their early uncultivated condition to the motions of the stars . . . it would nevertheless appear that the remarkable scientific activity manifested by the Arabs in all branches of practical astronomy is to be ascribed less to native than to Chaldean and Indian influences. Atmospheric conditions merely favoured that which had been called forth by mental qualifications, and by the contact of highly gifted races with more civilized neighbours. How many rainless portions of tropical America as Cumana, Caro, and Payta, enjoy a still more transparent atmosphere than Egypt, Arabia, and Bokhara! A tropical sky and the eternal clearness of the heavens radiant in stars and nebulous spots, undoubtedly everywhere exercise an influence on the mind, but they can only lead to thought and to the solution of mathematical propositions, where other internal and external incitements, independent of climatic relations, affect the national character.[1]

Humboldt's attitude had little influence on the general stream of geographical thought at this time and the theorizing continued. In geography, however, just as in history and political science, the conjectures were almost incidental; ingenious suggestions or rough theories based on a few correlations, they were not developed in any systematic way and consequently could make no claim to scientific validity.

Haeckel and Buckle

This situation changed suddenly with the rapid expansion of biological knowledge in the second half of the nineteenth century. After Darwin had successfully established the theory that life had evolved from the amoeba through multitudinous forms to man under the selective action of natural forces, it was inevitable that geographers, along with other scientists, should begin to see in the differentiation of man the operation of natural laws.

Haeckel elaborated this theme and outlined a new science, *Ecology*, the study of the mutual relations of all organisms living in one and the same place and of their adaptation to their environment.[2] This science, which immediately attracted the attention of geographers, was saturated with Haeckel's materialistic philosophy. Man was only one of the organisms to be studied, and was, along with all other living things, equally in the grip of the surrounding forces.

About the same time the study of social statistics began to reveal an extraordinary regularity in social behaviour. Crimes, such as murder and suicide, were found to occur with the 'regularity of the tides or the rotation of the seasons', and the number of marriages in England to bear a

---

[1] Ibid., p. 393. [2] Haeckel, *Natürliche Schöpfungsgeschichte*, 1867.

fixed and definite relation to the price of corn. Everything seemed to point to one and the same conclusion, that man was not so free as had been thought, his actions were largely controlled by natural or economic laws. Science in short provided a basis for the brilliant conjectures of earlier writers, and scholars turned to the old problem armed with new method of research and a vast amount of new data, and dominated for the time being by a mechanistic materialistic philosophy. The result was a spate of deterministic theories. All the sciences that dealt with man contributed; history and geography and sociology were particularly generous. However the various theories varied in their interpretation of nature's laws all were fundamentally at one in that they assigned a predominantly passive role to man.

Environmentalism in history is well illustrated by Buckle's *History of Civilization in England* (Vol. I, 1857; Vol. II, 1861). Buckle's aim was to elevate history to the level of other branches of inquiry. Other scientists faced with a great mass of data had studied it with the view to discover in it pattern or regularity, and in that way had been led to the recognition of fundamental laws. Historians on the other hand had failed to do the same, being convinced that the facts of history were incapable of being generalized, and had contented themselves with laboriously recording events. A science of history, he argued, must adopt similar methods and strive towards similar ends, that is to say, towards the discovery of laws or regularity in the affairs of men.

'The believer in a possibility of a science of history,' he continues, 'is not called upon to hold either the doctrine of predestined events or that of freedom of the will, all that he must concede is'

that when we perform an action we perform it in consequence of some motive or motives; that these motives are the results of some antecedents; and that therefore if we were acquainted with the whole of the antecedents and with all laws of their movements we could with unerring certainty predict the whole of their immediate results (p. 13).[1]

Hence:

We are driven to the conclusion that the actions of men, being determined solely by their antecedents must have a character of uniformity, that is to say, must, under precisely the same circumstances, always issue in precisely the same results. And as all antecedents are either in the mind or out of it, we clearly see that all the variations in the results, in other words, all the changes of which history is full, all the vicissitudes of the human race, their progress or their decay, their happiness or their misery, must be the fruit of a double action, an action of external

---

[1] Page numbers from the second London edition published by Appleton & Co., 1885.

phenomena upon the mind and another action of the mind upon the phenomena.
. . . Thus we have man modifying nature and nature modifying man, while out
of this reciprocal modification all events must necessarily spring (p. 15).

Proof that the actions of men are regulated by law is then offered in
the form of statistics showing the regularity in number and nature of
crimes, suicide, &c.; and the argument continued by suggesting that the
science of statistics is not the only one capable of inquiring into and
demonstrating the regularity. Physical sciences too are applicable to
history.

Indeed when we consider the incessant contact between man and the external
world it is certain there must be an intimate connexion between human actions
and physical laws, so that if physical science has not hitherto been brought to bear
upon history it is either that the historians have not perceived the connexion, or
else having perceived it they have been destitute of the knowledge by which its
workings can be traced (p. 25).

Buckle then proceeds to state the physical agents which have powerfully influenced the human race. These are climate, food, soil, and the
general aspect of nature, 'by which last I mean those appearances which
though presented chiefly to the sight have through the medium of other
senses directed the association of ideas and hence in different countries
have given rise to different habits of national thought' (p. 29).

The first three, which are closely interdependent, mainly affect the
accumulation and distribution of wealth. Their relative importance varies
however from one area to another. Civilizations in Africa and Asia have
been most powerfully influenced by the fertility of the soil, those in
Europe by climate. Climate influences labour in many ways. Excessive
heat enervates the labourer, a more moderate temperature invigorates him
while a short summer broken by a long winter in which low temperatures
interrupt work encourages desultory habits. Less obvious but equally
closely connected is the relationship between climate and wages.

The rate of wages fluctuates with the population, increasing when the labour
market is under-supplied, diminishing when it is over-supplied. The population
itself, though affected by many other circumstances, does undoubtedly fluctuate
with the supply of food; advancing when the supply is plentiful, halting or receding
when the supply is scanty. The food essential to life is scarcer in cold countries
than in hot ones and not only is it scarcer, but more of it is required; so that on
both grounds smaller encouragement is given to the growth of that population
from whose ranks the labour market is stocked. To express, therefore, the conclusion in its simplest form, we may say, that there is a strong and constant tendency
in hot countries for wages to be low, in cold countries for them to be high.

In a country like India where climate and fertility combine to produce dense population and low wages, there is inevitably an unequal distribution of wealth which in turn creates inequality in the distribution of political power and social influence.

In India slavery, abject eternal slavery, was the natural state of the great body of the people, it was the state to which they were doomed by physical laws utterly impossible to resist.

The energy of these laws is, in truth, so invincible that whenever they come into play they have kept the productive classes in perpetual subjection. There is no instance on record of any tropical country in which wealth having been extensively accumulated, the people have escaped their fate, no instance in which the heat of climate has not caused an abundance of food, and abundance of food caused an unequal distribution, first of wealth and then of political and social power (p. 58).

Civilization in the New World reflects the power of climatic influences. In North America the western part has heat but no rainfall, the eastern part rainfall but no heat; and therefore in no section were the two great conditions of fertility united. But Mexico, lying near to the equator, has heat and because of the shape of the land has humidity, and therefore in Mexico civilization flowered early.

Whereas climate, soil, and food affect the incidence of wealth, the fourth factor 'Aspects of Nature' affects the accumulation and distribution of thought. Aspects of Nature are divisible into two classes.

The first class being those which are most likely to excite the imagination, the other class being those which address themselves to the understanding so called, that is to the more logical operations of the intellect. For although it is true that in a well-balanced mind the imagination and the understanding each play their respective parts and are auxiliary to each other, it is also true that in a majority of instances the understanding is too weak to curb the imagination and restrain its dangerous licence (p. 86). Thus where nature inspires wonder or awe man contrasts himself with the force and majesty of Nature and becomes painfully conscious of his own insignificance, 'A sense-of inferiority steals over him' . . .

On the other hand, where the works of Nature are small and feeble man regains confidence; he seems more able to rely on his own power as the phenomena are more accessible, it becomes easier for him to experiment on them or observe them with minuteness; an inquisitive and analytic spirit is encouraged and he is tempted to generalize the appearance of Nature and refer them to the laws by which they are governed (p. 87).

The effects of earthquakes and volcanoes furnish excellent illustrations. Earthquakes and volcanoes inspire terror and excite imagination even to a painful extent; overbalance of judgement and predispose men to superstitious fancies (p. 87). Earthquakes and volcanic eruptions are far more frequent and more destructive in Italy and in the Spanish and Portuguese peninsula, than in any other of the great countries; and it is precisely there that superstition is most rife, and the superstitious classes most powerful. These were the countries where the clergy first established their authority, where the worst corruptions of Christianity took place and where superstition has during the longest period retained the firmest hold (p. 89). To this may be added another circumstance indicative of the connexion between these physical phenomena and the predominance of the imagination. Speaking generally, the fine arts are addressed more to the imagination, the sciences to the intellect. Now it is remarkable that all the greatest painters and nearly all the greatest sculptors modern Europe has possessed, have been produced by the Italian and Spanish peninsulas.

In regard to science both areas are of small importance.

So the argument is developed to the conclusion

that in the civilizations exterior to Europe all nature conspired to increase the authority of the imaginative faculties, and weaken the authority of the reasoning ones. With the materials now existing, it would be possible to follow this vast law to its remotest consequences, and show how in Europe it is opposed by another law diametrically opposite, and by virtue of which the tendency of natural phenomena is on the whole to limit the imagination and embolden the understanding, thus inspiring man with confidence in his own resources, and facilitating the increase of his knowledge, by encouraging that bold, inquisitive and scientific spirit which is constantly advancing and on which all future progress must depend (p. 94).

This contrast between European and non-European environments is seen in all aspects of life and illustrations are given from literature, religion, and art.

'In India, Mexico, Peru, Egypt, where Nature overpowers man religion is one of complete and unmitigated terror'; the people

did not desire to represent their deities in human forms or ascribe to them human attributes. Even their temples are huge buildings often constructed with great skill but showing an evident wish to impress the mind with fear, and offering a striking contrast to the lighter and smaller structures which the Greeks employed for religious purposes. Thus even in the style of architecture do we see the same principle at work; the danger of the tropical civilization being more suggestive of the infinite, while the safety of European civilization was more suggestive of the finite (p. 106).

Everywhere the hand of Nature is upon us, and the history of the human mind can only be understood by connecting it with the history and the aspects of the material universe.

The evidence that I have collected seems to establish two leading facts which unless they can be impugned, are the necessary bases of universal history. The first fact is, that in the civilizations out of Europe, the powers of Nature have been far greater than in those of Europe. The second fact is that those powers have worked immense mischief; and that while one division of them has caused an unequal division of wealth, another division of them has caused an unequal division of thought, by concentrating attention upon subjects which inflame the imagination. So far as the experience of the past can guide us, we may say that in all the extra-European civilizations, these obstacles were insuperable; certainly no nation has ever yet overcome them. But Europe constructed upon a smaller plan than the other quarters of the world, being also in a colder region, having a less exuberant soil, and less imposing aspect and displaying in all her physical phenomena much greater feebleness, it was easier for man to discard the superstitions which Nature suggested to his imagination; it was also easier for him to effect, not indeed a just division of wealth but something nearer to it, than was practicable in the older countries.

Hence it is that looking at the history of the world as a whole, the tendency has been, in Europe to subordinate Nature to man; out of Europe to subordinate man to Nature . . . thus to understand, for instance, the history of India we must make the external world our first study because it has influenced it. If on the other hand, we would understand the history of a country like France or England, we must make man our principal study, because Nature being comparatively weak, every step in the great progress has increased the dominion of the human mind over the agencies of the external world.

This final extract is very revealing. It shows that though Buckle could see historical events as the outcome of 'man modifying Nature and Nature modifying man' (p. 15), yet it is Nature itself which determines when and how man shall be so active, in other words natural powers are in every instance dominant, the determinism is complete.

Demolins and the Environment

The second example, furnished by Edmond Demolins' two-volume *Essai de géographie sociale, Comment la route crée le type sociale* (1901–3), illustrates the strict environmentalism in geography which sprang out of the teaching of Frederic Leplay (1806–82).

Leplay's insistence on the influence of natural forces on society was epitomized in the formula place, work, folk, which may be expanded somewhat as follows: Environment (place) conditions the type of work, and work shapes, at least in part, the social organization (place). This formula only holds for rural communities. In urban centres work loses its immediate link with the natural environment; it depends more on the human group and so the formula is revised. However, this modification need not be examined here since it is the influence of environment that is our main concern.

Henri de Tourville, a pupil and disciple of Leplay, developed these ideas and transmitted them to his student Demolins. Demolins concentrated on the study of environmental forces and wrote his book to prove that the route, defined by him as including not just the regions passed through by migrating folks but also the place where they eventually settled, moulds the character and social institutions of the people (Vol. 2, p. iv).

His preface sets forth the thesis in no uncertain terms:

The populations found on the surface of the earth are infinitely varied. What has produced this variety? The answer usually given is Race. But Race explains nothing, for it still leaves to be discovered what has produced races. The first and the decisive cause of the diversity of peoples and the diversity of races is *the route that people have followed*. It is the route that has created both race and the social type. The routes of the earth like powerful alembics have transformed in this manner or that, the people who have entered upon them.

It has not been a matter of indifference whether a people has followed one route or another, the route of the great steppes of Asia, or that of the Siberian Tundra, or that of the American grassland, or that of the African forests. Insensibly and inevitably these routes have fashioned the Tartar Mongol, the Lapp-Esquimaux, the Redskin, the Indian, or the Negro type. There is nothing to advance against this statement. It will be seen that here is a well-established law. Nor has it been a matter of indifference that a people should start out on the route of the deserts of Arabia and the Sahara, or that of Southern or Eastern Asia. Insensibly and inevitably these routes have fashioned the Arab type, the Assyrian and Egyptian type, or the type of the Medes and Persians, of the Chinese, Japanese, or Hindu.

Similarly it has not been a matter of indifference whether folk followed the route of the Mediterranean or that of Central Europe, the first has moulded the Phoenician, the Carthaginian, the Greek, and the Roman; the second the Celt and the German. In Eastern Europe the northernmost route has created in detail the Finnish type, the route of the Great Russian Plain the type of the Northern Slav, and that of the Southern Mountains the Southern Slav.

Always the route has set on man its inevitable and rigorously exact imprint. In Western Europe to which we belong, the Scandinavian, Anglo-Saxon, French, German, Greek, Italian, and Spanish types are likewise the products of the routes along which our ancestors wandered on their way to our present habitat. The diversity of these routes alone explain the diversity of the peoples of the West and that which we call, too glibly, the national genius of each one of them. Modify any one of these routes, elevate or depress it, replace the type of production in one place by another type, change in any way the form and nature of the work, immediately the social type is modified and another race produced.

I go much further; if the history of Mankind began again and the present surface of the earth were to remain unchanged, that history would be repeated in all its main traits. There would be many secondary differences, as for example, in certain manifestations of public life, in political revolutions, to which we attach too much importance, but the same routes would reproduce the same social types and would impose the same essential characteristics on them.

Doubt did not exist for Demolins and every step in the exposition of the thesis manifests the supreme confidence of the preface.

Steppeland folk are studied first. The argument runs roughly as follows. The steppeland climate produces grass vegetation, 'the presence of an exclusive grass cover determines a uniform mode of work—the art of pastoralism'. This means a complete dependence on animals, chief among which is the horse. The steppeland is the ideal environment for the horse, elsewhere for example, in mountain areas it loses some of its special qualities. Only on the steppe can all its special qualities be fully developed. We see here a law. The horse cannot develop normally in large numbers and with the essential qualities of a courser save on the boundless and inexhaustible pastures of the steppe. The steppe is essentially adapted to the horse and it is the horse that adapts the steppe to man. (*La steppe est essentiellement adaptée au cheval, et c'est le cheval qui adapte la steppe à l'homme*, pp. 11 and 15.) The horse fills many roles; it provides food, it confers mobility. Mobility makes possible the work of the shepherd, preserves the link between families, maintains religious unity of the steppe and on occasion enables the great hordes of a Genghiz Khan or Tamburlaine to assemble and to conquer.

Animals determine the diet and the type of crafts. Raw materials for crafts are all by-products of the flocks and herds; the need of frequent movement in search of fresh pasture determines the finished articles; they must be portable, they must not be luxury goods (frequent movements would damage them and 'moreover the isolation in which the people live gives the family little interest in the satisfaction of vanity'), they must be produced by simple processes. Machinery is excluded. 'Pastoralism by imposing a nomadic life and obliging man to continual displacement is opposed to the use of all complicated machinery; it is only adapted to the use of a very simple type of mechanical force, one requiring no special knowledge and one not difficult to install.'

Of all mechanical forces the hand best satisfies these requirements. Hence hand crafts dominate in pastoral societies. This in turn has important social effects. It results in the family workshop; each family working for themselves, by themselves; this means there is no division of labour, no problem of wage rates, no unemployment. Communal work of this type is neither intensive nor progressive. None of the stimuli necessary for improvement are present, there is no temptation to accumulate stores (need for mobility), no problem of market, no competition.

Just as the steppe produces the community for work, so it 'stamps the same communal character on property and the family'. The patriarchal family is characteristic of the steppe. This analysis then concludes with the statement, '*Mais on ne crée pas à volonté ce type sociale, pas plus qu'on ne crée à volonté la steppe; il faut cette route pour créer ce type*' (p. 66).

Pastoral nomads move outwards from the steppelands and according to the route they follow the type of food, work, and society is modified. In North America the Huron, Iroquois, and Algonquin tribes were typical of these who entered by Alaska and followed the route of the Great Lakes. The characteristic trait of these people was their divisions into two groups for work; one a mobile group of men devoted exclusively to hunting and war, the other a sedentary group of women devoted exclusively to agriculture. 'This curious dualism can only be explained by the route these people followed.'

As they moved from the Tundra towards the south-east they found their path blocked by innumerable lakes teeming with fish. Consequently these people acquired the habit of using canoes, made of bark because they must be light enough to be portaged from one waterway to another. Women, children, and old men who would be encumbrances on portages were left at some central, easily defended spot. This sedentary group needed food and therefore turned to agriculture, encouraged by the presence of an excellent grain, maize. The old men, sachems, exercised authority over this group, but the direction of agriculture was entirely in the hands of the women.

Several consequences resulted from the establishment of these two groups. First society became a Matriarchy. 'Matriarchies develop among populations which have been brought by circumstances to confide to women the exclusive control of some branch of production [*atelier de travail*]. This explanation is equivalent to a law' (p. 159). Secondly, marriage was a partnership involving a producer of maize and a hunter.

Among the Algonquins, who occupied a territory rich in game but of low fertility, the produce of the chase was abundant, that of cultivation very meagre. A man, a hunter, could thus feed several women. Hence the Algonquins practised polygamy. Among the Hurons the hunt gave inadequate returns. Consequently one hunter could not feed several women. Hence the Hurons practised monogamy. Now we can prove all this by the Iroquois. Among the Iroquois hunting gave even smaller returns. But maize cultivated by the women on the contrary yielded abundantly and was the basis of the diet. One woman could thus feed several men and more than that, she needed several to assure for herself a supply of game.

Hence certain Iroquois practised polyandry. Thus the ratio between maize and game controlled matrimonial conventions (p. 160).

Advanced societies betray the influences of the route the people have followed just as clearly as the more simple societies. Demolins' treatment of the Chinese is a remarkable specimen of determinist logic. Among the Chinese he recognizes two elements, one the ruler-conquerors of steppe-land origins; the other the peasants. The peasants, engaged in intensive agriculture and small-scale trade and industry, cannot have arrived by the steppe routes. If they had they would have developed a social type fairly analogous to that of the Northern Slavs who even on the most fertile areas still cultivate as little as possible, practise extensive agriculture, attach themselves as little as possible to the soil, are averse to industry and have little skill in commerce. In all these ways they differ from the Chinese.

So one must seek a route capable of preparing a people for agriculture, industry and trade, more precisely for *petite culture, petite industrie* and *petite commerce*' and all of intensive nature. It is also necessary that this route should not cause people to abandon the communal family grouping, but must strengthen it. All this is necessary for these traits characterize Chinese society, and this form of society did not spring up from the soil of China, for it was not adopted spontaneously by the immigrants who arrived from the steppe.

I first sought this route in the direction of India, but I was quickly convinced that an immigration of Hindus could not produce the Chinese type, it is quite impossible, the two types are too different. It was then that my friend, Mons. Henri de Tourville, suggested an entirely novel hypothesis, causing me to examine it and to verify it. Today for me doubt seems no longer possible. I believe that we have at last the route which has brought to China its basic population, and which alone explains this curious and mysterious country. It is the route of Tibet (pp. 248-9).

(i.e. the longitudinal trench occupied in part by the head waters of the Indus and Brahmaputra.) The nature of the route and its effect on the proto-Chinese are then described in detail.

One more illustration. Among the westward-moving peoples who settled on the Mediterranean coast-lands one group developed the trading community. Of this we see the prototypes in Phoenicia and Carthage, and the more developed form in Venice. Maritime commerce in every case of course, a direct product of environmental forces all carefully enumerated, when adopted as the basis of life created social instability.

Instability arises in three ways. There is instability in the relation with the soil; man is no longer closely bound to the soil, he simply sets his dwelling thereon. There is instability in the family. Trade demands and fosters individual initiative; the more competent trader breaks loose from the family group to work for himself. There is instability in the broader extra family group relation. Leadership and social importance are based on success measured by wealth or more precisely by credit, the most unstable of all social bonds. Trading empires are similarly fragile. They are merely a number of trading depots serving vague hinterlands, and each as insecurely rooted in the region it serves as the mother city.

Wars are purely business affairs, fought by mercenaries, and since there is no deep feeling for the land the trading community, at the least set-back, is always ready to cut its losses, and bargain for peace. Social instability of this type gives the government of the community a despotic character. This in turn engenders feuds between the leading families, rivals for the control of absolute power, and political life is poisoned by distrust, suspicion, and endless plotting. Such were conditions in Phoenicia and Carthage. Venice presented a rather different pattern. Venetians were a branch of the Southern Slavs who were organized into family communities and consequently the family unit retained its importance in Venice.

But above the family was the typical despotic government, the presence of a closed (after 1315) oligarchy of wealth. The inevitable distrust and fear led to an excess of precautions, evidenced by the absurdly involved electoral procedure and the complicated system of checks and counter-checks which clogged the machinery of government. 'Has there ever existed a political régime at once more artificial, more arbitrary, and more despotic?' asks Demolins, and concludes, 'the régime could only maintain itself at that price. It was not man who was responsible for it, but things' (p. 371).

Here is a determinism bold, confident, and quite unqualified. Like Buckle but with fewer scruples Demolins seeks the 'laws' which govern man's actions. He doubts not that they exist, indeed he seems quite certain that he has discerned them. His arguments have the form and certainty of a Euclidean demonstration. The theorem is stated tersely in italics, each step in the proof is italicized, staccato sentences reiterating some important phrase lead irresistibly to the triumphant conclusion 'Society is fashioned by the environment'; 'quod erat demonstrandum'.

Ellen Semple

As a third and last exponent of determinism let us examine Miss Semple's *Influences of Geographic Environment* (1911), an example of the determinism of the Ratzelian school. Miss Semple studied with Ratzel and wrote her book to introduce his ideas in *Anthropogeographie* to the English-speaking world.

Published almost a decade after Demolins' study it is less extreme. Miss Semple admits that the progress of research had brought the need for modifying many of Ratzel's generalizations. Spencer's organic theory of the state and deductions therefrom are, for instance, eliminated. Nevertheless Ratzel's deterministic cast of thought is retained, and throughout is plain to be seen. Planned as a statement of anthropo-geographic principles it is none the less (as the title shows) an examination of the old theme, the influence of the physical environment on man. The book thus starts with the assumption that such influences do exist, which to some degree robs the study of scientific impartiality. Note the opening paragraph.

Man is a product of the earth's surface. This means not merely that he is a child of the earth, dust of her dust; but that the earth has mothered him, fed him, set him tasks, directed his thoughts, confronted him with difficulties that have strengthened his body and sharpened his wits, given him his problems of naviga- tion or irrigation, and at the same time whispered hints for their solution. She has entered into his bone and tissue, into his mind and soul. On the mountains she has given him leg muscles of iron to climb the slope; along the coast she has left these weak and flabby, but given him instead vigorous development of chest and arm to handle his paddle or oar. In the river valley she attaches him to the fertile soil, circumscribes his ideas and ambitions by a dull round of calm, exacting duties, narrows his outlook to the cramped horizon of his farm. Up on the wind- swept plateaux, in the boundless stretch of the grasslands and the waterless tracts of the desert, where he roams with his flocks from pasture to pasture and oasis to oasis, where life knows much hardship but escapes the grind of drudgery, where the watching of grazing herd gives him leisure for contemplation, and the wide- ranging life a big horizon, his ideas take on a certain gigantic simplicity; religion becomes monotheism, God becomes one, unrivalled like the sand of the desert and the grass of the steppe, stretching on and on without break or change. Chewing over and over the cud of his simple belief as the one food of his unfed mind, his faith becomes fanaticism; his big special ideas, born of that ceaseless regular wandering, outgrow the land that bred them and bear their legitimate fruit in wide imperial conquests.[1]

Man, be it noted, is a 'product' of the earth's surface. In mountain areas he does not develop leg muscles of iron, or in coastal areas a vigorous development of chest and arms, nature *gives* them to him; he is the plastic form which nature moulds.

Religious ideas are not exempt from nature's control. This idea recurs over and over again. 'Buddha born in the steaming Himalayan piedmont,

[1] Semple, E. C., *Influences of Geographic Environment*, pp. 1–2.

fighting the lassitude induced by heat and humidity, pictured his heaven as Nirvana, the cessation of all activity and individual life.'[1]

'The evidence of history shows us that there is such a theory as a desert born genius for religion.' Here is a psychological effect of environment.

Judaism has always suffered from its narrow local base. Even when transplanted to various parts of the earth, it has remained a distinctly tribal religion. Intense conservatism in doctrine and ceremonial it still bears as the heritage of its desert birth. Islam too shows the limitations of its original environment. It embodies a powerful appeal to the peoples of arid lands, and among these it has spread and survives as an active principle. But it belongs to an arrested economic and social development, lacks the germs of moral evolution which Christianity, born in the old stronghold of Hebraic monotheism, but impregnated by all the cosmopolitan influences of the Mediterranean basin and the Imperium Romanum, amply possesses.[2, 3]

The opening paragraph sets the tone of the whole book, and every chapter contains examples of deterministic interpretation. In the discussion of the effects of a mountain habitat is the following.

'Mountains are seldom equally accessible from all sides. . . . Mountain barriers are therefore rarely by nature impartial.' The northern slopes of the Alps are gentler than those facing Italy hence

with the exception of the illmatched conflict between the civilized Romans and the barbarian Gauls, it is matter of history that from the days of Hannibal to Napoleon III, the campaigns over the Alps from the north have succeeded whilst those from the steep-rimmed Po Valley have miscarried (p. 547).

(Where the theory breaks down the contestants are ill-matched, where it fits equality is assumed.)

'The mountain dweller is essentially conservative. There is little in his environment to stimulate him to change and little reaches him from the outside world. . . . Hence innovation is repugnant to him' (p. 600). (This, though a little earlier (p. 570), we read, 'A mountain environment often occasions a forced development in the form of agriculture among peoples who still linger in a low stage of barbarianism or savagery, e.g. the terrace cultivation of the Igorots in Central Luzon.')

---

[1] Ibid., p. 41.   [2] Ibid., pp. 514–15.

[3] Semple is by no means alone in thus asserting environment forces in religion. Kirchoff (*Man and Earth*), another student of Ratzel, writes, 'Men that inhabit woodland and seafaring races also are usually polytheistic, while monotheism is the natural product of the desert.'

With this conservatism of the mountaineer is generally coupled suspicion toward strangers, extreme sensitiveness to criticism, superstition, strong religious feeling, and an intense love of home and family. The bitter struggle for existence makes him industrious, frugal, provident; and, when the marauding stage has been outgrown, he is peculiarly honest as a rule. Statistics of crime in mountain regions show few crimes against property though many against person. When the mountain-bred man comes down into the plains, he brings with him therefore certain qualities which make him a formidable competitor in the struggle for existence—the strong muscles, unjaded nerves, iron purpose, and indifference to luxury bred in him by the hard conditions of his native environment (p. 601).

The concluding chapter dealing with the influence of climate abounds in similar statements.

The warm, moist air of the Gulf and South Atlantic State is attracting back to the congenial habitat of the Black Belt the negroes of the North, where moreover, their numbers are being further depleted by a harsh climate, which finds in them a large proportion of the unfit (p. 617).

The influence of climate upon race temperament both as a direct and indirect effect, cannot be doubted, despite an occasional exception, like the cheery, genial Eskimos, who seem to carry in their sunny natures an antidote to the cold and poverty of their environment. In general a close correspondence obtains between climate and temperament. The northern peoples of Europe are energetic, provident, serious, thoughtful rather than emotional, cautious rather than impulsive. The southerners of the sub-tropical Mediterranean basin are easy-going, improvident except under pressing necessity, gay, emotional, imaginative, all qualities which among the negroes of the equatorial belt degenerate into grave racial faults. If, as many ethnologists maintain, the blond Teutons of the north are a bleached-out branch of the brunette Mediterranean race, this contrast in temperament is due to climate. A comparison of northern and southern peoples of the same race and within the same Temperate Zone reveals numerous small differences of nature and character, which can be traced back directly or indirectly to climatic differences and which mount up to a considerable sum total. The man of the colder habitat is more domestic, stays more in his home. Though he is not necessarily more moderate or continent than the southerner, he has to pay more for his indulgences, so he is economical in expenditures. With the southerner it is 'easy come, easy go'. He therefore suffers more frequently in a crisis. The low cost of living keeps down his wages, so that as a labourer he is poorly paid. This fact, together with his improvidence, tends to swell the proletariat in warm countries of the Temperate Zone; and though here it does not produce the distressing impression of a proletariat in Dublin or Liverpool or Boston, it is always degrading. It levels society and economic status downward, while in the cooler countries of the Temperate Zone, the process is upward. The labourer of the north, owing to his providence and larger profits, which render small economies possible, is constantly recruited into the class of the capitalist (pp. 620–1).

The contrast between the energetic, enterprising, self-contained Saxon of the Baltic lowland and the genial, spontaneous Bavarian or Swabian is conspicuous, though the only geographical advantage possessed by the latter is a warmer temperature attended by a sunnier sky. He contains in his blood a considerable infusion of the Alpine stock and is therefore racially differentiated from the northern Teuton, but this hardly accounts for the difference of temperament, because the same Alpine stock is plodding, earnest and rather stolid on the northern slope of the Alps, but in the warm air and sunshine of the southern slope, it abates these qualities and conforms more nearly to the Italian type of character. The North Italian, however, presents a striking contrast to the indolent, irresponsible, improvident citizens of Naples, Calabria, and Sicily, who belong to the contrasted Mediterranean race, and have been longer subjected to the relaxing effects of sub-tropical heat (pp. 621–2).

Climatic monotony, operating alone, would have condemned South Africa to poverty of development, and will unquestionably always avail to impoverish its national life. South African history has been made by its mines and by its location on the original water route to India; the first have dominated its economic development, and the latter has largely determined its ethnic elements—English, Dutch, and French Huguenots, while the magnet of the mines has drawn other nationalities and especially a large Jewish contingent into the urban centres of the Rand. In the background is the native Kaffir and Hottentot stocks, whose blood filters into the lower classes of the white population. The diversity of these ethnic elements may compensate in part for the monotony of climatic conditions, which promise to check differentiation. However, climatic control is here peculiarly despotic. We see how it has converted the urban merchants of Holland and the skilful Huguenot artisan of France into the crude pastoral Boer of the Transvaal (p. 623).

A book with the scope of Miss Semple's and so packed with detail cannot be summarized in a few lines, but the excerpts, given above, and picked almost at random, will suffice to illustrate the deterministic mode of thought.

Before closing the discussion of these exponents of determinism one should in all fairness try to see them against the background of contemporary thought. All three writers were concerned with bringing to the attention of scholars one factor that had been too frequently ignored in the past. With limited data at their disposal they were trying to prove a theory, and one cannot wonder that they overstated their case, nor that their illustrations should seem, in the light of later knowledge, to be poorly chosen. Whatever the defects, their work was valuable; Miss Semple's book in particular will always stand out as one of the great formative works in the geography of the English-speaking world.

Objections to Early Determinism

The deterministic thesis is not one that geographers can hold for long, at least not in the crude form in which the foregoing extracts present it. Closer examination of the works of man on the globe reveal many facts for which environmental forces alone can give no satisfactory explanation. Similar environments do not always evoke the same response. Eskimos differ markedly from the Tundra tribes of Siberia; Pygmy hunters share the equatorial forests of Central Africa with agricultural Negroes in a remarkable symbiosis.

Doubts too about the simple environmental explanation of racial differentiation are raised by the persistence of people in Amazonia for several thousand years without the development of any of those negroid features that we generally assume to be physiological adjustments to a tropical climate. Miss Semple attempts to explain this racial fixity.

Contrasted geographic conditions [she states] long ago lost their power to work radical physical changes in the race type because man even with the beginnings of civilization learned to protect himself against extremes of climate. He therefore preserved his race type which consequently in the course of ages lost much of its plasticity and therewith its capacity to evolve new varieties (p. 119).

But this does not apply to the primitive tribes of Amazonia.

Then again, though environment undoubtedly influences man, man in turn changes his environment, and the interaction is so intricate that it is difficult to know when one influence ceases and the other begins. Many landscapes that appear natural to us are in truth the work of man. The wheat, barley, olive, vine, and irrigated fruit trees which dominate the land use in Mediterranean countries is entirely the product of human effort; none of those plants, for instance, was native to Italy or Spain. The wheat fields of the New World are the creation of man, who in his desire to expand production to the limit has bred quick-ripening and drought-resisting hybrids for cultivation in marginal districts.

Man's preference for certain foods has thus stamped itself on the agricultural patterns. The French, by preference *mangeurs de pain blanc*, cultivate wheat wherever possible, even on poor siliceous soils better suited to rye; and the low yield in such areas reduces the national average until it is only two-thirds that of Britain (14 quintals per hectare compared with 22 quintals per hectare, average of 1923–7). Preference for rice similarly shapes the agricultural pattern in Japan and China.

Buddhist objections to taking life, according to Brunhes, sets a man-made limit to the cultivation of the mulberry and the rearing of silkworms.[1] Hindu religious beliefs have similarly hampered the development of a cattle industry in India. Nor is man's influence on nature transitory. Agricultural lands if abandoned are not necessarily reconquered by the original flora. Garigue and maquis have replaced the Mediterranean High Forest; in the Selva brush frequently succeeds to forest.

Environmental factors by themselves can rarely explain the distribution of population. Chinese overpopulation with all the resultant effects on land use and settlement is directly related to ancestor worship, as can be clearly seen when the trend of population in the eighteenth and nineteenth centuries is compared with that of Shogunate Japan, with its very different social philosophy.

Do natural factors alone explain the predominance of the white man in Cuba and Puerto Rico alongside the Negro population of Jamaica and Barbados, or of the exclusive white population of Australia? Or can one even affirm that in these instances environment has played the dominant role?

Was the dense population of medieval Flanders, its thriving industries, and intensive agriculture the result of 'telluric selection', to borrow Kirchoff's phrase? The economic development of nations provides numerous instances of the decisions of man overruling the dictates of environment.

When cheap grain from the New World flooded European markets England sacrificed her agriculture to concentrate on industry; France and Germany sought the protection of tariffs; Denmark clung to free trade and built on the import of cheap foodstuffs a highly organized dairy production based on small holdings. The decision to reject a protective tariff was carried after heated debates by a very small majority, it was by no means the only policy the statesmen of that period believed practicable. Moreover it is generally agreed that but for the preparatory work in the Folk Schools the fundamental co-operative structure could never have been successfully built. It is impossible to see Danish agriculture as man's fulfilment of the plan Nature had conceived for that area.

Industrial location provides yet clearer evidence of man's decision. Tariffs can and do create patterns of industry out of harmony with environment. Industrial development in southern Ontario has been dominated by Canadian tariff policy, not the physical environment. Demangeon in his study of Picardy failed to find geographical reasons for the iron industry there. Clear geographic reasons for the rubber industry of Clermont Ferrand likewise have been sought in vain. The partial transfer of the textile industry of Alsace along with many other

[1] Brunhes, *Human Geography*, p. 300.

industries (chemical, pottery, &c.) after 1870 was not dictated by physical controls, nor can one agree that such a transfer was part of Nature's plan. Was it Nature's plan that Detroit should be the centre of the American automobile industry,[1] or that rubber should be manufactured at Akron? —though of course one can see reasons for the concentration of both industries in the Middle West. There can be no more enlightening experience for a strict determinist than to visit a new industrial plant and interview the owner with the view to discovering his reasons for choosing that particular location. Geographical controls are rarely mentioned.[2]

Town sites frequently present curious problems to the environmentalist. Did Nature or man decide Zeebrugge and Gdynia should develop where they did, that Manchester should be a port, that capital towns should arise on the site of Madrid and Canberra?

Was it predetermined by Nature that Moscow should triumph over its nearby rivals and become the capital of Russia, or that Jerusalem should rise from its ashes and be a city of international importance while Nineveh and Ur remain shapeless mounds of ruins? Can one explain the growth of Lourdes by geographical facts, or the continued importance of Mecca?

Space relations that one might easily assume to be beyond the limits of human manipulation are none the less transformed. A study of the Near East and Western America before and after the Suez and Panama Canals were cut will show this. The list of such instances where human choice has obviously played a part, equal, if not greater than Nature, could be greatly extended. Sufficient, however, have been given to make clear the doubts that inevitably beset a student of human geography when the thesis of strict determinism is examined. Such doubts were known to the authors quoted earlier.

Demolins after describing steppeland society as 'derived directly from the place and imposed by the place', adds 'but when man has changed the soil he modifies the influence of place'. Then work, he continues, becomes more important in moulding society than place and 'man ceases to be the slave of the soil, he acts upon it and imposes on it the most varied transformations'.[3]

Semple in the introduction to her study says :

The eternal flux of nature runs through anthropogeography, and warns against

---

[1] Russell Smith, *North America*, 1st edition, p. 379. 'It is probably an accident that made Detroit the centre rather than Toledo, Cleveland, or another city.'

[2] *Editor's Note.* Surely this definitely illustrates the stupidity of the owner!

[3] Demolins, op. cit., Vol. I, p. 195.

precipitate or rigid conclusions. But its laws are none the less well founded because they do not lend themselves to mathematical finality of statement. For this reason the writer speaks of geographic factors and influences, shuns the word geographic determinant, and speaks with caution of geographic control.[1]

Kirchoff speaking of the causal relationship between natural opportunities and the pursuits of man in any region concludes with the warning: 'To invest this relationship with the compelling force of a natural law were inane pseudo-geographical fanaticism. Man is not an automaton without a will of his own. The suggestions thrown out by the nature of his birthplace sometimes find him a docile, sometimes an indifferent pupil.'[2] Some measure of human freedom which increases with every advance in agricultural and industrial technique is conceded, but this freedom is always seen as sharply circumscribed by Nature.

Since progress in civilization involves an increasing exploitation of natural advantages and the development of closer relations between a land and its people, it is an erroneous idea that man tends to emancipate himself more and more from the control of natural conditions forming at once the foundation and environment of his activities. On the contrary, he multiplies his dependencies upon Nature, but while increasing their total sum he diminishes the force of each. As his bonds become more numerous, they also become more elastic. Civilization has lengthened his leash and padded his collar so that it does not gall; but the leash is never slipped.[3]

The freedom in other words is more apparent than real.

The Rise of Possibilism

Other geographers, particularly those who entered the field after training in history, instead of natural science, have tended to stress this freedom of man to choose. For them the pattern of human activity on the earth's surface is the result of the initiative and mobility of man operating within a frame of natural forces. Without denying the limits every environment sets to man's ambition, they emphasize the scope of man's action rather than these limits.

Febvre has named this point of view 'Possibilism' and a very vigorous statement of its principles is to be found in his *Geographical Introduction to History*. The development of Possibilism is closely linked with the writings of Vidal de la Blache and Brunhes in France, and of Isaiah Bowman and Carl Sauer (among others) in the U.S.A. Some account of the growth of this philosophy will be found in later chapters, here only a statement of the main tenets will be given.

[1] Semple, *North America*, p. vii.   [2] Kirchoff, *Man and Earth*, p. 37.
[3] Semple, p. 70.

In common with the Determinists, the Possibilists start with the concept of the terrestrial 'whole', and the interrelation of all phenomena on the earth's surface.

This (idea of relationship) must dominate every complete study of geographical facts. One cannot be content with the observation of a fact by itself or of an isolated series of facts. After this initial observation, it is important to place the series back in its natural setting, in the complex ensemble of facts in the midst of which it was produced and developed. We must investigate the manner in which it is connected with the series of facts which are its neighbours; we must ascertain in what measure it has determined them, and in what measure on the other hand it has been affected by their influence.[1]

The 'geography of the whole—is in truth the highest goal of geographic study'.[2]

The dominant idea in all geographical progress is that of terrestrial unity. The conception of the earth as a whole, whose parts are co-ordinated, where phenomena follow a definite sequence and obey general laws to which particular cases are related was long confined to the dominion of mathematics. It did not become part of other branches of geography till our own day.... Friedrich Ratzel very wisely insists on such a conception making it the corner-stone of his *Anthropogeographie*. The phenomena of human geography are related to terrestrial unity by means of which alone can they be explained. They are related to the environment which is itself created by the combination of physical conditions in every part of the earth.

Geography getting its inspiration, like its kindred sciences from the idea of terrestrial unity, has for its special mission, to find out how far the physical and biological laws which govern the world are combined and modified in their application to different parts of the surface of the world.[2]

In this terrestrial unity (*ganzheit*), however, a greater emphasis is placed on the works of man than by the determinists. The works of man, not the earth and its influence, are the starting-point. This is strikingly brought out by comparing the form of Brunhes' book with that of Miss Semple's. Miss Semple's 'simplified paraphrase' of Ratzel's *Anthropogeographie* is devoted to the study of how area, location, mountains, climate, &c. affect man. Brunhes attempts to classify the essential facts of human geography under three headings: Facts of Unproductive Occupation of the Soil (Houses and Roads); Facts of Plant and Animal Conquest (cultivation of plants and raising of animals); Facts of Destructive Exploitation (plant and animal devastation, mineral exploitation.)

[1] Brunhes, op. cit., pp. 14–15.
[2] Vidal de la Blache, *Ann. de Geog.*, 1913, p. 291; quoted by Febvre, op. cit., p. 62, and *Principles of Human Geography*, p. 7.

Geographical influences are Miss Semple's chief concern, they are to be sought out and expounded. Brunhes' interest is focused on the facts of human occupation of the earth, irrespective of whether they show environmental influences or not. In the second part of his book, where the link between the earth and man is examined, it is not influences that are sought but 'geographical relations between physical facts and human destinies' (p. 52). His approach is certainly more conducive to unbiased research.

But not only are the works of man given more prominence, his activity is also stressed. Man is not looked upon as a passive being, he is seen as an active force, reacting on his environment and changing it.

Man is a geographical agent and not the least. He everywhere contributes his share towards investing the physiognomy of the earth with those 'changing expressions' which it is the special charge of geography to study. Through centuries and centuries, by his accumulated labours and the boldness and decision of his undertakings, he appears to us as one of the most powerful agents in the modification of terrestrial surfaces. . . . And this action of man on his environment is the part which man plays in geography.[1]

We must add to the group of material forces whose incessant interplay we have seen this new force, human activity; which is not only a material thing, but which also expresses itself through material effects.[2]

In this way we are in a position to appreciate better the role which should be assigned to man as a geographical factor. He is at once both active and passive. For, according to the well-known phrase '*natura non nisi parendo vincitur*' (Vidal de la Blache, *Principles of Human Geography*, p. 19).

Human activity modifies both the inorganic and organic features of the earth.

Man utilizes not only inorganic agencies in his work of transformation. He is not content merely to make use of the products of decomposition in the soil by ploughing, nor to utilize the waterfalls, the force of gravity brought into play by inequalities of relief. He further collaborates with all living forces grouped together by environmental conditions. He joins in nature's game (*op. cit.* p. 20).

Vidal de la Blache returns to this point later and expands it as follows.

Civilization has appropriated its favourite crops. Their original habitats have been enlarged far beyond what could have been foreseen. From the original plant countless varieties have been perfected to suit the requirements of different climates, with the result that its importance is often greater in regions where it has been acclimatized, than in those where it originated. For instance, wheat does not today have the largest yield in regions where it was first cultivated; the harvests of Mediterranean countries cannot be compared with those of the plains of Central

---

[1] Febvre, op. cit., pp. 63–4.   [2] Brunhes, op. cit., p. 27.

Europe. The largest ears of corn are no longer grown on tropical plateaux, but in the United States, on the prairies of the Middle West (p. 234).

Bowman gives another illustration of this type of human activity.

As knowledge of the world spread, the associations of event or condition with place widened, they become more complex, they had less or more significance with respect to mankind. The potato and maize plants were unknown to pre-Columbian Europe. Their discovery raised the question, 'Are they useful to the rest of humanity and where can they be grown?' The whole known world was in a sense resurveyed by the rough processes of trial and error and the result has been astounding. These two plants largely changed the economy of Europe. The soil had not changed; man had gained a little more knowledge of it through a new plant. An element of one environment had been added to the elements, long fixed of many other environments.[1]

In this way man gradually replaces the variety of nature by uniformity.

The modern European is an indefatigable labourer at a task which tends to render uniform, if not the whole planet, at least each of the zones of the planet.[2]

The action of man raised to the level of one of the powers of nature leads to the core of the Possibilist philosophy, namely the contention that nature is not 'Mandatory but Permissive'.[3]

Nature is never more than an adviser.[4]

The unrelenting power of natural agents reigns in the physical world alone. Human geography is a field of compromise; nothing is absolute or definitive for the human species on the earth except these general laws and those fundamental conditions which determine the limits beyond which all life is excluded; and if men are not able to push back indefinitely all these limits in altitude, latitude, depth, &c. they are at least able somewhat to force or modify some few of them.[5]

The forces of physical nature are bound to each other in their consequences, in their relations and in the consequences of these relations. Man does not escape the common law, his activity is included in the network of terrestrial phenomena. But if human activity is thus circumscribed, it does not follow that it is fatally determined.[6]

There are no necessities, but everywhere possibilities; and man as master of these possibilities is the judge of their use. This by the reversal which it involves puts man in the first place, man and no longer the earth, nor the influence of climate, nor the determinant conditions of localities.[7]

It has been the custom for many years to speak of human society in the great climatico-botanical regions as adjuncts, so to speak, of plant and animal societies,

---

[1] Bowman, *Geography and the Social Sciences*, p. 36.
[2] Vidal de la Blache, *Ann. de Geog.*, 1898; quoted also by Febvre, p. 157.
[3] Whitbeck and Thomas, *The Geographic Factor*, p. 12.
[4] Vidal de la Blache, p. 321.   [5] Brunhes, op. cit., p. 607.
[6] Ibid., p. 27.   [7] Febvre, op. cit., p. 236.

which were themselves, it was assumed, strictly dependent on meteorological phenomena. But these regions, into which man was thrown as a kind of extra have nothing tyrannical or determinant about them. Although he reviews and criticizes them along with many others, there is no necessity for the historian or geographer to look on the facts, which he retains in his descriptions and on which his studies are essentially based, as component parts of a pre-established order.

Still less have those facts any determining value for men and their existence. Even plant societies, which are less adaptable to environment than human ones, do not suffer exclusion from external conditions, a fortiori human societies are capable of protecting their own existence from that tyranny.[1]

The geographical elements of the environment are fixed only in the narrow and special sense of the word. The moment we give them human associations they are as changeful as humanity itself. That is why modern geography has so definitely steered away from determinism and towards a study of types of actually working regional combinations of human and environmental conditions.[2]

Earth facts do not determine the form and nature of human society in development. They condition it. New earth facts are continually being discovered and old earth facts given new significance as human knowledge thought and social action develop. The relations are reciprocal.[3]

These quotations, to which numerous others could be added from Possibilist statements published during the last fifty years, make quite clear the contention that Nature does not drive man along one particular road, but that it offers a number of opportunities from among which man is free to select.

This number, however, is never unlimited, and environmental influence is definitely shown in this limitation. Possibilists do not, nor have they ever claimed, that man can free himself from all environmental influences. To attempt, to refute Possibilism by reiterating that 'You can't grow bananas at the Pole, nor pineapples in Greenland', as is sometimes done, is to ignore the real character of the Possibilist thesis. Even Febvre, probably the most insistent on man's power of conscious choice, writes in this regard:

Men can never entirely rid themselves whatever they do of the hold their environment has on them. Taking this into consideration they utilize their geographical circumstances more or less according to what they are, and take advantage more or less completely of their geographical possibilities. But here as elsewhere there is no action of necessity.[4]

Brunhes strikes the same note:

The power and means which man has at his disposal are limited and he meets

---

[1] Febvre, op. cit., p. 172.　　　[2] Bowman, op. cit., p. 37.
[3] Ibid., p. 225.　　　[4] Op. cit., p. 315.

in nature bounds which he cannot cross. Human activity can within certain limits vary its play and its movements; but it cannot do away with its environment, it can often modify it, but it can never suppress it, and will always be conditioned by it (p. 603).

At times Brunhes' statements are couched in language closely similar to that of Determinist writers, as for instance when he says, 'Those who seem to be most independent of local conditions and who escape the geographical imprisonment of our sedentary life . . . the nomads, the shepherds, do not escape the tyranny of water.' Vidal de la Blache speaks of the 'sovereign influence of environment' and says:

Human societies, like those of the vegetable and animal world, are composed of different elements subject to the influence of environment. No one knows what winds brought them together, nor whence, nor when; but they are living side by side in a region which has gradually put its stamp upon them. Some societies have long been part of the environment, but others are in process of formation, continuing to recruit members and to be modified day by day. Upon such, in spite of all they can do, surrounding conditions leave their impress, and in Australia, at the Cape, or in America, these people are slowly becoming saturated with the influence of the regions where their destinies are to unfold. Are not the Boers one of the most remarkable examples of adaptation?[1]

This final paragraph from Bowman.

While the 'physical laws' to which mankind responds are variable in their application and in degree of effect, yet this is also true that all men everywhere are affected to some degree by physical conditions. The drought of 1930 in the United States threw into strong relief the fact that it is only in regions of optimum climatic conditions that men may say 'I am free of those extreme conditions that have more nearly continuous effects upon man elsewhere.' How circumscribed are such optimum areas, and how much history, and what deep cultural relations have flowed out of the contrast between well-favoured and ill-favoured regions.[2]

The limits set by Nature to man's action vary from place to place on the earth's surface and from one historical period to another. In marginal environments, such as the hot and cold deserts, and at low stages of culture man's choice may be extremely restricted. In the more favourable areas of the warm and cool temperate zones, and in periods when man's techniques are highly developed the possibilities are more numerous. But however many skills man acquires he can never free himself entirely from Nature's control. This is emphasized over and over again by Possibilists. Thus Brunhes writes:

Is it not at least in part an illusion to believe that by increasing his means of

[1] Op. cit., pp. 17–18.   [2] Op. cit., p. 161.

control and conquest of the earth man throws off its tyranny and increases his own independence? Is it not on the contrary a sort of contract with more exact, and one might almost say, more Draconian terms that is signed by civilized men as they make their relations with the earth closer and more productive? (p. 616).

Thus everything on the surface of the globe is for men a matter of habit, of sound understanding, of physical facts, and of skilful adaptation to these facts. Moreover, the adaptation must take place promptly, and at the right time, preceded, prepared for, and brought about by exact scientific investigations.

These investigations should also tend to moderate our ambitions and turn us away sometimes from undertakings that would mean such bold opposition to the forces of nature that men would run the risk of seeing sooner or later his patient work annihilated at a single stroke. The more imposing and glorious man's conquest the more cruel the revenge of the thwarted physical facts (p. 611).

Brunhes illustrates this with the example of the drainage of coastal lowlands causing the land to sink and to be reflooded by the sea, or the bursting of dykes, &c.

Bowman similarly points to the experience of the farmers on the High Plains, who having crossed the isohyets that fixed the boundary of agriculture by breeding better seed and using dry farming methods find topography setting a limit to the use of agricultural machinery on which the new technique depended (pp. 144–5).[1]

Great emphasis of this element in Possibilist thought is necessary in view of the misunderstanding of some critics who appear to think a Possibilist denies that environment influences man at all. What is important is to realize that a recognition of the power of environmental influence is very different from an acceptance of the full determinist thesis. Carl Sauer has given this point masterly treatment in his papers on methodology.[2]

Conscious of the selective power exercised by man Possibilists are cautious in approaching the problem of environmental factors in history. Though Brunhes sees 'human history deeply rooted in the material things of the earth' he does not believe that all history can be explained by geography. 'History evolves upon the earth, but it is made up of complex and involved elements, that are removed as far as possible from elementary geographic conditions' (p. 44). He also asks if geographers are to be satisfied 'with indicating some large and obvious relationships, exact though it be, between the general geographic situation of a country and

---

[1] See also Whitbeck and Thomas, *The Geographic Factor*, Chap. I.

[2] 'Recent Developments in Cultural Geography', in *Recent Developments in the Social Sciences*, ed. Hayes, 1927. Morphology of Landscape, Univ. of California Publications in Geography, II, No. 2.

its general historical destiny' (p. 45), which is so obvious that anyone with an open mind can perceive it.

Yet if more precise investigation is to be undertaken it is an exceedingly delicate task. The search for causal relations is always hazardous unless there is a repetition of circumstances with identical results. But no two parts of the earth's surface are identical; each region presents a unique combination of physical and human features and therefore each region must be separately studied when the intricate interrelations of man and his environment are to be analysed. This is the *raison d'être* of regional geography. Brunhes bases his work on studies of island regions; Vidal de la Blache, inspired by his teaching, the brilliant regional monographs of Demangeon (*La Plaine Picardie*), Blanchard (*La Flandre*), Vacher (*Le Berry*), and Gallois (*Régions naturelles et noms de pays*).

Precisely the same problem is met in history. Attempts continue to be made to distinguish cycles or patterns in history, and critics continue to point out that such cycles can only be established by an arbitrary selection of facts in each period; a different standpoint, resulting in a different selection, and the pattern is spoiled or another established. Each historical epoch is in fact a unique succession of events. This does not mean that causal relations or cycles cannot be found, it merely stresses the difficulties inherent in the search.

One factor stressed by Possibilists in the study of historical geography is the importance of habit. Man is a creature of habit and habits once established become a part of his environment and exert considerable influence on his later development.

Nature does not act on the needs of man [writes Febvre], it is man who by choosing two or three out of several means of satisfying his needs, and by clinging obstinately to what he has chosen, acts in the long run on nature, digs into it a trench, so to speak, always the same and in the same direction, of no great volume at first perhaps, but evergrowing deeper and wider. In other words what has to be brought out clearly is the manner of life of the various human societies.[1]

Habits, especially mental habits, modes of thought, long cherished ideas, may hamper man quite as seriously as deficiency in the physical environment. 'Between the desires and needs of man and everything in nature that can be utilized by him beliefs, ideas, and customs interpose. The origin of cultivation and of animal domestication is intimately bound up with religion and magic.'[2]

Ideas may even enclose a developing civilization in man-created isolation.

[1] Op. cit., p. 239.   [2] Febvre, p. 167.

But there is also another isolation, one which man forges about himself by his own acts, by whatever structures he builds upon his own achievements. His feelings, prejudices, and all his conceptions of social life are wrought into his inventions, into which he has put much of himself, and the modes of life which absorb his entire activity. To these may further be added a religious consecration through ancestor-worship and respect for a past which is shrouded in mystery. The result is that he weaves a thick shroud which envelops and paralyses him.[1]

In a most significant paragraph, Bowman refers to the part habits of thought play in precipitating crises in civilization.

It may be shown that there has never been a civilization that declined because it exhausted the possibilities of the land. No nation ever declined because it exhausted the possibilities of the land. No nation has ever fully developed its 'frontier'. The earth has never gone back on man, but man has found himself entangled in 'the unpredictable effects of his own system'. What really happens is that knowledge at the moment of strain, is not great enough to control the forces of nature and of systems of government combined.[2]

Present-Day Determinism

Such in brief are the main tenets of Possibilism to which the majority of present-day geographers subscribe. Very few still hold the Determinist thesis. Those who claim to do so, on examination are found to speak a language very different from those Determinists quoted earlier. The terms they use are more moderate, 'control' is replaced by 'influence' and 'influence' by 'response' or 'adjustment'.[3] Often the very core of their argument has been so changed that it approximates very closely to Possibilism.

Let us examine the views of Professor Griffith Taylor, the editor of this book, who describes his point of view as 'Stop-and-Go Determinism'. This he defines as follows:

Protagonists of the Possibilist Theory instance the carrying of fertilizer to the Canadian prairies, or the remarkable development of somewhat sterile northern Denmark as examples of human control, which have determined the utilization of the regions concerned. I do not for a moment deny that man plays a very important part, but he does not take fertilizer to the 'barren grounds'; nor would the Danes have developed their less attractive regions, if they had been free to choose among the good lands of the world. They have merely pushed ahead in Nature's 'plan' for their terrain. Even when their example is followed in other similar parts of the world, it will only indicate that man has advanced one more stage in his adjustment to the limits laid down by Nature. Man is not a free agent.

[1] V. de la Blache, p. 327.   [2] Bowman, *The Pioneer Fringe*, pp. 42–3.
[3] See Sauer, articles quoted earlier, for discussion of this point.

The writer then is a determinist. He believes that the best economic programme for a country to follow has in large part been determined by Nature, and it is the geographer's duty to interpret this programme. Man is able to accelerate, slow or stop the progress of a country's development. But he should not, if he is wise, depart from the directions as indicated by the natural environment. He is like the traffic-controller in a large city, who alters the *rate* but not the direction of progress; and perhaps the phrase 'Stop-and-Go Determinism' expresses succinctly the writer's geographical philosophy.[1]

It will be noticed that Nature has only 'in large part' determined the programme, man 'who plays an important part' determines the rest. Moreover, man only follows Nature's programme if 'he is wise', presumably he can act foolishly, which admits the possibilist contention that within broad limits set by environment man can choose, at the very least Professor Taylor concedes him the choice between wise and foolish action.[2]

But wisdom and folly are human concepts. The natural environment knows nothing of them. In Nature there is only the 'possible' and 'impossible', finer categories are man-made.

Man, not environment, judges an action as wise or foolish by reference to some aim or goal he considers desirable. Until such a goal has been set up wisdom and folly have no exact meaning. Professor Taylor's definition suggests that the goal must be adjustment to Nature's plan, the carrying out of Nature's programme. From among the possibilities of wise and foolish action how can man recognize this plan?

Obviously, as the proponents of Possibilism admit, the opportunities offered by any environment are not all equal. Some demand little effort from man, others continual struggle, some yield large, others meagre returns. The ratio between effort and return can be looked upon as the price Nature exacts from man for the particular choice he makes. But recognition of this inequality of opportunities gives no clue to which of them Nature prefers, and the wise man should take.

Should he always take the line of least resistance, or should be tread the harder road? Is he to be guided by the prospect of high or low returns? Environment gives no hint. Decision is always taken by man, and is influenced by purely man-made ideals.

History has shown that mankind does not always think it wise to take the easier road, nor to buy in the cheapest markets. To achieve certain desires no price is considered too high, not even the loss of life.

[1] G. Taylor, *Australia*, p. 445.
[2] Possibility of choice is also suggested by the name 'Stop-and-Go Determinism', since traffic lights are not usually placed on one-way streets which have no intersections.

At the present moment there are many who would prefer to unleash the destructive forces of war and to risk the annihilation of both themselves and their environments than to lose their way of life. Are they wise or foolish? The answer is not to be found by studying the natural environment to discern Nature's plan; it involves the assessment of human aspirations.

Once the possibility of alternative action is conceded,[1] then it is difficult to see how 'Stop-and-Go Determinism' can claim that man is not a free agent. That his liberty is curtailed all agree. In no environment are the possibilities limitless, and for every choice a price must be paid; proponents of Possibilism admit this (see pp. 161–2), but within these limits freedom to choose exists. Man makes his choice, and man himself judges its relative wisdom or folly by reference to goals he himself has established. Limits to man's freedom beyond those generally recognized by Possibilists are, according to Professor Taylor's definition, those imposed by man's conception of wisdom. (See the discussion of habit and modes of thought on man's action, pp. 158–9.) There is nothing indeed that contradicts the assertion of Febvre that 'there are no necessities but everywhere possibilities and man as master of these possibilities is the *judge* of their use'.

Despite the extreme Deterministic phraseology closer examination thus reveals 'Stop-and-Go Determinism' to be very different from the old Determinism. It introduces the idea of choice, and since it conceives of choice being guided by consideration of a goal that is to be attained, it could just as logically be named 'Pragmatic Possibilism' as 'Stop-and-Go Determinism'.

Pursuing this line of thought we see that the range of possibilities in any region are limited more by the price man is willing to pay for what he wants than by the dictates of environment.

If the nations of the world believed that their continued existence depended on growing bananas at the Pole, who can doubt that cost would be ignored, an artificial environment created and bananas grown?[2]

[1] Professor Taylor's example of the Danes is not too well chosen. During the years 1870–1900 when the reorganization of Danish agriculture was carried through, the Danes had access to the richer areas of the earth by emigration, a course thousands of them adopted. (*Editor.*—Those who could move to a better environment!)

[2] (*Editor's Note*): It is a modified form of such foolish action which the modern 'determinist' is trained to prevent—as witness my experiences in Australia from 1910 to 1928 in relation to unwarranted railways and settlements. What the Possibilist fails to recognize is that Nature has laid down a *Master Plan* for the World, as I pointed out in my study of Future World Settlement in 1922 (*Geog. Review*, July 1922, p. 384, Fig. 6). This pattern will never be greatly altered; though man may modify

In this regard Bowman writes: 'He [i.e. man] can build a comfortable and well-lighted city and provide education, opera and games at the South Pole, or build an artificial rain-compelling mountain range in the Sahara at an expense equivalent to that of cutting a few Panama Canals. But will it pay?'[1]

It is fundamentally a matter of price. This consideration must be borne in mind when thinking of the role geographers play in planning.

Their function is not that of interpreting Nature's plan and then regulating the speed of development as Professor Taylor suggests. It is rather that of seeing the possibilities any environment holds and estimating the price that must be paid for each. In a democracy the choice between them should only be made by society as a whole, for it is the society that pays the price and only society knows the value it places on its ideology.

Once the choice has been made geographers can then help to plan so that the desired policy may be carried out in closest harmony with the natural environment. The geographer's role in fact is basically advisory, and his work must be dominated by recognition of the totality (*ganzheit*) of Nature.

The old dichotomy between man and Nature, the view that environment is an antagonist that must be conquered, or to which one must passively submit can only lead to disaster or stagnation.

'The ideal of science must be harmony not force',[2] writes Schrader, and in human geography the Possibilist would suggest the maxim should be not conquest of, nor submission to, but co-operation with Nature.

one or two per cent of the desert areas, and extend the margins of settlement, as shown by Bowman in the present volume (Fig. 10). It is the duty of geographers to study Nature's plan, and to see how best their national area may be developed in accord with temperature, rainfall, soil, &c., whose bounds are quite beyond our control in any general sense. The Possibilist says, in effect, 'Little America (in the Antarctic) was a fairly comfortable camp: therefore man can, if he desires, do the same thing all over Antarctica.' The Determinist says, 'Nature has decided that Antarctica shall never be of any value to man except in a few negligible areas, and the sooner we recognize it the better.' A number of arguments for Possibilism, such as some of those on pages 149–50, suggest that this concept is often based on irrational and haphazard actions, which would have been avoided if scientific deduction had been employed. Moreover, Nature's control, though sure, is slow in action. It is arguable that Nineveh and Ur were badly sited, and so (given time enough) reaped the result of foolish human choice.

[1] Bowman, *Geography in Relation to the Social Sciences*, p. 164.

[2] Schrader, F., *The Foundations of Geography in the Twentieth Century*, First Herbertson Memorial Lecture.

PART II

THE ENVIRONMENT AS A FACTOR

Scire vere est per causas scire.
FRANCIS BACON
(To understand thoroughly, we must study cause and effect.)

CHAPTER VII

THE PROGRESS OF GEOMORPHOLOGY

S. W. WOOLDRIDGE

Professor Wooldridge was educated at King's College, London; B.Sc., 1921; D.Sc., 1927.
He became a Lecturer there in 1927; Professor at Birkbeck College 1944, and recently
Professor at King's College, University of London. He has written Physical Basis of Geo-
graphy *(with R. S. Morgan),* Structure of Southeast England, 1937 *(with D. L. Linton).*

Introduction

GEOMORPHOLOGY, like many subjects in the scientific curriculum,
had a double birth or, if we prefer another metaphor, distinct phases of
germination and flowering. Much, if not all, that geomorphology teaches
is implicit in the pages of Hutton and Playfair and they are normally
accounted the founders of the subject. Yet the real nature and extent of
'denudation' was by no means fully grasped by their successors. Throughout his earlier life, at least, Lyell held fundamentally erroneous views on
the origin of valleys. British geology was, perhaps, too preoccupied with
the philosophical and biological implications of the new earth knowledge
to have time or mind for a really close scrutiny of the existing landscape.
The general nature of sub-aerial wastage was accepted as manifest; its
efficacy as compared with the erosive powers of the sea was not acknowledged. Nor was the notion that valleys were in general modified tectonic
fissures at all lightly abandoned. Half a century's progress still left it
possible for George Greenwood in his *Rain and Rivers* (1857) to claim the
defence of 'Hutton and Playfair against Lyell and all comers'. Such a claim
administers a salutary shock to those who have lightly concluded that
Lyell was the lineal descendant and disciple of Hutton. It has been far
too readily assumed that because the 'cycle of erosion' was implicit in
uniformitarian doctrine, its corollaries were explicit in the minds of the
earlier geologists.

But new facts and sounder reasoning came quickly to hand. In 1862
the paper by J. B. Jukes[1] on the rivers of Southern Ireland, with its
prescient postscript on the Weald, established the nature of subsequent
streams and the general mode of 'adaption to structure.' Three years
later Le Neve Foster and Topley[2] presented the first sound and clear

[1] J. B. Jukes, *Quart. Journ. Geol. Soc.*, 18, 1862.
[2] Le Neve Foster and W. Topley, ibid., 21, 1865, p. 443.

picture of the origin of the Wealden landscapes. Before the end of the decade, Archibald Geikie had refuted the 'structuralist views' of the Duke of Argyle on the origin of the Highland valleys,[1] and elsewhere[2] had written the oft-quoted words 'Before the sea could pare off a mere marginal strip of land—the whole land would be washed into the ocean by atmospheric denudation.' In the same year (1867) Whitaker[3] wrote on 'Sub-aerial denudation' and carefully established the differences between marine cliffs and escarpments. That the older ideas were still not without influence is clear from the fact that his paper was rejected by the Geological Society of London and published in the Geological Magazine.

As is now universally recognized the bolder landscapes of the American South-west provided example and stimulus for the final vindication of the opinions struggling for acceptance in Britain. In a few brief years, Powell, Dutton, and Gilbert transformed accepted views on land sculpture; in particular the luminous discussion by Gilbert of the 'natural history' of river erosion provided the staple theme for a long lineage of physiographic texts.

It is also agreed that the co-ordination of geomorphology as an intellectual discipline, the flowering of the subject of which we have spoken, was primarily the work of one man, William Morris Davis. It is as difficult, as it is perhaps needless, for any disciple of his to deal at all fitly or adequately with the debt which we owe him. His own concise and modest estimation of the work was that he 'systematized the sequence of forms through an ideal cycle and provided a terminology'.[4] His aim was the explanatory description of land-forms. His method and mode of thought is amply evident in the persuasive pages of *Geographical Essays*, of which a new edition is long overdue; but the only formal presentation of his doctrine is found in *Die Erklarende Beschreibung der Landformen* (1912), embodying the matter of his lectures to the University of Berlin.

The views of W. M. Davis were at best rather tardily received in Europe; and in Germany, they were actively opposed. Though geomorphology is today often regarded as a natural and attractive introduction to geology, it was in fact a later growth than the main science. So it was that Archibald Geikie, himself no mean contributor to the science of scenery, wrote the brief 'appendix' on Physiographical Geology to the great two-volume *Textbook of Geology*. Though dignified as

---

[1] A. Geikie, *Quart. Journ. Geo. Soc.*, 18, 1865.
[2] A. Geikie, *Geolog. Magazine*, 1868, p. 249.
[3] W. Whitaker, ibid., 4, 1867, p. 474.
[4] J. Bowman, *Geolog. Review*, 24, p. 180.

Book VII, it occupies little more than 10,000 words, a limitation implicitly justified by the statement 'The rocks and their contents form one subject of study, the history of their present scenery forms another.'[1] We shall not, however, pursue further here the subject of the role of geomorphology and its relations to geology and to geography. The question is still of interest in Europe; for American readers 'geomorphology is a distinct branch of science'.[2] As such for present purposes we will regard it and, if this be its status, few will deny that W. M. Davis established its core of doctrine and laid down its methods of work. Within the limits of space here assigned, we may best proceed to inquire as to the progress of the subject during the twentieth century following its flowering late in the nineteenth century.

River-Profiles and Slopes

A first question of prime importance depends on the evident fact that geomorphology includes or should include, both the comparative study of land-forms and the analytical study of the processes concerned in their formation. The latter aspect has been too generally ignored. The position is thus curtly summarized by J. B. Leighly;[3] 'Davis's great mistake was the assumption that we know the processes involved in the development of land-forms. We don't, and until we do we shall be ignorant of the general course of their development.' Signs have not been wanting of a realization of the truth of this statement. A basic thesis in the writings of Gilbert and Davis was the conception of 'grade' in a river, defined as a 'balanced condition brought about by changes in the capacity of a river to do work and in the quantity it has to do', which changes continue 'until the two reach equality'. This conception has been criticized latterly in America by J. E. Kessili,[4] and in Britain by D. L. Linton in a manuscript not yet published; but which the present writer has been privileged to study. The doubts which these writers express have been fairly widely shared as is evident from a comparison of current text-books. The subject is treated in a varying and on the whole tentative manner. It is probable that the charge lies not so much against the founder of the doctrine as against those who have sought to interpret and use it as a working tool. Here certainly grievous mistakes have been made.

It may perhaps be fitting and fair if the writer's own account of the

[1] A. Geikie, Textbook of Geology, London, 1903.
[2] A. P. Howard, Journ. of Geomorphology, III, 1940, p. 173.
[3] J. B. Leighly, Ann. Assoc. Amer. Geog., XXX, 1940, p. 225.
[4] J. E. Kessili, Journ. of Geology, 49, 1947, p. 561.

matter[1] be cited for criticism rather than that we should engage in the self-righteous sport of claiming to detect the mistakes of others. The tacit assumptions are, that for a given rate of river flow, there is a definite limit to the load which can be carried, that the power for work is used alternatively in transport *or* corrasion, so that increased load means reduced power of corrasion. Both assumptions are evidently false. It is true that the calibre of load—i.e. the size of particle carried depends on the rate of flow, but under no expectable conditions short of 'earth flow' can a river be fully loaded. The second assumption, carrying the corollary that if the supply of debris slackens an excess of energy will be set free for downcutting, is no more acceptable. We cannot believe that halving the load will increase the power of corrasion, and to make any statement at all on the subject necessitates a much closer scrutiny of the nature of the load and the manner of its transport than has yet been undertaken.

Most, but not all, writers have avoided the final *reductio ad absurdum* of concluding that since a graded stream is by definition fully loaded, when grade is attained vertical corrasion ceases. If any sort of equilibrium at all is involved it is, as Davis recognized, and Baulig has clearly maintained,[2] a shifting equilibrium, the stream would attain grade and thereafter maintain its condition though flowing down an ever gentler slope and carrying ever finer debris. It must seem very doubtful, however, whether this or any other sort of equilibrium has a real existence. At best it can be predicated, but not demonstrated. If there be any hope for the conception of grade as a state of quantitative balance it can be found only in the special if recurrent case, noted by Baulig, of a river in active flood. Then it may set in motion the whole of the superficial drift layer of its flood-plain and make at least the nearest approach that it ever can make to full loading. Even in this supposition there are innumerable untested assumptions. Meanwhile the concave curve of water erosion is, in the qualitative sense, an observed fact. The other observed fact, and one on which the practical diagnosis of grading in fact rests, is the existence of flood-plains. Perhaps the most fundamental criticism of the creed of 'grade', for creed and little more it has in fact become, is, as emphasized by Linton, that both concave profiles and flood-plain derive from the simple fact of control by base-level; but this in itself in no wise involves grading as it has commonly been understood.

An alternative line of attack on the morphometry of river profiles is afforded by J. F. N. Green's[3] mathematical discussion. It may well be

[1] S. W. Wooldridge and R. S. Morgan, *The Physical Basis of Geography*, 1937.
[2] H. Baulig, *C. R. Cong. Intern. Geogr.*, 1925.
[3] J. F. N. Green, *Quart. Journ. Geol. Soc.*, 92, 1936.

true, as Miller[1] has maintained, that extrapolation of river-profiles by 'curve fitting' is subject to too great an error, to avail in terrace-correlation or base-level fixing. Nevertheless, an expression of the type used by Green gives indications at least of how, if not why, a river changes its profile during its life-history.

Our ignorance of the real nature of transport of river loads is paralleled by an ignorance even more profound of the processes concerned in the growth and grading of slopes in general. The ebullition of questioning on this point is a valuable by-product of the renewed interest in the views of Walther Penck. The general question here at issue, the supposed anti-thesis of the doctrines of Penck and Davis, has been so fully treated in a recent symposium and by O. D. von Engeln[2] in a valuable text-book that we can treat the matter briefly here.

There are two distinct though not unrelated strains of thought in Walther Penck's *Die Morphologische Analyse*. On the one hand, he believed that the form of slopes depended upon interaction between the relative rates of uplift and valley erosion. Were this demonstrable, valley-forms would embody a complete and highly valuable record of recent uplift-history. There is virtual unanimity that no such reading of the facts is valid. Douglas Johnson's[3] judgement was that 'the conception that slope profiles are convex, plane, or concave according to the uplifting action . . . is one of the most fantastic errors ever introduced into geomorpho-logy'. It can hardly be deemed too harsh. Penck's further contention that, in the stage of waning development (*Absteigende Entwickelung*), slopes were subject to parallel retreat rather than 'flattening with age' is receiving more serious consideration. Here Penck's view of the general cycle runs generally parallel with that of Davis, in the stages of late maturity and old age. Earth movement is at an end and relief is fading primarily through the wasting of divides. It is the manner of such wasting which is in doubt. Kirk Bryan[4] argues convincingly that under arid conditions, 'parallel retreat' is common and probably the rule, quoting the cogent fact that residuals when made of the same rock have the same angle of slope regardless of size. He gives reasons for supposing that parallel retreat may also characterize humid tropical regions and is prepared to regard it as the probable prevailing mode even in humid temperate regions which are much more familiar and fully studied. Here it is probable that many will wish to join issue with him.

[1] A. A. Miller, *Journ. of Geomorphology*, II, 1934, p. 95.
[2] O. D. von Engeln, *Geomorphology*, Macmillan, 1942.
[3] D. W. Johnson, *Ann. Assoc. Amer. Geog.*, XXX, 1940, p. 231.
[4] Kirk Bryan, *Ann. Assoc. Amer. Geog.*, XXX, 1940, p. 254.

British geomorphologists would probably unite in saying that, unless their eyes radically deceive them, the landscapes of Britain, whether of scarpland, lowland plain, or upland peneplain are wholly consistent with Davis's conception of the wasting of divides. Work now proceeding may modify this view. The clay plains both east and west of London admittedly show residuals of several sizes, but with substantial similarity of form. The escarpments of the Hythe Beds in the Western Weald might seem to lend some colour to the belief that 'slopes of hills are characteristic of the climate and the rocks, and once formed persist in their inclination as they retreat', independent of the structural attitude of the scarp-former and of the stage of the current erosion cycle locally reached. But in both these regions as in many others the existing morphology carries a heavy legacy of former periglacial conditions, of solifluction wastage and other forms of 'mass-movement'.

It is clear at least that the general subject of slope evolution is a fit one for active research. Further studies such as those of Kirk Bryan[1] on 'Gully Gravure' are urgently needed. Nor must sight be lost of the possibility urged by Crickmay[2] that peneplanation is in the last analysis wholly or partly panplanation—the integrated product of long-continued lateral corrasion by rivers. This idea seems to have found little favour; mention of it was unaccountably omitted from the symposium noted above. It involves ideas significantly kindred to those of D. W. Johnson on pediment formation; and so far as it is valid it would, like the processes imagined by Penck, imply the survival of steep-slopes into a late stage of the cycle.

Denudation Chronology

A significant development of geomorphology in the present century has been the attempt to link its record with that of stratigraphical geology. As a pedagogic device designed to assist the explanatory description of land-forms the concept of the cycle of erosion can afford to deal in purely qualitative terms. Though Hutton could find in the record of the earth 'no vestige of a beginning, no prospect of an end', the Davisian method was content to assume the beginning of a cycle—an initial surface—and to predict an end—a peneplain, making full allowance for 'accidents', climatic or volcanic, and interruptions, i.e. changes of base-level. Each interruption is regarded as initiating a new cycle of erosion, though its predecessor may be incomplete; it is in this sense that 'valley-in-valley' forms are spoken of as exhibiting polycyclic relief.

[1] Kirk Bryan, *Journ. of Geomorphology*, III, 1940, p. 89.
[2] C. H. Crickmay, *Geolog. Magazine*, 70, 1933.

Though the qualitative method has its merits in elementary teaching, it fails altogether to face the need of employing morphological evidence to elucidate earth-history. While cycles or 'part-cycles' have been running their course on the lands, the cumulative record of deposition has completed the stratigraphical story. To borrow a phrase of T. H. Huxley's we are involved in the problem of using 'sea-reckoning for land-time', or alternatively of concluding that no satisfactory correlation can be made between them.

In some few regions adjacent to Cretaceous or Tertiary outcrops it has proved possible to attempt a rough equation between geological periods and cycles of erosion. In southern England, it has been widely assumed, following Davis, that the accordance of the higher summits marks a former peneplain which terminated an earlier cycle of erosion and of which the uplift initiated the current cycle. Since the last major folding of the area is post-middle Oligocene, and the peneplain, if such it be, is demonstrably pre-lower Pliocene, the Miocene period is, in round terms, available for the first cycle, while the evolution of the existing hills and valleys has occupied the Pliocene and Pleistocene periods.

Similarly D. W. Johnson[1] regarded the Fall-zone peneplain as marking the end of a long-continued cycle in which the original Appalachian relief was destroyed during early and middle Mesozoic times. Following Cretaceous deposition on this surface, renewed uplift initiated a cycle which culminated in the Schooley peneplain, the existing summit plane over wide areas. This presumably dates from some stage of Tertiary times. No precise date seems ever to have been assigned to it; it might be regarded as either early or middle Tertiary and the current cycle dates from its first uplift.

Over wide areas correlations even as broad as these have proved unattainable. Cowper Reed[2] in the Sedgwick Prize Essay for 1900, divided the history of the rivers of eastern Yorkshire into six 'cycles', but forbore to attempt stratigraphical correlation. In general it may be said that most regions of diversified relief give evidence of a 'summit-plane' and of an incomplete physiographic stairway of lower erosion surfaces or platforms which punctuate the 'current cycle' or which, alternatively, may be regarded as the closing terms of separate cycles. Concerning both the summit plane and the lower platforms there arises the prior question as to whether they are sub-aerial or submarine in fashioning. There has been a tendency, in Europe at least, to revert to marine agencies in explanation of these forms. A similar conclusion was

---

[1] D. W. Johnson, *Stream Sculpture on the Atlantic Slope*, Columbia, 1931.
[2] Cowper Reed, *The Rivers of East Yorkshire*, Cambridge, 1901.

implicit in Barrell's[1] work on the 'Piedmont terraces' of the Appalachians, though it seems to have been received with little favour. Whatever be the relative long-period efficacy of sub-aerial and marine attack, there is strong reason to suppose that over short periods marine erosion may write the more definite and legible record. While differences of opinion will persist on this question, there is virtual unanimity that multiple platforms whether sub-aerial or submarine imply discontinuous changes of base-level. The attempt of Walter Penck to represent such platforms as a normal corollary of continuous uplift is obscure and unconvincing.

But the record, if discontinuous, proves remarkably accordant over wide areas. Hollingworth[2] has demonstrated by statistical methods that the same succession of 'platforms', whether marine or sub-aerial, char-acterizes large parts of upland Britain, south of the Scottish Border; and this work has been supported by field studies in Cornwall, Wales, south-east England and elsewhere. Doubt persists as to the number of platforms to be recognized in many areas. The only satisfactory criterion is to find them separated by relatively steep slopes, but in this respect the evidence is often incomplete. It is to be remembered that, even if untilted, both marine and sub-aerial surfaces must be presumed to show appreciable slopes. The average slope of the continental shelf itself is about $1°$, and few sub-aerial surfaces, even those of alluvial origin, are much less steeply inclined than this. Locally the platform record is confused by the exhuma-tion of 'fossil surfaces'—old planes of unconformity. On the whole, how-ever, there has been too great a tendency to dismiss surfaces as 'fossil', as has been clearly demonstrated by Trueman[3] in the Bristol district. Here elements of fossil landscapes undoubtedly contribute to the existing surface, but many planes of erosion formerly attributed to the 'conti-nental' agencies of the Triassic period, or to the waves of the Jurassic seas, are demonstrably of later origin, since they pass on to rocks of later date. In any case the ascription of quasi-horizontality to surfaces so ancient would be highly implausible.

The evidence in Britain suffices, on the interpretation here adopted, to demonstrate the essential stability—i.e. absence of warping over much of the area since Mid-Tertiary times. This conclusion is unwelcome to many geologists, and if it concerned only this small area, might be relatively unimportant. It should be noted therefore, that Baulig[4] notes essentially the same conditions over much of Western Europe, especially

[1] J. Barrell, *Amer. Journ. Sci.*, 49, 1940.
[2] S. E. Hollingworth, *Quart. Journ. Geol. Soc.*, 94, 1938, p. 55.
[3] A. E. Trueman, *Proc. Bristol Nat. Soc.*, VIII, 1938, p. 402.
[4] H. Baulig, *Inst. British Geography*, No. 3, 1935.

the recurrence over wide areas of platforms at about 180, 280, and 380 metres respectively. More distant correlations extending even across the Atlantic are beginning to suggest themselves. It is not too much to claim that, in its contribution to earth-history, geomorphology seems within grasping distance of a great unifying generalization. Just at the point where the stratigraphical record fails or becomes incomplete, an alternative principle of inter-regional correlation is offered in the fact that old sea-levels have engraved their mark on the margins of the lands and that the same levels are recognizable inland as 'terraces' or 'platforms'. The latter-day record of the continents seems to have been one of 'uplift' starting long before Pleistocene times,—or, more probably, in view of the uniformity of the record, of successive negative eustatic shifts of sea level. Here, in one of its major fields of advance, geomorphology converges upon geo-physics. The simplicity and regularity of the record cannot of course be valid in regions of recent or continuing earth-movement in the orogenetic sense. The remarkable fact is that such regions seem so limited in extent and so clearly bounded.

The Arid and Coastal Cycles

Davis laid the foundations of systematic thinking, not only in the field of 'normal erosion'. The collected papers of his *Geographical Essays* included also the record of his work on glacial, desert, and coastal erosion. In seeking to trace later developments, we may pass over the case of glacial erosion, which will receive attention elsewhere in this volume, though it may be permissible to note here that the work of E. J. Garwood[1] on 'glacial protection' seems to have been little understood or appreciated outside Britain; and his arguments have certainly never been effectively answered.

Detailed study of desert landscapes has been largely the work of the present century. Davis's[2] own sketch of the 'cycle' in an arid climate came in 1906, shortly after the study by Passarge[3] of the Kalahari. Kirk Bryan's[4] very important *Erosion and Sedimentation in the Papago Country*, published in 1922, was followed closely by J. Walther's great work on deserts.[5] These works, and more of still later date, have characteristically concentrated attention on the processes of desert erosion and are of high

[1] E. J. Garwood, *Geogr. Journal*, 36, 1910, p. 310.
[2] W. M. Davis, *Journ. of Geology*, 14, 1906.
[3] S. Passarge, *Die Kalahari*, Berlin, 1904.
[4] Kirk Bryan, *U.S. Geol. Survey Bulletin*, 370, 1922.
[5] J. Walther, *Das Gesetz der Wustenbildung*, Leipzig, 1924.

interest, not only in themselves, but for the light they throw on 'normal' erosion. It is probably true to say that the work of water was under-rated in earlier studies; its efficacy in the desert is not now in doubt, and by analogy, its mode of operation in more humid conditions is illumined.

If we are to select a central problem which focuses much recent discussion it may well be that of the origin of desert rock-plains or pediments. It was in connexion with these that D. W. Johnson[1] brilliantly revived the observation of G. K. Gilbert on lateral river planation and sought to show that pediments are essentially river-cut surfaces. This conclusion does not find universal acceptance, but is none the less a stimulating one, kindred to that of Crickmay on 'panplanation'. It is still clear, in any case, that, however desert plains are formed, they are independent of regional (marine) base-levels. Hence the growing tale of an orderly denudation chronology is halted at the borders of the arid lands. It is particularly in Africa, where arid and humid terrains are juxtaposed, that the problem may yield to study, throwing light on the relative rates of humid and arid degradation and enabling the erosion record of the watered lands to be matched within the desert borders.

In the field of coastal morphology a major landmark is provided by D. W. Johnson's *Shore Processes and Shoreline Development* (1919) and its sequel in *The New England–Acadian Shoreline*. These works employ the essentially comparative method of pure geomorphology. Meanwhile, J. A. Steers[2] and W. V. Lewis of the Cambridge School of Geography in England have concentrated patiently, not only on the forms, but the processes of select portions of the English coast, noticeably in East Anglia and the English Channel. The keynote of their work has been insistence on the primacy of wave-action, as distinct from a vaguely apprehended and probably non-existent 'long-shore current'. It would be premature to exclude all forms of current action in shaping coastal forms; but it is at least clear that breaking waves are answerable for much if not most of the 'forms of accumulation' along our coasts. By comparison with such forms, those of cliffed coasts have been neglected, though Alan Wood of Aberystwyth has completed important work on this topic, which will shortly be published.

Geomorphology and Structural Geology

Traditionally the geomorphologist has averted his ken from the field of earth-movements or structural geology, regarding the structure as

[1] D. W. Johnson, *Geogr. Review*, 22, 1922.
[2] J. A. Steers, *The Coastline of England and Wales*, Cambridge, 1946.

'given' as a starting-point for erosion. This position can no longer be logically maintained. As von Engeln fitly emphasizes, relief forms of the first order are a proper part of the geomorphologist's field, and he must necessarily take account of the rapidly widening field of research and speculation in geophysics and igneous geology. At the end of the nineteenth century little was known of the understructure of the 'crust', the implications of isostasy were not realized; and the fascinating if debatable theses associated with the names of Wegener and Joly, implying both lateral and vertical mobility for the continents as a whole, had not been entertained.

Closely associated with these is the growing body of doctrine concerning the orogenic cycle and its associated vulcanicity. All this raises anew an issue which may be tersely summarized as 'endogenetic' versus 'exogenetic'. To the structural geologist and geophysicist taking the standpoint of such a writer as Umbgrove in *The Pulse of the Earth*,[1] the work of surface agents appears as little more than an evanescent and superficial fretwork wrought upon forms of deep-seated origin and essentially 'structural' expression. This is no doubt one aspect of the truth. Yet it is merely confusing to attempt to include within geomorphology, as it has, in fact, grown, the whole of the methods and results of geophysical and tectonic investigation. The geomorphologist must necessarily be keenly aware of the findings of these other fields and this for two reasons. They form part of the background of his own work, but further, that work, in its own right, will throw light on geophysical questions. Knowledge is no doubt one and indivisible, but it is best pursued, not by defining the logical boundaries of 'compartments', but by perfecting converging methods of attack upon outstanding problems.

Walter Penck was, beyond question, right in conceiving that erosion and earth movement must often overlap in time, and that the resulting forms must bear the stamp of both processes. Yet in general practice, the standpoint of Davis was neither unreasonable nor unacceptable. In general, or at least over wide areas, earth movement is rapid, judged on the scale of the vast expanses of geological time, while erosion is slow and long-continued and starts essentially where earth-movement finishes. To this statement, no doubt, more qualification should be made than space will here permit. Bertrand's luminous conception of 'posthumous movement' warns us of the existence of regions of persistent, or at least recurrent, instability.

Yet one cannot but be impressed by the cogent evidence for the recent stability of such a region as the Alpine zone of southern England. This

[1] J. H. Umbgrove, *The Pulse of the Earth*, Nijhoy, The Hague, 1947.

region[1] (the Weald and 'Wessex') is traversed by powerful mid-Tertiary folds, yet reveals throughout evidences of Pliocene marine planation and relics of a Pliocene marine cover at closely identical elevations over an area of thousands of square miles. It seems most unlikely that further light, however strong, on the antecedents of the Alpine movements here, or on the understructures of the 'crust' beneath can in any way affect our conclusions as to the nature and course of the current cycle of erosion during which the actually existing land-forms have been shaped. It is in this sense that the geomorphologist, while not adopting the role of Gallio and keeping, indeed, a wary and informed eye upon commotion and dispute in the tectonic field, will rest content with saying, 'This at least you must explain and unless or until you can, so much the worse for geophysics.'

On the occasion of the recent Geomorphology tour of the International Geological Congress in London, no fact more strongly impressed the party than the clear evidence that much of southern and western Britain has stood essentially stable, subject only to eustatic changes of sea-level or 'epeirogenetic uplift' if such exists, for a large part of late Tertiary times. Yet it closely adjoins the geosynclinal area of the North Sea which presents a wholly different record. Pliocene deposits which cap some of the highest hills of southern England and maintain their elevation over distances of 100 miles and more, are 1,200 feet below sea-level at Utrecht. Here, indeed, are thesis and antithesis waiting urgently for synthesis and a fair field for future research in which the geomorphologist must play his part.

The foregoing pages constitute no more than a slight and allusive essay on a wide field, inevitably reflecting the interests and the ignorance of the writer. The emphasis throughout has been on geomorphology as the complement of stratigraphical geology—a tool in the elucidation of earth-history. On any showing this is one of its chief roles, and therein it is unmistakably part of geology. This fact periodically disturbs American and British geographers who are led to doubt its relevance in their proper field. Here lies the basis of a seemingly endless and wearisome argument which need not be rehearsed here. Let it suffice to re-state the strongly-held view of many, that the methods and conclusions of geomorphology are necessary alike to the geologist, in reconstructing the history of our planet and to the geographer concerned with what has been called its 'areal differentiation'; that is not the least, but it is also not the only agent responsible for differentiating surfaces of the earth into contrasted regions. The geographer cannot take land-forms as given without

---

[1] S. W. Wooldridge and D. Linton, *Inst. Brit. Geography*, No. 10, 1939.

intelligent scrutiny of their genesis, any more than the chemist can rest content with molecules and ignore the worlds of atomic and sub-atomic physics. It is perhaps the geographer of 'humanist' proclivities rather than the geologist who needs to take 'straight upon the chin' these forceful words of Davis.

CHAPTER VIII

GEOGRAPHICAL ASPECTS OF METEOROLOGY

F. KENNETH HARE

Professor Hare was born at Salisbury, England, and educated at King's College and the London School of Economics. He joined the staff of the Geography Department of Manchester University in 1940; and the Meteorological Service in 1941. He worked first as a forecaster, and later in the Investigations Branch. He joined the staff of the Department of Geography at McGill University in January 1946.

Meteorology and Climatology

GEOGRAPHY shares a common frontier with meteorology in the broad territory of climatology. It would be an exaggeration to say that this has led to conflicts between geographers and meteorologists, but there is no doubt that the exact position of the boundary between them is poorly defined. The geographer tends to keep as far away as possible from meteorology, which deals too much in terms of mathematics and physics for his comfort. The meteorologist, on the other hand, is normally a specialist in mathematical physics with very little training in the basic facts of physical geography. With both parties tending to shun one another it is little wonder that their mutual boundary is ill-defined.

The isolation of the meteorologists from the geographical field was disrupted by the recent world conflict. Forced to extend their activities over a wider field than ever before, the meteorological services of the allied nations acquired a width of outlook and a sense of the world's differentiation far more precise and practical than in pre-war days. Many American forecasters, for example, have worked first in Europe, then in North Africa, finally in the Pacific islands or the Far East before returning home. With such a background, it is difficult for the meteorologist to preserve the parochialism which his training naturally tends to create.

Another link has been the employment of geography graduates as forecasters side by side with those of mathematical or physical training. In normal times the meteorological services recruited their young forecasters, either from the honours schools of mathematics or physics, or else from those who had gone on to graduate work in meteorology. This prejudice in favour of mathematical physics was natural and desirable, since the fundamental theory of meteorology is in effect atmospheric physics. It is quite possible for a young man to become a competent forecaster purely by accepting the theory as gospel; the actual mathematics employed by a forecaster at work is within the powers of a child of ten. But the official services rightly felt that a professional man should work from an understanding of the processes involved, and not by rule of thumb. A training in advanced hydrodynamics and thermodynamics is thus indispensable, and so is the mathematics that goes with them.

The Second World War, however, created an acute shortage of manpower with the necessary training; there were many fields as high in priority that called for the same qualifications as those demanded by the meteorologists. It was soon realized that it would be necessary to accept other skills—in fact any evidence of the capacity of the individual concerned—in those assigned for training. The geographers, with their more than rudimentary training in climatology, were obvious candidates, and they were recruited in large numbers in several countries. The influx was especially large in Great Britain, where geography honours schools have a large enrolment. The training given them, though necessarily less thorough than that received by the peacetime entrant, was none the less intensive, and many of them have returned to geography with a very good grounding in both applied and theoretical meteorology.

Considering their initial disadvantages, these young men and women made a remarkably good showing in their new field. They were used to handling maps for one thing—the main working tool of the forecaster is the synoptic chart—and they knew more about the form of the ground than those with a mathematical training. In certain cases attempts were made to direct these geographically-equipped meteorologists to work in which they could use their special training. The writer, for example, was for some time engaged in work on the prediction of the 'going' across country for tracked military vehicles: this work entailed both the ability to use the synoptic chart for forecasting the weather, and also a familiarity with soil types, superficial geology, and hydrology. More often, however, the sheer pressure of circumstances made it necessary to use the geographers exactly as the mathematicians were used—on general forecast duties—and there is no doubt that they carried out this task very ably.

With the return of so many of these wartime meteorologists to the geographical profession, the latter has gained a new reservoir of special skill on which it may draw. Climatology in a university geography department is now very likely to be taught by a competently trained meteorologist with a much deeper understanding of his special field than was generally the case before the war. Since a training in climatology is an integral part of the geographers' systematic studies, it is vital that the development of the field should make good use of this new interest in meteorology. In this chapter the writer makes a brief review of present-day developments in meteorology and tries to relate them to the needs of the geographer.

Modern Developments in Synoptic Meteorology

It is fashionable today to talk about the 'old' and the 'new' meteorology, as if some sweeping revolution had overtaken the science, involving the complete rejection of the past. This talk is misleading: the 'new' ideas developed naturally out of the old, and were for the most part clarifications and extensions of familiar concepts. Nor is the word 'new' justifiable in 1948; the Bergen school's methods—the basis of the change —were developed fairly completely by 1925, and there have been few fresh developments since 1930. George R. Stewart, in his novel *Storm*, portrays two real characters, an 'old-timer' of the pre-revolutionary days, and a junior meteorologist of the newer school. The old-timer talks in terms of cyclones and anticyclones, of the look of the sky, of the feeling in his bones: the junior meteorologist, on the other hand, is full of fronts and airmasses, waves and occlusions, circulation indices, and all the jargon of the up-to-date weather student. Yet this imaginary conflict—which is daily reproduced in many forecast offices in all countries—is essentially one of terms rather than facts. As we shall see, the new must pay tribute to the old.

The old-style weather map is familiar to all of us. The basic designs visible upon it are made up of isopleths of pressure—*isobars*, that is— which are arranged in large patterns or 'systems' of high or low pressure, often roughly elliptical in shape. Because of the well-known relation of wind to pressure, such a map gives us an excellent synoptic picture of the circulation of the atmosphere over wide areas. Outside the tropics (where the weather map is a dubious ally) the wind blows strictly parallel to the isobars except near ground-level or when pressure is changing. In force the wind is proportional to the pressure gradient—the closer together the isobars, that is, the stronger the winds. Finally in direction the wind blows in such a sense that the observer with his back to it has the lower pressure on his left in the northern hemisphere and on his right in the southern. This fortunate natural law enables us to see the atmosphere's movements with great clarity from afar, and with no actual measurement of the wind. The barometer was then, and is now, the king-pin in the forecaster's machinery.

At first sight the new-style weather map looks different. Fig. 7 contains

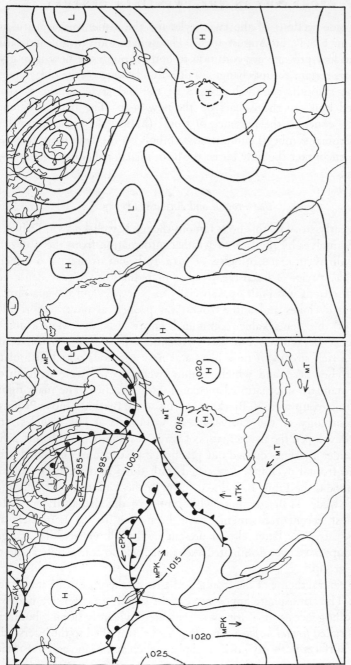

Fig. 7.—Comparison of new (Polar Front) and old Canadian weather maps. (Data at 13.30 E.S.T. on 26 August 1948)

side by side sections of the two styles for the same weather situation (1.30 p.m. E.S.T., 26 August 1948). The isobars and symbols indicating high and low pressure are common to both, though the new map gives the isobars certain abrupt changes of direction lacking on the old; in many cases the smooth, rounded troughs of the old style appear as sharp V-shaped kinks in the isobars on the new map. The main difference, however, concerns the presence of fronts (indicated by the heavy lines with marginal symbols) and airmass symbols on the new map. It is here that we encounter the new ideas: the term *frontal and airmass theory* sums them up.

The Frontal and Airmass Theory

The early story of this now famous theory is well-known. Driven in upon themselves by the lack of weather information from the war zone, the Scandinavian meteorologists of 1914–18 began to practise a hitherto impossible species of intensive weather map-analysis. A very dense network of stations was built up, especially in Norway, and the anatomy of travelling cyclones and anticyclones was probed as never before. The centre of this remarkable communal effort was the Meteorological Institute at Bergen, on Norway's Atlantic seaboard. From this centre flowed a rich stream of new ideas and new methods which stimulated research elsewhere, and which, within twenty years, were to form the basis of standard international meteorological practice. The main figures among this group were V. Bjerknes and his son J. Bjerknes (now Professor of Meteorology at the University of California at Los Angeles); the former developed the mathematics of wave development on fronts, while the younger Bjerknes carried out practical investigations on frontal structure and frontal cyclones. Associated with these two were H. Solberg, G. Swoboda, the Finn, E. Palmen (now in the University of Chicago), and the Swede, T. Bergeron, to whom most of the airmass theory is due. The most recent refinements have been due to S. Petterssen and C-G. Rossby, the latter also at present in the University of Chicago.[1] Few groups have ever dominated a scientific field so completely as did the Bergen group.

The central theme of the frontal and airmass theory can be stated very simply. The atmosphere appears to consist largely of extensive bodies of fairly homogeneous air—*airmasses*—separated by gently sloping boundary surfaces called *frontal surfaces*. The term 'front' is applied to the intersection of these surfaces with any horizontal plane, such as the land and sea surface.

[1] See note on bibliography at the end of the chapter for details of publications.

A frontal surface is hence analogous to the visible surface which separates oil from water when the two are poured into a tumbler; the chief difference is that this latter surface appears horizontal, whereas frontal surfaces slope gently at angles varying from ½ to 2 per cent. In effect, when a cold airmass is in contact with a warm, the cold mass forms a very thinly tapering wedge beneath the warm.

One speaks of the 'frontal theory': in reality fronts have passed the stage of theory and have become respectable realities. Fig. 8 shows an

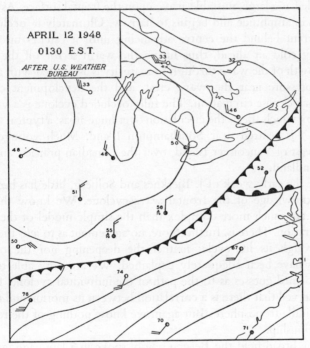

APRIL 12 1948

0130 E.S.T.

AFTER U.S. WEATHER BUREAU

FIG. 8.—A well-marked Front in eastern North America.

example of a front lying across the Central United States with a striking contrast in temperature on the two sides. Because of the cloud and precipitation which is normally found within the warm air above the frontal surface, fronts are visible to the naked eye as well as identifiable on the weather map. The older meteorologists referred to 'rain-areas', 'squall-lines', &c., when confronted with frontal phenomena: the latter were well enough known before the days of the Bergen school, but only with the emergence of the frontal theory was the physical mechanism of linear rain areas understood. Today the tendency among practising meteorologists is to overload the weather map with fronts: if it rains, then there must be a front about. This natural tendency is regrettable in that it often hides real complexities deserving explanation.

The extension of the frontal theory into the field of cyclone-formation was chiefly the work of J. Bjerknes and his collaborator H. Solberg. The Bjerknes diagram of the life-cycle of the frontal wave-cyclone is almost too familiar, and will certainly not bear reproduction here. The cyclone is regarded as a large, unstable wave upon the frontal surface. As it travels it grows in amplitude and begins to narrow. Ultimately it 'occludes', the cold current behind the centre advancing until it catches up with the retreating cold air ahead, thus lifting the warm sector off the ground. This growth of the wave through to maturity is associated with a marked fall of pressure near the wave crest, and the development of strong counter-clockwise circulation. The fully occluded cyclone is a vast rotating vortex which affects the circulation over huge areas; a typical specimen on Fig. 7 is centred near Southampton Island. Much younger waves appear west of Vancouver Island, over the Canadian prairies, and east of Newfoundland.

Since the early work of J. Bjerknes and Solberg, little has been added to our knowledge of the frontal wave-cyclone. We know that many cyclones are much more complex than the simple model of the original demonstration. There is, furthermore, no agreement as to *why* the cyclone goes through its life-cycle: neither the deepening nor the occluding processes have been adequately explained. We are now able to hazard well-informed guesses as to the path of the individual cyclone, for it has been observed that there is a correlation between its motion and the wind in the middle troposphere. But again we know nothing of the reason for this relationship.

In one broad field the Bergen school spoke in a language familiar to the ear of the geographer. If we define an airmass as 'a large body of air fairly homogeneous in physical characteristics in the horizontal plane', it is plain that we are in effect defining atmospheric regions analogous to the natural regions of the geographer. The systematic study of such atmospheric regions or airmasses has been mainly the work of the Swede Tor Bergeron,[1] whose classification of airmasses has acquired international status. The division of airmasses into four groups is now all but universal; the primary classes are referred to Polar and Tropical origin,

[1] See bibliography.

and both may be divided according to whether they come from maritime or continental areas. The four groups are hence:

Maritime Polar (mP)
Continental Polar (cP)
Maritime Tropical (mT)
Continental Tropical (cT)

Bergeron also discussed the primary source regions for airmasses in relation to the general circulation; he proposed[1] that the airmass and frontal concepts should form the basis of a new approach to the study of world climate: 'dynamic climatology', the term he suggested for the new approach, was to comprise the explanatory description of world climates in terms of the airmass theory. His suggestion has not been followed up, to the detriment of the geographer.

The airmass principle is now universally accepted among meteorologists, though its limitations have become very clear. We do not in practice find the huge bodies of homogeneous air required by the original definition: instead we find between successive fronts bodies of air in which sharp variations of temperature and humidity are lacking, and it is this second form that we now prefer as a definition of an airmass. Furthermore, we realize that airmasses rarely or never move about the earth's surface as compact and continuously united bodies of air. Within any given airmass there is almost always a variation of wind with height, so that a column of air existing at point x at moment t can hardly ever move to point y as a unit; it is at once broken up by the shear of wind. When, for example, Toronto is covered by a cool outbreak of continental polar air, we may find that the surface air has come down from central Ungava, the air at 5,000 feet, from Churchill and the Barrens of Keewatin, and at 10,000 feet, from northern Alberta. It is plainly impossible in such an instance to regard the airmass covering southern Ontario as a concrete, semi-rigid body. Yet it does have a certain value to refer to the airmass concerned as a unit, and to discuss its properties as though it were capable of possessing and maintaining, as it were, a personality peculiar to the general class of air we call 'continental polar'.

Unworried by these doubts, several meteorologists have worked out climatological normals for the principal airmasses. Petterssen[1] has presented mean surface and upper air conditions in each airmass in several different parts of the world. Showalter[1] and Willett[1] have made very detailed studies of North American airmasses, and Tu and Huang[1] have applied similar methods in the Far East. The airmass has come to stay,

[1] See bibliography.

for it has been treated climatologically; there is no better sign of longevity in meteorology.

In short, we can say that in 1948 the Bergen ideas have been thoroughly knit into the fabric of modern meteorology, and are taken almost for granted by its practitioners. Today their place in the vanguard of theory has been taken by the broad field of upper air analysis, associated chiefly with Rossby and his associates. To that field we must now turn.

The Upper Air

The Horace Greeleys of the meteorological profession constantly exhort: 'Look up, young man!' Therein, we are told, lies the ultimate salvation of the forecaster and the dynamic meteorologist. The surface weather map has for over half a century served as the main weapon of both, but today the surface map is usually supplemented by three or four equally significant upper air charts covering a similar area. High-flying aircraft have forced this revolution on a none-too-enthusiastic profession, which has never been unanimous as to the value of upper air analysis. The change has been made possible by the development of the radiosonde, the instrument employed in carrying out observations in the upper air. A large body of entirely new theory has arisen out of this unavoidable exploration of high-level weather. Just as the Bergen school's ideas became well defined as soon as really adequate surface weather maps were drawn, so today we are in the midst of finding an immense amount of useful material on the upper air charts.

The simplest, most venerable, and least useful of the ways in which we can gather information from the upper air is by means of the pilot balloon, always used by newspaper photographers to illustrate the meteorologist at work. The principle involved is familiar to us all: the ascent of a balloon with a fixed rate of climb is followed through a theodolite, and its horizontal displacement measured. This gives us approximate wind velocities for each level penetrated by the balloon. The objections to the method are many: for one, it is inaccurate, even in the hands of a well-trained observer; for another, it can be carried out only in clear weather below cloud-base; and for a third, it is rarely possible to follow the balloon beyond 10,000 to 12,000 feet even in clear weather. One suspects that its continued use in many modern services in addition to the more refined methods available is partly conservative and partly because the regular computation of PBA's, as the ascents are nicknamed, is good for the morale of the observers!

The accepted modern method of upper air observation is, of course, the radiosonde, or its newest relative, the rawinsonde. The principle of these instruments is the sending aloft of small radio transmitters by means of balloons: the signals sent out by the transmitters are controlled by small sensitive elements responding to changes in pressure, temperature, and humidity, the three fundamental atmospheric variables. Receiving apparatus on the ground automatically records and deciphers the signals, so that within about ninety minutes the meteorologist has at his disposal an accurate record of conditions up to 50,000 feet or above. The radiosonde does not measure the wind directly, but is employed indirectly in the construction of upper air synoptic charts. The rawinsonde, on the other hand, can be followed directly by radar, since it carries a small radar 'target'; direct measurement of the upper winds is hence obtainable.

Within the past ten or fifteen years the upper air synoptic chart has become a standard method of all efficient forecast services. Made possible by the refinement and multiplication of radiosonde ascents, the upper air chart is a necessity in these days of high-altitude flying. The charts are usually constructed for the 5,000-, 10,000-, 18,000-, and (sometimes) the 30,000-foot levels, the exact procedure differing somewhat from place to place. In form they closely resemble the surface weather map, the main lines being the isobars, which indicate the flow of the atmosphere at each level. It may come as a surprise to many non-meteorologists, however, that the familiar cyclones and anticyclones of the surface weather map rapidly change their form as one ascends; many of the winter anticyclones of Canada and the U.S.A., for example, though intense on the surface synoptic chart, are entirely absent from the 10,000-foot and higher charts.

The most recent developments in dynamic meteorology have largely been concerned with this new field of upper air analysis. Most of the new ideas—of the greatest interest to climatologists and geographers—are associated with C.-G. Rossby and his Chicago school of meteorologists, and with the experimental long-range forecast units of the U.S. Weather Bureau. In middle and high latitudes the upper atmosphere normally forms a gigantic circumpolar whirl of westerly winds—the 'circumpolar westerlies'—which overlie travelling cyclones and anticyclones at lower levels. Rossby and his colleagues have studied variations in the strength of this great whirl, and also the wavelike oscillations and perturbations which affect the westerlies. They have been able to show that the behaviour of the lower atmosphere—which most concerns us as geographers—is largely governed by the intensity of the overlying circumpolar westerly circulation.

It has been in this direction that recent progress has been made, in extending the period within which forecasting is possible. The intensity or 'index' of westerly circulation has been computed on a numerical scale for many years, and is found to vary within astonishingly wide limits for reasons as yet unknown. At times of 'low index', viz. when the upper westerlies are weak over the earth as a whole, there is likely to be a large meridional component in the motion of the lower atmosphere: great outbreaks of polar air will sweep south across middle latitude lands, with equally broad sweeps of tropical air moving northward between the polar masses. The route taken by the main polar outbreaks is also believed to be related closely to the circulation index. With a high index, on the other hand, westerly winds prevail even down to ground level; travelling cyclones and anticyclones move rapidly eastwards, but there is no marked meridional movement of either polar or tropical air.

It is along such lines as these that present-day research and modern practice are trending. Meteorology is a very young and immature science, and its practitioners are only now beginning to feel their way along the right paths of inquiry. But already the new ideas are affecting our views of the general world circulation, just as did those of the Bergen school twenty years ago. The reader is especially urged to read Rossby's paper 'The Scientific Basis of Modern Meteorology' to meet face to face the unfamiliar language and stimulating approach of the pioneer of a new field. Moreover, we should remember that *climates*, which are geographical entities, are explicable only in terms of the general world circulation: and if our ideas about the latter change, we shall have to think again about our stock explanations of climates. Why, for example, is the Mediterranean rainless in summer? The air is moist, and on the face of it should yield heavy thunderstorms: that it rarely does so is an example of the climatic facts which can only be explained by the newer meteorological techniques.

Radar Storm Detection and Rain-making

The network of reporting stations of the ordinary kind is quite dense enough in Europe and North America to enable us to draw adequate surface synoptic charts on which pressure, a smoothly distributed quantity, is the fundamental variable. The 'present-weather' observations also enable us to sketch in the approximate limits of the main precipitation belts. Detail, however, can never be obtained when the individual observing stations are more than 50 miles apart. Moreover we should have very little use for the detail even if it were available, for it changes too quickly to be of much real use—or at least so we thought.

An accidental by-product of wartime research in radar techniques,

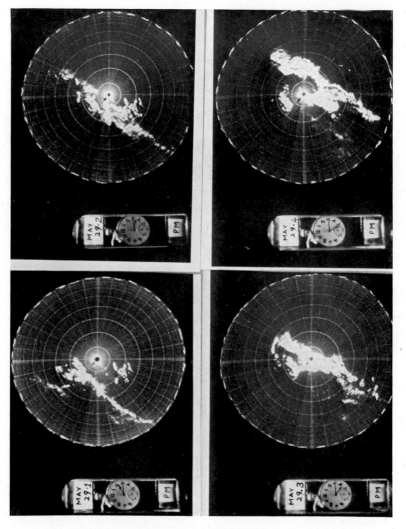

A thundersquall at Ottawa as seen on the Radar-scope. It moved 70 miles in three hours. (K. Hare)

however, has presented us with a tool that gives an extremely detailed picture—quite literally a picture—of rain and snow, especially the former. It has been known for five or six years that falling precipitation 'scatters' the radar beam and produces on the radar scope a signal similar to that produced by an aircraft in flight. A normal 10-centimetre wavelength radar set shows on its scope a map of the surrounding countryside out to ranges of as much as 160 miles in which falling rain appears as brightly glowing patches. A thunderstorm fifty miles away can hence be precisely delimited, and its motion observed and photographed. An example appears in Plate 1. Snow can be detected only out to very short ranges, and the main value of radar observations is with rain and hailstorms.

The forecasting fraternity has found little use for this new technique of observation; as one forecaster put it to the writer, 'it simply tells us our forecast is wrong before the public does'. A forecaster who has to issue a forecast twelve hours in advance has little use for an instrument unlikely to give him more than three hours' warning of bad weather approaching. Extensive use can be and has been made, however, of radar detection for research purposes, especially in the study of the mechanics of rain formation. The Thunderstorm Research programme recently carried out under official sponsorship in Florida and Ohio, for example, maintained photographic records of storms. So also in Canada the Defence Research Board has for several years employed radar as a main method of research into cloud physics, and storm propagation.

Much attention has been paid recently to the artificial production of rain. Scientists of the General Electric Company in Schenectady, N.Y., and others have apparently induced artificial rain by 'seeding' certain types of very cold cloud with crystalline carbon dioxide, silver iodide, and certain other substances. These successful experiments have raised anew the old question of climatic control—whether, in the words of a publicist, 'we can air-condition and irrigate a continent as readily as we can air-condition a train or irrigate the Imperial Valley'.

Such claims are, of course, preposterous, as were the schemes formerly touted to increase the local rainfall by flooding parts of the Libyan, Australian, and South African deserts. All that the meteorologist is at present able to achieve is to provide the trigger which starts off rain from a pre-existing cloud; the problem of creating the cloud is the step which eludes us, because of the vastness of the energy transformations involved.

Nevertheless, these two things—the use of radar in storm detection, and the artificial production of rain—are typical of the slowly extending technical resources of the meteorologist, hitherto something of a Cinderella among the experimental scientists. Though outstanding progress in fundamental knowledge rarely comes suddenly through new technical developments, such progress cannot ultimately be made without steps like these.

Meteorology and the Earth Sciences

There are few 'pure' meteorologists. Almost all professionals are actively engaged in applying their talents, some as forecasters, some in industry and many in one or other of the military fields. Many modern developments in meteorology have their birth in such applied fields as, for example, the Bergen theory of wave cyclones. Much of what we have said so far has dealt with the field of synoptic meteorology, where 'pure' dynamics and thermodynamics are inextricably mixed with the applied field of weather forecasting. Of the remaining applied fields, the most significant to the geographer and the student of earth sciences is that of hydrology, where the meteorologist has begun to make significant progress.

The hydrologic cycle involves a large group of important atmospheric processes; of these the advection of moisture by travelling maritime airmasses and its subsequent precipitation fall within the broad field of synoptic meteorology already discussed. At the opposite end of the cycle, however, comes the process of evaporation or evapotranspiration. This weather-element—for such it is—is only now emerging in our minds as one of the fundamental climatic factors. Increasingly the attention of meteorologists is being turned towards the measurement and prediction of natural evaporation, the hitherto neglected counterpart of precipitation. These efforts are of outstanding interest to hydrologists, water engineers, and farmers, since they offer a real hope of the prediction of such things as soil moisture content, run-off, the fire danger in forests, and crop-yields.

Though many have contributed to this field, two groups stand out. In North America, C. Warren Thornthwaite and Benjamin Holzman[1] of the U.S. Soil Conservation Service have carried out experiments at Arlington (Va.) and elsewhere aimed at actually measuring the upward flux of water vapour off field surfaces. From this and other work, Thornthwaite has developed a general theory of soil-atmosphere relationships upon which he has based his new[1] and in some ways revolutionary rational classification of climates. It is true that at present he does not use a sound functional relationship to predict evaporation, preferring an empirical form, but this he states to be a temporary expedient. In Europe his work has been closely paralleled by scientists working at the

[1] See bibliography.

Rothamsted Experimental Station, Harpenden, England. Here the prime mover has been H. L. Penman,[1] working closely with the official British meteorological service.

To comprehend the work of these specialists it is necessary to keep carefully in mind the role of natural evaporation in the soil climate. At any point on the earth's surface we have for humid climate the relation:

$$\text{Rainfall} = \text{Evaporation} + \text{Run-off} + \text{Percolation}$$

which holds good over any period in which the retained moisture of the soil is the same at both ends of the period. Run-off we can measure by the measurement of stream-flow, percolation ultimately reappears as run-off from spring-fed streams, and rainfall may be measured directly. But evaporation eludes us; the evaporating pans employed by many meteorological services are of little value because of various special local conditions set up by the pans themselves. Yet the relation between evaporation and rainfall at a given station is plainly a fundamental climatic quantity: if evaporation exceeds rainfall there can be neither run-off nor percolation, and the climate must be arid.

The efforts of the meteorologist have been directed towards finding an indirect way of estimating the amount of natural evaporation. Evaporation is essentially a by-product of atmospheric turbulence; the evaporating water vapour is carried away from the soil by the gusts and eddies of the windy airstreams. In essence the process is one of eddy diffusion, and in the absence of wind, the alternative process of molecular diffusion is almost negligibly slow. Sutton, Pasquill,[1] and other British meteorologists have in the course of the past fifteen years applied the general theory of turbulence to problems of atmospheric diffusion, and have arrived at a functional expression for the evaporating power of the atmosphere in terms of temperature, humidity, and windspeed, all readily measurable quantities. Penman, however, has demonstrated that this formal analysis is inconsistent with observation, and has given an empirical solution based on the same variables which gives a remarkably close approximation to observation. Thus we have arrived at the point at which it is possible to predict the evaporating power of the atmosphere from normal meteorological observations.

But natural evaporation differs from the power of the atmosphere to absorb water vapour; the living plant-cover, through the physiological process of transpiration, is the agent of real evaporation—hence Thornthwaite's term 'evapotranspiration'. Since transpiration is largely confined to the daylight hours, the plant-cover can plainly avail itself of only the

[1] See bibliography.

evaporating power of the atmosphere. Thus Thornthwaite's fundamental unit 'potential evapotranspiration' is based on the assumption that only during daylight does significant evaporation occur. Similarly Penman has estimated that a turf-cover is able in England to evaporate only about three-fifths in winter and four-fifths in summer of the total possible evaporation.

Though the detail entered into here may seem out of place in a general review of this kind, the potential value of this new meteorological field is great enough to justify our greatest interest in it. Not only does our understanding of climatic influences on vegetation, soil, and stream-flow increase, but we may shortly discover that agricultural meteorology has become an economically valuable science, through these and other researches. If we can satisfactorily follow the progress of soil moisture content during the growing season—and this is within sight—we can go a long way towards forecasting crop-yields.

Conclusion: The Future

In very brief compass we have reviewed the progress of both theoretical and applied meteorology in recent years. We have seen how the ideas of the Bergen school of meteorologists have slowly but finally become an integral part of the science, and we have seen also how the increasingly searching investigation of the upper air is leading to new ideas and methods in their way as original as those of the airmass and frontal concepts. We have glanced at some new techniques, and at the embryonic field of meteorological hydrology. But the question 'whither next' has not been answered.

The fundamental knowledge of the meteorologist is, of course, physical: he says he 'knows' something only if he can express that knowledge in the exact form of a mathematical equation or identity. To this precise knowledge may be added information capable of statistical analysis in the light of the theory of probability. Yet in practice we are forced to admit that by these standards meteorology is barely embryonic in its development as an exact science; the atmosphere is so complex in its properties that the latter are almost 'unknowable' by the rigorous standards just defined. We add to our knowledge only if we are prepared to concede its approximate character. In this respect meteorology is much more akin to the earth and biological sciences than to physics. We know quite well that the facts of the landscape, the lithosphere, and the living cell are quite beyond mathematical expression. Conceding this, the geologists and biologists have succeeded in erecting respectable sciences;

we might name them the 'detective sciences' from their manner of collecting evidence.

The writer believes that a similar concession from the meteorologist is necessary before much further progress can be made. An immense body of fact awaits a study of the atmosphere from the 'detective' point of view. By all means let us explore the physical approach to its limits, but we must not neglect other avenues of approach. Of these the attitude of the professional geographer and the climatologist is one of the most telling. Bergeron's 'dynamic climatology', discussed briefly a few pages back, is an example of an approach to the study of the atmosphere which combines the viewpoints of the dynamic climatologist and the geographer in a manner of outstanding value to both. Yet so far the meteorologist has worked very little in this field, and the geographer shuns it because of his fear of mathematics.

As climatology becomes more and more an analytical science, more and more explanatory, the geographer is faced ever more urgently with the decision 'how far must I go?' The same problem arose forty years ago when W. M. Davis's technique of explanatory description revolutionized the teaching of physiography; the latter was transmitted into geomorphology, and today we assume a broad familiarity with evolutionary landscape analysis in all geography students. Similarly in climatology, we cannot afford to neglect the explanatory aspect of our descriptions. It is not enough for the honours student to be aware that the Mediterranean summer is dry: he should also know why. That knowledge is available to him without advanced training in mathematical physics, though his appreciation of the facts will be immeasurably increased if he has a little learning in that field.

It is possible that the educated public still underestimates the significance of the work of the meteorologist in the recent world war. The preparation of forecasts for bomber operations, for trans-Atlantic ferry flights and other purely tactical activities have been well publicized. But in practice much of the most valuable work was strategic in character, and went on behind the scenes. No operation of any scale was allowed to begin without prolonged advance planning, and in the latter climatological advice was always sought. Such advice was couched in very different terms from the typical operational forecast: it had to cover such diverse things as the clothing necessary for personnel, the effectiveness of insulation on electrical apparatus, the hardness of terrain for cross-country operations, and the like.

A major test of the capacity of the profession to rise to the requirements of modern war came with the Normandy landings. For many months prior to the landings the climatology of the possible sites was carefully examined, and the moment chosen for the actual landings was picked with a full knowledge of its potentialities for both good and bad weather. Ultimately the responsibility for advising the Supreme Commander on the weather at the time rested with a small group of senior and experienced service meteorologists of both the United States and Great Britain, under the chairmanship of Group-Captain J. H. Stagg. It happened that the period chosen for D-Day was stormy and unsettled to a degree that June has brought only once in many years. Stagg's task was one of the most nerve-racking of the war, for to his natural anxiety as chief meteorologist was added the perennial anxiety of a profession that deals with an inexact and qualitative science. As things turned out, however, the forecasts were closely paralleled by the actual weather.

BIBLIOGRAPHY

The references listed below are fundamental papers referred to in the text. Each represents something of a milestone in its particular field. They do not, however, in any sense form a complete reading list in modern meteorology. A note on further reading follows the bibliography.

T. Bergeron: 'Uber die dreidimensional verknüpfende Wetteranalyse', *Geofysiske Publicationer*, Vol. V, No. 6, Oslo, 1928.
    'Richtlinien einer dynamischen Klimatologie', *Meteorologisches Zeitschrift*, Vol. 47, 1930.
J. Bjerknes and H. Solberg: 'Life Cycle of Cyclones and the Polar Front-Theory of Atmospheric Circulation', *Geofysiske Publicationer*, Vol. LII, No. 1, Oslo, 1922.
V. Bjerknes, J. Bjerknes, H. Solberg, and T. Bergeron: *Physikalische Hydrodynamik*, Berlin, 1933. Reprinted by Edwards Bros., Ann Arbor, Mich.
H. C. Huang: *The Airmasses of North China*, Publication of the California Institute of Technology.
F. Pasquill: 'Evaporation from a plane, free-liquid surface into a turbulent airstream', *Proceedings of the Royal Society*, Series A, Vol. 182, 1943.
H. L. Penman: 'Work . . . on Natural Evaporation', *Annual Report* for 1946, Rothamsted Experimental Station, England.
    'Natural Evaporation from open water, bare soil and grass', *Proc. Royal Soc.*, Series A, Vol. 193, 1948.
S. Petterssen: *Weather Analysis and Forecasting*, New York, 1940.
C-G. Rossby: 'The Scientific Basis of Modern Meteorology', in *Climate and Man*, Yearbook of U.S. Dept of Agriculture, 1941.
A. K. Showalter: 'Further Studies of American Air Mass Properties', *Monthly Weather Review*, July 1939.
O. G. Sutton: 'Wind Structure in a Turbulent Atmosphere', *Proc. Royal Soc.*, Series A, Vol. 146, 1934.
C. W. Thornthwaite: 'An Approach toward a Rational Classification of Climate', *Geographical Review*, Vol. 38, 1948.

C. W. Thornthwaite and B. Holzman: 'Measurement of Evaporation from Land and Water Surfaces', U.S. Dept. of Agriculture, *Technical Bulletin*, No. *817*, 1942.

C. W. Tu: 'Chinese Airmass Properties', *Quarterly Journal of the Royal Meteorological Society*, Vol. 65, 1939.

H. C. Willett: 'American Air Mass Properties', Papers in Physical Oceanography and Meteorology, Vol. II, No. 2, 1934, *Massachusetts Institute of Technology*.

'Characteristic Properties of North American Air Masses', in 'Air Mass Analysis', J. Namias, ed. *American Meteorological Society*, a revised summary of the above.

FURTHER READING

A few reliable and up-to-date studies are listed below, with the approximate scope described. They are arranged under the main sub-divisions of meteorology.

(1) *Dynamical and Physical Meteorology*

S. Petterssen: *Introduction to Meteorology*, New York, 1942. Simple introductory study by an outstanding authority.

H. R. Byers: *General Meteorology*, New York, 1944. A comprehensive but not unduly technical study.

D. Brunt: *Dynamical and Physical Meteorology*, Cambridge, 1937. The standard reference work in English, severely mathematical in approach.

(2) *Synoptic and Applied Meteorology*

H. C. Willett: *Descriptive Meteorology*, 1944. Written essentially from a forecaster's standpoint.

S. Petterssen: *Weather Analysis and Forecasting*, New York, 1940. This book is indispensable: it constitutes the major reference work on all applied techniques.

(3) *Reference Books*

Berry, Bollay, and Beers (editors): *Handbook of Meteorology*, New York, 1945. A very useful and wide ranging reference book, of value to the non-specialist.

Climate and Man. Yearbook of the U.S. Dept. of Agriculture, 1941. A unique and almost priceless collection of general articles, climatic statistics, and other material of the highest value.

CHAPTER IX

CLIMATIC INFLUENCES

STEPHEN SARGENT VISHER

Dr. Visher, Professor of Geography at Indiana University since 1919, is the author of several climatic volumes, including Tropical Cyclones of the Pacific, *1925,* Climatic Laws, a Summary of Climate, *1924,* Climate of Indiana, *1944, and* Climatic Atlas of the United States, *1950. He is co-author with Ellsworth Huntington of* Climatic Changes, their Nature and Causes, *1922. In addition, he has contributed numerous climatic articles to leading journals.*

PART I.—INTRODUCTORY

OF all the geographical influences to which man is subjected, climate seems to be the most potent. It is an influence that no individual or race can escape. On land or sea, on plain or mountain, in savagery or civilization, man must meet the climate virtually on its own terms. Those terms are sometimes easy and generous, and sometimes extremely vigorous. . . . In a large measure, climate determines where man may live and thrive, what crops he may raise, what type of home he may appropriately build, what sort of clothing he needs, and what pests and diseases he must combat. The influence of climate reaches into the social, political, and religious life of mankind. There is a direct connection between climate and the type and degree of civilization.[1]

'Climatic control', assigned by the editor, connotes determinism, a concept repellent to many persons, who contend that no environmental influence is deterministic. Despite the fact that most climatic influences are 'permissive, not deterministic', various aspects of the climate are so highly restrictive as to be in effect controls.

In the subsequent pages, after a brief historical résumé, various climatic elements are considered one by one, with illustrations of their influence.

Historical Résumé

Throughout the ages observers have recognized that weather and climatic conditions are powerful influences. For example, Hippocrates, 'The Father of Medicine' (about 400 B.C.), concluded that regional climatic differences explain several significant differences of peoples. His writings (*On Airs, Waters, and Places*) presented evidence which was con-

---

[1] R. H. Whitbeck, *The Geographic Factor*, Century Co., New York, 1932, p. 87.

sidered convincing to many writers over the centuries. Indeed a distinguished medical professor in a leading American medical school, W. F. Petersen, has recently published a translation of Hippocrates' conclusions, with extended, appreciative notes.

Other ancients supplemented Hippocrates' claims. For example, Aristotle (about 350 B.C.) believed that the people of relatively cold climates have more spirit (energy) than do those of mild climates. Pliny (about A.D. 60) explained by climate the Negroes' dark skin and frizzled hair and the blond complexions of northern Europeans. He also believed that people in warm climates are relatively dull. Vegetius, a Roman writer of the fourth century, contended that people of hot climates are relatively weak and lacking in courage, vitality, and resistance; that people of cool climates have greater vigour and courage.

The Arab historian-geographer, Ibn Khaldun (ca. 1360), divided the northern hemisphere into seven climatic zones. The zone farthest north he considered too cold for man; the one nearest the equator, too hot. The people of the warmer zones are noted, Khaldun asserts, for their passionate natures and their ready abandonment to physical pleasures. Those of the colder climates incline to stolidity and lack of vivacity. Those in the middle zone excel in wisdom and are neither excessively passionate nor markedly stolid. He also explained skin colour as due to climate.

The most famous social writer of France of the eighteenth century, Montesquieu (1689–1755), greatly popularized, in his *The Spirit of Laws*, the generalizations that the people of cold climates tend to be brave, vigorous, physically strong, phlegmatic, monogamous, while the people of warm climates tend to be weak, timid, indolent, vivacious, sensitive to pain or pleasure, inordinate in their sexual indulgences, and lacking in mental ambition. Reclus (1830–1905), often characterized as the greatest of French geographers, recognized clearly that climate is a major environmental influence. He gives more attention than do the earlier writers to aridity versus excessive humidity.

A succession of English writers who discussed this subject recognized additional climatic influences and ramifications. Buckle (1821–62) in *The History of Civilization in England* contended that climate, generally working indirectly, is a major environmental influence. He stressed its influence upon the energy of people, the attribute which he recognized as of almost supreme importance. Herbert Spencer (1820–1903) recognized that many of the statements of earlier writers as to climatic controls were too sweeping. He presented many data refuting various early generalizations, but clearly recognized climatic conditions as highly potent influences. He led in noting that humidity is scarcely less significant than warmth.

German scientists also recognized that climate is highly influential. For example, Ratzel (1844–1904) recognized it as a chief environmental influence but pointed out that its effects are often indirect, affecting man by way of its influence on plants, animals, and soil. He noted that within the intermediate or temperate zone, the regions where the isothermal lines are relatively close together are more stimulating than are those regions where the isotherms are farther apart. He also realized that winds are important, discussing the influence of the Trades in the early development of commerce. Storms too receive attention, but chiefly as intensifiers of the struggle for existence.

Among the American students of climatic influence, Dexter and Huntington merit special mention. E. G. Dexter (1868–1938) published in 1904 (while he was Dean of the School of Education of the University of Illinois) an empirical study of weather influences which attracted wide interest, and which significantly affected later workers. He compared the daily temperature, atmospheric pressure, humidity, wind, sunshine, and precipitation with the records in New York City and in Denver, Colorado, in respect to the behaviour conditions investigated, and found statistically significant correlations between weather and conduct, suicides, and other crimes.

Ellsworth Huntington (1876–1947) made extensive factual studies of climate and weather and human behaviour. He studied, in a series of volumes and numerous papers, many more aspects than any previous investigator, and assembled an imposing mass of data which is convincing to many investigators. His successive studies revealed increasing complexity of the subject, with the result that it is now obvious that the simple relationships announced by most earlier workers are inadequate, if not incorrect. In Huntington's work on the subject five stages may be recognized. He recognized that climate, a highly important influence, has varied in the past, with profound consequences. He did much to establish the fact that there have been significant post-glacial changes of climate and that these played an important role. His *Pulse of Asia* (1907), *Palestine and its Transformation* (1911), and *The Climatic Factor as Illustrated in Arid America* (1914) were early volumes dealing with this subject, to which he returned from time to time for decades. *Climatic Changes, Their Nature and Causes* (1922) summarizes much such evidence.

The second great phase of Huntington's work on climate was on the nature of the changes and their cause. He concluded that changes in the sun have been major causes of changes of terrestrial climate. Although many of the changes occur so unpredictably as to be classed as pulsations rather than cycles, he early saw that the solar (sun-spot) cycles are significant, and he became increasingly interested in an ever-increasing number of cycles. Despite present inability to predict the future (because of the complexity and overlapping of the cycles), he believed it worthwhile to study all sorts of cycles affecting climate and weather. His books *Climatic Changes* (1922 with Visher) and *Earth and Sun* (1923) present many of his findings in this field, but some are presented, not long before his death, in articles, and in his last major book. Thirdly, Huntington, in his studies of climatic and weather influences on production and health, *Climate and Civilization* (1915), *World Power and Evolution* (1919), *Weather and Health* (1930), *Season of Birth* (1938), and *Mainsprings of Civilization* (1945), presented many concrete data on the influences of weather and climate. His *The Character of Races* (1925) also includes a significant discussion of climate and the origin of civilized man and his subtypes.

In these several volumes he, of all the students of weather influences, devoted most attention to the influence of the complex changes incidental to the passage of cyclonic disturbances. The beneficial effect of sudden drops in temperature received special attention in various medical journals. One of his articles in a medical journal was awarded a prize as the most significant contribution of the year published therein. Many lives have already been saved, of people close to death, by the simple expedient of a sharp cooling of the sick room. The fifth phase of Huntington's investigation of climatic influences was his consideration of the effect of ozone, almost ignored by previous investigators. He presented in 1941 (*Climatic Pulsations and an Ozone Hypothesis of Libraries and History*) a highly provocative theory, with many supporting data. This is supplemented in his last book (*Mainsprings of Civilization*, 1945).

PART II.—SOME CURRENT IDEAS ON CLIMATIC CONTROL

As is invariably the case, increased investigation reveals increased complexity. Hence it is desirable to discuss successively a considerable number of aspects.

Average Temperature

The annual average temperature has little significance in regions which possess well-marked seasonal contrasts. The early emphasis on average temperatures reflects the fact that the writers dwelt in a region of moderate seasonal contrasts. (Western Europe, because of the great marine influence, is exceptionally temperate.) What influences living

14

things are actual conditions, not averages. Hence, for example, North Dakota's January average temperature of about 5° and its July average of 68° is vastly more significant than its annual average of 40°. Its summer warmth permits much more agriculture than is possible in various regions having considerably higher annual averages but less seasonal contrast.

Instead of the annual average temperature being highly important, as commonly assumed by persons who know little about climate, it is a minor influence in much of the world. The seasonal temperature is much more significant. In the higher latitudes, the amount of summer warmth counts much more than the degree of winter cold. Conversely, in tropical and subtropical regions, the occasional presence of cool spells is more significant than the amount of heat characteristic of most of the year. For example, the large population of much of northern India and southern China is possible partly owing to the presence of relatively cool winter spells, which tend to offset the excessive heat of the long hot season.

For many plants and animals, and presumably also for primitive mankind, when shelter from cold and heat were inadequate, the seasonal extremes are even more significant than are the seasonal averages. Insofar as this is true, for example, North Dakota's occasional 50° below zero, and its occasional 110° above zero, are even more significant than its January average of nearly zero and its July average of nearly 70°.

Extremes of Temperature

The hardship that extremes of temperature cause upon mankind are illustrated almost everywhere, as throughout all the world there are notable extremes of temperature. The chief variation in the tropics is largely between day and night, but cloud, rain, and hail cause appreciable variation. Hail occurs occasionally even at sea-level well within the tropics, and is not very rare at elevations of two or three thousand feet. The variations due to wind are also significant, though less in the tropics than in higher latitudes, because the winds from different directions tend to have similar temperatures. In middle latitudes winds from high latitudes are generally relatively cold, while in high latitudes winds from warmer latitudes normally are comparatively warm. The amount of nocturnal cooling varies of course with the clearness of the sky, the relative humidity, the altitude, and, where snow occurs, with the existence of a snow-cover.

Even near the equator, many people suffer from the cold at night. For example, near sea-level in Fiji many of the natives, who wear little clothing during the day, gladly wear heavy overcoats in the evening.

Many tropical natives suffer so much from the cold, partly because their resistance to cold is low, that one widely travelled geographer concluded that cold causes more suffering in the tropics than in the sub-polar regions. In consideration of the fact that there are many more people in the tropics than in high latitudes, this conclusion appears not only justified but conservative.

The sharp nocturnal cooling at high altitudes causes much suffering. Even under the equator, freezing temperatures occur frequently at night at elevations of a few thousand feet, while at high altitudes, decidedly low temperatures occur. Though average temperature of day and night there may be near the optimum for man, this average is generally derived from bitter cold nights and early mornings and quite hot midday temperatures.

The amount of nocturnal cooling varies significantly also with the topography. Even at sea-level in the tropics the nights may be relatively cool if cold air drains down a valley from a nearby mountain. Excellent examples of climatic control due to nocturnal cooling of this type occur in the Hawaiian Islands. In Honolulu, for example, residential sites at the end of valleys from the adjacent mountains are far more desirable and hence more valuable than are sites only a few rods away on the same street but so situated that the cold air draining down the valleys does not affect them. Where the cool nocturnal valley breezes blow, residents can obtain more restful sleep than can those who reside only a stone's throw away, at the same level but not opposite to the end of a valley. Hilo, a fairly large city on the north coast of the island of Hawaii, has an exceptionally low death rate partly because (though its average temperature is high and its humidity is great) its nights are relatively cool, due to the cool nocturnal breezes which drain down a valley from nearby Mauna Kea (13,784 feet).

The most conspicuous effect upon plants and animals of extremes of temperature are those involving frost. Many plants and small animals are killed by even a little frost. The damage done to crops by freezing temperatures runs each year into billions of dollars. Five segments of great damage are (1) the northern zone of extensive agriculture in Europe, Canada, and Asia, where wheat, oats, and most other crops are much damaged by frosts that come during the time of flowering, or when the kernels are still soft. (2) The northern limit of corn production in North America is largely set by frost, as corn is harmed by frost at all stages of its growth. (3) Fruit-tree blossoms are seriously damaged by frost, and frosts during the blossoming season often do great harm. (4) In the American South and in many other places, delicate fruit trees and winter vegetables are much harmed by frost. Indeed in Florida, for example, a single night's freeze has done more than $100,000,000 of damage by killing orange trees in addition to the fruit and winter vegetables. (5) Freezing of the top of the soil causes much heaving, breaking some of the roots of winter wheat and other shallow-rooted winter crops and even grass, and also loosening the soil so that it is eroded much more readily by subsequent rain. In brief, frost is a major factor or control in the distribution of many crops.

Although man has withstood the lowest and the highest temperatures experienced on the earth's surface, many people each year freeze to death, and every exceptionally hot spell causes a number of deaths in each well-populated area.

The abruptness of the change of temperature is significant. For example, various dormant fruit trees, such as the apple and the peach, may withstand temperatures well below zero if they come after a prolonged cool spell. Conversely, if sub-zero temperatures occur early in the autumn, before sufficient 'seasoning' has occurred, parts of the tree or even all of it may be killed.

The most sudden erratic cold spells, for example, 'blizzards', are decidedly harmful to animals and man, while the sudden coming of relatively high temperatures, as in chinooks, may cause considerable harm. This is partly indirect, by inducing undue development of plants or exposure by animals to the cold which generally follows the warming. In general, extremes of temperature within short periods (diurnal and from one day to the next) are relatively greatest in arid regions, at high elevations and near mountains from which cold wind or warm chinooks may blow. The seasonal extremes are greatest, on the average, in continental interiors at rather high latitudes.

The great changes of temperature, both seasonal and from day to day, which are characteristic of the northern interior of North America are harmful to many people. Clarence A. Mills, M.D., contends that although that region (Kansas to northern Manitoba) has a relatively low adjusted death rate it is distinctly less healthful than are the regions to the south and south-east. The lower death rate in the region of exceptional great change presumably is, as Bowerman points out, a consequence of other factors which are favourable to health.

Although the actual temperatures rather than averages are what matters, the readily available conventional climatic data on average temperatures correlate, in regions of moderate change, with certain human responses. Detailed physiological examinations by Mills and others indicate that, for example, in parts of the tropics where high average temperatures occur, the human body functions less efficiently than in cooler regions. Of special interest is the evidence that the bodily need for protein and fat are less readily supplied by the diet.

Adjustments to high temperatures are made by the body, though they are not made so well by the very young, the aged, the sick, and those with weak hearts; these are the individuals most likely to succumb to heat. The process of acclimatization to heat consists largely in learning to sweat more volume with less salt in it, and this must be accompanied by taking more water and more salt. Other adjustments are involved, too, though some of the ones suggested are questioned by some authorities. The basal metabolism may decrease somewhat; the number of sweat glands may increase; some of the internal glands may alter their level of secretion. There seems to be a lowering of blood pressure; the volume of blood presumably increases, but it is more diluted; sweating takes a toll of plasma, fluid, and salts which must be made up; there is a decrease in gastric secretions, accompanied by constipation and impaired appetite and digestion; there is also reduced energy for work, but this may often be only a sign of malnutrition or some other trouble. Those who have high energy production because of an over-active thyroid are likely to become neurasthenic in the Tropics. There is less oxygen per cubic foot in hot than in cold air, and this may reduce the effectiveness of all bodily functions unless the body becomes adjusted to it.

The most important conclusions seem to be that the constant sweating and the increase of blood flow to the capillaries induced by warmth have a harmful effect on blood chemistry and the tone of the internal organs, lowering resistance to infection.[1]

The fact that some men have survived in the hottest and coldest regions of the earth has led some people to assert that man is not subject to a temperature control. Survival, however, is biologically inadequate. Reproduction and the maintenance of culture and of some cultural progress are essential. The almost complete lack of population in Antarctica and in most arctic areas suggests that such regions are too cold. The cultural stagnation of the Eskimoes points the same way. The hottest areas of the world likewise are obviously distinctly unfavourable for mankind. The maintenance of culture and cultural progress depends, of course, largely upon mental energy. Much evidence indicates that few people can be mentally active in hot climates. Huntington concluded, and no one has refuted the evidence, that for mental vigour, an average outdoor temperature of 50 to 60° is better than one above 70°. Much of the tropical half of the world has an average temperature well above 70°, with the result that

[1] Adapted from Robert G. Stone: 'Health in Tropical Climates' in *Climate and Man*, Yearbook of U.S. Dept. of Agriculture, pp. 246–61, Washington, 1941.

intellectual activity is handicapped. Conversely, in the cooler parts of middle latitudes, man's intellectual activity has been comparatively great, wherever other conditions are fairly favourable. Indeed, it appears that average outdoor temperatures of about 50° are generally associated with appreciably more mental activity than are temperatures above 70°.

A northward shift during the last 3,000 years of 'Civilization' has occurred as man has been able partly to overcome by buildings, clothing, and more adequate diet some of the ill effects of relatively low temperatures. As civilization has spread into cooler latitudes it has risen to higher average levels, intellectually.

Huntington was apparently the first to observe and effectively state the fact that a general improvement in quality and productivity occurs for many crops and domestic animals toward the cooler margin of their range. This generalization has been supported by such a mass of evidence in recent years that it is increasingly recognized as highly significant. Crops and domestic animals improve in cooler regions partly with the increased mental vigour of their masters, man. Other factors are the more severe selection of improved strains, better care, and the greater relative cost of failure. An inefficient dairy cow, for example, is much more of a financial burden in Minnesota than in Louisiana. Similarly, small yields of crops are more serious in cool regions than in warm ones. Thus the causes for this northward increase in quality and yield almost to the northern limit (in the northern hemisphere) of the range of each are not simple, but they certainly are real.

Related to the improvement in domesticated animals is the fact that for many widely distributed wild birds and mammals the largest varieties of each species, or the largest species of a genus, are found near the northern margin of the range of that type. Many examples of this are known to biologists. Three examples will serve as illustrations. The very widely distributed song-sparrow increases progressively in size northward; those of southern Alaska and Canada are more than half again larger than those of the Gulf of Mexico coast. Of all the brown bears, the largest are the Kodiak; of all the tigers, the Manchurian is much larger than those of India.

Conversely, the smallest types of man, the pygmies, and the smallest birds, the humming-birds, and the smallest rodents are found in tropical regions.

Small bodily size is conducive to the radiation loss of bodily heat. In hot regions the problem of overheating is serious for many warm-blooded animals, with the result that individuals of any particular type which are relatively large are handicapped in this respect. Conversely, the larger the body is, the more internal heat is retained, giving a survival advantage to the larger forms in relatively cold regions.

Of course other factors may overcome this heat loss or retention advantage. For example, although cows become progressively larger in Europe, up to Friesland and southern Scotland, smaller varieties prevail in Iceland and northern Norway. The largest horses are found, also, on the borders of the North Sea, but the smallest in the Shetlands.

A northward increase in the average weight of adult men occurs also to near the northern limit of considerable population. This is despite the fact that some African natives are relatively tall, though thin. In Asia there is a fairly regular increase in human bodily size from the equator to subpolar latitudes.

Humidity

Atmospheric humidity notably affects all sorts of non-aquatic life. The rate of evaporation and transpiration are sharply influenced by the relative humidity, as are likewise the water requirement and the internal temperature. Most plants grow best in humid air and most animals prefer it. Man suffers from high relative humidity whenever the temperature is high. He objects also to high humidity whenever the temperature is relatively low, but it appears that moist air is conducive to health whenever moderate temperatures occur. One of the characteristics of the world's most healthful type of climate is that, with moderate temperatures, it has a high relative humidity.

When both temperature and humidity are high, many forms of life normally multiply rapidly. Included are fungi, bacteria, and most other low forms of life, as well as insects and 'weeds'. Hence food and many other items useful to man commonly soon decay, mould, or rust.

When humidity is great but the temperature is relatively low, there normally is much condensation of moisture as dew, frost, fog, or mist. Hence it is difficult to keep clothing and other equipment sufficiently dry.

Conversely, when the humidity is low, the mucous membranes of the nostrils and bronchial tubes and the skin often crack, permitting the entrance of disease-causing germs. The damage done to most plants and many animals by exceptionally dry air is great, whenever there is considerable wind. When the temperature is high at the same time that the air is dry and in rapid movement, the damage to crops, for example, may be devastating. Forests also are greatly damaged at such times, particularly by fire.

Humidity is significant in numerous additional ways, one of which is its influence on the efficiency of artificial cooling. Where the relative humidity and the temperature are high (as in humid tropical and sub-tropical regions) artificial cooling by 'air conditioning' often results in the condensation of moisture on the walls and other objects, with undesirable results. For example, air at 85° with 90 per cent relative humidity (a frequent condition in large regions) becomes saturated upon only a little cooling, rendering impracticable a cooling to such a comfortable temperature as 70°.

Wind

Another climatic element which often exerts considerable 'control' is the wind. The more violent wind storms do great damage to most sorts of property. For example, hurricanes, typhoons, and the other stronger tropical cyclones have strongly affected human utilization of large regions. The damage that they do is sometimes partly offset by the adjustments they require; after each devastating storm, wiser adjustments result in progress. In most devastated areas, however, the damage wrought by a destructive storm is incompletely overcome.

The destructive influence of strong wind upon the growth of trees in exposed places is often accomplished with the help of salt spray or desiccating air. Similarly much of the damage wind does on the coast or on the sea is by means of the waves. But the fact that the wind uses 'tools' to help in its control does not reduce its significance.

The sand blast in various coastal and desert areas are other effects of the wind of considerable local significance, notably shortening the life of telegraph and other posts, for example.

An interesting correlation between strong winds and flightless birds and insects has been noticed. On various oceanic islands, especially in the Trade Wind Belt, a considerable number of kinds of insects and some birds whose relatives elsewhere fly have become relatively or completely flightless. This is attributed to the fact that on such islands the wind carries out to sea and destruction those individuals who fly, while those who do not use their wings survive to reproduce.

The influence of the wind upon navigation decreased as sailboats were replaced by steamboats. But with the increased use of air travel, wind is becoming increasingly significant, especially in landing and taking off. The use of gliders is even more conspicuously influenced by wind direction and velocity than is true for power-driven planes.

Wind is highly significant also with respect to the tillage of land which is often dry. Dust storms are a dramatic manifestation. Considerable tracts of fertile land have lost much or all of their top soil, and vast tracts have been badly damaged. Indeed it may be safely asserted that the relatively high winds which frequently occur there are a powerful factor in discouraging the tillage of much of the Great Plains. To be sure, the wind alone would not be a control, but the wind significantly supplements occasional dryness.

In numerous small areas the wind alone is a control, practically preventing settlement. This is true in exposed elevated and coastal areas, and in parts of 'The Roaring Forties'.

The lack of wind interferes, of course, with sailing, the use of windmills, and locally even with fishing. Small lakes surrounded by elevated land or woods may be almost without fish because the water contains too little oxygen partly because there is not enough wind to stir it up. The decomposition of the organic matter washed into such small lakes often uses up the dissolved oxygen almost as rapidly as it is supplied by wind-induced waves or by aquatic plants. This is especially the case when the lake is frozen over, preventing waves, and when the ice is snow-covered, keeping out the light which is required by the aquatic plants that liberate oxygen when they grow.

Wind, of course, plays a potent role in fires; most catastrophic fires occur when the wind is exceptionally strong. The amount of damage done each year by fires presumably is many times greater than would have occurred if wind had been lacking or even moderate. Fear of devastating forest fires and prairie fires have significantly retarded the utilization of many areas, and such fires have rendered of little value many areas. The cost of fires in other places, even cities, is greatly increased by winds.

Windstorms

Four types of windstorms clearly merit separate mention. The locally most destructive type, the tornado, causes an average of more than 200 human deaths a year in the United States, and considerable numbers elsewhere. The damage done to buildings and other structures and to trees total an average of many millions of dollars a year in the United States alone.

Thunderstorms are the most numerous type of storm. The damage which they do is only partly caused by the wind, much of it being due to lightning, hail, and torrential rainfall. Many thousands of thunderstorms occur each day somewhere in the world, more in the humid tropics than elsewhere. Undoubtedly the squall winds of thunderstorms are a highly significant environmental influence, causing a considerable number of deaths and much property loss. Much more important than the harm they cause is, however, the good they do by inducing rainfall.

Tropical cyclones which have strong winds, namely the hurricanes, most typhoons, and many 'cyclones' of the Indian Ocean are also highly significant. It is estimated that they kill many thousands of humans per decade and do many millions of dollars' worth of property damage. Single typhoons have killed as many as 30,000 people (Swatow, China, August 1922, or even as many as 100,000, Yokohama, Tokio, 1 September 1923). The Galveston, Texas, hurricane of September 1900 cost more than 6,000 lives and property damage in excess of $30,000,000. An earlier hurricane killed an estimated more than 50,000 persons in the West Indies. One severe cyclone near Calcutta, India, caused more than 200,000 deaths. The hurricane of September 1938 that struck New England and nearby coastal areas caused an estimated more than $400,000,000 of property loss. Many of the heavy tolls caused by these violent windstorms were due to drowning by waves or other floods, and some were due to fire, instead of by wind alone, but the wind induced these other phases.

Less destructive than the foregoing three types are the cyclonic lows which cause most of our day-to-day change of weather. These 'storms', while causing much less harm to the areas they affect than do the three types mentioned above in their respective areas, nevertheless are highly significant. The winds, besides producing notable changes of temperature and cloudiness, bring in the moisture which falls as rain or snow. By producing the change of weather they complicate man's life and put a premium on adaptability. Much evidence indicates that they are stimulating. At any rate the regions which have relatively many cyclonic storms are relatively progressive in the opinion of most persons who are considered to be qualified judges of this matter.

Atmospheric Pressure

Although near sea-level the variations in atmospheric pressure due to weather changes are small and have perhaps only minor direct influence upon men, altitudinal changes of pressure are great and potent. Indeed, one of the most obvious controls caused by climate is that induced by change in air pressure whenever there are rapid changes in altitude. The strongest men become sick at sufficiently high altitudes. Conversely, when persons somewhat adjusted to thin air descend to lowlands, they are for a time notably different. Part of the effect of low air pressures is a shortness of breath. Hence those who remain long at high altitudes develop increased lung capacity. Although some strong adults live at altitudes of 15,000 feet in the Andes, it is stated that children cannot be reared there from birth.

Average Annual Precipitation

The significance of this factor is so great that by common consent much of the world's land is divided into three great types: humid, arid, and semi-arid. Each of these types has distinctly different flora and fauna. Despite man's great adaptability, the people generally are appreciably different in their mode of life, habitation, clothing, domestic animals and plants, and equipment. Even physically, the average desert nomad differs from representative inhabitants of humid regions, is thinner, more 'wiry'. Hence it has long been recognized that the amount of precipitation received in an average year is highly significant.

In addition to arid, humid, and semi-arid, two other types are occasionally recognized: sub-humid and super-humid. The former is transitional between semi-arid and humid, while the latter comprises regions that are excessively wet, either because of large amounts of precipitation or considerably less evaporation than precipitation.

Arid regions have many plants which are characterized by resistance to water loss, as for example the almost leafless cactus, and many plants with thick-skinned or hirsute leaves. Many desert plants are thorny or have a bitter taste. Of the edible desert plants many are short-lived, growing quickly after the occasional rains.

Semi-arid regions have, characteristically, grasses or relatively insignificant shrubs. Trees are almost lacking except some along streams or on rocky hills. Humid regions are generally naturally forested, while the super-humid often is moorland or boggy, though certain types of forest sometimes occur.

Seasonal Precipitation

Regions which have almost the same annual totals of precipitation but receive it in different seasons exhibit notably different responses. For example, where most of the precipitation falls in the summer or at least in the warmer half-year, many conditions differ from those characteristic of regions where the precipitation falls largely in the winter half-year. Still other human responses are characteristic of regions in which the precipitation is rather evenly distributed throughout the year.

Where little precipitation falls in summer, as in the Mediterranean type of climate, irrigation is strongly encouraged wherever sufficient water and warmth are available; also the growing of winter crops and of trees, shrubs, and vines. There is also generally much drying of fruit. Also characteristic are living in villages about the scattered permanent water supplies, and a relatively early development of community life. The winter rainfall of such regions also facilitates soil erosion, with the result that most such regions soon lose much of their hillside soil except where the slopes are terraced. Hence terracing is especially widespread.

Where most of the precipitation falls in the warmer months, as in the monsoon regions and in parts of the Great Plains and the Ukraine, crop growing is encouraged and soil erosion is comparatively slow unless the rainfall is largely torrential, as it is in the monsoon regions. The natural hay formed by the dry autumns and preserved by the dry winters of the Great Plains facilitates grazing, as does the relatively light snowfall. Cities and industrial development is interfered with, however, in this type of climate by the months with little precipitation. Hence most cities are located on rivers and few become large or industrial.

Where the precipitation is distributed fairly evenly throughout the year, man is able to carry on successfully many more activities than are feasible in regions having chiefly winter or summer precipitation. As a partial result, the more advanced modern civilizations are largely in such regions. As these generally have numerous cyclonic disturbances, to induce the rains in all seasons, they are sometimes called the cyclonic regions. Their cultural advancement may be due chiefly to the changeableness of the weather, as Huntington believed. However, the year-round water supply certainly has favoured the development of cities and factories as well as diversified agriculture. The forest wealth characteristic of such regions has also contributed to their advancement. (Most regions with either dry summers or long dry winters have inferior forests, if any.)

Precipitation, Dependability and Intensity

The average precipitation amounts considered in the preceding paragraphs are, of course, the accumulation of individual rainstorms or snow storms. The amount that falls in any given short time is normally much more significant than the average amount. Hence, as was true with temperatures, averages should not be stressed; what counts is the actual occurrence. In large regions the precipitation is highly erratic, one summer receiving, for example, several times as much as another. Arid regions experience wide extremes but the humid regions differ widely in rainfall dependability. In general, there is much more variability in the tropics, with a comparable annual total, than in middle latitudes. The most dependable regions are rather cool and 'cyclonic'. The significance of dependability is tremendous. Although the individual men of regions of erratic precipitation are physically much like the men of regions of dependable rainfall, human psychology and responses are conspicuously different. Since droughts have caused millions of deaths in the monsoon regions, early marriage, high birth rate, and 'ancestor worship' have been encouraged. In arid regions, notably south-western Asia, the fluctuation in rainfall has contributed to the development of religions that recognize an overpowering force called God. In semi-arid and sub-humid regions, the wide fluctuations in rainfall have helped develop radical political doctrines. In the United States and Canada, for example, many of the more radical governmental programmes have emanated from regions where erratic rainfall often makes the people, who have done their best, desperate.

Rainfall deficiencies and excesses cause damage partly because most human responses to the environment are to average or normal conditions. It is a serious task to make wise adjustments to ordinary or usual conditions; to adjust wisely to unusual conditions requires a great deal of additional knowledge, effort, and capital. Although Americans have by no means yet succeeded in effectively adapting many of their activities to normal conditions, the cost of failure to prepare for unusual conditions is so great as to make it highly desirable that increased efforts be made along that line. The body of knowledge now available to serve as a guide as to what adjustments are wise is far greater than it was even two decades ago. This is partly because, with the help of capable people previously unemployed because of the depression, various costly studies were made (during 1934–40) of Weather Bureau data.

In a relatively wet year shallow wells yield abundant water, springs are bountiful, water supply reservoirs overflow; there is plenty of water for man, livestock, industrial uses, fire fighting, canal navigation, and hydro-electric production. In a relatively dry year, however, serious water shortages develop as many wells, springs, reservoirs, marshes, and even rivers go dry. Many hydro-electric power plants fail for lack of water, and some steam power plants are seriously interfered with by lack of sufficient water for steam production. Forest fires usually spread widely in a dry year, whereas in a wet year there usually are few serious forest fires.

The effects of variation in precipitation, while important in all regions, differ significantly. A relatively wet year usually is a bad year in humid regions, is generally a good year in sub-humid areas, and often is a 'wonderful' year in the semi-arid and arid regions. Such a wet year may produce a drastic change in the economy and attitude of the people.

In a region which has already received enough rain, the extra amount characteristic of a wet year produces floods, drowns low-lying land, interferes with planting, cultivation, and harvest. It may also interfere with hydro-electric development by raising the water level below the dam sufficiently to reduce the head of pressure. The extra rain of a wet year may therefore be a real liability in a humid region.

By contrast, the extra rainfall of a relatively wet year in a dry region may be almost entirely beneficial, increasing manyfold the growth of grass and hastening the development of range stock (chiefly because of better feed but partly by the greater availability of drinking water). Crop yields are increased greatly. This is most conspicuously true when the summer is wet (considered below), but occurs to a lesser degree when the other seasons have exceptionally heavy precipitation even if the summer does not. This is because the native grass and hardy crops of dry regions usually can grow rather well if the soil contains much moisture accumulated in autumn, winter, or spring, even if the summer is not rainy. This is especially true of winter wheat and the grain sorghums, but even corn can grow rather well in the fertile soil of the sub-humid plains, provided the soil is well filled with moisture at the beginning of the summer, and the summer is not too hot and has no scorching winds.

The effects of dry years are profound and almost completely detrimental in normally sub-humid or semi-arid regions. Pasture and water for livestock decrease alarmingly or critically; crop yields shrink locally to almost nothing, wind erosion of the soil is greatly accelerated; discouragement and poverty tend to undermine morale and health of the people. Inability to water and feed the livestock—the most dependable source of income in such regions—leads to their being sold, greatly retarding economic recovery when wet years do return. For example the number of cattle in Nebraska decreased 1,100,000 head between 1934 and 1938 (1934 and 1936 were very dry years). The decline in Montana in those years was relatively even greater; there were only a few more than half as many cattle in Montana in 1938 as in 1934, despite the fact that irrigation is important in that state. Such a decline in cattle as occurred in Nebraska and Montana, and also in most neighbouring states, represented a very serious decline in source of income.

The decline in the number of hogs which occurred in the corn belt following the drought years of 1934 and 1936 was even more drastic than the decline in cattle. Iowa had about 4,000,000 fewer hogs in 1935 than in 1934, Nebraska about 3,000,000 fewer; even Indiana (which had the poorest corn yield on record in 1934) had 1,300,000 fewer; Kansas had only a third as many hogs in 1935 and in 1938 as in 1933.

Following relatively wet years, the number of hogs and cattle increase sharply; for example South Dakota and Kansas had about twice as many hogs in 1940, after the good corn year of 1939, as in 1937, after the drought year of 1936.

In Kansas the average corn yield has varied 1916–40 from 3 bushels per acre in 1934 and 4 bushels in 1936 to 30 bushels in 1927 and 27 bushels in 1928. The yield in wheat has ranged from 8·5 bushels per acre in 1933 and 9·1 in 1935 to 18·5 bushels in 1931 and 16·3 in 1928. These great differences are of profound local economic importance.

The serious effect of the severe drought of 1934 is illustrated in other states by the following data. Nebraska grew less than half as much wheat in 1934 as in 1935; North Dakota less than a third as much; South Dakota less than a sixth as much. Rye yielded 2½ times as much in 1935 as in 1934 per average acre in Minnesota; 2¾ times as much in North Dakota.

The advantage of a relatively dry season in a humid region is illustrated by the following data: Wisconsin's potato crop was nearly three times as large in 1934 as in 1937. In semi-arid South Dakota, however, the potato crop was 43 times as large in 1933 as in 1934; 11 times as large in 1935 as in 1936.

In much of the country the chief cause of variation in crop yield from year to year is the amount and distribution of the rainfall in summer. In Indiana, for example, the state average yield of corn was 51·5 bushels per acre in 1939, a wet summer, but was less than three-fourths as great (37 bushels) in 1940, a dry summer, and less than half as great (24·8 bushels per acre) in 1934, a very dry summer. Likewise Indiana's oat crop has varied from a state average of 45 bushels per acre in a favourable season to little more than a third as much (15·5 bushels) in the bad drought year of 1934. For wheat, the range in yield in Indiana has been from 26 bushels per acre for the state average in 1931 to less than 10 bushels in several years. Likewise, the soy bean crop varied from a state average of 20 bushels per acre in 1938 to 13·5 bushels in 1940. Similarly tomatoes show a wide range largely associated with summer rainfall; in 1922, when July was wet but June and August relatively dry, the yield averaged just twice as much as in 1923 when August was very wet.

The range in the state average yield of corn is greater in Iowa than in Indiana, from 20 bushels per acre in 1936 to 52 bushels per acre in 1939. This meant a difference in output of about 300,000,000 bushels which is equivalent to about $750 per average farm family in the state.

The variation between the crop production in wet and dry summers is much greater in the Dakotas, Nebraska, Kansas, and Montana than in Iowa. In those western states, wet summers produce large yields, dry ones very little. For example, South Dakota's wheat crop was only a ninth as large in 1934 as in 1932, and half of the small 1934 crop was winter wheat, the spring wheat being almost a complete failure. The large yields of the wet seasons often produce reckless extravagance, especially in ploughing up additional sod, while the dry seasons produce poverty, land abandonment, political unrest, and perhaps dust storms which carry to the humid East clear evidence that something serious is wrong in the 'Dust Bowl'. A useful result was the great expenditure via W.P.A. and A.A.A. for the construction of dams for reservoirs for stock water and domestic supplies. These reservoirs are so valuable in the more effective use of the dry plains in ordinary years as well as in dry ones that their construction is a substantial advantageous result of 'Dust Bowl' conditions of dry years.

Many of the serious floods of the rivers in the north-eastern United States were caused by the fall of more than 10 inches of rain in a month. The flood of the Miami River through Dayton and of various Indiana rivers in March 1913 was caused by the fall, mostly in a week or two, of about 12 inches of rain. The loss of life was 732 persons. The great flood of the Ohio River in January 1937 was caused by a month's total of 15 to 20 inches received over a considerable tributary area. About 10 inches fell in a five-day period. Property loss was estimated at $417,000,000 not including soil damage; 137 lives were lost. Floods of the Mississippi River in April, May, and June 1927, caused by prolonged hard rains, took several hundred lives, and did more than $270,000,000 worth of property damage.

The washing out of dams is one result of excessive rainfall. Some examples are the Johnstown, Pa., dam which broke, after several days of excessive rain, on 31 May 1889, with the loss of about 2,200 lives. The Austin, Pa., dam broke, following a tropical cyclone, on 30 September 1911, killing 150 people and doing damage estimated at $8,000,000; the St. Francis dam, near Los Angeles, Calif., broke following several days of very heavy rainfall, on 13 March 1928, killing about 400 people and causing property damage estimated at more than $12,000,000.

Some Effects of Torrential Rains

Buildings may be damaged by flooding of basements and weakening of foundations by run-off and by water soaking. Buildings on lowlands may be partly submerged by the floodwaters of torrential rains. For example, the storm that brought 10 to 20 inches of rain in 24 hours to much of south-eastern Alabama (14–15 March 1929) flooded many towns.

City and town water supply, whether from shallow wells, reservoirs, or streams, and sewer disposal systems are seriously interfered with by torrential downpours. Heavy rainfalls injure roads, railroads, bridges, airports, and pipe lines by flooding, softening, and eroding. Although large-scale floods are caused by prolonged rains rather than by 24-hour falls, the briefer storms often cause serious local floods. For example, on 29–30 June 1940, much damage was done to roads, railroads, and bridges in an area 50 miles by 100 miles in Texas, where from 8 to 20 inches of rain fell in 24 hours and a number of people were drowned.

The damage to telephone, telegraph, and electric lines by torrential rains is partly due to the force of the water-laden winds that accompany most such downpours. But the damage is much increased by the excess softening of the ground caused by the large amount of water that runs down the poles. Electric light and power services may be disrupted by damage to the generating plant. If the plant is a hydro-electric one, the damage may be gradual, due to silting of the reservoir, or very rapid, due to breaking of the dam. Or the excessive rainfall may raise the water level enough to put the plant temporarily out of order. Fuel-powered plants, too, may suffer flood damage because their water requirements encourage location close to a stream.

Crops are damaged in several ways. Planting may be delayed; seeds and small plants may be washed out or buried beneath sediment; growth of weeds is facilitated, partly because cultivation is hindered. The value of unpicked cotton is greatly diminished when the open bolls are soiled with mud spattered by a hard rain. The great rain of 24–25 July 1933 in Louisiana did crop damage officially estimated at more than a million dollars, chiefly by flooding some 20,000 acres of cropland.

But the most serious long-term damage is that done by erosion and leaching. The South is the large American region where soil erosion is most widely serious. Except for Florida and the low-lying land along the coast, fully four-fifths of the South has widespread 'serious' or 'harmful' erosion. By contrast, less than one-third of the North has either. It is obvious that the relatively extensive soil erosion in the South is due in part to the larger and more frequent hard rains.

Soil leaching is also accelerated by heavy rains, even where there is little soil erosion. On sandy and level lands, excessive rains dissolve soluble soil materials. The most extensively leached soils in the world are found in the rainy tropics. But the average soils of the South to the east of central Texas are little better than those of the Amazon basin, said C. F. Marbut, who did extensive field work in both regions. The South uses far more mineral fertilizer than any other American region, largely because of the low average natural soil fertility.

Soil erosion in one place necessarily results in soil deposition elsewhere. If only fertile soil is eroded, its deposition renews the underlying soil.

15

Examples are seen along the lower Mississippi River and on many other flood plains. But if, as has happened extensively in the South, subsoil and other relatively infertile materials are eroded, their deposition may damage fertile lowlands. Indeed, an appreciable part of the fertile valleys of the southern Appalachians and other rugged southern areas has been covered with subsoil, sand, or coarser materials eroded since the steeper slopes have been cultivated. Deposition in reservoirs reduce their capacity. One of the compelling demonstrations made by the Soil Conservation Service in recent years is that of the rapidity with which most southern reservoirs are silting up. Some of them have lost at least a quarter of their original water capacity in two or three decades.

Thus, in conclusion, the precipitation conditions here briefly described have varied and far-reaching consequences.

Precipitation variation is greater in much of the world than in most of the United States. Hence the illustrations given in the foregoing section of effects are 'conservative'. It is extracted from the author's articles in *Economic Geography*, 19: 1–15, 1943; and *Geographical Review*, 31: 644–52, 1941.

Sunshine and Cloudiness

By general agreement of those who have studied the subject, there is a rough correlation between the amount of sunshine and human skin colour; the blond people are found in regions of inadequate sunshine and the dark-skinned peoples chiefly in regions of intense sunshine. Huntington found that though most northern people welcome bright days, they accomplish less work on such days than on the partly cloudy ones. Dexter found that suicide is more common on bright than cloudy days. The strong influence of sunshine on tuberculosis germs is well known. Lack of sunshine also is associated with rickets. However, rickets is widespread among the poorer people of various tropical lands, Puerto Rico, for example. This is because the infants are kept from the sun, which is so intense that serious damage is done to the retina if the sun shines upon it. It is pathetic that rickets should be common where there is plenty of sunshine.

Ozone

The following quotation from Huntington's *Mainsprings of Civilization* is appropriate as an ending.

Atmospheric ozone in extremely small amounts, one part in twenty or thirty million of air, is known to be a most effective physiological stimulant. It gives to the air the delightful quality known as freshness. Practically every kind of air that is considered especially desirable has more than the average amount of ozone. Thus it appears to be a genuine stimulant to health and especially to mental alertness. In warm, moist regions the ozone largely disappears before it reaches the earth's surface. This appears to be one of the reasons why tropical air is enervating. By midwinter the concentration of ozone in the far north has reached a high level. In summer, too, the amount at high latitudes is still large. This may be one reason why crops which escape frost grow luxuriantly in high latitudes, giving yields per acre that are almost unparalleled elsewhere.

PART III.—SOME TRENDS AND TECHNIQUES

As the opening historical résumé pointed out, one of the great trends as to the knowledge of climatic influences is an increased realization of complexity. Average temperatures, average annual precipitation, and normal winds, for example, are now seen to be far less significant as influences than various other climatic conditions formerly ignored. Hence the difficulty of assembling, depicting, and analysing the requisite data is becoming more and more obvious. Accordingly few geographers now attempt to analyse climatic influences as such, and the work of studying and depicting climatic conditions has become a matter for specialists making specific correlations, a matter of far greater validity and more importance than the sweeping generalizations about influences which were made in the past.

In the graphic presentation of climatic data, there has been striking increased complexity. A couple of generations ago, few areas had more than about a dozen climatic maps. Depicted, perhaps, were average seasonal temperatures, precipitation, wind directions, and amount of sunshine, supplemented by a map perhaps of the average length of the growing season. Now, however, many persons realize that a dozen maps can only very inadequately depict the climate. As a result, an ever-increasing number of maps are being made. For example, Visher's *Climate of Indiana* has more than 300 maps, and *Climatic Atlas of United States* more than 1,000; each of which helps significantly to illustrate some aspect of the climate, and hence helps contribute to an understanding of climatic influences. Although such large numbers of different climatic maps seem excessive, a careful consideration of the complexity of climate and its fluctuations leads gradually to a realization that attempted simplicity is misleading.

Efforts to obtain simplicity are of three main sorts: (*a*) to ignore 'unimportant' conditions, (*b*) to synthesize in one or few maps a number of significant types of climatic data, (c) to make many maps, each of which shows a single body of climatic data, and shade that map so that the regional contrasts are conspicuous. The first type of simplification, ignoring most of the data, has been proven so unsatisfactory that it is being abandoned by all those who know much about climate. The second technique has been used by Koeppen, Thornthwaite, and various others. Koeppen, for example, arbitrarily decided to use the average January and July temperatures and the seasonal amounts of precipitation, ignoring other aspects of the climate. He gave ritualistic names to certain types of arbitrary combinations of the selected data. His climatic regions map is attractive for its concise simplicity. But it did not commend itself to those who were not too carried away by its stereotyped simplicity, and sought evidence in the field as to how effectively it presented existing regional climatic differences.

C. W. Thornthwaite, working in areas clearly not satisfactorily delimited and characterized by the Koeppen maps, proposed significant changes in the formulae, most notable of which is a consideration of the amount of water loss by evaporation and transpiration. Consequently, his earlier climatic regionalization (*Geographical Review*, 1931, 1933) were conspicuously better than Koeppen's. Thornthwaite continued to improve on his system, considering additional data and making increasingly complicated calculations. His recent climatic maps ('A Rational Approach to Climatic Regions', *Geographical Review*, 1948) are a vast improvement over Koeppen's and earlier simplifiers. In effective presentations of dominating climatic conditions he has found it necessary, however, to abandon an attempt to present only one map. Instead he gives four: moisture regions, seasonal variation in effective moisture, average annual thermal efficiency, and summer concentration of thermal efficiency.

The present writer has not attempted to depict regional climatic differences by a few maps, instead he has used many, each of which is easily read. However, it is seldom practicable to present numerous maps, and hence some selection or consolidation is desirable. Maps that are desirable, besides those of thermal efficiency and effective moisture, include those showing the dependability of precipitation, of the frequency of killing frosts, of torrential downpours, of droughts, of hail, of destructive winds, and of stimulating changes of weather.

An increasing number of diagrams has been used to depict climatic conditions. Vertical bar graphs for monthly temperature and precipitation were almost the first type used. Numerous refinements have been introduced to this type, including the use of daily, seasonal, and annual data to supplement the monthly. Extremes are also indicated. Various groupings of the data have been helpful in showing trends, for example five-year, ten-year, and twenty-year moving averages. Curves made thus often greatly supplement simple bar graphs in making clear what changes have occurred.

A technique of notable utility is the climograph (Fig. 9). It was invented by John Ball of Egypt, and independently by Griffith Taylor in 1915 in Australia. It was widely used by Taylor[1] and later by Ellsworth Huntington, Visher, and some others in the U.S.A. The first main use

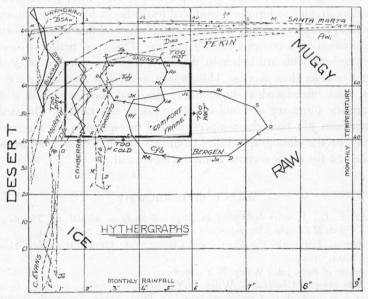

FIG. 9.—The main environmental conditions of any stations in the world can be readily compared by drawing their 'Hythergraphs' on this base

Each graph is a twelve-sided figure charting the rainfall and temperature conditions for each month. The well-known climatic formulae (Cfb, &c.) used by Koeppen are added. (From Griffith Taylor: *Our Evolving Civilization*, 1947)

of the climograph was to show by a single closed curve the temperature and rainfall, or any other two climatic conditions, throughout the twelve months of the year by plotting one of the conditions, say precipitation, horizontally from left to right and the other, say temperature, vertically from bottom to top (Fig. 9). Curves connect the dots (where the plot lines cross). The climograph is a great improvement over bar graphs for those who understand them. Climographs are especially effective in

[1] For instance, the seventy climographs illustrated in *Bulletin No. 14*, Meteorology Bureau, Melbourne, 1916.

disclosing correlations between two climatic conditions and some non-climatic conditions. For example, the base of the diagram may represent the amount of rainfall, increasing from left to right and the vertical height may represent the temperature. If the yield of corn for the year is indicated by a dot at the point where the rainfall and temperature of July occurred that year, and similar dots are located for the yield in numerous other years, a diagram develops which shows effectively the correlation between yields in that area and those two elements of the climate. (Hythergraphs are similar graphs applicable to crop ecology, Fig. 9.) A refinement of this climography technique introduced by Visher is to show the normal (average) temperatures by a conspicuous horizontal line and the normal precipitation by a conspicuous vertical line. This cross makes it easy to see whether yields are better in months which are warmer or cooler, wetter or drier than average. Huntington, instead of two heavy crossed lines, later introduced a single heavy diagonal line, which is a diagrammatic summary of London's temperature and rainfall. This makes conspicuous just how the temperature and precipitation for the station plotted on the climograph differs from that of London, selected as close to the best for many sorts of human achievement.

SHORT BIBLIOGRAPHY

Dexter, E. G.: *Weather Influences, an Empirical Study of Mental and Physiological Effects of Definite Meteorological Conditions*, Macmillan, N.Y., 1904.

Huntington, Ellsworth: *Civilization and Climate*, Yale Univ. Press, New Haven, 1915, 1924.
  Season of Birth, John Wiley, N.Y., 1938.
  Mainsprings of Civilization, Wiley, N.Y., 1945.

Kincer, J. B., and others: *Climate and Man*, U.S. Dept. Agric., Yearbook, Washington, D.C., 1941.

Markham, S. F.: *Climate and the Energy of Nations*, Oxford Univ. Press, N.Y., 1942, 1944.

Mills, Clarence A.: *Climate Makes the Man*, Harpers, N.Y., 1942.

Petersen, W. E.: *Hippocratic Wisdom*, C. C. Thomas, Springfield, Ill., 1946.
  The Weather and the Patient, Edwards Brothers, Ann Arbor, 1934-5.
  Man, Weather and Sun, C. C. Thomas, Springfield, Ill., 1947.

Price, A. G.: *White Settlers in the Tropics*, American Geographic. Society, N.Y., 1939.

Taylor, Griffith: *Our Evolving Civilization*, Univ. of Toronto Press, 1946.

Thomas, Franklin: *The Environmental Basis of Society*, The Century Co., N.Y., 1925.

Visher, S. S.: *Climate of Indiana*, Indiana University, Bloomington, 1944.

Ward, R. DeC.: *Climate and Man*, Putnam Co., N.Y., 1908, 1918.

CHAPTER X

SOILS AND THEIR GEOGRAPHICAL SIGNIFICANCE

D. F. PUTNAM

Donald Fulton Putnam, B.S.A., Ph.D. (Toronto, 1935), Associate Professor of Geography, University of Toronto. Born Lower Onslow, Nova Scotia. Nova Scotia Agricultural College, 1924 (Diploma); McGill University 1929–30. Engaged in agricultural investigation in Nova Scotia 1924–30, and in British Columbia 1930–1. Demonstrator in Botany, University of Toronto 1931–8.

GEOGRAPHY may be defined as 'human ecology' or it may be considered simply as a description of the earth. A most graphically phrased explanation attributed to Isaiah Bowman states that 'geography tells what is where, why and what of it'. In the words of Griffith Taylor, 'Geography is the correlative science.' One might continue to quote the attempts of eminent geographers to define the field of geography, yet no matter what approach is made to the subject it will be found that soil is one of the important factors of the environment. Its importance, however, has not yet been clearly recognized by all geographers. There are still in use standard geography text-books in which no useful mention is made of soils; others which do not regard it as necessary to explain what soils are, or how they are classified. In those recent texts which do recognize the importance of soils knowledge, it may be allotted from 3 to 5 per cent of the space. In books on land settlement and conservation of resources, in which geographers are becoming increasingly involved, possibly 10 to 12 per cent will be devoted to the subject. It is, therefore, not out of place that in a symposium on modern geography there should be a discussion in which soil science should contribute its share towards the moulding of geographic thought.

No student of civilization forgets for an instant the fundamental importance of the soil. It is the source of practically all man's food, clothing, and an ever-increasing list of other needs and desires. In spite of all the great advances in manufacturing technology, agriculture is still the world's most important industry—a fact which, though often neglected, becomes appreciated anew in each historic crisis. Such considerations apart, however, approximately two-thirds of the population of the world are still farmers, living on and deriving their living directly from the soil. There are many problems of land-use adjustment to be dealt with in the near future. Geographers expect to contribute to the solution of these problems, and it behoves them to acquire a working knowledge of soil science and to develop a lively appreciation of the geographical significance of soils themselves.

In the eyes of some geographers, soils have one further function worthy of mention. Being, as they are, the expression of all factors of the environment acting in unison, they constitute an important clue to that elusive geographical concept, the natural region. To this end, however, it is necessary for the geographer to understand very well indeed the principles upon which soil scientists have based their classifications.

Definitions

Like many common words, 'soil' is given various meanings by the writers of dictionaries. The lexicographers give as synonyms such terms as 'the loose top layer of the earth's surface', 'land', 'dirt', 'earth', &c. As a concept it seems vague enough. To most people soil is just something to walk on, if it hasn't already been covered over by pavement. To the geologist and miner, it is a nuisance, an overburden upon the rocks which must be removed before work can proceed. To the highway builder and foundation engineer soil has recently become most important, and to them the concept includes all the unconsolidated mantle rock. To the botanist and agriculturist, on the other hand, it is but the upper part of this mantle, the all-important medium in which plants grow.

Our search for definitions, however, must properly be addressed to the soil scientists, those individuals who see in the soil itself something worthy of serious investigation and have made it their business to attempt an understanding of the soil. Even among them, however, there is no universally accepted definition (let geographers not waste their pity— what is geography?) and we must examine several in order to note the various angles of approach of the experts themselves.

Hilgard, the foremost American soil scientist of the last century, defined *soil* as 'the more or less loose and friable material in which, by means of their roots, plants may or do find a foothold and nourishment, as well as other conditions of growth'.[1]

Ramann of the University of Munich wrote, 'soil is the outermost layer of the solid earth consisting of rock material mixed with organic remains'.[2]

[1] Hilgard, E. W. (1906), *Soils*, Macmillan, New York.
[2] Ramann, E. (1905), *Bodenkunde*, Julius Springer, Berlin, ed. 2.

Dokuchaev, the founder of the Russian school of soil science gave the following definition,

> Soil is the surface and adjoining horizons of parent material (irrespective of kind) which have undergone, more or less, a natural change under the influence of water, air, and various species of organisms—living or dead; this change is reflected to a certain degree, in the composition, structure, and colour of the products of weathering.[1]

Marbut, long the chief of the U.S. soil survey, who compiled an English translation of the classic work of K. D. Glinka[2] and thereby grafted the ideas of the Russian school upon an earlier American geological concept, wrote:

> The soil consists of the outer layer of the earth's crust, usually unconsolidated, ranging in thickness from a mere film to a maximum of somewhat more than ten feet; which differs from the material beneath it, also usually unconsolidated, in colour, structure, physical constitution, chemical composition, biological characteristics, probably chemical processes, in reaction and morphology.[3]

Joffe, who may be regarded as a link between the Russian and American schools of soil science, has modified Marbut's definition to read as follows:

> The soil is a natural body, differentiated into horizons, of mineral and organic constituents, usually unconsolidated, of variable depth, which differs from the parent material below in morphology, physical properties and constitution, chemical properties and composition and biological characteristics.[4]

While it is undoubtedly true that it would be impossible to draft a definition agreeable to everyone, nevertheless the definitions given above illustrate the trend of thought in soil science. The soil has come to be recognized as a natural body about which there may be accumulated a more or less independent body of knowledge. In one word this body of knowledge is known as *pedology* (πεδον) while its adherents are termed *pedologists*.

While accepting the soil as a natural body and pedology as a natural science, it would perhaps be well to avoid too great claims for the independence of either, although such are sometimes made. The soil is,

---

[1] Dokuchaev, V. V.; quoted by Jacob Joffe in *Pedology* (1936), Rutgers University Press, New Brunswick, New Jersey.

[2] Glinka, K. D., *The Great Soil Groups of the World and Their Development* (trans. by C. F. Marbut), Edwards Bros., Ann Arbor.

[3] Marbut, C. F. (1928), 'A Scheme for Soil Classification', *Proceedings and Papers of First International Congress of Soil Science*, 4: 10–31.

[4] Joffe, J. (1936), *Pedology*, Rutgers University Press.

of course, not completely independent of the earth's crust, although differentiated therefrom in its development under the influence of environmental factors. Neither can the science exist in ignorance of the other natural sciences from which it derives its fundamental ideas. In turn, pedology contributes its findings to the enrichment of biological and agricultural studies. It is probable that most soil scientists are rather impatient of this attempt to narrow the field, even for so worthy an object as independence, consequently 'soil science' and 'soil scientist' remain recognized terms. An attempt to express these wider relationships in single words has resulted in the use of the words 'edaphology' and 'edaphologist'[1] but their polysyllaby is a distinct handicap.

The geographer is naturally interested in the wider relationships but, in order to make use of them he must make himself familiar with the language and principles of soil science. This is just what he has to do in the case of geomorphology, climatology, botany, and many other fields of knowledge.

The term *pedogeography* is introduced herewith, not exactly as a mere synonym for soil geography, but as indicating a branch of geography which has to do with the distribution of soils and soil associations, much in the same way as the term phytogeography is used in writing of plants.

The Russian Contribution to Soil Science: Dokuchaev

To many it may not be apparent why it should have been Russian scientists and not those of the more erudite nations of western Europe who discovered the true nature of soil development. The answer, of course, is to be found in geography. Western Europe in the nineteenth century had just experienced the industrial revolution. Becoming increasingly urban, it faced the problem of feeding a growing population while its man-to-land ratio was becoming ever narrower. Moreover, in this land of small farms and gardens the soils had been tilled for centuries until their original characteristics had been lost. They were, in fact, no longer natural bodies. The essential problem involved not their origin but their fertility. Production per acre must be increased even at the expense of decreased labour income. Western Europe was more interested in soil chemistry than in either soil morphology or soil geography. The Russian Empire, on the other hand, was a huge sprawling territory with many empty spaces and many kinds of soil. Within her occupied zone however, population pressure was increasing and people were pushing out to occupy the empty spaces. For the purposes of settlement administra-

[1] Lyon and Buckman, *The Nature and Properties of Soils*, Macmillan, New York.

tion it was necessary to have some information about these new lands, and men were sent out to report upon the natural resources.

Among those observers was Vasilii Vasielevich Dokuchaev,[1] destined to become the father of modern soil science. His definition of soil has already been quoted. Dokuchaev was a remarkable man. He was born 17 February 1846, the son of a village priest in the province of Smolensk. He, also, was expected to enter the priesthood but, after his first year at St. Petersburg, he became interested in natural science and graduated as a specialist in geology and mineralogy. He became curator of the geological laboratory in the University of St. Petersburg in 1872, and in the ensuing years conducted many expeditions into various parts of the country to study soils. Articles from his pen began to appear in scientific journals about 1877 and, in 1883, his famous book *Russian Chernozem* was published. Many other pedological papers followed before his death in 1903. Dokuchaev was not only an observer and recorder, he was also a teacher and the founder of a new school of soil science which is now perpetuated in the Dokuchaev Institute. About him there grew up a devoted band of investigators to whom not only Russia, but the whole world, stands in debt.

Dokuchaev did not discover the chernozem (which can be translated as *black earth* in English). Previous investigators had seen and described it, but their bewilderment concerning its origin was great. Some saw it as a separate geological stratum laid down in former bodies of water, bogs, or floods. Only one man is credited by Dokuchaev with being on the right track. Ruprecht in 1866 had declared that the organic matter in the black soil originated from the plant cover growing upon it.

Dokuchaev was a keen observer. He was also a philosopher. He saw that the chernozem occurred in a belt or zone, always under a grass vegetation, never under forests. He saw, also, that the chernozem occurred upon many types of parent rock, and that the limits of its zone were closely related to the climatic factors of precipitation and evaporation. Dokuchaev was firmly convinced that the climate, vegetation, and soil of the Russian steppes were all elements of an indivisible geographical complex.

The soils of the forested region of Russia were also investigated. In fact Dokuchaev, himself, began his soil studies in the region of Smolensk. Here the dominant soil colour was grey, not black. Beneath the litter and mould of the forest floor was a horizon of 'white sand'. In Russian this is known as podzol or 'ashy soil'. The name *podzol* has been accepted, the world over, to designate leached forest soils, just as *chernozem* has

[1] Joffe, J., op. cit.

been accepted as the name of the black soils of the natural grasslands. Previous investigators in northern Europe had also described the occurrence of podzols, and were inclined to the view that the 'white sand' was a separate geological stratum. The genetic theory of soil formation advanced by Dokuchaev and his followers finally provided the explanation that podzol formed *in situ* under the coniferous forest type of vegetation cover.

Later Russian Pedologists

Among the many followers of Dokuchaev, only a few may be selected for special mention. Sibirtzev (1860–99) died before his master and his book was published posthumously in 1900.[1] He it was who finally consolidated the zonal theory of soils and showed that soil zones are correlated with climatic zones. He pointed out that there were, also, *intra-zonal* soils, that is, soils that for some genetic reason had not developed normally for the zone. This idea of the geographical zone, foreshadowed by Dokuchaev and promulgated by Sibirtzev, has done more to make clear the soil pattern of the globe than any other contribution to soil science.

Starting from the recognition that the podzol soils of the northern forests were part of, and were specific to, their own environment; moreover, that they were representative of that environment as were the chernozem soils of their steppe environment, the Russian workers drew up scheme after scheme in which the soils of the world might be classified. In most of these the predominant influence in soil formation is acknowledged to be climate.

K. D. Glinka (1867–1927), more than any of the other pupils of Dokuchaev, has been recognized as the leader of the new school of soil science. His point of view was not primarily geographic, but rested upon the characteristics of the soil itself. Some soils he found were inherently amenable to the influence of climatic factors, these soils he termed *ectodynamomorphic*, others because of certain inherent characteristics were able to resist, or at least to modify, the influence of outside factors and these he termed *endodynamomorphic*.[2] Later he changed these terms to *ectodynamogenous* and *endodynamogenous* in order to emphasize the formation rather than the form of the soil. At the same time he laid down this postulate: 'The geography of soils, namely the distribution of soil zones, sub-zones and provinces and the topography of soils, namely their dis-

---

[1] Sibirtzev, N. M. (1900), *Pochvovedenie*, St. Petersburg.
[2] Glinka, K. D., op. cit.

tribution within the zones, are perfectly regular.' He also states that the intrazonal soils show characteristics specific for the zone, or in other words, each soil zone has its own intrazonal soils.[1]

Upon the death of Glinka, Professor L. I. Prasolov became the leader of the Russian School. He, also, has made many contributions to soil geography, but most of them still remain obscured behind the 'iron curtain' of the Russian language.

Even the views of Glinka, which revolutionized the soil philosophy of the rest of the world, are very imperfectly represented by the Marbut translation of his book, because it in turn was based upon a German translation of 1914. All Glinka's later ideas have passed unnoticed, and even his revised scheme of soil classification translated by Abashkin in 1933 has not served to modify his influence in any very noticeable manner. American pedology had already received its inspiration and had set off on its own course of development.

Joffe[2] provides a later link with Russian literature but even he fails to take notice of Glinka's amended ideas. So much seems to depend upon timing.

The Progress of Soil Geography in America: Hilgard

It has been intimated in the previous pages that soil classification and differentiation developed in Russia because of the range of geographical conditions to be found under one administration. It should cause no surprise, then, to find that the contributions to soil geography, which rank with those of the Russian school, should come from the soil scientists of the United States of America. For, in the U.S.A., we find conditions which parallel most of those found in the U.S.S.R., except for the far northern and agriculturally most useless areas. The latter, of course, are found in Alaska, which is under American jurisdiction, and in Canada, which is just as accessible to the scientists from across the border as it is to Canadians themselves. In addition, the southern part of the U.S.A. offers a greater variety of sub-tropical conditions than do the southern regions of the U.S.S.R. In fact, it is rather remarkable that a more or less parallel science of the genesis and distribution of soil types had not grown up independently before the impact of Russian ideas had been received. Much basic work, of course, had been done which was capable of correct interpretation when the code had been supplied.

[1] Abashkin, B. J., 'Translations from Chapter III of Prof. Glinka's Posthumous Edition of *Soil Science*', *The American Soil Survey Association, Bulletin XIV*: 97–102, 1933.   [2] Joffe, J., op. cit.

That modern soil science might just as easily have arisen in America is shown from the work of Hilgard. Having worked in Missouri and in California, this scientist was well aware of the fundamental differences between the soils of humid east and arid west. His pioneer work appeared in 1892[1] and was later embodied in a text-book published in 1906, and now one of the most frequently quoted reference works.[2] Hilgard, however, was a prophet in the wilderness, a man come before his time, the true significance of whose work was not realized until some years after his death.

Hilgard's ideas did not immediately sweep the continent and inaugurate a new era because American soil science, along with that of western Europe, was still under the domination of the teachings of the great German agricultural chemist of the nineteenth century, Justus von Liebig. To him the soil was a storehouse of nutrients. It was necessary only to analyse the soil and the plants which grew upon it, apply a little calculation and the whole productive capacity of the soil stood revealed. When one removed a crop containing stated amounts of nutrient elements one returned the equivalent in fertilizer. If not, one faced the inevitable result of soil exhaustion. This is the often quoted 'theory of the balance sheet'.[3, 4, 5] Along with the chemical theory of soils went the system of geological classification. After all, if the soil were merely a storage bin it was important to know what minerals and rocks were contained therein. The characteristics attributed to soils from limestones, soils from shales, soils from granites were therefore carefully tabulated and remembered.

Nevertheless, the U.S. Soil Survey had been initiated and had been

[1] Hilgard, E. W. (1892), 'A report on the relations of soil to climate', *U.S. Dept. Agric. Weather Bureau Bulletin 3*, 59 pp., Washington, D.C.

[2] Hilgard, E. W. (1906), *Soils, their formation, properties, composition and relation to climate and plant growth in the humid and arid regions*, XXVII, 593 pp., The Macmillan Co., New York.

[3] Harding, T. S. (1947), *Two Blades of Grass—A history of scientific developments in the U.S. Department of Agriculture*, XV, 352 pp., University of Oklahoma Press, Norman, Oklahoma, U.S.A. (see Chapter XI).

[4] Kellogg, Charles E. (1948), 'Conflicting doctrines about soils', *The Scientific Monthly*, Vol. LXVI, pp. 475–87.

[5] The effectiveness with which the adherents of the Liebig school presented the balance-sheet theory can be well attested by the writer. As an undergraduate student of agricultural chemistry he was inspired to undertake the task of preparing a complete chemical balance sheet for his father's farm. In the process, of course, much was learned about agricultural chemistry, but the same effort spent on studying soils might have been more productive. Under the same teachers soil classification and soil geography were embodied in agricultural geology.

working many years before it received the inspiration of the Russian theories. Canada, also, had begun soil surveys in a small way under American influence.

Whitney and Marbut

Milton Whitney was appointed chief of a new Division of Soils in 1894. He had been in charge of an experimental farm in North Carolina and had been interested in problems of soil fertility. Under his direction work was undertaken which finally led to the establishment of a soil survey. Whitney leaned strongly towards a geological definition of soil. He wrote: 'Geology defines the limits and areas of these different rocks, and as I have shown that these rocks determine the texture of the soil, a thorough and detailed geological map of the state should answer for a soil map.'[1] It is interesting to note that this bulletin appeared in the same year from the same office and in the same series as the one by E. W. Hilgard.

It would be more interesting still to speculate upon what might have happened had Hilgard, and not Whitney, been placed in charge of the soil survey. Whitney's ideas changed as the results of his investigations unfolded. He had soon discarded the 'balance-sheet' theory of fertility; but, in spite of the fact that he also soon came to recognize that climate was highly important in the formation of soils, the soil survey continued to work along geological lines.

Towards the end of his life Whitney wrote a book which summarized his ideas on the philosophy, geography, and historical significance of soils.[2] In it he maintains that there is a strong parallelism between the soil type and the animal species. Some of the statements seem a bit far-fetched but, as he says, 'Analogies are helpful in conveying ideas and impressions but they are harmful if taken too literally as meaning the same thing.' In another place he writes, 'Each soil type is a distinct, organized entity— a factory, a machine—in which the parts must be kept fairly adjusted to do efficient work.' He actively combated the idea that the soil could be considered a static dustbin; to him, 'the soil is dynamic and a living thing rather than the dead, inert and wholly uninteresting material that is too often known as dirt'. He acknowledges the importance of climate in the development of soil characteristics, yet his geographical ideas about the

[1] Whitney, Milton (1892), 'Some physical properties of soils in relation to moisture and crop distribution', *U.S. Dept. Agric. Weather Bureau Bulletin 4*, 80 pp.

[2] Whitney, Milton (1925), *Soil and Civilization—A Modern Concept of the Soil and the Historical Development of Agriculture*, D. Van Nostrand Company, Inc., New York.

distribution of soil types remain tied to the often-quoted map of the soil regions of the U.S.A., prepared by his workers in 1912.[1] This map, or a modification of it, still does duty as a map of soil materials. It is interesting to note, however, that in the glacial and loessal province, for instance, it groups together Carrington and Miami soils which, while the book was in writing, were being segregated into fundamentally different Great Soil Groups.

The last sections of Whitney's book constitute an attempt at an historical account of agricultural civilizations, which, while extremely interesting, is somehow not very closely correlated with the chapters on soil. Of course, world knowledge of soils was not great twenty-five years ago.

Interest in soils was strong during the first decade of the 20th century under the stimulus of such men as Whitney and Hilgard. A product of this era is 'Forest Physiography' by Isaiah Bowman, for many years director of the American Geographical Society.[2] Significantly, it is dedicated to 'Eugene Waldemar Hilgard, leader in agrogeology'. As his title implies, Bowman was writing a physiography, but the emphasis upon soils, climate, and vegetation indicate a brilliant effort to achieve a geographic synthesis. Bowman was then, as he always has been, a true geographer and he recognized the geographical value of the soil.

We return now to the development of geographical ideas in the United States Soil Survey. Whitney, as we have seen, initiated the survey in hope of finding out about soils for the purpose of growing crops. Indeed it was because of the troubles of the tobacco growers that the work was started. In 1910, however, he brought into his organization a man whose viewpoint was and always remained that of pure science, a point of view which could conceive of the soil as a natural body worthy of study for its own sake.

Curtis F. Marbut (1863–1935)[3] was already a man of middle age when he accepted Whitney's invitation to work for a couple of years in the Bureau of Soils. Behind him was a successful career of fifteen years as Professor of Geology at the University of Missouri. He had had the experience of graduate work under W. M. Davis and N. S. Shaler, and he had had the privilege of travel in Europe.

On the professional side he had already accomplished a notable amount

[1] Marbut, C. F., et al. (1913), 'The Soils of the United States', U.S. Dept. Agric. Bureau of Soils Bulletin 96.

[2] Bowman, Isaiah (1911), Forest Physiography, John Wiley & Sons, New York.

[3] The Life and Work of C. F. Marbut. A memorial volume published by the Soil Science Society of America.

of physiographic work in his native state of Missouri, including the first attempt at a soil map of the state. In 1905 he was appointed director of the newly established Missouri Soil Survey, and since then had been engaged in general soil surveys.

When Marbut entered the Bureau he was still a geologist and geomorphologist, as is clearly to be seen in his first publication under the auspices of the Bureau.[1] From the first, however, Marbut's endeavours had a dual purpose, on the one hand to accomplish a geographical presentation of the soils of the whole country, and on the other hand to develop the art of pedological description to the point where each and every soil type would have a fully documented personality. The crux of the situation, of course, lay in the development of a system of classification based upon the characteristics of the soils themselves. Marbut saw, much more clearly than Whitney, that the borrowed geological system was inadequate. Another must be found, for, as Harry Buckman aptly remarks, 'A pedologist must be a systematist.'[2] It was at this crucial point, then, in 1914 that the German translation of Glinka's book appeared. Marbut devoured it eagerly and proceeded to put its principles into practice. On the one hand the genetic classification with its dependence upon climatic zones gave him the clue for the geographical interpretation; while, on the other hand, the emphasis upon the *profile* provided the proper vehicle for the description of the individual soil types.

Marbut's Classes of Soils

It remained, however, for the genius of Marbut to work out the details. There is an inherent difference in Russian and American objectives, the former being always concerned with the establishment of large-scale geographical differences, whereas the U.S. soil surveyors had always been trying to delimit small geographical units. Marbut could not and did not adopt a Russian system of soil survey or even a complete Russian system of soil classification. He adopted certain guiding principles and proceeded to create his own scientific structures. Over the years a series of papers appeared to mark his progress.

With convincing logic he shows why the old geological classification is inadequate. The soil is a natural body developed from, and therefore different from the parent material. The climatic classification is equally invalid because, while climate determines certain broad features, it does

[1] Marbut, C. F., *et al.*, op. cit.
[2] Lyon, T. L., and Buckman, H. O. (1943), *The Nature and Properties of Soils* (4th edition, revised by Harry O. Buckman), The Macmillan Company, New York.

not provide a basis for minor differentiation. There is, therefore, only one correct method, soils must be classified on the basis of soil characteristics. Thus he focused the attention of his surveyors upon the virgin profile (or uncultivated profile).

Recent studies of soil profiles developed under a wide range of geographic conditions have brought to light the existence among them of two fundamental kinds of differences. These may be called: (1) differences in *kind* and (2) differences in *degree of development*. The former concern *mature* soils only and the differences are those of well-defined characteristics. The latter concern soils with imperfectly developed profiles, so that differences are those not of different kinds of features, but of the same kinds of features imperfectly developed. The imperfection of development may extend to complete absence of a given feature in extreme cases. These are *immature* soils.

Soils with fundamentally different kinds of features or profiles, occupy regions more or less widely separated from each other and in which different geographic conditions prevail. Soils with profiles differing only in the degree or perfection of the development of their features occur in the same region and in very close associations. Mature soils are found associated with immature, but fundamentally different kinds of mature soils are not found in the same region. This is a necessary consequence of their immobility.[1]

Dr. Marbut achieved a complete classification of soils, based upon the philosophy set forth in the preceding paragraphs. In a tentative form it was presented to the First International Congress[2] and in its final form it is incorporated in his great work *The Soils of the United States*,[3] published the same year in which he died.

Marbut's classification makes use of a number of ascending categories or steps in the grouping of soils. Briefly they may be defined as follows:

Category I—Differentiation upon the basis of the texture of the surface soil—*soil type*.

Category II—Differentiation upon the morphology of the soil profile —*soil series*.

Category III—Differentiation upon the basis of certain features of the profile brought about by local rather than general environmental factors,

[1] Marbut, C. F. (1927), Outline of a scheme for the study of soil profiles. Report of Subcommission II of Commission V: Classification, Nomenclature and Mapping of Soils in the Americas, *Proceedings, First International Congress Soil Science*, Part I.

[2] Marbut, C. F. (1927), 'A Scheme for Soil Classification', *Proceedings and Papers, First International Congress of Soil Science*, Commission V, pp. 1–31, Washington, D.C., U.S.A.

[3] Marbut, C. F. (1935), *The Soils of the United States. Atlas of American Agriculture*, Part III, Bureau of Chemistry and Soils, U.S. Dept. Agric. Washington, D.C., U.S.A.

for example, similarity of parent materials, drainage status, presence of a high content of calcium carbonate, &c.

Category IV—Differentiation based upon features of the profile wholly independent of parent material or site and therefore due to climatic influences—*great soil groups*.

Category V—Differentiation based upon the general core position of the inorganic colloids produced by the weathering process.

Category VI—Differentiation based upon the presence or absence of a zone or horizon of calcium carbonate accumulation in the soil profile. Soils are thus separated into two groups which Marbut designated *Pedocals* (soils accumulating calcium) and *Pedalfers* (soils accumulating aluminium and iron).

In his final work Marbut does not use the word *order* to identify the members of his highest category although he does so in an earlier paper. In the same article he uses the term *family* for the units of the category above the series and states:

> Each varying soil profile associated with a given mature profile, to whatever stage in development it may be due or whatever variation in character of parent material may have produced its variations, constitutes a distinct kind, or, as we designate it, series of soils; and the whole group of soils consisting of the mature and its related and associated immature soils constitutes what could be designated as a soil family.[1]

The *Soils of the United States* is accompanied by a map of the U.S.A., in twelve sections, drawn on a scale of 1 : 2,500,000, showing by means of a complex colour scheme the locations of all the important soil series in the country. The legend contains about 250 different colour blocks. Obviously, on such a scale the area allotted to each series represents an association of soils designated by the name of the dominant or most representative series. In the text the principal soil series are described and their geographical and taxonomic relationships are discussed. In the words of Dr. Charles E. Kellogg, his successor, 'The result is the most complete work by one man on the classification and geography of the soils of the United States or of any other large continental area.' Later he terms it 'the ideas and results of the work of the man who did more than anyone else for soil science in this country'.[2] Both of these statements are eminently true, but they do not imply that the work of the soil classifier or soil geographer is by any means completed.

[1] Marbut, C. F. (1922). *Soil Classification: Bulletin III*, American Soil Survey Association. Reprinted in *Life and Work of C. F. Marbut* (op. cit.), pp. 85–94.

[2] Kellogg, Chas. E., 'Soils of the United States' in *Life and Work of C. F. Marbut*, pp. 265–7.

It is perhaps not out of place to state here that Dr. Marbut probably did more than any other man to make American geographers conscious of soils. He was a charter member of the American Association of Geographers and his name appears on the programme of the first meeting. His paper on the soils of the Great Plains is a classic of soil geography.[1] It was followed by a number of authoritative geographical papers. A most important service to geography, however, was the series of lectures which he delivered each year to the graduate school of geography in Clark University. 'He added one more vital element to the attributes of place with which geography, and particularly human geography, is concerned.'[2]

Kellogg's Work: 'Soils and Men'

Soil classification in America was not completely crystallized by Marbut, this was accomplished about three years after his death by the workers of the Survey under his successor Dr. C. E. Kellogg and published in *Soils and Men*.[3]

This classification retains the category system devised by Marbut but with many changes and adjustments.

Categories I and II remain unchanged.

Category III is designated the *family* and is made up of soil series showing morphological similarities.

Category IV is equivalent to Marbut's *great soil groups* but with many additions.

Category V is based upon a grouping of units of Category IV which are related to one another by climatic origin and surface colour. These groups are termed *sub-orders*.

Category VI is made up of three great classes of soils named according to the scheme of Sibirtzev,[4] *zonal*, *intra-zonal*, and *azonal*. These three divisions are designated as *soil orders*. Marbut's fundamental divisions, *Pedocal* and *Pedalfer* are given subordinate rank as divisions of the zonal soils.

The groundwork for this classification was laid by Kellogg in an

---

[1] Marbut, C. F. (1923), 'The Soils of the Great Plains', *Annals of the Association of American Geographers*, XIII, No. 2.

[2] Ekblaw, W. E., 'Dr. Curtis F. Marbut at Clark', *The Life and Work of C. F. Marbut* (op. cit.), pp. 36–9.

[3] Baldwin, Mark, Chas. E. Kellogg, and James Thorp (1938), 'Soil Classification', *Soils and Men*, pp. 979–1001, U.S. Dept. Agric. Yearbook for 1938.

[4] Sibirtzev, N. M., op. cit.

earlier publication.[1] In it he postulates and describes seven general processes of soil development:

1. *Calcification*, the accumulation of calcium and magnesium carbonates in the lower part of the soil under conditions of restricted rainfall and a grassland type of vegetation.

2. *Podzolization*, which is the process of removal of soluble salts, including those of calcium and magnesium from the soil profile, under humid climatic conditions and forest vegetation.

3. *Laterization*, a process active under humid tropical climates, whereby not only are the soluble bases removed but the content of silica is greatly reduced. In contrast high percentages of iron and aluminium oxides accumulate. This process is admitted by Kellogg to be, probably, more in the nature of geological weathering than soil building. Nevertheless the products and coloration produced by this process characterize a large part of soil cover of the globe.

4, 5, and 6. *Salinization*, *solonization*, and *solodization*, a chain of processes operating in the genesis of intrazonal soils, in sub-humid and arid regions, where high concentrations of bases accumulate within the soil. In the first instance, under restricted drainage and high evaporation, salts accumulate in the soil giving rise to a saline soil or *solonchak*. In addition to calcium and magnesium, salts of sodium are usually present, but the soil is only mildly alkaline, colloids are flocculated and organic matter not dispersed. In the second stage which takes place with a slight improvement of drainage the excess soluble salts are removed, hydrolysis of sodium salts takes place with the formation of sodium hydroxide, colloids are deflocculated and organic matter dispersed throughout the profile. This is the condition of the 'black alkali' soil or *solonetz*. In the third stage leaching continues until the profile becomes acid, the upper soil taking on a whitish powdery appearance. It is underlain abruptly by a columnar B horizon. This type of profile is known as *soloth*. (Joffe[2] uses the term *solodi*.) Eventually general climatic conditions assert themselves and bring about the formation of a normal *pedocal*.

7. *Gleization*, the process by which an impermeable, structureless, sticky clay-like mass or 'clay-pan' is formed in the subsoil under conditions of poor drainage. At the same time partially decayed organic matter accumulates upon the surface. Among other compounds the *glei*

---

[1] Kellogg, C. E. (1936), 'Development and Significance of the Great Soil Groups of the United States', *U.S. Dept. Agric. Miscellaneous Publication No. 229*, Washington, D.C.

[2] Joffe, J. (1936), *Pedology*, op. cit., p. 454.

horizon usually contains a considerable amount of deoxidized iron compounds.

The first three of these processes are involved in the formation of *zonal* soils while the last four are concerned in the development of intrazonal soil profiles.

Soils and Men contains a map of the soils of the United States, including Alaska, the Canal Zone, Puerto Rico, and Hawaii. It is compiled on the basis of associations of soil series, over 160 being shown. By means of the colour scheme on the map the associations are identified with the great soil groups. In the accompanying discussion[1] the *association* is stated to be a geographical area in which several or many soil types are associated together in an individual pattern. It is not to be considered as a category in a logical taxonomic classification. Soil associations may contain both zonal and intrazonal soils as, for instance, in the Miami-Crosby-Brookston and Miami-Keewannee areas.[2] In all cases, the association contains areas of other soil types than those named, the latter being either the most prevalent or most characteristic of the associated members.

The map and discussions constitute a condensed 'soils atlas' which is, in many ways, much more usable than Marbut's magnificent work. At the same time, by its modifications, and especially by some of its usages, it does obscure some of the fundamental distinctions which Marbut laboured hard to establish. Nevertheless, it does, together with the sections which precede it, constitute an invaluable guide to the pedological and pedogeographical philosophies of the group of workers whose influence is paramount in the scientific world of today.

Pedogeography

Pedogeography is an even younger science than pedology. It embraces both the principles of the distribution of soils themselves and the influence of the soil upon other geographical features. It is, as it should be, the geographical approach to soil science. Whitney[3] was intrigued by the historical significance of soil as others have also been. Marbut in a single address[4] uses the historian's approach, but for the most part, when he

[1] Soil Survey Division, Bureau of Chemistry and Soils—'Soils of the United States', in *Soils and Men*, U.S. Dept. Agric. Yearbook, pp. 1019–1161, 1938.

[2] *Soils and Men*, op. cit., pp. 1040–2.

[3] Whitney, Milton (1925), *Soil and Civilization*, op. cit.

[4] Marbut, C. F. (1925), 'The Rise, Decline and Revival of Malthusianism in relation to Geography and Character of Soils', *Annals of the Association of American Geographers*, XV: 2–29.

stepped out of the role of pedologist, he became a geographer; as witness his articles on the Amazon Basin[1, 2] and on Russia.[3, 4, 5]

The first strictly, consciously directed effort towards the establishment of a pedogeographic viewpoint, however, is contained in a little book by Wolfanger.[6] Briefly, and with very little of the tabular underbrush so beloved of some soils writers, he sets forth the background of soil classification, passing on to descriptions of the Great Soil Groups and their environments and a discussion of some geographical relationships. It has done much to make geographers soils-conscious; but its appeal is sadly reduced by the fact that it has only two illustrations, a profile photograph of a black earth and a very much generalized soil map of the U.S.A. Wolfanger's achievement lies, for the most part, in defining the concept of the attributive system of classification and in stressing the geographical relationships. His closing sentence expresses a hope that 'Though manifestly incomplete, the study may serve to open further the vast, almost untouched, field of soil geography.' It has eminently justified its sub-title, 'A Pedologic-Geographic Survey'.

The second and distinctly meritorious effort in this direction comes from the pen of Charles E. Kellogg.[7] In quite non-technical language he explains the history of soil knowledge, the characteristics of soils and the factors of their development. The pattern of distribution is explained by maps of the Great Soil Groups of the United States and the zonal soil groups of the world. Chapters on the soils of the grasslands, deserts, cool temperate and the warm and tropical forests give the details about the chief great soil groups. Cultural, geographical, and historical relationships are discussed in the latter chapters. The book is almost without references, and he might have stopped there with a nicely balanced well-organized 'soils for the layman'. Instead he adds some appendices on classification, description, and reference material which really make the book. In

---

[1] Marbut, C. F., and C. B. Manifold (1925), 'The Topography of the Amazon Valley', *Geographical Review*, XV: 617–42.

[2] Marbut, C. F., and C. B. Manifold (1926), 'The Soils of the Amazon Basin in Relation to Agricultural Possibilities', *Geographical Review*, XVI: 414–42.

[3] Marbut, C. F. (1931), 'Russia and United States in the World Wheat Market', *Geographical Review*, XXI: 1–21.

[4] Marbut, C. F. (1931), 'Agriculture in United States and Russia: A Comparative Study of Natural Conditions', *Geographical Review*, XXI: 598–612.

[5] Marbut, C. F. (1935), 'Soils of the Union of Socialistic Soviet Republics', posthumously printed in *Life and Work of C. F. Marbut*, op. cit., pp. 227–44.

[6] Wolfanger, Louis A. (1930), *The Major Soil Divisions of the United States—A Pedologic-Geographic Survey*, John Wiley & Sons Inc., New York.

[7] Kellogg, Charles E. (1941), *The Soils that Support Us*, The Macmillan Company, New York.

particular, this writer will always be grateful for the exceedingly well-selected list of U.S. soil survey reports, from which may be gathered authentic detailed information about all the important soil groups in the country. There are other equally valuable survey reports available, but the list is well selected although it should now be supplemented by a few later reports.

After all, in the final analysis, the student of soil geography must get down to the study of soil reports, just as the student of structure or geomorphology must examine the detailed geological reports of the areas in which he is interested. All the text-book materials constitute merely a background study which enables the student to understand the various phases of his problem. Besides, some of the finest pedological explanations and pedogeographical interpretations are to be found in the soil survey reports.

No better exposition of effect of the factors of soil formation or evaluation of the pedologic significance of soils in the Red and Yellow Podzolic Soil zone can be found than that of A. C. Orvedal in the Jefferson County Report.[1] His analysis of the profile relationships of the Talbott, Decatur, Dewey, Fullerton, and Clarksville soils deserves to be regarded as classic. It is a convincing demonstration that even in mature zonal soils, the influence of parent rock may remain a highly significant factor.

D. R. Kunkel et al.[2] summarize very logically the effects of age especially as it concerns the development of soils upon the tills of different Pleistocene glaciations in southern Indiana. The effects of drainage conditions are well discussed by Johnsgard et al.[3] for the Grey Brown Podzolic zone, and by Swenson et al.[4] in the Red and Yellow Soil zone. The effects of high lime content upon profile development are well brought out by Swenson also, and by Templin and Huckabee[5] in their discussions of Black Prairie Soils. Edwards and Ableiter[6] give one of the best descriptions

[1] Orvedal, A. C., 'Morphology and Genesis of Soils' in Soil Survey of Jefferson County, Tennessee, U.S. Dept. Agric. Bur. Plant Ind., 1941.

[2] Kunkel, D. R., et al. (1940), 'Soil Surveys of Jennings County, Indiana', U.S. Dept. Agric. Bur. Plant Ind., Series 1932, Report No. 40.

[3] Johnsgard, G. A., et al. (1942), 'Soil Survey of Clinton County, Michigan', U.S. Dept. Agric. Bur. Plant Ind., Series 1936, Report No. 12.

[4] Swenson, G. A., et al. (1941), 'Soil Survey of Sumpi County, Alabama', U.S. Dept. Agric. Bur. Plant Ind., Series 1936, Report No. 18.

[5] Templin, E. H., and J. W. Huckabee (1940), 'Soil Survey of Kaufman County, Texas', U.S. Dept. Agric. Bur. Plant Ind., Series 1936, Report No. 3.

[6] Edwards, M. J., and J. K. Ableiter (1942), 'Soil Survey of Mackenzie County, North Dakota', U.S. Dept. Agric. Bur. Plant Ind., Series 1933, No. 37.

extant of the conditions surrounding the formation of intrazonal soils influenced by high salt content. Another section on the morphology and genesis of soils is that of Nikiforoff et al.[1] in which the complicated soil conditions of the Red River region are discussed. This treatment is especially good in its illustrative material.

A great advance in the understanding of the soils of tropical regions is made in the Soil Survey of Puerto Rico.[2] On this small island, because of its position and relief, a great variety of moisture conditions, and hence of soil profiles, are found. Naturally many of the conditions are similar to those of parts of the mainland, but the development of laterites and lateritic clays goes beyond anything found on the mainland. The soil scientists of the U.S. Department of Agriculture are thus privileged to widen the scope of their experience.

State Summaries

There is yet another type of soil bulletin from which a great deal of pedogeography may be derived, albeit sometimes of a rather skeleton sort. These are the state summaries, usually emanating from the state agricultural college and experiment station, which in practically every case is partner with the U.S. Dept. Agric. in undertaking area soil surveys within the state.

One of the earliest of these was the 'Soils of Wisconsin' by A. R. Whitson.[3] It is accompanied by a general soil map of Wisconsin in which a very complicated soil pattern is reduced to twelve associations. These associations take the name of the dominant soil series in some cases, in others are designated by some dominant characteristic, and delineated on a scale of ten miles to one inch. This work shows little evidence of the modern concept of classification, the only category above type and series being a division into glacial and residual classes of origin. Nevertheless it has 270 pages of soils data much of which is geographical.

A somewhat similar account for Texas was written by W. T. Carter.[4] Texas being a large area, the accompanying map is drawn on a scale of

[1] Nikiforoff, C. C., et al. (1939), 'Soil Survey (Reconnaissance) of the Red River Valley Area, Minnesota', U.S. Dept. Agric. Bureau Chem. and Soils, Series 1933, Report No. 25.

[2] Roberts, R. C., and party (1942), 'Soil Survey of Puerto Rico', U.S. Dept. Agric. Bur. Plant Ind., Series 1936, Report No. 8.

[3] Whitson, A. R. (1927), 'Soils of Wisconsin'; 270 pp. and map; Wisconsin Geological and Natural History Survey Bulletin No. 68. Soil Series No. 49.

[4] Carter, W. T. (1931), 'The Soils of Texas'; 192 pp. and map; Texas Agric. Exp. Sta. Bulletin No. 431.

twenty-four miles to one inch. The soils are arranged in groups or associations and the associations identified with the geographic (physiographic) regions of Texas. The pattern of this map is more easily identifiable on the national maps of Marbut's Atlas or *Soils and Men*, than that of the Wisconsin Bulletin but, of course, it was drafted five years later.

Conrey, Paschall, and Burrage[1] issued a key to the soils of Ohio with a small sketch map of general soil regions. Here again they find it convenient to generalize on the basis of glacial drift areas and types of underlying rock.

A recently issued bulletin by McMiller discusses the soil regions of Minnesota.[2] It contains two maps of soil regions within the state, both of which differ in a number of respects from the soil map accompanying *Soils and Men*. Many of the differences occur in the north-western part of the state where little soil mapping had been done. In fact when it is remembered that, even yet, only 40 per cent of the area of Minnesota has been covered by soil survey, it is seen to be inevitable that several new versions of the soil region map will probably have to be issued as time goes on. McMiller does not dwell very heavily upon the detailed profile characteristics of the soils in his various regions, even though they are named for associations of soil series. He emphasizes the geographical rather than the pedological factors. Climate, parent material, relief, natural vegetation, and agricultural potential are the points most often stressed.

T. M. Bushnell's story of Indiana soils deserves special mention.[3] It has already been brought to the notice of geographers through an enthusiastic review by Wellington Jones in the *Geographical Review*, January 1947. By the use of many 'single feature' maps including classification of parent materials, land forms, native vegetation, texture, and various land use data, he provides pedogeographical interpretations of the general soil regions of the state. The agreement with the national map[4] is almost perfect, but the explanations are much more explicit. Indiana is a region of comparatively uniform climatic conditions, hence one is not surprised to find that the maps of parent materials and land forms are the ones that really provide the key to general soil regions. Emphasis is also put upon the range of drainage conditions in the general relief

[1] Conrey, G. W., A. H. Paschall, and E. M. Burrage (1934), 'A Key to the Soils of Ohio', *Special Circular No. 44*, Ohio Agric. Exp. Sta., Wooster, Ohio.

[2] McMiller, P. R. (1947), 'Principal Soil Regions of Minnesota', University of Minnesota Agric. Exp. Sta., *Bulletin 392*.

[3] Bushnell, T. M. (1944), 'The Story of Indiana Soils', Perdue University Agric. Exp. Sta., *Special Circular No. 1*, Lafayette, Indiana.

[4] *Soils and Men*, op. cit.

classes designated as 'high ground' and 'low ground'. Jones's suggestion that this booklet be used as a text-book is, perhaps, over-complimentary but, for the facts of soil geography in Indiana and as an example of method, it probably has no equal.

It is not possible here to evaluate all the state treatments, these have been chosen as examples to indicate that information of a regional nature, which the geographer requires, is often to be found in such publications.

Soil Conservation

It is rather a paradox that geographers and, in fact, people in general have paid more attention to soil conservation than they have to soil. Almost countless books, bulletins, and pamphlets recount the ravages, present and potential, of soil erosion in all parts of the world. High school science programmes include a section on soil conservation, but nothing on how soils are formed.[1] College departments of geography, also, may list courses in conservation but none in the geography of soils. The present writer would be the last to deprecate an interest in soil erosion and counteractive conservational measures. The conservation of all natural resources is, inherently, within the province of geography but so is a knowledge of the nature and distribution of those resources.

The prophet of soil conservation in America and indeed of the world is Hugh Hammond Bennett, the head of the U.S. Soil Conservation Service. Bennett was nurtured in the soil survey in its early years, but almost from the first his attention became fixed upon the fact that soil resources were being wasted away at an enormous rate. While this was first impressed upon Bennett in his native South,[2] it is, of course, true in varying degree throughout the world. His crusade on a nation-wide basis[3, 4] had a great deal to do with bringing about a programme of action,[5] and the establishment of a Soil Conservation Service. It would appear that for some years Bennett was regarded as rather a troublesome agitator by many of his co-workers in the Bureau of Chemistry and

[1] Putnam, D. F. (1947), 'Educational Materials in the Field of Soil Science', *Ontario Research Commission Interim Report*, pp. 65–8, Toronto.

[2] Bennett, H. H. (1921), *The Soils and Agriculture of the Southern States*, The Macmillan Book Co., New York.

[3] Bennett, H. H., and W. R. Chapline (1928), 'Soil Erosion, a National Menace', *U.S. Dept. Agric., Cir. 33*.

[4] Bennett, H. H. (1928), 'The Wasting Heritage of the Nation', *Scientific Monthly*, Vol. 27, pp. 97–124.

[5] Bennett, H. H. (1931), 'National Program of Soil and Water Conservation', *Jour. Amer. Soc. of Agronomy*, Vol. 23.

Soils; and, when given the job of organizing soil conservation, it was, at first, under the Department of Interior. When finally it was properly launched, it came back to the Department of Agriculture with the status almost, of a rival bureau. It was but natural, perhaps, that a number of younger soils surveyors should become soil conservationists. The official steps in the historical process of setting up the service are related by Bennett in the preface to his monumental book.[1] The nation-wide survey conducted in the mid-thirties disclosed an alarming condition of the agricultural resources. Approximately 50,000,000 acres of former crop land were ruined for all time, another 50,000,000 acres severely damaged, 100,000,000 acres with half its top-soil gone and erosion beginning on a third 100,000,000 acres. The damage is, of course, much more critical in some areas than others. Later chapters in the book are devoted to details about the various physiographic divisions of the U.S.A.

Bennett has also written a briefer volume in which soil erosion is discussed and conversational practices are outlined.[2] Other manuals on soil conservation are those of Ayers[3] and Gustafson.[4] Another book by Graham[5] discusses soil conservation from the viewpoint of the student of wild life, an angle with which geographers should be familiar. It is valuable also because of its well-selected bibliography.

While broad scale surveys of the nation and of the various states have been made and maps have been published showing the extent and degree of soil erosion, the objective of the Soil Conservation Service is action on the individual farm. Seldom however is the individual in a position to do very much; and if he were, in all probability his hard work might be undone by the negligence of his neighbour. Consequently, the soil conservation service assists in the setting up of soil conservation districts whose members attack the problem. By 1946 more than 1,600 districts had been formed, embracing 875,000,000 acres of land and including around 3,900,000 farmers.[6]

Each farm, eventually, must be planned and remodelled. As an aid to planning, a preliminary survey of the district may be made such as, for

[1] Bennett, H. H. (1939), *Soil Conservation*, McGraw-Hill Book Co., New York and London.

[2] Bennett, H. H. (1947), *Elements of Soil Conservation*, McGraw-Hill Book Co. Inc., New York.

[3] Ayers, Q. C. (1936), *Soil Erosion and its Control*, McGraw-Hill Book Co., Inc., New York.

[4] Gustafson, A. F. (1937), *Conservation of the Soil*, McGraw-Hill Book Co., Inc., New York.

[5] Graham, E. H. (1944), *Natural Principles of Land Use*, Oxford University Press.

[6] Bennett, H. H. (1947), op. cit.

instance, that made for Schuyler County.[1] The basis of such a survey is the so-called *land-capability* class of which eight are recognized with definitions as follows:[2]

Land Suitable for Cultivation:

Class I—Land of good productivity practically free of erosion and suitable for cultivation without special practices; some areas may need to be fitted for cultivation, as by clearing or simple drainage.

Class II—Land of moderate to good productivity suitable for cultivation with ordinary or simple practices to prevent erosion or effect satisfactory drainage, as by contouring, growing protective cover crops and carrying out rather easy drainage operations, as with small ditches, where needed.

Class III—Land of moderate to good productivity suitable for cultivation with intensive practices, such as terracing, strip cropping, heavy fertilization, and installation of extensive drainage facilities.

Land Suitable for Limited Cultivation:

Class IV—Land of moderate productivity suitable chiefly for pasture and hay because of steepness of slope, with occasional use for row crops. When it is cultivated, intensive erosion-prevention practices usually are required.

Land Not Suitable for Cultivation:

Class V—Land not suitable for cultivation but useful for grazing or forest with normal precautions to insure sustained use.

Class VI—Land not suitable for cultivation but suitable for grazing or the growing of trees with strict precautions for sustained use.

Class VII—Land not suitable for cultivation but suitable for grazing or forestry when used with extreme care to prevent erosion.

Class VIII—Land not suitable for cultivation, grazing or forestry, although it may have some value for wild life. This land is ordinarily extremely rough, stony, sandy, wet, or susceptible to severe erosion.

The report on Schuyler county is accompanied by a map on the scale of 1 : 15,840 on which land-capability class areas are shown in colour. By the use of symbols, soil type, slope, erosion, and land use are shown within these areas. Generalized maps of land-use capability and soils on a scale of two and one half miles to the inch are also included. The reason for the latter is that Schuyler county was one of the few counties in New York which had not had a soil survey.

[1] Bonsteel, A. J., and B. J. Patton (1943), Physical Land Conditions in Schuyler County, New York; U.S. Dept. Agric. Soils Conservation Service, *Physical Land Survey No. 31*, Washington, D.C.

[2] Bennett, H. H. (1947), op. cit., p. 160.

Soil conservation surveys do not, of course, offer as much information on soil geography as do soil survey reports. They are, of course, not designed to do so, although they must repeat much of the information contained in soil bulletins. They are aimed towards showing the erosion and land-use condition in preparation for land-use planning, and further discussion of them can perhaps best be conducted within such a framework.

The soil conservation service through its many research projects has made numerous contributions to physical geography. The study of gully erosion in the Piedmont[1] deserves to be regarded as a classic, giving evidence, not only on the mechanism of the common physiographic process of water erosion, but also showing the protective action of the soil cover upon the easily eroded, disintegrated regolith beneath. The numerous climatic studies carried on by the service are worthy of mention, but, being somewhat removed from our theme of pedogeography, will not be stressed at the present time.

Problems and Trends

The greatest problem in pedogeography has been the concept of the fundamental soil unit, the series and its component types. In the beginning it was based on underlying geological material and might have a number of types conditioned by surface texture. *Soil series*, therefore, were easily recognized and broadly distributed. The development of classification on the profile basis has led to the continued splitting of series, until now strictly speaking it can contain only one textural type and a strictly defined profile morphology conditioned by a very narrow range of drainage or permeability. It has, therefore, in many areas become almost impossible to map soil types, and other higher units (i.e. more generalized units) are sought. Such units are always patterns of areas of profile types, they are geographic and not taxonomic units. This problem is world-wide, of course, and not confined to American soils.

Patterns observed in East Africa led Milne[2] to propose the term *catena* for a complex which might be mapped as a unit. His concept is vague enough and, in fact, can be taken to mean that he recognized patterns. Adopted by American pedologists it has been defined as: 'a group of soils within one zonal region developed from similar parent material, but differing in characteristics of the solum, owing to differences in relief

---

[1] Ireland, H. A., C. F. S. Sharpe, and D. H. Eargle (1939), 'Principles of Gully Erosion in the Piedmont of South Carolina', *Technical Bulletin 633, U.S. Dept. Agric.*

[2] Milne, G., et al. (1936), *A provisional map of East Africa (Kenya, Uganda, Tanganyika and Zanzibar) with explanatory memoir*, 34 pp. illus., London.

or drainage'.[1] In actuality, it is degree or rate of soil moisture percolation which is responsible, whether this difference is due to relief or some condition of the substratum. Some years earlier, Ellis[2] in Canada, proposed the term *association* to cover almost the same concept, but this term has been adopted by Americans to mean a more generalized grouping.[3] The concept of the *catena* has probably received as much study by Bushnell[4, 5] as by anyone. In his hands it is, very definitely, a range of profile development upon the same type of parent material, under conditions ranging from very wet to very dry, whether occurring in pattern sequence or not. In none of this work is the catena given any status in the taxonomic classification of soils, except in the case of Ellis's association. It has great geographic value in the field and for this reason the concept deserves study by geographers.

Another attempt to find a geographical unit which would be of value in a rapid inventory is the *land type* proposed by J. O. Veach[6, 7] and used in the work of the Michigan land inventory.[8] Lately it has also been used in the work of the Michigan Soil Survey.[9] It is defined by Veach as a naturally occurring pattern of soil types, but its value lies in its rapid recognition in the field as a combination of geomorphic forms without stopping to examine soil profiles. A modification of this concept was used by the writer in reconnaissance work in areas where soil surveys had not been made,[10, 11] and is found very useful in local area studies by graduate students and other workers.

Each and every concept which tends to make pedogeography more

[1] *Soils and Men*, op. cit., p. 1164.

[2] Ellis, J. H. (1932), 'Field Classification of Soils for Use in the Soil Survey', *Scientific Agriculture 12*, pp. 338–45.

[3] *Soils and Men*, op. cit., p. 1163.

[4] Bushnell, T. M. (1942), 'Some Aspects of the Soil Catena Concept', *Proceedings of the Soil Science Society of America*. Vol. 7: 466–76.

[5] Bushnell, T. M. (1946), 'The Catena Cauldron', *Proceedings of the Soil Science Society of America*, Vol. 10: 335–40.

[6] Veach, J. O. (1933), 'Classification of Land on a Geographic Basis', *Papers of the Michigan Academy of Arts, Science and Letters*, XIX, pp. 359–65.

[7] Veach, J. O. (1933), 'Agricultural Land Classification and Land Types of Michigan', *Michigan State College. Agric. Exp. Sta. S.P. Bulletin 231*.

[8] *Land Classification in the United States*, Report of the Land Committee to the National Resources Planning Board, Washington, 1941.

[9] Foster, Z. C., et al. (1939), 'Soil Survey of Cheboygan County Michigan', *U.S. Dept. Agric. Bureau of Chemistry and Soils*, Series 1934, No. 15.

[10] Chapman, L. J., and D. F. Putnam (1937), 'The Soils of South Central Ontario', *Scientific Agriculture*, 161–197.

[11] Chapman, L. J., and D. F. Putnam (1942), 'The Soils of Eastern Ontario', *Scientific Agriculture*, 608–636.

intelligible should be welcomed by both pedologists and geographers. It is still necessary to issue a warning, however, to the effect that these are geographical concepts and every attempt to incorporate them into a logical taxonomic classification of soils should be stoutly resisted. They are analogous to the plant associations which the ecologist and phytogeographer make use of in describing vegetation. They also have a very close relationship to the geographer's 'natural landscape'.

Hans Jenny[1] may be regarded as the prophet of the new universal approach to the problems of soil formation. Divested of its mystical pseudo-mathematical formulae, his thesis is that soil is the product of the interaction of all the soil forming factors: time, parent material, topography, climate, and organisms. All are of equal rank, and Jenny sees little logic in a division into active and passive factors as suggested by Joffe.[2] The soil is a physical system and part of a much larger system which may be termed the environment. Any boundary lines must be purely arbitrary. There is, for instance, no real dividing line between the processes involved in the formation of the weathered rock or parent material and those involved in so-called pedological processes. Neither is there any definite boundary between one soil type and its neighbour. All are related parts of the larger system, and it is by studying the relative influences of the different soil factors that one arrives at a true understanding of soil development.

Soil therefore is simply a product and a part of geographical environment. Physicists, chemists, biologists, and other specialists may have techniques for obtaining detailed knowledge concerning the formation and characteristics of soils or their capabilities for crop production; the soils man adopts such information, regardless of its origin, and incorporates it into the tissue of soil science. The geographer does likewise, finding that the soils man, with a growing sense of geographical relationships, continues to find more interesting facts to add to his soil descriptions. The Soil Survey of Puerto Rico for instance, is probably the best collection of geographical facts about that island. The geography and, in particular, the agricultural geography of the great plains, the valleys of the Appalachians or the Black Belt of Alabama cannot be fully understood without the information contained in the publications of the soil survey and the soil conservation service.

There are, naturally, innumerable problems of soil science upon which we have not touched which either directly or indirectly may have

---

[1] Jenny, Hans (1941), *Factors of Soil Formation*, McGraw-Hill Book Co., New York.

[2] Joffe, J. (1936), op. cit.

pedogeographical significance. They include all the modern work in soil physics, soil chemistry, mineralogy and microbiology, in all of which recent great advances have been made. This survey of soil literature has been highly selective with the objective of showing how the pedologist, that is, the man who studies the soil as a natural body, has become more and more geographically minded. Secondarily it indicates the growing value to geography of soil investigation, hence the necessity of scientific fellowship between geographically minded soils men and soil-conscious geographers.

In historical fashion the trend of these ideas in soil science may be summarized as follows:

1. The pre-survey period of dependence upon the Liebig school of soil fertility in which soil was seen only as a sort of inert holder for plant nutrients while native soil characteristics, if recognized, were related to the geological material.

2. The Whitney period of soil survey, in which the 'dustbin theory' was rejected and soil series recognized by geological analogy.

3. The Marbut period of independence in which, under the influence of the Russian climatic school, the dependence upon geology was formally disclaimed and the emphasis placed upon the soil profile.

4. The recent period of geographical correlation, in which, while still independent, soils workers are not afraid to note, in the soil characteristics, evidence of the influence of any and all possible soil-forming factors. Furthermore, in this period the soil survey feels that it can now make a much more direct contribution to the problems of crop ecology and land utilization by way of soil ratings and physical systems of land classification.

The future seems to promise much.

Author's Postscript.—A most important contribution to this subject has appeared since this chapter was sent to press. It is a symposium on 'Soil Classification' by leading American soil scientists, published as the February, 1949, issue of *Soil Science* (Vol. 67, pp. 77–191). It contains the most recent version of the soil classification used by the U.S. Soil Survey, as well as a great deal of further information about many topics which are but lightly touched upon in the foregoing discussion.

CHAPTER XI

SETTLEMENT BY THE MODERN PIONEER

ISAIAH BOWMAN

Isaiah Bowman was born at Waterloo in Ontario, and graduated at Harvard and Yale. He later became Assistant Professor of Geography at Yale, and led a number of scientific expeditions to various parts of South America from 1907 to 1913. He became Director of the American Geographical Society in 1915, and after the First World War was engaged on research at the Peace Congress at Paris. In 1935 he was appointed President of Johns Hopkins. He has published a number of important books, such as Forest Physiography, *1911;* Andes of S. Peru, *1916;* New World, *1921;* Geography and the Social Sciences, *1934. (Bowman died in January 1950.)*

The Frontier of Settlement

THE idea of systematic and concentrated study of contemporary pioneer life on the active border of settlement throughout the world began to take form in my mind in 1905, while I was engaged in hydrologic work for the U.S. Geological Survey and first saw the surprising realities in the drier parts of Kansas and Oklahoma both on and beyond the discontinuous fringe of the wheat belt. The idea developed rapidly in succeeding years of study and university teaching. In 1907 it became a major inquiry in further field work in the diversified and somewhat extreme environments of parts of Peru, Bolivia, and northern Chile. In the course of more intensive work in the same general area in 1911 and 1913 the idea was extended. Regional examples will be found in two books that were among the results of these three expeditions to South America. My first paper on the broader political implications, entitled 'The Pioneer Fringe', was published in 1928 in the quarterly journal *Foreign Affairs*.

A certain professional urgency marked these studies. The historians of the Turner school were producing a genre of writing, marked by sound research, that was distorted by popular commentators who margined the historian's tale with imaginative or inferential elements that in many cases outran the realities. Pioneer conditions but little different from classic examples of the widespread westward movement of English-speaking peoples across the continent were readily observable; yet the commentators (including not a few historians and economists), kept repeating so often the error that pioneering in the United States ended in 1890, that it was as if they walked about with closed eyes in a world where there were still 3,000,000 square miles of land capable of settlement, and wrote as if no such land lay in the United States. They did not look at the real experiments of contemporary pioneer life so much as at the life of records paled by time and complicated by changing human motivations. Reconstructions from documents could not fail to be less vivid and full than field studies in the present, each form of research having, of course, its own merits. Often the key to the present—or at least one key—can be found in history, in what lies behind. Again, depth and relative completeness of understanding in many cases are realized only when historical and geographical research are blended. This could hardly have been the conviction of the American geographer who told me that my book *Desert Trails of Atacama* (1924) had so much history that he sent it to the library of the history department of his university to be accessioned!

The error of supposing the United States frontier of settlement to have closed in 1890 will no doubt continue to appear in print for a hundred years, so persistent is the habit of copying ideas and phrases in text-books and so general is the popular belief. How the error arose is an interesting example of the incompleteness of historical interpretation that deals in part with the environment when such interpretation is unchecked by geographical observation. It is no less important that geographers realize the shallowness of many studies of human institutions in their modern aspects only. Our ancestors speak through us with remarkable constancy. A distinguished historian, Sir John Meyers, concludes that ' . . . it has been Nature, rather than Man, hitherto, in almost every scene that has determined where the action shall lie'.[1]

The error grew out of the misreading of two sentences in the Compendium of the Eleventh U.S. Census, 1890:

Up to and including 1880 the country had a frontier of settlement, but at present the unsettled area has been so broken into by isolated bodies of settlement that there can hardly be said to be a frontier line. In the discussion of its extent and its westward movement it can not, therefore, any longer have a place in the census reports.[2]

Because a certain 'line' was no longer shown on a census map of a certain year the human reality that it was said to represent was thought to be as suddenly extinguished! The Census report did not say that the frontier had vanished. Free or cheap land was still abundant in 1890. Tens of millions of acres have been homesteaded since then. Pioneer conditions

[1] Quoted by A. L. Rowse in *The Use of History*, 1948, p. 98. ('Teach Yourself' series, English Universities Press).

[2] Compendium of the Eleventh Census, 1890, p. xlviii.

still prevail in some localities.[1] The report said only that the line separating territory with a population density of less than *two* to the square mile from territory having a higher density was so *irregular* that it would no longer be drawn on the census map. It was not pioneering that ended, only the habit of showing one of its supposed elements on a map! Perhaps hundreds of economic, political, and historical papers have since been written which refer to the end of settlement and cheap land and the opening of a new era in 1890—as precisely and suddenly as that!

Theodore Roosevelt had a sounder view of the *process of pioneering* as against any cartographical expression of it. His *Winning of the West*, like Willard D. Johnson's classic monograph[2] on the High Plains (1899) drew no sharp dividing line of settlement in time or place. *Through the Brazilian Wilderness*, which records Roosevelt's tropical journey of 1910, has sections written from the standpoint of a practical cattleman who had seen life on the move in the Badlands of Dakota, and never lost the sense of that motion. He particularly commended one review of his book which brought out this point. His African book is likewise flavoured with frontier life and thinking—the receding yet persistent past as well as the dynamic present. In *South America: Observations and Impressions*, Lord Bryce's interpretations likewise followed a two-way street—the past ever thrusting forward into the present, and a knowledge of the present enlarging and clarifying the historical record—environment and life at their interactive work.

In the 1920's geography began to have much wider representation in our universities and lack of depth was an immediate and unexpected result. A narrow view of time, process, field observation, and analysis gained favour. 'Human' geography became the fashionable phrase. In some schools the physical elements were minimized, and the subject largely confined to human societies and general ideas about their motivations, habits, rhythms, rise and fall, laws of behaviour, and forecasts of their fate. Few geographers are qualified for such wide excursions. A thin brew results if observational or experimental methods and the expert handling of environmental data and physical principles are lost to sight. Surely the geographer works best in the medium he knows best, and his unique expertness is in the interpretation of those elements of the environment that, varying in time and place, affect, and long have affected his life and organization. This is the part of his subject in which the un-questioned 'scientific' element is most evident and needs especially critical

[1] Isaiah Bowman, *The Pioneer Fringe*, 1931.

[2] Willard D. Johnson, *The High Plains and Their Utilization*, Twenty-first Annual Report of the U.S. Geological Survey, 1899–1900, pp. 601–741.

treatment, if it is to be used in historical and social interpretation. Beyond the environmental analysis the geographer competes with the economist, the historian and the sociologist. The day of easy generalizations about 'man' is over. A sounder method is well illustrated in a recent book, by Dr. Carlos Monge of the University of San Marcos at Lima, Peru, on *Acclimatisation in the Andes*. By combining the techniques of medicine, history, and geography and by conducting experiments on animals and men in both high and intermediate altitudes, he has given us indirectly an answer (in terms of altitude) to Sorokin's scepticism of 1928[1] on one element at least of the geographical environment at work.

The Frontier in Canada

The frontier of settlement—what I have called the pioneer fringe—offers one of the best posts of observation on the environment at work upon an intruded culture system that is almost at once modified in outer detail and eventually in inner spirit. It is a priceless laboratory for the study of cause-and-effect with a minimum of city influence. In 1928 an opportunity arose to enlarge pioneer studies through the interest and support of the Social Science Research Council. Funds were allotted to support a programme of research for which the American Geographical Society became responsible. It was thought best to concentrate the work in Canada. The Canadian Pioneer Problems Committee was then formed, upon my invitation, and under the chairmanship of Professor Mackintosh of Queens University at Kingston, Ontario. It had a distinguished membership that included Dawson of McGill, Martin of Manitoba (now Toronto), Lower of Queens, and Innis of Toronto. In this committee historians, economists, geographers, sociologists worked together with widening outlook. The results were published in a series of nine volumes by the Canadian Pioneer Problems Committee.

The Council of the American Geographical Society contributed liberally to the general programme of pioneer studies that I had drafted in 1928 and out of which the Canadian plan grew. With this quite free fund it was possible at once to broaden the studies by engaging regional experts in many parts of the world. Two volumes were produced by the American Geographical Society which set new standards of critical work in this field. The first, *The Pioneer Fringe* (1931), was an introductory systematization of observations and possibilities looking towards a science of settlement. The second, *Pioneer Problems* (1932), was a symposium by thirty scholars in which each author dealt with the region he knew best.

[1] Pitirim Sorokin, *Contemporary Sociological Theories*, 1928.

In 1937 a third volume was prepared at the request of the Conference of Institutions interested in International Affairs held in Spain in 1936. Nine scholars were good enough to join me in this endeavour. The result was *The Limits of Land Settlement,* published by the Council on Foreign Relations in New York.

Chiefly through this book, a wide discussion took place as to the suitability of the remaining areas of potential settlement in relation to the refugee problem then rising to alarming proportions as a result of Nazi policies. It was also clearly recognized by President Franklin D. Roosevelt that the general migration problem would assume new urgency after the war and that quite detailed settlement studies, with engineering data well organized, would be promptly required. At his request, made in 1938, I prepared and later directed special studies on a considerable scale and advised him on regional settlement possibilities and policies from that time until his death. Much of the resulting material, both outside and inside the government, is unpublished. A summary of one part of it edited by F. Julius Fohs, was issued in 1948 by the Refugee Economic Corporation of New York under the title *Quest for Settlement.*

The Frontier in Australia

Placed in the stream of politics, studies in pioneering possibilities thus took on a practical aspect wholly unintended at the beginning. They were conceived as scientific and critical analyses with direct practical applications to be made by governments only after detailed field surveys plot by plot. Our studies were to be useful to all settlers, while government has to be responsible for the individual settler, migrant or otherwise. Griffith Taylor in Australia had made an approach to both theoretical and practical applications in the period 1910 to 1940. National policy there turns on water to a large extent. Water deficiencies had repeatedly reached crisis proportions; and Taylor's early climatological work was directed towards the appraisal of risk in the zone of more highly variable dryness that includes the vast interior of the continent.

The classification of the lands of Australia made by Taylor thirty years ago[1] is now generally accepted by Australians, and was as follows:

About 42 per cent of Australia is *arid*, of which
    20 per cent of the whole is almost useless for stock,
    22 per cent is fair pastoral country, except in drought years.
About 34 per cent is *good pastoral country*.

[1] *Australia, Physiographic and Economic*, Oxford, 1919, p. 261.

About 21 per cent is *fair temperate* farming land suitable for close settlement; of which

13 per cent receives over 20 inches of rain per annum

8 per cent receives less than 20 inches per annum.

About 3 per cent of *Tropical* Queensland has a uniform rainfall through most of the year, and has crop possibilities.

A later estimate gives 50 per cent as *arid*, and 26 per cent as *good pastoral* country.[1]

The future millions of Australia are going to find their dwelling-places and occupations in the lands already known by 1865. The 'Empty Lands' of Australia are a burden to the Commonwealth rather than an asset, and their vast potentialities exist only in the minds of the ignorant booster. Yet the seven millions of Australia possess in the south and east of the continent one of the best areas in the world for white settlement.[1]

In this quarter of Australia Taylor expects that some twenty millions will dwell when the land is developed to the same extent as the United States.[1]

A recent paper by The Hon. C. L. A. Abbot,[2] Administrator of the Northern Territory of Australia for nine years (1937–46), has been published which the present-day student will find of special interest. Mr. Abbot claims for a part of the Northern Territory development possibilities that are substantial. One-fifth of the Northern Territory is good pastoral land and one-fifth is second-class pastoral land, each approximating 100,000 square miles or a total of 200,000 square miles. He thinks that over 50 per cent of the whole territory of 523,000 square miles could be put to use and settled (thinly of course), a proportion about equal to that of some of the adjoining states in a more advanced stage of development. The pastoral industry is the backbone of such development, but the standard difficulties are the lack of railways and the failure of the federal government to act upon expert surveys such as that of 1937.

Mr. Abbott concludes that the Northern Territory could double the number of its cattle, carry millions of sheep, and increase its population from 5,000 to 50,000,[3] with an eventual national income of £4 million. These are not inconsiderable results for a territory of a half-million square miles that is a vital link in Australia's advance, and which has benefited to some extent from highway and aerodrome construction during the

---

[1] *Australia, a study of warm environments*, London, 1940, p. 444.

[2] The Hon. C. L. A. Abbott, 'Australia's Frontier Problems', *The Geographical Journal*, Vol. CXI, Nos. 1–3, July 1948.

[3] *Editor's Note:* This is small compared with one million folk in Queensland today and half that amount in West Australia.

last war. Naturally the area in question is chiefly the northern portion with its regular monsoon rains that extend over one-third of the territory and where there are irrigation possibilities in a variety of valley situations. By these conjoined means he believes that Australia can work its way out of having too much land and too few people over an area of 'unpeopled north', that is 'a definite danger to Australia'. A not inconsiderable political difficulty will be the sub-division of pastoral holdings required for closer settlement.

Every element of pioneer land settlement sets it apart from more highly organized communities with respect to land occupation and use. The objects in view in adopting a pioneer life are many, some sordid as in land speculation, some noble as is the effort to provide a better future for children. The opening sentence of *The Pioneer Fringe* is 'Pioneers are young people with children'. The demographic picture is quite different in pioneer lands from that in settled communities where social services and amenities attract or hold the infirm, the aged, the timid, the avaricious, the pleasure-loving as well as the prosperous and the average. In the more systematic census-taking of the future (the sort now encouraged by international collaboration through the Population Committee of the United Nations), we may hope to have in time the raw data by which we may better evaluate the contribution of pioneer lands to national welfare, perhaps in part on a quantitative basis. The youthful quality of the population has important effects especially in health and strength, hopefulness, time in which to build, and in general longevity. So too must there be recognizable effects of the experimental nature of pioneer living. A recent statement by an historian comes to mind.[1]

The Frontier in Brazil

The physical environment of the remaining pioneer lands of the world is mostly marginal, one large-scale exception being a part, possibly a large part, of the interior of Brazil southward from the lower Amazon right across the interior plateau. The studies now in progress by Leo Waibel and his associates in Brazil should test and evaluate this exception in the near future. His results should have an important bearing on migration policies in Brazil and they will certainly lead to a re-study of transport and communications policies. Such is the fragmented road and railway situation in Brazil that the country is an archipelago of population groups. The railway map shows the dependence of each population group

[1] Dexter Perkins, 'Geographical Influences in American History', *Geographical Journal*, 1948, Vol. CIX, Nos. 1–3, pp. 26–39.

upon river or sea or soil and climatic types. Interconnexions are almost non-existent, despite the fanfare that has greeted each new spurt of road-building. What use will be made of good land in the interior depends far less in the next fifty or one hundred years upon favourable land and climate than upon the character of the people and the degree of continuity in government policies respecting roads and settlement. The high growth rate of Brazilian population and the slowness of industrial development are among the factors that have long kept Brazil's millions at a low economic level. Pioneering has been most active in Brazil in the coffee zone north-west of São Paulo, where production has been controlled by national restrictions that have operated for at least forty years. Excess coffee production confronted the Brazilian government with much the same kind of problem in dealing with the fringe settlers of São Paulo as confronted the governments of the Canadian Prairie Provinces in the 30's, when settlement pushed continuously into new and northerly wheat lands even in the depression years.

A marginal environment in modern times produces interesting states of mind in the pioneer. He wishes comforts and securities to follow him promptly, and is conscious that he is adding to the taxable wealth of his country and to its future strength. The Trans-Appalachian pioneers were also aware of their large future importance. So swift was their growth that it was natural to look ahead with confidence to a time of greatness, which included enhanced land values and profits. With the end of the Revolutionary War, western land policies became urgent. Land grants to soldiers, the construction of canals and railways, statehood, farm loans, and later homesteading—all were elements in the life of a nation with a wide and continuing frontier with plenty of room in which to move forward. Not all the new land lay in the 'west'. Governor Wentworth of New Hampshire, just before the Revolutionary War, wrote that in his colony 'A man that has £100 and can labour, in three years will be very easy and independent', and forecast an increase of 400 per cent in land values in five years.[1]

The modern pioneer regards more highly the paternal element of subsidized transport and state support for community services, in a word economic support in the venture and personal security regardless of results. When comforts and risks were but slightly smaller on the frontier—before telephones were known and when bathtubs and corner drugstores were rare—life was not too different in the new and largely tax-free communities, and time and growing density of population would assuredly bring substantial increments in land value. Today pioneering is more largely

[1] L. S. Mayo, *John Wentworth*, 1921, p. 96.

a matter of getting the government to assume the risks. Close economic calculations are made to reduce risk. All degrees of this process are illustrated on the many diversified fronts of the world's far-flung newer settlements. The arithmetic of pioneering is growing more complex everywhere, as political, economic, and social conditions grow more complex everywhere.

The Frontier in Rhodesia

The case of Northern Rhodesia is selected to point up some of these factors. It introduces the special feature of a 'native' population and the white man's moral relation thereto. The railway is the base-line of settlement there. Its construction was a matter of colonial policy, a link in the Cape to Cairo chain of transport, and a factor in imperial economic interest and defence. Mines (copper) played their due part. Native labour was desired and it was mutually advantageous to conserve it. Territorial reserves were set up for native use, white settlement being excluded from them. So far as possible the reserves were given natural boundaries based on want and use. What was left of good land was open for white settlement, due regard being paid to forest growth and conservation, the better to serve long-run housing and mining interests. The capital required of the settler to invest in tools, fences, house, and a working fund reserve to assure a native labour contract, and to tide over crop failure or bad market conditions, varies with circumstances, but is not under £500, and may be as high as £1,500 according to the acreage taken up. While production in most lines is optional, maize production is subject to the maize control ordinance. This is pioneering by close government supervision and support. It is settlement by contract. Physical fitness and courage are not enough. Risk is reduced by advising the new settler to take employment on, or purchase, an established plantation so that he may learn crop practices and labour management before enlarging on his own account.

The Northern Rhodesia government maintains an office in London, and eagerly consults a likely pioneering candidate. But what is offered is not a poor man's opportunity.[1]

Government and the Pioneer

Potential land settlers, like all the rest of us, are conscious of the market place today. Growing densities of population everywhere demand attention from science, society, and government. We see this in the newly

[1] Information for Intending Settlers, Land Board, Northern Rhodesia, November, 1947.

reclaimed areas of the Zuyder Zee project where a group of students in 1938 took me to see *their* 'pioneer fringe' as they proudly called it. The work was done necessarily by government which here preceded the settler and set the conditions of his life. Control is perhaps inescapable on today's frontier—control of the market through production and price restrictions and relief from either over-supply or the pressure of population upon the food reserves. Industrialization alone is not the answer in new countries long dependent upon European markets for the sale of their agricultural surpluses and their supply of manufactured imports. The uses and effects of industrialization are various and not to be forecast accurately. The unexpected scrambles the lines of logic and government control.

Oddly enough, control has given even the densely settled United Kingdom a sort of pioneer quality as experimental as Northern Rhodesia or the Hylean Amazon and certainly more complex. This is especially true of the iron-ore territory of northern England where the levelling and reconditioning of worked-over areas has become imperative. On 1 July 1948, the new Act defining the powers of the Department of Town and Country Planning went into effect. Theoretically, no acre of land is now free to be used in any way its owner chooses. The national need has crept out over all Britain from coast to coast. With 10,000 more mouths a month to be fed, depressed areas still troublesome, housing shortages still acute, and the individual caloric intake lowered on the average from 3,400 to 2,700,[1] it matters to everyone that timber be grown and agricultural production schedules be maintained in balance with import schedules, the latter being controlled in turn by the strength or weakness of the domestic economy.

The market place as a means of maintaining (1) a balanced economy and (2) an acceptable standard of living is now of large concern to the settlers of tropical lands. No longer is the question of settlement answerable in terms of good land or the willingness of a government to admit immigrants destined for land settlement. In the Amazon 75 per cent of the consumption is imported and 85 per cent of the production is exported. In neither case is the market price determined by Amazon inhabitants. The price-fixing machinery is in the hands of governments, and industries that merge Amazon supply and demand into world supply and demand, or at least those large parts of the world where the economic impulses and controls are determinative for the rest of the world. 'We should control our own prices', says the Amazon producer or merchant, but with what machinery, on what commercial principle, by what investment in ships

[1] Sir Charles Close, 'Our Crowded Island', *Eugenics Review*, 1948, Vol. 40, No. 1, pp. 23–30.

and roads and port facilities? The Soviet technique is to balance the economy at the centre *and control the published reports on it* which are generally favourable. When unfavourable, the system is not criticized, only the individuals who failed to do the impossible. When the inevitable mistakes are made the books are balanced, so to speak, by taking the deficit out of the standard of living and shooting a few officials.

The pioneer settler cannot keep the books of the world. Wherever his community be located it is but a fragment of a larger economy, a thread in a web, not a completed garment. By overlooking these basic economic facts, the ardent advocate of a specific settlement venture can make any spot seem attractive to the unwary. Put in capital enough, screened houses, a purified water supply, fertilizer perhaps, tools, preferably 'native' labour, *an assured price for export products in the world market*, and add the hope that there will be tolerance for high temperature and humidity, and almost any tropical lowland area can be made to look like home. What is astonishing is not that such schemes are devised but that some men are willing to put money into them.

Defence may make any settlement investment 'pay' without reference to local or world markets or the expense of non-productive facilities and comforts. An adverse conclusion on settlement, that rests on engineering analysis, may be set aside for military reasons. The long-run intention of defence policy may be to meet an expected condition in which room for military staging is more important than financial dividends. Australia's white-man population policy recognizes that every land settlement potential must be exploited even to uneconomic limits. Nothing less than full use is the primary aim. Whether or not it pays is secondary. More population means greater military strength. Australia with seven millions is on the flank of South-east Asia with half the world's population. A white man's policy is thus challenged by hundreds of millions with a far lower standard of living. When a high-standard population reaches the end of land-and-water exploitation a low standard population can pick up the job at that point and go further. Australia's form of economy must change to gain over-all strength. Further industrialization (already advanced by war) is thought to be part of the change required. The inevitable effect of such a change on British economy is yet to be calculated.

The motives and impulses of intending settlers reveal some promising recent changes. After World War I, overseas settlement was encouraged in Britain. The efforts of the 1840 Settlers' Association were supplemented by the Overseas Settlement Office of the British government. The Empire

Settlement Act of 1923 was meant to give an impulse to migration from the United Kingdom without loss of manpower to the Empire. Dominion and colonial governments at the receiving end lent such facilities as they had. They were too small in every instance for large-scale immigration which requires special services even when free or cheap and good land is available. The Empire Settlement Act, costing tens of millions, failed in the end. Settlers were few in number. Some lost interest when they were asked to exchange their customary weekly wage for the enterprise and risk called for by the pioneer conditions of West Australia, to take a specific example. From southern Africa came reports of homesickness and disillusionment, when the comfortable steamship on which the settlers had taken subsidized passage was exchanged for life on the veldt or a plantation with its heavy and unaccustomed labour and its term of apprenticeship.

By contrast the settlers of today are more numerous and more willing to take risks than those of twenty-five years ago. The bombing of England and the continuation of rationing, plus the lowered calories of the post-war period and the political risks of an elusive peace, have turned more minds towards a new life outside the British Isles; even if cinemas and shops and doctors are few and far between in pioneer lands. In June 1948 it was reported in Parliament that 150,000 emigrants had left the United Kingdom during the preceding two years to settle in the Dominions (the Government reserving the right to check too great a flow of certain types of highly skilled workers). This illustrates the generalization one drew sixteen years ago during the depression that hard times are one of the powerful causes of migration. Drought in Saskatchewan and failure of crops as well as city jobs led to an unusual influx of settlers into northern Alberta and eastern and north-eastern British Columbia, in the depression of the early thirties.

Conditions of Pioneer Life

Much thought has been expended upon the economic results of diminishing amounts of free or cheap land in the world, with little thought given to the process of living (varying from region to region), and the structure of life in the continuing pioneer fringe still of large aggregate extent. National conclusions have been drawn without looking closely at their validity in terms of local life. In history writing the relatively stationary frontier has been all but overlooked. San Pedro de Atacama in Chile has had a pioneer life for nearly 400 years. Even with the coming of the railroad from the east (across the Andean Cordillera) in 1948 the change is special, not general.[1] In 1930 when I visited Jordan, Montana, it was as definitely a frontier town in appearance, social organization, outlook, and population composition as if it were a town in Missouri on the Oregon Trail of a hundred years ago.

The distinguishing features of pioneer life depend locally upon the civilization involved, the production system, the form of land tenure, the food habits of the population, and the climatic limitations, to name a few conditioning elements. Therefore, one should not put a halter on a field observer by insisting upon a preconceived mode of inquiry. In any event, an ounce of insight is often worth more than a pound of technique. For example, there is the principle of dominance, that control of the situation so largely exercised through one or two outstanding conditions, not by a host of little things all to be set out in the serried ranks of an outline. Pedagogical array at once over-taxes the memory and the available time as if a complete list of things that might be observed were itself an objective. The *weight* of an observation is important; and weight is determined by a theory to be tested or an induction to be drawn by an assemblage of dominances.

The dominant things in Northern Rhodesia, for example, are distance from market, high freight rates, and a strongly-fluctuating world market price. Secondary to that is the character of the labour supply. Also dominant are a succession of well-marked good and bad crop years, the social habits of the English settlers, the degree of prosperity of the local mining industry, and government controls in the interest of a fairly well-balanced economy. There are a baker's dozen of other conditions of secondary importance. They are all in the files of the local government officials, who inspect, issue licences, locate and bound desirable plantation sites, or approve and endorse labour contracts. With the main elements in mind, government prescribes that a pioneer settler must have capital of a given amount. If the government of the United States had made a similar prescription in the settlement of the West it would have been both impossible to carry out and grotesque for the period. The Northern Rhodesia government, as we have seen, prescribes *a standard of living* for both the settler and the native labourer whom he employs, and this ties land settlement to an economy whose centres are far distant and whose workings, moral as well as economic, are as complex and invisible to the settler as they are uncontrollable by him. He is not in any sense or degree the pioneer of the Tennessee or Kentucky lowlands, though the trans-Appalachian settlers soon passed out of the solitary log-cabin stage

[1] Isaiah Bowman, *Desert Trails of Atacama*, New York, 1924.

into the stage of pressure upon Washington for canals, roads, railways, and other amenities.

You may teach a man a technique but you cannot teach him to discover. This is well shown by a conversation I once had with a government land investigator. I told him, on the basis of my own farming experience, that a good local farmer could drive through a new region and tell as much about it in a week and give as reliable a forecast of farm use, as a government investigator who spent $25,000 of public money and took a field season or two to apply his formalized techniques in a systematic manner. He agreed, but added that when a Congressional appropriation is requested you have to explain *in advance* in most instances just what and where you propose to observe and how this bears on local welfare. It should be added that a good deal of 'scientific' writing on land classification is generalization based on local *experimentation* by the settler himself. The scientist, with funds, can explore the unsettled tracts and say how far local tested conditions may be extended in the field. The settler experiments, the scientist maps the possible field extension of the settler's results. At a later stage, as a rule, the scientist tells *why* the settler got his results. The re-study of the results of agricultural effort as science advances may show up earlier errors of course. Recent studies in microclimatology seem to modify some earlier conclusions on plants as indicators of soil fertility, for example.

The typical colonial prospectus of the eighteenth century—whether expressed in terms of a better home, the plea of a proprietor for more settlers, or a printed tract—dwelt on the advantages of a free new society and the productivity of the available acres. Get good land and enjoy liberty. It was not overlooked that a man had to work hard. Settlers had therefore to be young and strong. They were generally at the child-rearing stage. Hands were needed. On the land a boy of ten can begin to earn his keep. In a new land a young man can begin to plan a more expansive future. It is remarkable how quickly in one settlement after another and on a rapidly expanding frontier the controls from which the migrating settler had thought to escape were re-established in the new environment. The Mayflower Compact was signed before the company had set foot to land at either Provincetown or Plymouth. It bound men to observe rules and gave power to a few 'for their better ordering and preservation' as Palfrey had expressed the idea long before. The vigilance committees of a later West are only the most melodramatic of a host of self-imposed 'rules' that local societies require, with leadership by minister or priest or soldier or sheriff or an obviously wise or aggressive member of the community.

A chapter could be written on labour in settlement, its division, its sources. To an extent not realized by a student who has been fed on American expansion only, the supply of local labour has often determined the form of a frontier society, especially in tropical situations.

Three broad groups of facts are required to be known in the analysis of pioneer societies. First, is the environment. The techniques for its study are in an advanced though incomplete state today with much regional work to be done and many anomalies to be explained. Second, is the settler's thinking. What led him to migrate into an experimental fringe, new or old? His impulsions and thoughts may be irrational, emotional, romantic, hard-headed, stupid, intelligent, or courageous. His conclusions may be denied by events and his reasoning frustrated by time. Yet he is a cell in the frontier organism, and it is important to know how he functions and why, as he sees the matter. An intelligent cross-examination that combines some of the elements of the F.B.I. and the psychiatrist is required by the field man who tries to find out why men live where they do.

The third required group of facts is the relation of a pioneer group to the outside world. Within every state are forces that affect the advancing pioneer, or the stationary marginal settler. Beyond national boundaries are economic forces and groupings, and also the changing tides of foreign affairs. Roads are the arteries of trade for frontier groups. Will they be built? Who must build them? What freight rates will be charged if a railway is constructed? These are life and death matters in all places and times on the frontier. Wheat at railhead at Pouce Coupe was selling for 22 cents a bushel in 1932, and it cost at least 30 cents to haul it from Rose Prairie, British Columbia, to the railway. Under these conditions the pioneer let it rot on the stalk, and all he had to show for the clearing of the land and the seed and the ploughing was one year off the five of residence required to gain a firm title.

Difficulties in Charting Pioneer Lands

The complexities of pioneering from place to place show how inadequate, even for the time, was the concept of the 'line' published in successive U.S. census reports down to 1880, to show the border of territory having a population of less than two to the square mile. The same kind of life was lived on both sides of the line. A broad belt, rather than a line, would have been nearer the reality. The significant thing was a process running its course. First in the process was the finding of the choicest location that limited knowledge and means could procure.

Second, a culture system to be thrust forward with elements that included the log or the sod hut and the hoe and the prairie plough, distant neighbours as a rule, primitive living, and roads that wound irregularly over the landscape of the plains or followed ridge tops and valley bottoms in the forested middle country. As late as 1915 all of these features could still be seen in some parts of the 'West'. During the next few years (which included the period of World War I), the prairie schooner had disappeared and a less primitive phase of pioneering took over.

There are many parts of the Plains country which have less than two to the square mile of year-round residents today. A mechanized agriculture has made it possible for many farmers to live in village or town and drive to the farm each day. With no stock to tend, such a farmer need have no barn for shelter and feed storage. The only building required is a tool-shed. Even the windmill is often absent or out of repair. That part of the town population that works the land must be spread over the land to get a density figure at all comparable with that of earlier times. But really comparable figures are not possible. The wheat 'farmer' with modern machines can do all the work of tillage, sowing, harvesting, and marketing in about ninety days. With sufficient capital for land, seed, and machines, he can avoid diversified farming with its round-the-clock duties. Under such a system population density expressed as a raw figure has no real meaning. The system back of the figure, the way of life, the interplay of machine, capital, and man are at the heart of the matter and *differentiation of production systems* on a map is required, not mere density of population. This reasoning shows the aridity of the attempt to get 'scientific' tables of population and area only, without reference to their local interpretations. There can be no valid comparative studies unless the things compared are first analysed.

A description and analysis of pioneering that runs all the way from parts of densely populated Britain to Northern Rhodesia and includes the world's diversified systems of culture calls for a definition. The desert affords an example of the difficulty involved. By definition a desert is an area of deficient rainfall, having a sparse or specialized vegetation and an 'adapted' animal life. Yet we all know of tracts of desert within the Sahara or Kalahari or Atacama that have dense vegetation and occasionally heavy and even normal rainfall. Local 'deserts' in Maine and Connecticut also come to mind. The key to a definition of pioneering is not experimentation alone, for the land-use practises now prescribed in Britain are equally experimental (because of crowding). The experiments of the pioneer settled upon new land are carried out where population is sparse and land-use and markets uncertain. Risk accompanies all land-use

18

dependent upon the weather. The risks of weather are greater for the pioneer because the undeveloped lands are largely marginal as to climate, soil, and location. They are the less desirable lands where rainfall variability is highest or where it rains in excess. To live in them requires a civilization to stand behind one, to share the risk, to give a running start by furnishing seed, tools, and duty-free imports for a time. Civilization can do this because it has other ends to serve and those of defence come first to mind. The outposts of power are everywhere. No territory is so small or remote today that it has no value. The swift aeroplane seems to skip territory, but like a bird it does not know where it may have to alight because of weather or war. Even floating ice is aeroplane 'territory'. The remote pioneer of today may be at the centre of a howling activity tomorrow.

There is a recognized 'border' of land settlement many thousands of miles long in the aggregate with large tracts in every continent but Europe, and where production risks are high. To meet them and to assure land occupation life must be simple, the standards relatively low, and government aid available. Social gravitation is more powerful today than ever—in Brazil or Rhodesia or in the United States. Military strategy now plays its often decisive part not here and there but everywhere. The pioneer is tied to world conditions and events which he does not control. He is no longer a breed, as it were, but any one of us trying to make a living under difficult conditions with risk offset by hope and promise.

This is far different from the earlier days when a man could move freely beyond the sight of his neighbour's smoke. One of the picturesque features of an earlier day is largely gone—the outpost pioneer who built, if native labour was available, a little kingdom of his own. Southern Africa had examples now warped out of shape or largely absorbed by larger forces. The border of the Amazon country has its scores if not hundreds of such personal domains. Australia and New Guinea supply other examples. The pioneer still creates a distinctive type of life and thought. He has still a large measure of imagination, independence, and self-reliance. He is still a young man (in general) trying to improve his position and future and not depending on job and wage from day to day. Pioneering adds strength to any nation when it has the element of progress in it and does not become a place of refuge for undesirables or a stagnant pool of defeated men.

The study or the administration of modern pioneering is strongly conditioned by the fact that the world is becoming socially minded. The discovery by a scientific study of soils that good agricultural land is available will not of itself create a rush of settlers. How 'comfortable' is the climate? How far is it from centres of culture? What cash crops can be

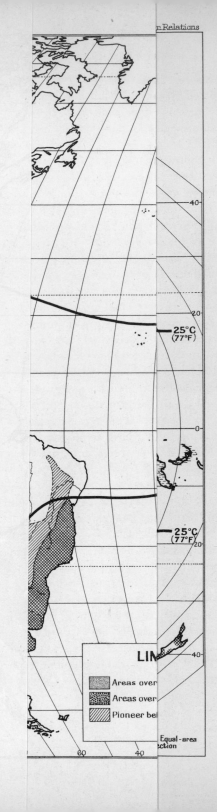

40-

20-

25°C
(77°F)

0-

25°C
(77°F)
20-

LIM

Areas over

Areas over

Pioneer be

40-

Equal-area
ection

60   40

grown for export? How austere will be the living while the land is prepared for crops? Will medical care be available? These are among the questions that must be answered in large part by government because social conditions are coming more and more under government control.

It follows that a map of the world, such as shown in Fig. 10, which shows *land* available for settlement tells only a few elementary facts. It shows *where* the pioneer operations take place. Beyond that point one must study the society in which the operation is projected. Is it stable? Will its government keep its promises? If health conditions in a country are bad, the pioneer who settles in it cannot expect high standards of medical care for his family in the new community. If government is unstable the promises of today may be broken tomorrow.

Thus the analyses of physical conditions of soil and climate, while vital to an undertaking, are minimized *in the initial phase of settlement* by social conditions. They are minimized further by the potentialities of step-up in productivity in better-favoured regions through chemistry. Often the apparent richness of the soil in a given element is deceptive. Pineapples require a soil rich in *available* iron. On some of the Hawaiian pineapple plantations with plenty of iron in the soil an iron solution is sprayed on to the growing plants, the iron of the natural soil being in insoluble form. Mere reconnaissance is not enough. The survey of pioneering lands must be thorough as to available plant food, trace elements, probable duration of natural soil fertility, and erodibility. In a recent paper the advice is given that a certain jungle area in Central America can be cleared by modern machinery and high production assured. Not a word is said about any of the critical social and economic factors that come into play once the work of clearing is completed.

Pioneer lands being generally marginal, their *relative* value in an organized country rises or falls as modernization proceeds or is retarded in the rest of the country. Population capacity is expressed in abstract statistics of population density and area. It is expressed in what is *done* with the natural resources available or creatable. The Dutch *make* their pioneer fringe out of sea bottom in their polders. They apply to it all the techniques of scientific agriculture. They extend into it (distance being no factor) a completely equipped society. Dutch communities have successfully used the same techniques in Holland, Michigan, and drained ponds, lakes, and marshes, raising the value of land in one lifetime from lowest to highest rank, in some cases from $20 an acre to $1,000 an acre. To the extent that *interior* pioneering—which includes spraying, hybridization, trace elements and fertilizer studies—becomes general the homesteads of marginal lands lose some of their advantages of cheapness and size.

The pioneer fringe is a laboratory of exceptional scientific worth because there the human intelligence is pitted against extreme or unusual environmental conditions. There men test their capacity to go farther. There governments determine how far aid may be extended in the endless process of reappraising the earth as new plants, machines, ideas, strategies, and transport facilities open new vistas of opportunity. City geography is at one end of the scale of settlement, pioneering at the other. City growth and a tight general economy plus the growth of amenities and pleasures have given new forms to pioneering, almost *de luxe* forms in some instances. While these conscious (because government-aided) forms of settlement effort come most often to public notice, the largest share of new land occupation is in the form of an unheralded slow advance of quiet people who go about their work with determination. The imagination that is in the pioneer's planning and thinking is reflected in literary works mainly. Accustomed to record 'facts', the scientist sometimes misses the most important fact of all—why people act in a given way. When a man moves from one place to another the reason he gives may not be sound but it is *his* reason. Imagination is like that too. Many a pioneer uses it who does not take the trouble to name it.

We hardly need add that pioneers are all sorts of people. I have given few detailed examples for lack of space. The reader will find them in abundance in the books mentioned at the beginning of this article. Almost every important population and government entity has its share of frontier living. Ibn Saud made his frontier in the Nejd and the instruments of it were water and the employment of a hydrologic engineer. The control of 'fly' opens still another under-developed territory in Africa. The U.S.S.R. early recognized the worth of northern Siberia for the production of minerals and for defence. In each case an economic system and a set of values migrate, as well as men. There is no one type of pioneer. Yet all have experimentation in common and all have scope for originality and imagination, thus giving the scientist a stream of changing raw material for analysis and generalization and for a deeper understanding of other folk as well as his own.

CHAPTER XII

GEOGRAPHY AND ARCTIC LANDS

A. L. WASHBURN

Washburn, A. L.—New York, 15 June, 1911. Ph.D. Yale 1942. Executive Director, Arctic Institute of North America. Geomorphology, glacial geology. Member, Nat. Geog. Soc. Exped. to Mount McKinley, Alaska, 1936; Boyd East Greenland Expedition 1937. Geological investigations Canadian Arctic 1938–41. Publications include: (With Flint, R.F., and Demorest, Max) 'Glaciation of Shickshock Mountains Gaspé Peninsula', Geol. Soc. Am. Bull., Vol. 53, 1942, pp. 1211–30. 'Opportunities for international cooperation in Arctic research', Biologia, Vol. 1, No. 6, pp. 23–4, 1947. 'Reconnaissance geology of portions of Victoria Island and adjacent regions Arctic Canada', Geol. Soc. Am. Mem. 22, 1947, 142 pages.

Aims of Arctic Exploration

ALTHOUGH seldom stated as aims, adventure, romance of the unknown, and freedom from the restrictions of civilization have often been underlying and compelling incentives for Arctic exploration, especially in the past. Even today they exert a strong, often unadmitted, influence over many persons. However, in general the fundamental aims of Arctic exploration are purely scientific—to learn more about the North, to solve the many problems that confront us there and which must be solved before we are in a position to describe the North accurately and completely. From this point of view the North differs from no other region; where it does differ is in the fact that we know so little about it compared with most other parts of the world.

The fundamental aims cover a number of practical objectives. The search for natural resources is a particularly important one. Only a very small proportion of the Arctic has been thoroughly explored geologically; large parts of it have never been seen by a geologist. When this situation is contrasted with the successful northern mineral developments in some parts of North America, Scandinavia, and the Soviet Arctic that are known, the imagination is challenged by the mineral wealth that may still lie concealed. Other natural resources such as fisheries, fur, timber in the Subarctic, water power—all remain to be developed to a greater or less degree. Hence this chapter, written in 1948, may soon need revision.

In addition to resources within the region there are important processes operating in the North that affect significantly people outside of the region. Enough is known about dynamic meteorology, for instance, to establish that Arctic weather has a profound influence on weather farther south and on forecasting, but the exact degree of influence is still uncertain.

In a way Arctic exploration must hitch itself up by its own boot-straps through formulating its own methods. Only those who have worked in the North can appreciate the great amount of time that has to be spent just seeing to the everyday necessities of life. A valid objective of Arctic exploration may therefore be said to be improvement in the techniques of living, travelling, and working. The experience gained on numerous expeditions has resulted in very significant innovations in design of vessels and aircraft for northern work. Only the dog team and sledge as used by the Eskimo have remained comparatively constant. Methods of polar navigation, too, have undergone considerable change for the better; the introduction of Radar and Loran have greatly simplified matters. Housing and clothing problems are less of a drag on research workers in the Arctic than formerly.

The importance of the North in military strategy is emphasized by those who point out that the shortest route between many strategic areas and centres of population lies over the Arctic regions. The rapid progress in developing long-distance flying and the possibility of atomic and bacteriological warfare make it essential for all nations with Arctic frontiers to know these frontiers intimately if just from the defence angle alone.

Fortunately peaceful trade and commerce provide an equally compelling reason for knowing the North. Now for the first time since the days when the North-west Passage was first sought, the 'short' polar air routes between centres of population are entirely practical from a mechanical point of view, and it remains only for future economic justification to develop them. As a result of both the military and civilian interest, the Arctic has become an important region in international affairs.[1] Although the Arctic presents certain diplomatic problems because of its international importance, it also offers the opportunity for friendly co-operation between nations, since scientific problems are generally the same regardless of international boundaries and some problems in the North can only be solved by joint effort. To the extent that such effort can contribute to understanding and good-will between nations this constitutes in itself a noteworthy by-product of Arctic exploration.

As our detailed scientific knowledge of the North increases, as new

[1] Bolles, Blair (1948), *Arctic Diplomacy*, Foreign Policy Association Reports, Vol. XXIV, pp. 58–67.

natural resources become known, and as research and living techniques improve, it may be possible usefully to accommodate more people there. Comparison of similar regions of climate and terrain in North America and the U.S.S.R. suggest that North America lags behind the U.S.S.R. in developing her Northland to the best possible use.[1] Whatever the population potential of the North, certainly the acquiring of factual information on which to base a sound, over-all utilization of northern lands for the benefit of mankind is one of the most important reasons for Arctic exploration, combining as it does fundamental scientific aims with practical objectives.

Taking the progressive growth of interest in the North since the development of long-range aircraft as a guide, the North will continue to grow in importance in world affairs. Clearly no nation fronting the Arctic Sea can afford to be unfamiliar with this still largely unexplored region.

The Arctic as a Geographical Unit

The term 'Arctic' is generally used loosely to indicate the Far North without implying a definite southern boundary. Some authorities employ the term more precisely to mean the tundra region north of the limit of coniferous forest (or north of tree line);[2] others, following Köppen, Trewartha, and Ackerman,[3] to mean the region that is north of the 50° F. (10° C.) isotherm for the warmest month and which has an average annual temperature of 32° F. (0° C.) or less (Fig. 55). In a rough way these two regions coincide although marked differences occur here and there. Away from rivers the forest limit tends to lie farther south than along major waterways where finger-like projections extend northward. As a result the forest-limit definition gives the Arctic a very irregular southern boundary but one that can be recognized on the ground. The temperature definition, because of the wide areal spacing of long-term temperature records, gives a smooth boundary having a spurious appearance of accuracy. Although this boundary also has the disadvantage that it cannot be readily recognized in the field, the temperature definition is an extremely useful one because it is not affected by soil conditions and other

[1] Taylor, Griffith (1946), 'Parallels in Soviet and Canadian Settlement', *Can. Inst. Internat. Affairs, Internat. Jour.*, Vol. I, No. 2, pp. 144–58.

[2] The northern limit of coniferous forest is somewhat south of tree line or northern limit of individual scattered trees. A difference of $1\frac{1}{2}$ degrees of latitude between the two limits is not uncommon.

[3] Ackerman, E. A. (1941), 'The Köppen classification of climates in North America', *Geog. Rev.*, Vol. XXXI, pp. 105–11.

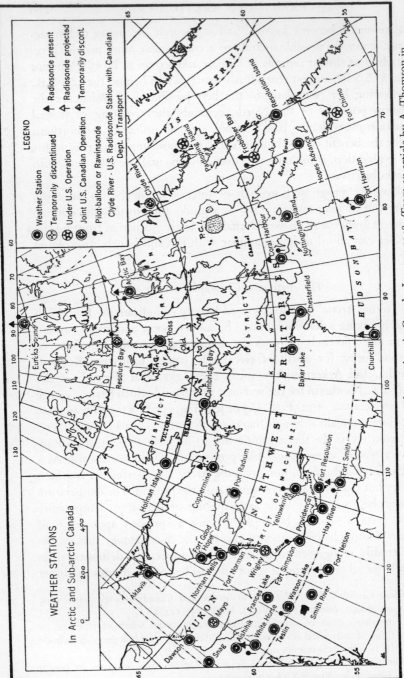

Fig. 11.—Distribution of Arctic and Subarctic weather stations in Canada, January 1948. (From an article by A. Thomson in *Arctic*, Spring 1948)

Isotherm 56° F. (July) runs from Aklavik to Radium and '100' on S. edge of map. The newly discovered Prince Charles Is.

ecological factors that cause local irregularities in tree line. Furthermore climate is the fundamental factor controlling the northward limit of trees.

Still a third concept of the Arctic, but applying only to the sea, is employed by some oceanographers. The criterion is the presence of Arctic water at the surface and in the upper layers, as determined by currents. Such water has distinctive characteristics of temperature and biological production, although its southern limit varies somewhat from time to time. This concept that the Arctic coincides with the region of Arctic water may become a very useful one for purely oceanographical purposes.[1]

The Arctic as delimited by any of the above definitions departs widely from the heterogeneous region encompassed by the Arctic Circle; being a mathematical concept that cuts across natural characteristics such as climate and terrain, the Arctic Circle has no particular significance in formulating a useful definition of the Arctic.

The Subarctic can be defined as the circumpolar belt of dominant coniferous forest (taiga), and also by temperature as the region where the average January temperature is below 32° F. and where the average temperature of the warmest month is more than 50° F., but where there are less than four months above this temperature. Here, too, the botanical definition is an extremely useful approximation but it involves even more irregularities than in the case of tree line. According to the oceanographical definition, the Subarctic is the region of mixed Arctic and non-Arctic water.

In the following pages the terms 'Arctic' and 'Subarctic' will be employed in the restricted sense to indicate respectively the regions north and south of the 50° F. isotherm for the warmest summer month. The term 'North' will be used in a general sense to indicate either one or both of these regions.

Arctic Characteristics

The climate of the Arctic varies considerably from place to place. The average temperature of the warmest summer month is by definition less than 50° F., but maximum summer temperatures of 70° to 80° F. are not uncommon on some days in interior areas. In these same areas minimum winter temperatures may drop as low as −50° to −60° F., giving a range of as much as 140° F. between a summer heat wave and winter cold spell. Coastal temperatures are generally less extreme because of the moderating

[1] Dunbar, M. J. (1947), 'Note on the delimitation of the Arctic and Subarctic zones', *Canadian Field-Naturalist*, Vol. 61, pp. 12–14; (1948) Personal communication.

effect of the sea. Precipitation in the Arctic tends to be slight. In the Canadian Western Arctic, for instance, it is ±10 inches and in the Canadian Eastern Arctic ±15 inches. As a result snowfall is moderate, and because there are no trees to break the force of the wind the little snow that falls is often swept away to be deposited as drifts in the lee of some obstacle.

The Subarctic climate tends to have greater seasonal temperature contrasts than that of the Arctic except in coastal areas where the moderating effect of the sea is more pronounced because of the absence of an ice cover. By definition the average temperature of the warmest summer month is greater than 50° F.; in the interior areas maximum summer temperatures are commonly 10° to 20° F. higher than in the Arctic whereas minimum winter temperatures are 10° to 20° F. lower. Precipitation in the Subarctic tends to be similar or only slightly greater in the interior areas, but considerably greater in the coastal regions as compared with the Arctic; at Tromsö, Norway, for instance, it is about 40 inches. Most of the Subarctic is well forested so that the force of the wind is broken and snow tends to accumulate where it falls rather than blow away. As a result the snow is much softer than the hard wind-packed snow of the treeless Arctic.

There are a number of different sorts of terrain features that are typical of the North. The general presence of tundra in the Arctic and of coniferous forest in the Subarctic, for example, not only emphasizes the difference between the two regions but also gives two distinct types of northern terrain. Characteristically the tundra consists mainly of grasses, sedges, and low-lying shrubs which cover hill and dale as a discontinuous blanket.

Another terrain feature typical of many parts of the Arctic is the permanent snow and ice that is generally, but not everywhere, associated with highlands. The Greenland Ice Sheet with an area of about 637,000 square miles and an altitude that may exceed 11,000 feet is the second largest body of snow and ice in the world, being exceeded only by the Antarctic Ice Sheet. Small ice caps and valley glaciers are common in the highlands of the Canadian Eastern Arctic and in many other comparable regions. Because the snow line descends northward, more glaciers from highland areas reach sea-level in the Arctic than in the Subarctic. Lowland areas unassociated with highlands are generally free of snow in the summer as illustrated by the low-lying islands of the Canadian Western Arctic.

Permafrost or permanently frozen ground is still another characteristic terrain feature. It is present throughout the Arctic and much of the Subarctic and has a very irregular southern boundary. Lakes are likewise

typical of the North. Most of them are the result of Ice-Age glaciers dis-
rupting drainage by erosion and deposition. Permafrost, by holding
water near the surface of the ground rather than permitting it to percolate
downward, also favours the development of lakes.

The Arctic Sea is a very important factor is making the North a
geographic unit because its peculiar features, like those of the land, are
also a result of the northern climate. Whether off the coasts of North
America, Europe, or Asia, the Arctic Sea has the same fundamental
appearance: a southern zone of alternating open water and sea ice, depending upon the season of the year, and a more northerly zone of moving
pack ice present at all times of the year. No matter if summer or winter,
this pack ice is always moving and always has some open water where the
ice has cracked open to form leads.

Difficulty of access is another characteristic of the North. Transportation problems caused by remoteness from centres of civilization and
aided by the peculiarities of climate and terrain give the Arctic an individuality all its own. A person is either in the Arctic and part of it or
he is 'outside'. In the Subarctic this individuality is of course much less
distinct, and as time goes on increased air travel will tend to diminish the
effect, even in the Arctic.

It is the geographic unity of the North that emphasizes the interrelation of the different aspects of exploration there. Almost every branch
of scientific investigation has a bearing on some other branch. To be sure
this is true of any part of the world, but it is particularly apparent where
geographic features are similar and where difficulty of access and consequent costs make joint efforts by scientists especially desirable. Geography is a great co-ordinator of information, and nowhere in the world
is this co-ordination more needed than in Arctic work.

Exploration Techniques, and Transportation by Ships

Up to the present time nearly all Arctic field research has had to be
approached on an expeditionary basis. The very nature of the region, its
difficulty of access, and its lack of population account for this fact. Because
of the expeditionary approach transportation problems have constituted
a critical limiting factor on the type and amount of work done. As a
result most Arctic research to date has been of a reconnaissance character,
although exceptions are offered by fixed research stations in the North
and by laboratory study of material that has been brought back from
the field.

As transportation methods improve, so will exploration techniques and knowledge of the North. Advances in boat travel, land travel, and flying now permit exploration of a kind never dreamed of a hundred years ago. Today a university group can spend a profitable summer field season on Southampton Island in the Canadian Eastern Arctic without interfering in the least with the university calendar. A few years ago such a trip would have required at least a year's leave of absence from a university.

Since the days of Pytheas and his famous voyage of about 330 B.C. and of the Viking voyages that led to the discovery, or perhaps rediscovery, of the Barents Sea, White Sea, and Iceland in the ninth century A.D. and of Greenland in the tenth century, the major features of the North have become gradually known largely because of stout sailing ships manned by adventurous souls.

Ships played a dominant role in outlining the Arctic coasts of Europe and Asia. While exploring for the North-east Passage in 1553, Willoughby and Chancellor sailed into the White Sea and discovered Novaya Zemlya. Voyages by others followed and almost a century later in 1648 Dezhnev sailed through Bering Strait. Weyprecht and Payer found Franz Josef Land (Zemlya Frantsa-Iosifa) in 1873, and several years later in 1878–9 Nordenskjöld in the *Vega* became the first to sail in one continuous voyage around the entire Arctic coast of Europe and Asia, and thus complete the North-east Passage or Northern Sea Route as it is now known. The Ob, Yenisei, and Lena rivers are great arteries draining northward whose deltas can be profitably linked by the Northern Sea Route. A number of ships have sailed along it since the *Vega*, and now the route is of considerable economic and strategic significance. A good deal of geographic information resulted from the many early voyages in this region, but most of the detailed scientific knowledge was obtained later by government expeditions bent on acquiring the information necessary to make the Northern Sea Route the potentially valuable asset to the Soviet Union that it has now become.

On the opposite side of the Arctic Sea the search for the North-west Passage gave a similar impetus to geographical exploration. Frobisher landed in Baffin Island on the first of his voyages which started in 1576, and ten years later Davis sailed through the strait (Davis Strait) separating Baffin Island from Greenland. In 1610 Hudson sailed into the body of water (Hudson Bay) that Frobisher had probably seen earlier, and which for many years after Hudson's voyage was believed to be the entrance to the North-west Passage. Actually the real entrance from the east, Lancaster Sound, was found by Baffin in 1616. One of the most remarkable polar voyages of all time was made two hundred years later in 1819 when

Parry sailed through Lancaster Sound and wintered at Melville Island, after passing through the heart of the Canadian Arctic Archipelago and making tremendous geographic discoveries.

It was a hundred years before Parry's voyage was duplicated, but in the meantime numerous other voyages had been made and the North-west Passage had become a reality. John Ross and his nephew, James Clark Ross, made notable contributions, the latter locating the North Magnetic Pole on Boothia Peninsula in 1831. Probably the expedition that led to the greatest advance in knowledge of the North American Arctic, even though indirectly, was the fateful voyage of Franklin in the *Erebus* and *Terror*. The ships were lost in the ice in the neighbourhood of King William Island in 1848, starvation set in and not a man survived. Numerous search expeditions were sent out before these facts were established and, in the course of their work, they explored the coasts of many of the Canadian Arctic islands, carefully mapping as they went along. It is note-worthy that the detail of some of the resulting maps is more accurate than that shown on some maps current today. Nansen's drift in the *Fram* from 1893 to 1896 and the work of the Second Norwegian Arctic Expedition from 1898 to 1902 added very significantly to the knowledge of the Arctic Sea.

Amundsen was the first to negotiate the North-west Passage by ship. His tiny *Gjoa* was several years *en route*, from 1903 to 1906, but the very slowness of Amundsen's voyage gave his party time to carry out signifi-cant studies in terrestrial magnetism. Long before Amundsen's voyage, however, it had been realized that the North-west Passage did not have the same economic advantages as the Northern Sea Route. The only large northern rivers in North America comparable to the Ob, Yenisei, or Lena are the Yukon and Mackenzie, and no strong economic motive exists for linking their deltas nor, in view of currently adequate overland transportation routes, does it require a North-west Passage to do so.

Most of the voyages mentioned above were carried out in the tradi-tional manner of sailing ships. The introduction of auxiliary power increased greatly the effectiveness of expeditions such as Amundsen's, yet vessels still could not fight the ice but rather had to pick their way through it with great care.

Ice-Breakers

The advent of ice-breakers materially extended the field of ship opera-tions. Ice-breakers vary considerably in construction from the type that wedges ice apart to the type that rides up over the ice and breaks it by the weight of the prow. True ice-breakers are all-steel ships, the largest ones having a gross tonnage of 10,000 tons or more. The Soviet Union, Canada, and recently the United States have been the principal countries interested in the development of these vessels for Arctic work; although Scandinavian countries have long used specially reinforced wooden ships for sealing in northern waters, and locally employed ice-breaking ships to lengthen the navigation season in harbours.

The fact that the commercial feasibility of the Northern Sea Route depends to a large extent on ice-breakers gave a particularly powerful impetus to their development in the Soviet Union, which probably has at its disposal some eight to ten large ice-breakers of about 10,000 tons and five to seven smaller ones of 5,000–7,000 tons. Since the North-west Passage is less fortunately endowed with commercial possibilities, there has been less incentive for the construction of ice-breakers in North America. In 1948 the *N. B. McLean* of the Canadian Department of Transport and the ice-breaking car ferry, *Abegweit*, designed for the Prince Edward Island service, were the largest ice-breakers in Canada; although two other large ice-breakers are planned by the Canadian Government, one of which is already under construction. Canada has also several smaller ice-breaking ships, including the *Sorel* and *Ernest Lapointe*, operating on the St. Lawrence River. The United States had no real ice-breakers before the last war, but during the war patrol work in Greenland waters and lend-lease aid to the Soviet Union led to the construction of the *Wind* ships, three of which were loaned to the Soviet Union. The United States has now four modern effective ice-breakers of the *Wind* class (two belonging to the Navy and two to the Coast Guard), and also the *Mackinaw* on the Great Lakes and the ice-breaker-buoy tender *Storis*, in Alaska. The *Wind* class ice-breakers can reportedly make their way through pack ice four to twelve feet thick depending upon conditions.

Although the advent and development of ice-breakers greatly extended the capabilities of exploration by ship in the Arctic, these vessels are so expensive that only governments can avail themselves of them. To date in North America their greatest contribution to scientific work has been to facilitate the establishment of Arctic weather stations such as the one at Cornwallis Island in the Canadian Arctic Archipelago. They constitute, however, a valuable technique of polar exploration that is being constantly improved and which should bring many worthwhile results. When ice-breakers are used in conjunction with aircraft that can spot leads and land exploratory parties ashore the capabilities of this technique are of course tremendously increased.

Another technique of Arctic exploration and research that would certainly yield most worthwhile results is the development of research ships—not necessarily ice-breakers but strongly built vessels especially fitted for the various types of research that should be carried out in the North. Generally scientists accompanying polar ships have had inadequate working quarters and equipment, and with rare exceptions like the *Fram* in the Arctic or *Discovery II* in the Antarctic, few polar ships have had scientific research as their sole objective. Another exception is the *Calanus*, built by the Canadian Government in 1948 for fisheries research in the Eastern Arctic.

Arctic exploration by submarine appeared to be a fantastic technique when first experimented with by Wilkins in the *Nautilus* in 1932, and the initial results were not encouraging, perhaps largely because of unsatisfactory equipment. However, modern improvements in submarine construction and further experimentation may prove Wilkins's idea completely practical. Certainly navigation beneath the ice of the Arctic Sea would eliminate many problems encountered by surface navigation.

Small boats and canoes have, of course, played a very significant role in exploration by boat. Much of the Arctic coast of the Canadian mainland was first delineated by the small boats of Franklin's expeditions of 1819–22 and 1825–7, and of Dease and Simpson's journeys of 1837–9. On the other hand in the interior of the North American Continent, the many rivers and lakes made canoe travel the most important method of exploration until the advent of aircraft, and it still retains many advantages for detailed local work.

Exploration by Sledge and Oversnow Vehicles

Arctic exploration by sledge is almost as old as exploration by boat and generally has gone hand in hand with it whenever a ship has wintered in the North. Much of the geographic knowledge resulting from the Franklin search expeditions of the 1850's was gained as a result of sledge travel covering many thousands of miles in the aggregate. M'Clintock and Mecham, especially, stand out for their excellent work during these sledging operations, all of which were dependent on man-hauling rather than dogs.

Peary during the twenty-three years that he devoted almost exclusively to Arctic exploration and the attainment of the North Pole between 1886 and 1909 developed sledging with dogs to a fine art. Stefansson carried out a series of remarkable sledge journeys during the Canadian Arctic Expedition of 1913–18, and Rasmussen also relied on sledging with dogs during the Fifth Thule Expedition of 1921–4, to cite just a few of the many names prominently associated with Arctic sledging history. The fact is that there is hardly an Arctic traveller who has not travelled by dog team at one time or another. The Eskimos are of course past masters of the art. Recent experiments by a Canadian National Research Council Committee have shown that Eskimo sledges are so perfectly designed that there is little room for improvement.

Man-hauling and dogs are slow cumbersome methods of sledge travel. Both require minimum loads and leave little opportunity, time, or even inclination for painstaking scientific work. Man-hauling has been almost entirely abandoned, and dogs will probably become less and less employed as mechanical means of oversnow transportation are improved. Early steps in this direction were tractor operations in both the Eastern and Western Canadian Arctic by the Hudson's Bay Company in the 1920's and propeller-driven sledges on the Greenland Ice Sheet by the Wegener Expedition of 1930–1.

None of the early experiments in mechanical oversnow transportation were particularly successful; technical problems were, and still are, legion. But the recent war saw many improvements ranging from motorcycle-like sledges to the American amphibious 'Weasel' and the Canadian armoured snowmobile. The last two are tracked vehicles which appear to have great potentialities. The Canadian vehicle, which is the heavier of the two, proved its capabilities during the Canadian military 'Exercise Musk-Ox' in 1946; when a party equipped with these vehicles, led by P. D. Baird, started in the middle of winter and went from Churchill on Hudson Bay to Victoria Island north of the mainland coast and then south to Grande Prairie, Alberta, a trek of 3,000 miles. This feat would have been impossible, however, without the aid of aircraft to supply fuel, food, and other equipment. The development of a reliable oversnow vehicle that could carry an adequate load and, if possible, also operate over tundra in the summer would introduce a most valuable new technique in Arctic exploration.

Exploration by Aircraft

The advent of flying and construction of reliable aircraft gave rise to by far the greatest advance in exploration techniques since the days of the Vikings. Byrd's flights in northern Greenland in 1925 and his flight to the North Pole in 1926, Amundsen's and Ellsworth's dirigible flight from Spitsbergen to Alaska in the same year, and Wilkins's and Eielson's flight from Point Barrow, Alaska, to Spitsbergen in 1928 started a trend whose culmination is not yet in sight. Although Arctic flying was considered a hazardous business for many years after these and other historic polar flights, it has developed to the point where it has now become the preferred means of transportation in the North.

Alaskan and Canadian bush-pilots deserve the greatest of credit for the development of safe northern flying. The fact that Berry, Crosson, May, Wien, and many other pioneer bush-pilots whose names have become almost legendary are still living proves the soundness of their flying technique. For the most part they operated on floats and skis with the result that emergency landings could be made in numerous places in comparative safety; the plane might crack up but the pilot and passengers could generally walk away. Thousands of passengers and millions of pounds of mining machinery and other freight led to the rapid expansion of bush-flying, most of it carried out with single-engine aircraft.

Today the trend in northern flying is towards multi-engine, wheeled aircraft and the construction of airfields, so that aircraft can operate the year around without the interruption caused by freeze-up and break-up. The North's peculiar environmental problems are gradually being solved and northern flying is becoming the same routine operation that it is farther south. Airfields have been constructed at a number of places in both the North American and Soviet Arctic, and commercial air lines operate regular schedules to many northern points. In North America, for instance, the Arctic coast settlements of Point Barrow, Aklavik, and Coppermine are all served by scheduled flights (Fig. 11).

Long-range flying has come into its own. In 1937 the Soviets landed four four-engine aircraft on skis within a few miles of the North Pole and since then the American B-29 has made Arctic history. United States Air Force aircraft are now making routine weather observation flights to the Pole, and Arctic flights of three to four thousand miles have become commonplace—a far cry from Wilkins's spectacular flight of twenty years ago. Such long-range flying has two particularly important effects: it gives a practical means of utilizing trans-Arctic air routes and it provides a way of investigating these routes geographically.

The peculiar problems of navigation in the polar regions have always been a handicap to Arctic flying; but improvements in navigation methods, including Radar and Loran, are gradually eliminating many of the problems. The Loran stations that have been established in northern Alaska and northern Canada should prove most useful in this respect.

The new techniques of Arctic exploration and research that have been opened up by flying are evidently manifold. The long-range weather flights mentioned above are one illustration; aerial mapping of the North

19

is another. Thousands of square miles can now be photographed in a single day and detailed maps constructed in a comfortable laboratory. The aerial supply of ground parties and even the setting up of complete ground stations are further illustrations. As already noted 'Exercise Musk-Ox' depended entirely on aerial supply for fuel, food, and other equipment, much of which was delivered by parachute without the aircraft having to land. The Soviet North Pole flight in 1937 left a completely equipped scientific party on the drifting sea ice. This party under the leadership of Papanin was thus able to carry out detailed observations for a number of months before being picked up off the coast of East Greenland by an ice-breaker. The weather station that was set up at Eureka Sound on Ellesmere Island in the Canadian Arctic in the spring of 1947 was also an air-lift operation. Dirigibles have never been extensively used in the Arctic but have advocates who point to their manœuvrability for observation purposes. Helicopters on the other hand are developing rapidly, and promise to be very useful for scouting ice conditions from a vessel and for ship-to-shore operations. By setting out and servicing field parties from a research ship they can save months of back-packing and supply operations. Present plans call for carrying a helicopter on the new Canadian Government ice-breaker now under construction.

From many points of view, therefore, not the least of which is rapid transportation from urban areas to the field, the advent of the aircraft has been a great boon to northern exploration, and the future promises many further innovations of technique as a result of it.

Research Stations

From the point of view of the detailed investigation of the North, by far the greatest promise of results is offered by a series of well-equipped research stations. According to Soviet figures there were 86 polar stations in the Soviet Arctic in 1946.[1] Most of them are essentially weather stations, but some are also general scientific laboratories where a variety of research is carried out in biological and physical sciences. Five stations, Bukta Tikhaya on Zemlya Frantsa-Iosifa, Matochkin Shar on Novaya Zemlya, Ostrov Dikson, Mys Chelyuskin, and Uellen—carry out geomagnetic, ionospheric, actinometric, and full aerological observations.[2] In addition Novaya Zemlya, Ostrov Dikson, Mys Chelyuskin, and Ostrov Vrangelya are reported to be radar stations operated in connexion

[1] Perevalov, V. A. (1946), *Sovetskaya Arktika posle voini*, U.S.S.R. Academy of Sciences, Priroda, No. 5, pp. 3–6.
[2] Shimkin, Demitri (1948), Personal communication.

with the Northern Sea Route.[1] There are a number of universities and other research installations in Subarctic Europe and Asia (Fig. 11). In Greenland the Danish Government has operated a magnetic observatory at Godhavn on Disko Island since 1926, and the former Director, Dr. Morton Porsild, also carried out detailed botanical studies.

Fixed research stations have many of the advantages of the specially equipped research vessel, such as adequate scientific equipment, a good library, and comfortable working quarters. To an even greater degree, however, all the comforts of home can be provided including accommodations for married couples. Such research stations have the great asset of permitting long-term observations with exact controls. When combined with an airfield as many of them are in the Soviet Arctic, the opportunity is offered for frequent exchange of scientific personnel as well as for the use of aircraft in aiding the scientific programme.

In contrast to the number of general research stations in the Soviet Arctic, only two were operating in Arctic North America in 1948. One, sponsored by the United States Office of Naval Research, is located at Point Barrow, Alaska;[2] the other, suggested by the Arctic Institute of North America and sponsored by the Canadian Department of Mines and Resources, is located at Baker Lake west of Hudson Bay. The adaptation of the various Arctic weather stations in North America to include facilities for other types of research, and the staffing of such stations with competent biologists, geophysicists, and other scientists as well as meteorologists, would contribute very materially to the solution of the many unsolved problems of the Arctic. In the Subarctic the United States has appropriated funds for a geophysical laboratory at Fairbanks, Alaska, to be operated in conjunction with the University there, and Canada has several agricultural stations, including Fort Simpson in the Mackenzie Valley and Bear Creek near Whitehorse in the Yukon. The Armed Forces' research facilities at Fort Churchill on Hudson Bay represent a joint Canadian-United States project (Fig. 11).

The Little-known North

The North is still one of the great unknowns geographically. It is amazing how little is really known about it. There are areas larger than whole States or Provinces which have never been traversed on the ground.

[1] *The Montreal Daily Star*, 9 June 1948.
[2] Shelesnyak, M. C. (1948), 'Arctic research laboratory, Office of Naval Research, Point Barrow, Alaska', *Science*, Vol. 107, p. 283. Irving, Laurence (1948), 'Arctic research at Point Barrow, Alaska', *Science*, Vol. 107, pp. 284-6.

The interiors of many of the Canadian Arctic islands are almost completely uninvestigated. It is true that the coasts of most of the islands have been travelled but there are significant gaps. On Victoria Island, for instance, which is one of the most southerly of the Archipelago and one of the best known, there is still a hundred-mile stretch along the northeast coast that has never been traversed on foot, except possibly by Eskimos. In the case of Bathurst Island it was only in 1947 that aerial observation disclosed that it actually comprises five islands rather than the single island shown on most maps. Lack of geographic and other scientific information is also one of the outstanding characteristics of large parts of the continental interior—for instance the Brooks Range of Alaska and the barren grounds of northern Canada east of the Coppermine River.

Even the areas in Arctic North America that have been seen or partially studied are not well known. With hardly an exception all the scientific work in the Canadian Arctic has been of a reconnaissance character. The number of expeditions that have carried qualified scientists, aside from medical men, is very few. The Second Norwegian Arctic Expedition of 1898–1902 under Sverdrup, Amundsen's expedition of 1903–6 in the *Gjoa*, the Canadian Arctic Expedition of 1913–18 under Stefansson and Anderson, and some of the official Canadian Government expeditions are among the few that have carried trained scientists into the Canadian Arctic.

The exploration of Greenland and the Soviet Arctic is probably far more advanced than that of northern North America. Yet in these places, too, large gaps in knowledge remain to be filled in. Many factors help to explain this general lack of knowledge concerning the North—all stemming from its remoteness and environmental characteristics. The factors include transportation problems and therefore difficulty of access, difficult shelter and working conditions and, especially in North America, necessity of economic justification for the large expenditures necessary to carry out large-scale research. Once a permanent white population is established in a region these conditions become ameliorated and detailed scientific work can be more easily pursued. The dilemma is that considerable research is often necessary before a region and its resources become well enough known to attract and justify a permanent population.

Gaps in Knowledge

Accurate geographic information is, of course, essential to planning the development of any area, for it is vital in locating flying routes, airfields, roads, railroads, harbours, water-power sites, and the many other important features that go hand in hand with economic development. Good maps are not only a vital element of accurate geographic information but are also a prerequisite for nearly all types of detailed scientific research. Yet in 1946 less than one per cent of Alaska was topographically mapped on a scale of one mile to one inch, although a large part of it is now covered by aerial photography. With a few exceptions such as parts of Baffin Island and Ellesmere Island, the interiors of Canada's Arctic islands are nearly complete blanks; and there are many places, both on the islands and mainland, which have never been seen much less mapped. Fortunately a large-scale government mapping programme is rapidly closing this gap in knowledge.

Meteorology is another vital subject. Standard meteorological expressions like 'Polar Pacific Air', 'Polar Continental Air', and 'Polar Atlantic Air' emphasize the fact that much of the weather of the Northern Hemisphere originates in the North. But there have been too few weather stations in North America for adequate reporting (Fig. 11). Stations extending across the extreme northern fringe of land, similar to stations that have been established in the Soviet Arctic, would give much worth-while information for long-range forecasting—information that would be of great benefit to areas much farther south. Agriculture, flying, and shipping are only a few of the important activities that would be benefited. Canada, with the support of the United States, took significant steps in this direction in 1947 when it established weather stations at Eureka Sound on Ellesmere Island and at Resolute Bay on Cornwallis Island, and in 1948 when it put additional weather stations at Mould Bay, Prince Patrick Island and at Deer Bay, Isachson Land (Ellef Ringnes Island).

Oceanographic studies have many practical applications. A detailed study of northern currents, for instance, might yield fundamental information related to climatic changes and to changes in marine faunas. A slight shift in the influence of the Gulf Stream is known to have introduced vast quantities of Atlantic cod into West Greenland waters with the result that commercial cod fishing has been possible there since 1917. It is evidently highly desirable to know if other changes of this nature are taking place in northern waters. The effects of tides, currents, and ice conditions on navigation constitute another oceanographic problem. The existence of a North-west Passage through Canada's Arctic islands has been amply demonstrated, but we still do not know if it is feasible every year or for large ships. Detailed oceanographic studies will help to solve the question. Strategic considerations make the matter an important one, and rich mineral deposits may some day be found in the North that would make the North-west Passage economically worth while.

Only detailed geologic work can definitely establish or disprove the existence of rich mineral deposits in the Arctic. Both in Alaska and in Canada profitable mines have been discovered in areas that were blank on geologic maps a few years ago. Many more blank areas remain to be investigated that are believed to contain promising types of rock similar to rocks which have been the source of rich mineral deposits farther south. Oil and coal occur in Arctic Alaska and in the Mackenzie Basin of northern Canada. Coal is also found on several of the Arctic islands and some of these islands may be favourable places for oil, too. In addition to the problem of finding such new fuel deposits, there is of course the problem of developing the ones that have already been found in the North but which are still inadequately explored. Permafrost or permanently frozen ground is likewise a northern geologic problem about which very little is known. Its practical importance lies in its influence on construction practices. Construction on permafrost may lead to thawing of the ground beneath, which then becomes the poorest kind of foundation and may collapse beneath the load it was able to carry when frozen. Not infrequently this subsidence has caused the sinking or collapse of structures such as buildings, dams, and mining shafts and has led to the loss of thousands of dollars. There is much further information needed about the distribution of permafrost and about its behaviour and control before the problem is solved.

There is still a great deal to be learned about the earth's magnetism and the North Magnetic Pole. Even the exact location of the Magnetic Pole is open to question. It was originally discovered on Boothia Peninsula by James Clark Ross in 1831 and more precisely located there by Amundsen on his expedition of 1903–6; the British *Aries* flight of 1945 questioned this location and suggested the Pole lay several hundred miles farther north. The United States Air Force in 1947 indicated the possibility of three poles on the basis of magnetic observations during B-29 flights,[1] but recent Canadian conclusions are more conservative.[2] It seems to be situated in the west of Prince of Wales Island, about 200 miles from the old site in Boothia Peninsula (Fig. 11). There are many other geophysical problems demanding careful study, such as ionospheric and cosmic ray research. Ionospheric phenomena are related to magnetic phenomena and to auroral activity, although the exact effect of one on the other is not well known. A wide practical interest in ionospheric research lies in its importance to radio communication, and continuous observations are

[1] *New York Times*, 20 Oct. 1947.

[2] Madill, G. R. (1948), 'The Search for the North Magnetic Pole', Arctic Institute of North America, *Arctic*, Vol. 1, pp. 8–18.

particularly important in the Arctic because there the ionosphere is at its lowest altitude. Cosmic rays are sources of energy that should be measured at all levels, and observations in the North are essential to confirm conclusions as to their nature and properties in relation to the earth's magnetic field.

There are many important biological problems in the North. Climate is naturally a major control in limiting the distribution of many species of animals and plants. Yearly variations in temperature tend to be greater in the North than in temperate regions, and their effect on biological phenomena is particularly important where a species is near the northern limit of its range. Detailed environmental studies are needed to give exact data on such questions.

Fur cycles constitute an interesting zoological problem, which is of considerable practical importance to fur-trading companies and trappers. For instance, Arctic fur-trading posts are largely dependent on white foxes, which are abundant in some years and scarce in others as the result of a cyclical influence that is still largely unexplained. Economic gain may also be derived from detailed studies of possible fishing grounds. Commercial fisheries already constitute a major activity in the waters of southeastern Alaska and western Greenland, and there may be still other fishing areas to be developed in northern North America.

Caribou and seals are the principal sources of food and clothing for Eskimos and are therefore essential to their well-being. However, a better knowledge of distributional factors than is now available is needed to safeguard an abundant supply of these mammals. In fact the whole question of original faunas and their conservation is a very important matter. In the Arctic, especially, original faunas are so delicately adjusted to their environment that any kind of northern development is likely to have unfavourable consequences for wild-life. The planning of sound conservation measures demands detailed scientific data concerning the many environmental and faunal factors that are involved, and this information must be available before the need for conservation measures becomes acute.

Botanical studies have a very practical application in determining the best grazing grounds for reindeer. Such studies made possible the introduction of reindeer from Alaska to the Mackenzie Delta where the reindeer are now being herded for the benefit of natives. But more knowledge of potential grazing grounds is needed before this work can be extended farther east. Northern botanical studies are likewise essential to agriculture which has been widely developed in the northern parts of Scandinavia, Finland, and the Soviet Union where experimental stations are located in many places. Although a good deal of agricultural research has been carried out in Subarctic North America, too, much remains to be learned. The farms of the Peace River country of Canada demonstrate that crops such as wheat, oats, potatoes, alfalfa, and flax can grow in some parts of the North, and the many private vegetable gardens of Alaska and northern Canada prove that agriculture on a much more limited scale is possible considerably farther north than the Peace River country. Additional experimental farms, such as the one at Fort Simpson on the Mackenzie River, maps of soil types, and more studies of organisms inhabiting permanently frozen soils are all needed for the further extension of northern agriculture.

The influence of the Arctic environment on the physiological processes of man is almost an untouched field of investigation. Yet this kind of research is essential to a proper understanding of the factors controlling man's adaptation to northern living.[1] Much could probably be learned from detailed physiological studies of native peoples. Natives are actually an important potential asset to a country. For instance, some ethnologists and others who have come into direct contact with natives claim that Eskimos, if given adequate training, are capable of becoming excellent weather observers and radio operators for Arctic weather stations.

All the problems mentioned above have a clearly defined practical value. In addition there are, of course, countless other problems in fields that may be regarded as pure science today but which may have most practical applications tomorrow. Most of the problems discussed have dealt with northern North America.[2] There are probably equally many problems in the Soviet Arctic and other northern lands, but the gaps in our knowledge of Arctic and Subarctic North America are perhaps the more glaring.

Summary—Co-ordinated Programme of Northern Research

From whichever way one looks at the North—whether from the point of view of economics, politics, strategy, or science—the North is growing in importance. New techniques of exploration are at hand, especially in the field of transportation, by which urgently needed knowledge can be much more easily obtained than formerly. Governments and private institutions are turning their eyes northward and devoting

[1] Shelesnyak, M. C. (1947), 'Some problems of human ecology in polar regions', *Science*, Vol. 106, pp. 405–9.

[2] The Arctic Institute of North America (1946), 'A program of desirable scientific investigation in Arctic North America', *Bulletin 1*, 65 pages.

considerable effort and money to research. Under these circumstances a co-operative attack on northern problems by specialists in the different scientific fields would be more productive now than ever before.

GENERAL REFERENCES

Arctic Institute of North America (1946), 'A program of desirable scientific investigations in Arctic North America', *Bulletin 1*, 65 pages.

Breitfuss, Leonid (1943), *Das Nordpolargebiet*, Springer-Verlag, Berlin, 180 pages.

Brown, Rudmose (1927), *The polar regions. A physical and economic geography of the Arctic and Antarctic*, Methuen & Co. Ltd., London, 245 pages.

Dawson, C. A. (Editor) (1947), *The New North-West*, University of Toronto Press, Toronto, 341 pages.

Greely, A. W. (1928), *The polar regions in the twentieth century*, Little, Brown & Co., Boston, 270 pages.

Joerg, W. L. G. (Editor) (1928), *Problems of polar research*, Amer. Geog. Soc. Spec. Pub. 7, New York, 479 pages.

Mirsky, Jeannette (1948), *To the Arctic! The story of northern exploration from earliest times to the present*, Alfred A. Knopf, New York, 334 pages.

Nordenskjöld, Otto, and Mecking, Ludwig (1928), *The geography of the polar regions*, Amer. Geog. Soc. Spec. Pub. 8, New York, 359 pages.

Stefansson, Vilhjalmur (1922), *The northward course of empire*, Harcourt Brace & Co., New York, 274 pages.

    (1944) *Arctic manual*, Macmillan Co., New York, 556 pages.

Taracouzio, T. A. (1938), *Soviets in the Arctic*, Macmillan Co., New York, 563 pages.

CHAPTER XIII

EXPLORATION OF ANTARCTICA

GRIFFITH TAYLOR

THE nineteenth century saw the exploration of the coasts of the *Arctic* regions almost completed. Only a few islands on the north-west edge of the Canadian Archipelago remained to be mapped by Sverdrup and Stefansson, and Peary reached the North Pole in April 1909 (see Chapter XII). Far different was the state of our geographical knowledge of *Antarctic* lands and seas at the close of the nineteenth century, so that this chapter describes the last years of world exploration. It was not till February 1899, that Borchgrevinck landed at Cape Adare, made his headquarters here for the following winter, and sledged inland a very short distance from this cape at the north-west corner of the Ross Sea.

The coasts had been sighted long before this time of course, and it will be worth while to traverse the aims and accomplishments of the earlier explorers very briefly. Captain Cook was the first navigator to cross the Antarctic Circle in January 1773. This was south of the Indian Ocean (Fig. 12) in the region where later Biscoe named Enderby Land (1831). Cook was primarily interested in geographical exploration, and it was his great achievement to wipe out most of the hypothetical continent which had cumbered the maps of the world (from the time of Ptolemy) in these far southern latitudes. But Cook discovered no part of the continent, though he placed South Georgia on the map on his last southern cruise in January 1775. His reports of the seals and other mammals near these islands did much to promote the whaling industry of the next century.

It is a controversial point as to who actually discovered the Antarctic continent. This occurred in 1820 somewhere on the long 'stalk' of Antarctica (Fig. 13) which extends from its pear-shaped outline to tie it to the similar 'stalk' of South America. Numerous whaling vessels were engaged in hunting the slow whales, who had all been killed off in *northern* waters by this time. In December 1819 Bransfield and a small naval staff were sent south in the brig *Williams* to survey the islands recently discovered by British whalers south of South America. On 30 January 1820, Bransfield discovered the mainland in 64° south latitude (longitude 60° W.) and he named it Trinity Land (*vide* A. R. Hinks, *Geog. Journ.*, p. 309, Oct. 1939). He indicated a coast with high mountains

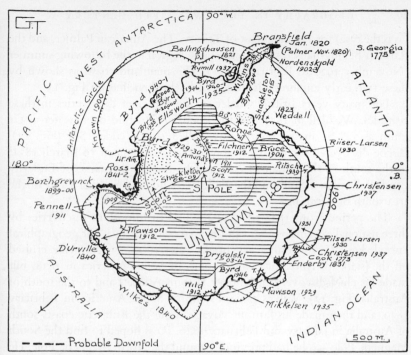

FIG. 12.—The progress of Antarctic Exploration from Cook (1773) to Ronne (1947)
Earliest coasts shown with heavy lines. Note the probable Downfold

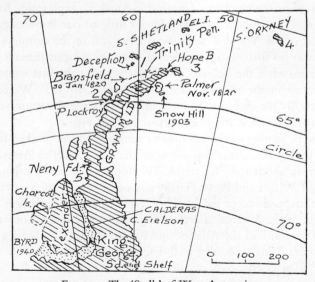

FIG. 13.—The 'Stalk' of West Antarctica

The coasts as charted by Bransfield and Palmer in 1820 are shown by broken lines, and
the five bases (1–5) of F.I.D.S., 1944–6. (From map in *Geog. Jour.*, p. 424, Dec. 1940)

(as is the case) for 100 miles east of Trinity. The American Palmer, and the Russian Bellingshausen were in the same region in the following summer (November 1920 to February 1921). The mainland coast, as shown by these two early explorers, is indicated by broken lines in Fig. 13.

For many years British whalers made the chief discoveries in these latitudes. Weddell in 1823 had the good luck to find open water as far south as 74° S., in the region now called the Weddell Sea (Fig. 12). Biscoe discovered the main portion of the continent on 16 March 1831, to the south of the Indian Ocean, and he gave it the name of Enderby Land. Balleny in 1839 found the Balleny Islands and Sabrina Land in the area south of Australia.

The period from 1838 to 1843 resulted in important discoveries by three national expeditions, sent out primarily to advance our geographical knowledge. We can only very briefly refer to these. D'Urville cruised off the 'stalk' of Antarctica to the south of South America in 1838, but made his chief discovery in January 1840 in Adelie Land to the south of Australia (Fig. 12). Wilkes cruised south of South America in February 1839, and then made his famous voyage along the Antarctic coasts south of Australia in January and February 1840. Ross hoped to find the South Magnetic Pole—as he had previously found the North Magnetic Pole. He discovered instead the open Ross Sea, Mount Erebus, and the front of the Ross Ice Shelf (Fig. 12).

A period marked by lack of interest in Antarctic exploration followed. Scottish and Norwegian whalers added a little to our knowledge of the west coast of the Weddell Sea towards the end of the century. Borchgrevinck on his first voyage landed on the continent in January 1895 at Cape Adare, while the Belgian, De Gerlache, spent the first winter in the south locked in the ice, and drifting from 80° to 102° W. off West Antarctica. By the end of the nineteenth century the Antarctic Seas were known as far south as the line marked 1900 in Fig. 12.

At the beginning of the twentieth century, a period marked for more detailed survey, the general position of the coast south of Australia was known from about 100° W. to 180° W. longitude, chiefly owing to the voyages of Wilkes and Ross. Hardly any other part of the vast continent had been mapped except the 'stalk' of West Antarctica, where it projects well north of the Antarctic Circle. Practically nothing was known of the coasts to the south of the Atlantic and Pacific Oceans, the latter quadrant of Antarctica being especially well-defended by dense and wide belts of pack ice, as is clearly indicated in Fig. 12.

Early Scientific Investigations

Early in the new century began a phase of exploration somewhat resembling that of 1838-43. Britain, Germany, and Sweden each sent down an expedition, and two of these were led by scientists. Drygalski was primarily interested in oceanography and meteorology, and his expedition was beset some distance from the coast near 90° E. longitude (Fig. 12). However, he made many valuable observations with regard to the circulation of Antarctic seas, finding three layers near Antarctica, of which the middle layer (below 400 metres) is much warmer than the northbound layers above and below it.

Nordenskjöld commanded the Swedish expedition in West Antarctica, and he had the good fortune to find many plant and animal fossils which showed great climatic changes in later geological eras. For instance at Hope Bay (Fig. 13) Jurassic fossils show that ferns lived there, of the same type as were found in Australia in those times. At Snow Hill his party obtained Cretaceous fossils showing relatively warm seas. In Tertiary times *Araucaria* and *Fagus* trees were common, where today not a single flowering plant can survive. In Miocene times or thereabouts, many different types of penguin lived in these regions. Near the close of the Tertiary, marine types now living in the seas near New Zealand were common off West Antarctica.

The first Scott expedition in 1902 added greatly to the knowledge of the geology and geography of the Antarctic. For the first time extensive journeys were made into the interior, notably one led by Royds which investigated the Ross Ice Shelf, while Scott himself made a long journey to the south. He skirted the base of the great Horst for 260 miles, reaching 82° 16′ S.; and prepared the way for Shackleton's journey a few years later. In the second summer Scott climbed the western glaciers, reaching the plateau by way of the upper Taylor Glacier (Fig. 15), and thus penetrated the great Antarctic Horst. He marched west over the high Ice Plateau for a distance of 150 miles. The geologist Ferrar made the first detailed geological map of this part of Antarctica, and gave the first descriptions of the 'ice slabs', which were later found to be cirque glaciers of a new type. Bernacchi made meteorological observations, which were of great value to later scientists in posing the problems peculiar to this region.

In 1903-4 Bruce commanded a small expedition which discovered 150 miles of the coast to the east of the Weddell Sea (Fig. 12). This was named Coats Land. They also carried out a geological survey of much of the South Orkney Islands, which lie in the ocean off West Antarctica, forming part of the immense submarine ridge called the Drake Loop. Charcot in 1908-9 continued his investigations to the west of Graham (or Palmer) Land and discovered Charcot Island, which lies to the north-west of the huge Alexander Island bounding King George Sound (Fig. 13). (This land had been discovered by Bellingshausen in 1820.)

The role of the great land expeditions so worthily started by Scott was carried on by his former sledge-mate Ernest Shackleton in 1907-9. Two famous geologists, Sir Edgeworth David and Sir Douglas Mawson,

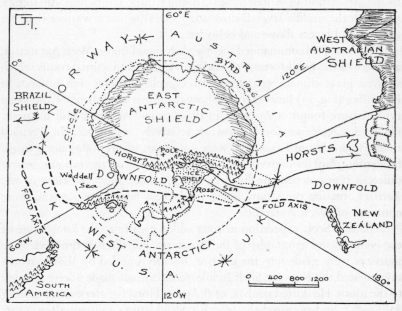

FIG. 14.—A simplified block diagram of Antarctica, showing the hypothetical 'Down-fold', and its relation to South America and Australia.

The extent of the survey in Byrd's 1946 expedition is shown by dotted outlines.

were members of his party, while Priestley and Wild were other notable members. Shackleton hoped to reach the South Pole, and was the first man to climb the giant Beardmore Glacier. He reached 88° 23′ S. on 6 January 1909, adding greatly to our knowledge of the Ice Plateau, which is here 11,000 feet above sea-level. Meanwhile David and Mawson made a long journey over the sea ice along the coast of the Ross Sea. They turned inland and reached the area of the Magnetic Pole (1909 on Fig. 12). David also led the first party to ascend Mount Erebus, the active volcano at whose foot many British expeditions have made their headquarters. It is not too much to say that the large memoir produced by David and

Priestley as a record of their scientific investigations, laid the basis for the glaciology, physiography, stratigraphy, and tectonic geology of East Antarctica.

David and Priestley demonstrated the structure of the great Antarctic Horst which extends along the west side of the Ross Sea and of the Ross Ice Shelf for a thousand miles (Fig. 14). David with his great experience and omnivorous interests linked meteorology and landscape in his studies of the *sastrugi* (snow ridges) of the Ice Shelf. He proposed the 'wicker-shield' theory as to the origin of the great Ross Ice Shelf, which still appeals to the writer as the most probable explanation. His knowledge of the smaller complex shelves and tongues along the west coasts of the Ross Sea led him to assume that the 'Shelves' were partly built of tongues of ice, and partly of drift snow. He discussed the various levels reached by the great Ice Cap at its 'flood periods', and showed that the ice is much less extensive now than formerly. The investigations of the small lakes and of wind erosion also marked important advances in the study of Antarctic environments.

The next large expedition to the Antarctic was that led by Scott during the years 1910–12, and it included more scientists than any earlier expedition. Simpson was the first senior meteorologist to join a British expedition; and the writer was lent by the Australian Weather Service, though his chief research was physiographic. Priestley and Debenham were other geologists, while Wright was interested primarily in Ice Physics, now studied in detail for the first time. Nelson and Atkinson studied invertebrate biology, while Wilson and Cherry-Garrard investigated the birds and mammals. Lillie remained with the ship and carried out research on the whales and sea mammals. Some of these investigations seem at first glance to have little relation to geography; but it is to be noted that the problems were largely concerned with migrations and distributions in biology; with structure and geomorphology in the geological field; with glaciology and meteorology in the physical field; and all these are in liaison with geography.

There were three main objectives in the 1910–13 Expedition. Captain Scott hoped to be the first to reach the South Pole, and he worked out an elaborate plan of transport and relays which was quite successful. He had no opinion of dogs as means of transport and preferred Siberian ponies, which had first been used by Shackleton in 1907. There is little doubt that this was a mistake, for a large part of the load dragged by the ponies consisted of their own fodder. The rival teams led by Amundsen used 52 dogs, and as these weakened they were used for food for the surviving dogs, thus materially reducing the original load. Scott however took down three motor sledges, almost the first 'caterpillar' motors used any-where. They had automobile engines, and one major fault was they moved so slowly (five miles an hour) that the motors overheated every few miles! Only one managed to travel some distance over the Ross Ice Shelf, but they paved the way for the much-used tractors of today.

On the journey to the Pole, the first relay party turned back at 81°. The second reached the foot of the Beardmore Glacier, where the ponies were shot, since they could not tackle the crevassed surface. The third party reached the top of the great glacier at 85°, while Lieutenant Evans (now Baron Evans) left the final party of five when they were about 145 miles from the Pole. Scott found that Amundsen had reached this long-desired objective on 14 December, about a month before the British party. On the return they were delayed by injury to seaman Evans, who died at the foot of the Beardmore. This meant that they could not reach the depots as rapidly as was necessary; and this in turn found them on the Ross Ice Shelf much too late in the season. The sun was setting, and the blizzards and low temperatures of the latter part of March were too much for them. Oates weakened, and finally they all died of starvation.

The sketches and fossils collected by Wilson, and the complete meteorological log recorded by Bowers greatly added to our knowledge of the environment in the far south. Permian coal with ferns, and Cam-brian corals, were found in Beardmore cliffs. Another major result was the very detailed research carried out by Simpson on the meteorology and climate of the vicinity of headquarters. He discovered peculiar pressure-waves, which travel more or less radially outward from the centre of the continent. He believed that surface air is thus forced upwards, and its moisture condensed giving rise to the snow, which in turn 'feeds' the great ice cap. Simpson did not agree with Hobbs's concept of an 'anticyclonic broom', and laid much stress on the cyclonic circula-tion which must develop above the Polar Anticyclone. Meinardus had developed a somewhat similar theory as the result of the weather data collected by Drygalski in 1901-2.

A considerable amount of research on the physiography of the Ant-arctic was carried on by the scientists in the smaller sledging parties. Priestley examined the glaciers and formations near Cape Adare, and later farther south, near the Drygalski Tongue, where he found interesting fossil tree-stems of Triassic age. Taylor, Wright, and Debenham studied the coastal regions between Mount Discovery and Granite Harbour, i.e. the coasts in the south-west of the Ross Sea. Here they found lakes and subglacial rivers, and cirques in all stages of development, some being drowned by the sea. Debenham discovered Devonian fish at Granite

Harbour; and many varieties of debris cones, lateral moats, ice divides, hanging glaciers, &c. were investigated and described. Perhaps the chief feature was the large 'Dry Valley' below the Taylor Glacier, and this is some 18 miles long and several miles wide (Fig. 15). This gives a perfect picture of a great glacial trough-valley immediately after the ice had left it, and before rain and vegetation have complicated the topography. The detailed plane-table surveys made by Debenham all round the Macmurdo Sound give us an unrivalled knowledge of the topography.

After the writer's return from the Antarctic he discussed fairly fully the major problem of continental structure in the *Geographical Journal*

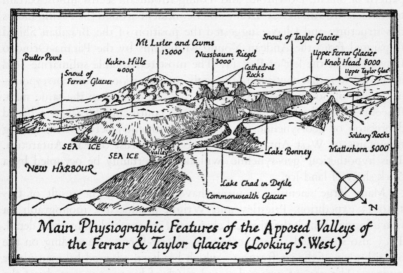

Main Physiographic Features of the Apposed Valleys of the Ferrar & Taylor Glaciers (Looking S. West)

FIG. 15.—Block diagram showing the ice-free Taylor Valley 18 miles long, and the Ice Divide between the Taylor and Ferrar glaciers. (*By permission of John Murray*)

(October 1914, p. 366). The map given in that paper still seems to illustrate quite clearly the most probable units of Antarctic structure. I have copied the main features of my 1914 map in Fig. 14. It will be seen that I postulated a close similarity between the structure of Australasia and that which would be found to characterize Antarctica. In Australia we find four meridional structural divisions, dominated by the resistant West Australian Shield in the west. Next comes a belt of Horsts shown most clearly in Victoria and the region near Kosciusko. Deep folds in the crust separate Australia from the high 'Young Mountains' of New Zealand.

It was the writer's belief—and he still holds it thirty-five years later

—that we shall find much the same arrangement in the Antarctic. The great Horst of Victoria Land was indicated by the explorations of Scott's and Shackleton's geologists—especially by David and Mawson. But in the following years more and more data have accumulated which support the thesis. The Filchner Ice Shelf, the relatively low icy plains which seem to link the Weddell and Ross Seas, and above all the numerous peaks seen by Ellesworth on his flight in November 1935 seem to be in harmony with this theory.

It is however when we look still farther afield—as in the map given in the writer's book *Environment, Race and Migration* (Fig. 3) that the pattern of Shield, Downfold, and Young Mountain seems almost certain to characterize Antarctica. Every other continent around the Pacific shows this structure; and I have suggested the position of the Brazilian Shield (separated from the Andean Young Mountains by the Parana-Orinoco Downfold) at the left of Fig. 14. The most remarkable submarine fold in the world is that connecting the 'stalk' of Antarctica to the corresponding 'stalk' of South America and this is also indicated in the same map. It seems likely that complete maps of the continent will show a broad depression or geo-syncline (as in other continents) between the young mountains of West Antarctica and the stable crust of East Antarctica. This hypothetical 'geo-syncline' will almost certainly be occupied by a thick sheet of land-ice.

Many large scientific memoirs have appeared as the result of this 1910–13 expedition. Priestley and Wright produced a monograph on Glaciology in which the physical changes of ice are studied in great detail. They also suggested a classification of glacier-forms—depending on the nourishment of the ice features—which has been adopted by many later students. The present writer devoted much of his time to a study of the evolution of cirques. It is clear that the cirques on Mount Lister some 10,000 feet above sea-level could not be produced under present climates; since the climate there is too cold for any nivation (freeze and thaw) erosion. They probably date back to a warmer Pliocene period. The Palimpsest Theory was propounded to account for the remarkable rock steps and rock bars—which are so striking a feature in the valley below the Taylor Glacier. This suggests that the topography of the trough valleys is in part inherited from an earlier phase of cirque erosion. At the 'flood stage' in the Ice Age the plateau ice overwhelmed the earlier topography, as sketched in the diagrams in Fig. 16.

The expedition led by Amundsen has already been referred to. His base was at Framheim at the north-east corner of the Ross Ice Shelf—within a few miles of what was later known as Little America (Fig. 12).

Amundsen made his way to the Pole by a route far to the south of the Beardmore Glacier, and added a good deal to our knowledge of the Antarctic Horst in that area. He made no collections, nor does science seem to have bulked much in the plans of his expedition. He had returned to his headquarters by the 25th of January 1912, and so met with none of the climatic difficulties or heart-breaking toil of the ill-starred British on their return from the Pole.

In 1911 twenty-six men, mostly young graduates from Australian Universities, under the leadership of Douglas Mawson left Hobart to

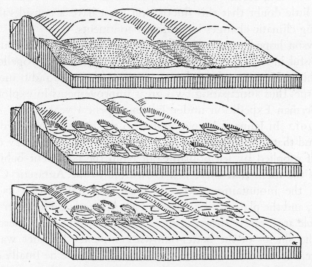

FIG. 16.—Block diagrams illustrating the 'Palimpsest Theory' of Glacier Erosion applied to the Royal Society range

In the upper figure the pre-glacial topography is suggested; in the central figure the advancing hemicycle with much cirque erosion by headward recession; in the lower figure the period of ice-flood when the outlet glaciers were at their maximum. (K.F.T. indicate Koettlitz, Ferrar and Taylor glaciers.) Each block is 180 miles wide.

explore the coasts immediately to the south of Australia. They made their headquarters at Adelie Land (Fig. 12), where D'Urville had found a coast free from ice. Captain Davis then took another party under Wild far to the west, and landed them in longitude 90° E. not far from the region seen by Drygalski. The outstanding feature of this region is the strength of the wind, for the average for the year was fifty miles an hour. During one period of eight hours the velocity was 107 miles an hour, and such figures have not been approached elsewhere. One party under Bage reached the area of the Magnetic Pole. Another made a hazardous journey along the coast, and found a suite of rocks very like those to the north in Australia. The two great glacier tongues were named after Ninnis and Mertz, who died on this expedition.

Davis noted that there is a strong tendency for the winds to blow to the west in accord with the general anticyclonic circulation. As a result he correctly deduced that there would be an open sea to the west of the great ice barrier named Termination Land by Wilkes. The western party found relics of the German Expedition near Mt. Gauss, and mapped many large glacier tongues. The pack ice was found to vary very greatly in width from year to year, along the coast of Antarctica; and there is little doubt that this fluctuation must have a considerable effect in causing climatic changes in southern continents.

Mawson hoped to use an aeroplane on this expedition, but he was unsuccessful in flying, though he used the engine on a propeller-driven land vehicle. However, he did manage to send simple radio messages to Melbourne, thus anticipating two great improvements in exploration.

A German Expedition under Filchner spent a year in the Antarctic during 1912. In January he penetrated to the head of the Weddell Sea, and found that it was blocked—as is the Ross Sea—by a very extensive Ice Shelf supplied by ice pouring out from the continent behind. This supports the thesis that there is a Downfold in the Antarctic Continent between the mountainous area of West Antarctica with its Andean affinities, and the plateau-like mass of East Antarctica. The latter seems to be a stable area, rarely showing signs of great folding, and therefore not unlike the Shields of the better known continents. Filchner was caught in the ice, and drifted far to the east and north before he finally emerged in the South Atlantic Ocean.

Shackleton's second Expedition hoped to land a party on the Filchner Ice Shelf, and march overland to meet another party on the Ross Ice Shelf. This plan, if carried out, would have solved the problem mentioned in the previous paragraph. Unfortunately Shackleton's ship was caught in the ice in January 1915, and drifted across the Weddell Sea somewhat to the east of Filchner's drift (Fig. 12). After losing the ship, and floating for weeks on pack ice the expedition reached Elephant Island (Fig. 13), and were rescued ultimately by the *Yelcho* in August 1916. In 1921 Shackleton made his last voyage in the *Quest*, but he died suddenly as they reached South Georgia, and he was buried on that sub-Antarctic Island. The expedition was unable to add much to our geographical knowledge in their attempt to explore the coasts east of Coats Land.

The Era of Flying begins with Wilkins

The new technique of Antarctic exploration, which was to complete the survey of the coasts within twenty years, began with the exploit of Sir Hubert Wilkins in December 1928. Wilkins had already been a member of two Antarctic expeditions, and he now chartered two mono-planes, which were carried to Deception Island (off West Antarctica, Fig. 13) where a runway was cleared on the rough lava fields. At 8.20 a.m. on 20 December they headed south and flew towards the South Pole for a distance of 600 miles. A survey was made of the whole east coast of the great Antarctic Peninsula. It was found to be narrow and plateau-like with many cross valleys. Wilkins thought that some of these depressions were at sea-level, and he named several straits right across the peninsula; thus converting West Antarctica into an archipelago. (Rymill and others later showed that there were no straits here.) In ten hours he was back again at his starting place, and had conclusively proved the value of the aeroplane for geographical survey in the south.

Whaling and Modern Antarctic Exploration

We first hear of whaling on a fairly large scale in the bay of Biscay in the tenth century, when the Basques became proficient in the industry. They hunted the slower whales throughout the North Atlantic, and soon were busy in the seas near Spitsbergen and Greenland. This phase lasted until the close of the eighteenth century, when the sperm whale was followed extensively into temperate and even tropical waters. In 1840 there were some eight hundred vessels so engaged, mostly from New England ports. All these whales were slow swimmers, and were harpooned from boats.

Before the end of the eighteenth century there were whalers near the Falkland Islands, and we have seen that Smith and Palmer and their fellows greatly extended our knowledge of the Antarctic Islands south of South America. They chiefly hunted the Right Whale (*Balena Australis*). Between 1804 and 1817 American ships harpooned 193 thousand Right Whales in southern waters. They also took sperm whales (*Physeter*) and humpbacks. This southern whaling lasted through most of the nineteenth century, the British firm of Enderby Brothers being one of the best known in the trade.

The northern swift whales were killed off after the invention of the grenade harpoon in 1886; and so the Norwegian and Scottish whalers voyaged to the Weddell and Ross Seas around 1893. In 1904 Captain

Larsen, who had seen many whales on the Nordenskjöld Expedition, founded a whaling company. In his first year he was very successful, and took full ships back to his headquarters near Oslo. The industry for a time was largely concentrated in the southern islands, such as South Georgia, South Orkneys, and South Shetlands. In 1923 Larsen extended his operations to the Ross Sea, and successful cargoes have been obtained off both West and East Antarctica.[1]

In recent years the industry centres about the large 'factory ship', each of which is accompanied by a fleet of small 'catchers'. Some of these factory ships are said to be over 20,000 tons register. With the rapid catcher-boats swift whales, like the rorqual and the finback, can be captured; and in 1925 it was alleged that there were not more than 12,000 whales surviving. In 1923 the famous ship *Discovery* was purchased by the British Government, and in 1925 began investigations in every phase of the whaling industry. Much oceanographic work was carried out by this ship, and also by her successor the *William Scoresby*. In 1929 a new steel ship was specially constructed for this southern research and was named *Discovery II*. From 1931 to 1935 the *Discovery II* circumnavigated the continent for the first time in the winter. On many occasions expeditions to the Antarctic were able to use these vessels to carry them to their chosen headquarters. At times the seas are remarkably free from ice, as was the case in February 1936. All the coast of MacRobertson Land was easily accessible, and the whaling ship was able to chart various bays and islands which had not been properly identified by land expeditions or from aeroplanes.

Meanwhile Sir Douglas Mawson and other Australians were anxious to obtain more detailed knowledge of the coasts lying south of Australia. In October 1929 the *Discovery* left Capetown, and visited Kerguelen and other smaller islands. On 26 December they approached land near longitude 72° E., and then sailed to the west to longitude 65° E. Here a plane was sent up from the ship and discovered Douglas Isles and a number of mainland peaks. This region was given the name of MacRobertson Land (Fig. 12). Next summer in January 1931 a new coast was surveyed from the air near 120° E., and this was named Banzare Land. A few days later another coast was surveyed in 117° E. and this is to be known as Sabrina Land. Sailing to the west it was found that much of the Ice Shelf at Termination Land had broken away. On 9 February in longitude 76° E. some new coasts were seen which have been named Princess Elizabeth Land.

[1] A good account of the whaling voyages appears in the *Handbook of Antarctica*, by Bayliss and Cumpston, Canberra, 1939.

Norwegian Flights from Whaling Ships

In December 1929 Riiser-Larsen flew over Enderby Land, and later on 16 January discovered a new coastland which extended from longitude 46° E. to 43° E. This is called Queen Maud Land (Fig. 12), but the ships were driven away from the continent, and the next flight was much farther to the west where Princess Martha Land was discovered in longitude 18° W. on 18 February 1930.

Next season the Norwegians searched for various islands reported in southern waters, and were able to show the non-existence of Nimrod and Dougherty Islands. Proceeding south in longitude 33° E. the aviators discovered Princess Ragnild Land on 21 February 1931. There was a lull in the whaling industry until 1935, when Mikkelsen landed on the continent in longitude 78° E. on Ingrid Christensen Land. On 4 February 1937 a flight to the south near longitude 34° E. led to the discovery of Prince Harald Land. On this occasion Mrs. Christensen (wife of the leader) was in the plane.

Ellsworth's Notable Flight over West Antarctica

In January 1934 the American explorer Ellsworth, accompanied by Sir Hubert Wilkins, journeyed to Little America in the hope that they could fly across Antarctica. But their plane was damaged, and it was not till November 1935 that this hazardous flight was started from the opposite side of the continent at Dundee Island. On the 21st they started south and had reached the Eternity Range, when heavy clouds made it necessary for them to return. On the 23rd they made a fresh start flying down the east coast of Graham Land. They could see open water in the Weddell Sea as far south as 69° S. They flew over the Eternity Range, which was found to be 100 miles wide, but finally merged into a snow plateau at an elevation of about 9,000 feet. Between longitudes 70° W. and 75° W. a wide valley was observed (Fig. 12).

The Sentinel Range rising to 13,000 feet was passed at 7.35 p.m. After flying for nearly fourteen hours they landed in longitude 102° W. where the plateau was about 6,000 feet above sea-level. Bad weather prevented them from proceeding far on their journey until 4 December when they made a flight of four hours, and on the 5th they reached the north end of Roosevelt Island close to Little America. Here they were picked up on 16 January by the survey ship *Discovery II*.

By this long flight Ellsworth traversed near the most interesting portion of the Antarctic, i.e. the region between West and East Antarctica.

He found—as in other continents—that a series of high mountains bounded (on the Pacific side) a broad lower belt. This latter is bounded on the side away from the Pacific by a level-bedded resistant area, which has many of the characteristics of a Shield. In Fig. 14 the probable axis of this crustal downfold is indicated by the heavy broken line. The recent flight by Ronne in November 1947 may give us some vital information as to whether Antarctica conforms to the pattern of the six other continents, i.e. with Young Mountains on the Pacific side and a resistant shield on the Atlantic (or Indian Ocean) side. The interval between always takes the form of a downfold.

Rymill Discovers King George Sound

Although somewhat out of place in chronology, some attention may now be given to the fine work done by a small British Expedition in West Antarctica. J. R. Rymill (an Australian) was in command of the *Penola*, a tiny ship of only 130 tons. A Moth aeroplane was taken south, and the ship was moored in the Argentine Islands for the winter. A few flights were made, but a better base near Neny Fiord (Fig. 13) was occupied in February of 1936. Several long flights were made which added greatly to our knowledge of this section of Antarctica. The most striking feature was the long Sound (named after King George) which separates Alexander Land (discovered by Bellingshausen in 1820) from the continent. Several sledging parties traversed the great peninsula, and they were able to show that there were no straits across, as Wilkins had reported. On the return voyage the *Penola* reached South Georgia on 3 April 1937.

Much collecting was done and our knowledge of the glacial geography of the area was greatly increased. Such an expedition shows that there is much to be gained by small ground expeditions, which can investigate problems which will never be adequately interpreted from a rapid flight across the terrain.

W. S. Fleming has discussed a number of interesting glacial features along the west coast of Graham Land.[1] A belt of glacier ice fringes the coast north of Adelaide Island, and this is less than a mile wide. Fleming thinks this fringe is a relic of a wider Ice Shelf of which Wordie Ice Shelf is a survival. He is inclined to think that the rock-flat below these 'fringing glaciers' is in part due to glacial erosion.

King George's Sound is filled with shelf ice, which has a height about

[1] *Geographical Journal*, London, June 1938 and August 1940.

500 feet above sea-level near its centre. The Shelf slopes gradually to the sea at both ends. Near Alexander Land Rymill's party found peculiar ice 'Calderas' (Fig. 13). These are oval depressions a mile wide, with cliffed borders up to 100 feet in depth. The floor of each is covered with ice mounds and ice blocks, and their origin is quite obscure.

Byrd's Four Expeditions to the Antarctic: The First Expedition, 1928-30

In May 1926 Byrd made the first flight to the North Pole, and we learn that he immediately began to prepare for a similar flight to the South Pole. In autumn 1928 his two boats left New York. They carried three monoplanes, and with the aid of the 17,000-ton whaling factory ship *Larsen*, these reached the Ross Ice Shelf late in December. 'Little America' was established at the east end of the Shelf close to Amundsen's former base at Framheim. Dog teams and a snowmobile (tractor) were used to transfer the supplies some seven miles inland from the edge of the ice. L. M. Gould, a geologist, was second in command, with B. Balchen in charge of aviation. The first flights were made on 15 January 1929, a few weeks after Wilkins first flight in West Antarctica. Byrd's party on land numbered 42 men (Fig. 12).

Early flights from the base resulted in the discovery of the Rockefeller Mountains—which seem to form the western extremity of the Antarctic 'Andes'. Gould flew to make collections here in March, but unfortunately his plane was wrecked in a blizzard. However, after some anxious weeks the party was brought back in another plane. On 4 November Gould sledged south to reach the southern Horst some 400 miles away. He was supported by a snowmobile, but it was not very satisfactory in heavy snow. A flight in this direction showed that Amundsen's 'Carmen Land' (which seemed to block the hypothetical 'continental downfold') was non-existent.

The famous flight to the South Pole was made on 28 November 1929 in a Ford aeroplane. A depot had been laid down at the foot of the mountains by plane previously. It is noteworthy that the date of the flight was in large part determined by wireless data as to the state of the weather sent back by the geological party. Byrd flew up Liv Glacier, and found some difficulty in rising to 10,000 feet, but by dropping most of their supply of food he gained the Polar Plateau. At 1.14 a.m. (Greenwich time) on 29 November they reached the Pole. They returned by way of the Axel Heiberg Glacier, adjoining Liv Glacier. At 4.33 a.m. they landed at their depot, and soon reached Little America after a journey of 1,600 miles, which had occupied nineteen hours. Meanwhile Gould found much the same suite of rocks in the Horst here as had been observed far to the north-west. Thick horizontal sandstones with carbonaceous layers seem to be the dominant formations.

Byrd's Second Expedition, 1933–5

Byrd considerably increased his transport on the second expedition. He had four aeroplanes, two light snowmobiles, and four caterpillar tractors. Proceeding south from New Zealand several flights were made near longitude 150° W., but no land was visible and on 17 January 1934 Little America was reached. An advanced base was established on the Ross Ice Shelf about 100 miles south of Little America, and here Byrd kept a solitary meteorological vigil through the winter until 10 August.

Three parties sledged to different parts of the Ross Ice Shelf. Siple's objective was to the east, where they made many valuable observations among the Haines Mountains. Blackburn in charge of the geological party proceeded up the Thorne Glacier and reached within 207 miles of the Pole. Here they climbed Mount Weaver (8,200 feet), and observed that the ice plateau was dropping from 7,000 feet to the eastward. Further flights by Byrd filled in details of the region near Sulzberger Bay, which separates Edsel Ford Mountains from Alexandra Mountains (Fig. 12). Another flight showed that the ice was only about 1,600 feet high between Edsel Ford and Queen Maud Ranges. If the ice is about 1,500 feet thick here (as Byrd suggests), the evidence in favour of a *low-level area* between the Antarctic 'Andes' and the Antarctic Horst is fairly strong.

Valuable work was done by Dr. Poulter in determining the thickness of the Ross Ice Shelf. At Little America the ice was 300 feet thick and was afloat over a sea 2,000 feet deep. No less than 510 soundings were made, which showed that the great Shelf is held by ice that is grounded in many places. A survey of the edge of the Ice Shelf showed that it was 13·8 miles north of its position as fixed by Pennell in 1911. The expedition left the Bay of Whales on 6 February 1935.

In very few instances have the details of the topography charted in the maps of the various expeditions been discussed and explained by the observers themselves. A welcome exception is to be made with regard to the findings of the first and second Byrd Expeditions. We owe to L. M. Gould a very interesting discussion of the features, which was published in the proceedings of the Sixth Pacific Science Congress, 1939. A summary appears in the following paragraphs.

Like most Americans Gould uses the name 'Palmer Land' for the peninsular portion of West Antarctica, whereas the British prefer the name

'Graham Land' given to this area in 1832. Gould stresses the similarity of the rocks in the Antarctic peninsula to those of the Andes, and indeed calls the Antarctic Mountains the 'Antarctandes'. We must note, however, that Rymill found Jurassic sedimentary rocks in Alexander Land, though most of the peninsula consists of igneous rocks. The ice mantle in West Antarctica is less complete than that in East Antarctica—which is the larger semicircular unit which lies in *eastern* longitudes, and includes the South Pole (Fig. 14).

Gould doubts if there is a strait linking the Ross and Weddell Seas, though he believes there may be a broad intermontane plain between the Horlick Mountains and the Antarctandes. He describes a great re-entrant on the east side of the Ross Ice Shelf, where tremendous floods of ice seem to pour down on to the Shelf. The smaller glaciers coming into the Shelf (i.e. Liv, Heiberg, and Bowman Glaciers) farther to the west, seem to be deflected to the west by the greater ice flood just mentioned. Near the Thorne Glacier—which may be as large as the Beardmore—the ice spreads through a number of connected valleys, and is very different in its plan from the relatively narrow glaciers described near Macmurdo Sound. At the outlet of these glaciers nearest the Pole, the ice merges into a continuous piedmont, and this presses the Ice Shelf into low open folds some 20 feet high.

As elsewhere along the Antarctic Horst Gould found cirques in every stage, high or low, filled with ice, or nearly empty. He shows that the topography in the far south is not favourable for colossal ice glaciers overwhelming former cirques, as explained in the writer's Palimpsest Theory (Fig. 16). But while faults and variations in the hardness of the formations may explain the origins of Gould's main valleys, I saw no evidence of such conditions in the valleys bordering Macmurdo Sound.

Gould gives some evidence that the horst was elevated far back in Tertiary times, and he suggests that the ice age in Antarctica existed much earlier than the Pleistocene Ice Age in our temperate lands. This agrees with the deductions made by the writer from the height of the cirques, which are in much too cold a zone to be produced there today. In fact Gould agrees with the writer that Antarctica is *much too cold* for major glacial erosion, though this seems a somewhat paradoxical conclusion.

Byrd's Third Expedition, 1939–41

The last major gap in the Antarctic coastline—that lying south of the Pacific—was filled as the result of the Third Byrd Expedition.[1] Two bases

[1] R. A. J. English, *Geographical Review*, July 1941.

were established in January 1940, one at Little America on the Ross Ice Shelf, and the other near Neny Fiord in Graham Land (Palmer Peninsula) close to Rymill's southern base (Fig. 13). In both cases lengthy sledge journeys were made, but the chief explorations were by plane. There were nearly a dozen scientists in each of these parties, including several geologists and a physicist.

The ship *Bear* on its voyage to the east sent off three flights between 90° W. and 110° W. longitude, which showed that the continent here lay approximately along latitude 73° S. Numerous flights from Little America reached as far east as longitude 130° W., and two prominent mountains projecting through the ice cap were named Mount Flood (10,000 feet) and Mount Sidley. A mountain, 15,000 feet high, on the coast was named Mount Ruth Siple. A sledging party traversed 450 miles of this region, reaching Mount Flood. Flights to the south reached Queen Maud Mountains in the Horst, and defined the eastern margin of the Ross Ice Shelf. Two low-level gulfs in 81° W. and 85° W. seem to be filled with extensions of the low-level ice. In March a plane ascended to 21,050 feet to make cosmic ray observations.

From the East Base at Neny Fiord three major sledging journeys explored the plateau of the peninsula, the east coast for 100 miles south of Cape Eielsen (Fig. 12), and the south-west end of King George Sound. Aeroplane surveys mapped the Pacific coast as far west as longitude 90° W., and showed that Alexander Land reached to longitude 70° W. Another flight extended our knowledge of the Weddell Sea, and mapped the Eternity Range (12,000 feet). The east coast was observed as far south as 77° S., where the mountains thin out, with summits about 7,000 feet. Open water to the south-east showed that the Filchner Shelf did not reach to this portion of West Antarctica.

Byrd's Fourth Expedition, 1946–7

In the southern summer of 1946–7 the United States Navy, as part of its training and research activities, organized an expedition under Admiral Byrd which dwarfed all previous efforts.[1] Thirteen ships including a submarine were employed, with a personnel of 4,000 men. The general figures before this date were one or two ships and about 100 men! This huge armada was divided into three groups. Two of them were supplied with plane-tenders, and their purpose was to cruise round the whole of

[1] Based on the article by Admiral Byrd in the *National Geographic Magazine*, Oct. 1947.

the continent, sending off survey planes to make an accurate survey of as much of the coastlands as possible. There was also a Central Group at Little America, equipped with a number of planes, who would carry out similar work from a land base.

The survey largely depended on the trimetrogon cameras carried by the planes, but much other remarkable apparatus was in use which will be referred to later. Novel features in the expedition were two ice-breakers which on many occasions forced a way through ice too heavy for the thin steel plates of the other ships.

The five ships of the Central Group met at Scott Island north of Ross Sea on 31 December 1946. They found some 600 miles of pack ice confronting their passage to the south. This was unusually wide, though the writer traversed 400 miles in 1910; but at times the pack ice has been traversed in a day or two, as in 1940. Most of the ships followed the ice-breaker, but the submarine was compelled to retreat to a position north of the heavy pack. A helicopter was used to find the best tracks for the ice-breaker. On arrival at the Bay of Whales the ice-breaker literally smashed out a safe harbour in the sea ice which filled the Bay. The latter was now only a tiny fraction of its size when first surveyed in 1911. It was found that Little America (built on the Ice Shelf) had moved more than 8,000 feet to the north-west in the last five years.

Flights from Little America surveyed the continent in every direction for a distance of about 600 miles (Fig. 14). One flight went 100 miles beyond the South Pole, but showed only the usual uniform ice plateau at an elevation of about 9,000 feet. There seems, however, to be a broad swell in the ice plateau about 150 miles on the Ross Sea side of the Pole, and this may rise to 11,000 feet. Another flight from Little America furnished aerial views of the glaciers mapped by the British expeditions near Macmurdo Sound. A new colossal glacier was seen which apparently enters Shackleton Inlet from the west. (These areas surveyed from the air are enclosed in dotted lines in Fig. 14.)

The most interesting region visited by the planes was that to the south-east of Little America (Fig. 14). Here a new Hourglass Glacier was discovered about 60 miles east of Scott Glacier. The new glacier was 15 miles wide, and had a very steep drop to the Ross Ice Shelf. Byrd found that high mountains continued indefinitely to the east in the general direction of the east coast of the Weddell Sea. The final point reached was near longitude 100° W. On February 14th Anderson flew 180 miles beyond the Horlick Mts. towards the Weddell Sea. He saw a *continuous scarp* of reddish rock, some of the mountains being 15,000 feet high (*Polar Times*, June 1947). There is, however, a large gap in our knowledge of this part of the continent, as is clearly shown by the ruled area in Fig. 12. Byrd fully recognized the importance of finding out whether a downfold separates the two sections of Antarctica as suggested in Fig. 13; and indeed has done more than any other explorer to inform us on this point.

The Western Group with a plane tender made a photo survey of all the coast from the Balleny Islands westward to Princess Astrid Coast in 10° E. longitude (Fig. 14). Of course most of this coast had been adequately surveyed, by Australian and Norwegian ships mainly; but much new data were discovered near Cape Adare, such as the deep bays which penetrate Oates Land. However, details as to the size and shape of the great glaciers reaching the sea were charted. On longitude 100° E. a considerable area of bare rock with small freshwater lakes (on which a seaplane descended) was seen on the margin of the ice cap. The writer sees no reason to invoke volcanic action, since small lakes (due to the sun acting on thin snow on north slopes) have long been recorded. In fact, Byrd found more of these lakes near longitude 78° E. Mountains, some as much as 10,000 feet high, extend for more than 100 miles along Ragnhild Coast in longitude 30° E.

The Eastern Group made the most spectacular discovery, since they found a deep bay between longitude 100° and 110° W. This penetrated nearly 250 miles into the continent, and had a breadth of over 150 miles. The bay is flanked by the Thurston Peninsula on the east, and by the Kohler Range on the west (Fig. 12). Here visibility was very bad, and a plane crashed on the ice with the sad loss of three of the crew. The weather was very unfavourable in the vicinity of Peter Island; but flights near Alexander Island resulted in better knowledge of this corner of the continent. Unfortunately the last stretch of unknown Antarctic coast—that South of the Weddell Sea—could not be reached by the Eastern Group. (Ronne has, however, since mapped much of this coast.)

Innumerable data of scientific value were recorded by the huge personnel. With the aid of radar, subglacial islands were detected. It was found that the South Magnetic Pole varies its position from day to day, and is best considered as an oval region of about 1,000 square miles in area. Two 10-ton tractors were tested on a journey of 280 miles to the east of Little America. The main purpose of this naval expedition was admittedly to test ship operations under the normal—but always difficult —conditions of a polar environment. The absurd rumours as to a hunt for uranium had no place in the plans of the last and largest expedition led by Admiral Byrd.

A few words may be added about the recent flight of Commander Ronne. This American explorer during November 1947 started from a base at Cape Keeler in Graham Land, and surveyed the hitherto unknown coast at the south-west of the Weddell Sea. He found that the Weddell Sea extends to 77° S. in longitude 60° W. Two women were in his party.

The Falkland Islands Dependencies Survey, 1943–6

We owe to J. M. Wordie (*Polar Record*, April 1947) a detailed account of the latest phase of Antarctic Exploration, which differs in several rather important respects from earlier investigations. Until 1939 research work in West Antarctica was carried out under the guidance of the 'Discovery Committee' of the Colonial Office, and the islands were visited every year from 1910 onwards. The new body, the F.I.D.S. (created in 1943), had as its objects the completion of the mapping of Graham Land, the setting up of wireless weather stations, and the carrying out of a detailed economic survey of this Antarctic sector.

Five bases were ultimately occupied in the sector south of the Falkland Islands (Fig. 13). The first was established at Deception Island in February 1944, where (during the great whaling period of 1910–30) a Falkland Island magistrate had been on duty during the season. The second base was placed at Port Lockroy on an island in latitude 65° S., and many geological and botanical specimens were collected. Next year in February a base was placed at Hope Bay at the very end of the 'stalk' of the continent. In the following August a sledge party from this base surveyed the east coast of the peninsula near where Nordenskjöld made his winter-quarters in 1902–3. Much information was gathered with regard to the numbers and habits of Antarctic birds.

In the third year a fourth base was established in the South Orkneys, not far from the Argentine meteorological station. About the same time the fifth base was built at Neny Fiord near the Debenham Islands. Here both Rymill and the Americans in 1940 had made some surveys and collections. From four to ten men occupied each of these five stations during the third year; and there was a meteorologist, and usually a geologist or surveyor, at each base. This steady systematic work is already yielding valuable data as to the Antarctic environment.

Political Aspects

In concluding this necessarily brief record of Antarctic exploration a few words will be in order regarding the political geography of the last continent to be charted. Ultimately control will, no doubt, be settled by international agreement—as was the case with Spitsbergen. The principle of 'sector divisions' (along the lines of longitude) seems to be the guiding criterion in many cases. Australia has sent many expeditions to the sector south of that continent, and a great deal of information has been gained on the possibilities of the region under the direction of Sir Douglas Mawson. The Australians seek control of the sector between longitude 50° E. and longitude 165° E. as shown on Fig. 14. France, however, claims a thin sector south of Adelie Land on the basis of D'Urville's discovery, while America points out that Wilkes charted various portions of this coast as far back as 1840.

The most definite pronouncements are those of the British concerning the lands south of New Zealand and again south of the Falkland Islands. These areas include most of the two large seas named after Ross and Weddell. The British have maintained survey ships, and placed a number of bases here, as described earlier in this account. Here again Chile and Argentina raise counter claims regarding much of West Antarctica.

Norway has certainly explored nearly all the coastlands south of the Atlantic, as indicated on Fig. 14; and has claimed this sector as her territory. For the same reason U.S.A. has a paramount claim to the sector between Little America and Alexander Land, almost all of which has been mapped during Byrd's four expeditions. Already some American writers have claimed much more territory for U.S.A. as a result of the enormous area of hinterland first surveyed by aerial photography on the last expedition. (These areas are enclosed in dotted lines in Fig. 14.) Germany has also entered claims for sectors near the meridian of Greenwich. The relative merits of these claims to sovereignty in the Antarctic will only be decided in the distant future.

BIBLIOGRAPHY

Balch, *Antarctica*, Philadelphia, 1902.
Brown, R., *Polar Regions*, London, 1927.
David and Priestley, *Geology of 1907 Expedition*, London, 1914.
Hayes, G., *Antarctica*, London, 1928.
Heawood, G., *Geographical Discovery*, Cambridge, 1921.
Joerg, W. L., *Brief History of Polar Exploration*, New York, 1930.
Mills, H. R., *Siege of the South Pole*, London, 1905.
Polar Record, published by the Polar Institute, Cambridge.
Polar Times, published by the American Polar Society, New York.
Problems of Polar Research (Various authors), New York, 1928.
Scott, R. F., *Voyage of the Discovery*, London, 1905.
Taylor, Griffith, *Physiography of Macmurdo Sound*, London, 1922.
Taylor, Griffith, *Antarctic Adventure and Research*, New York, 1930.
Wright and Priestley, *Glaciology*, London, 1922.

CHAPTER XIV

GEOGRAPHY AND THE TROPICS

KARL J. PELZER

Karl J. Pelzer, Associate Professor of Geography, Yale University. Author of Economic Survey of the Pacific Area, *Vol. I.* Population and Land Utilization, *New York, 1941, and* Pioneer Settlement in the Asiatic Tropics, Studies in Land Utilization and Agricultural Colonization in Southeastern Asia, *New York, 1945.*

Introduction

EXPANSION of the peoples of the middle latitudes into the low latitudes of Africa, America, and Asia has brought almost every part of the tropics at one time or another under foreign political control. This expansion, which was made possible by a great development of material culture, began some five centuries ago in Western Europe, but it did not remain the prerogative of Western Europe. The United States, Japan, and other countries such as Australia and New Zealand, too, entered the scramble for political control of the tropics. China, on the other hand—due to political weakness—did not stake any claims in the tropics, despite the fact that millions of its peoples settled in tropical countries.

In the course of these five centuries of expansion the economy of the countries in middle latitudes has become increasingly dependent upon the tropics for foodstuffs as well as for industrial raw materials. The natural monopoly of the low latitudes in spices, stimulants such as coffee and cacao, sugar (prior to the nineteenth century), and more recently certain fibres and vegetable fats, and rubber, has been an important motivation for the peoples of the mid-latitudes to establish their economic and political control over tropical latitudes. They did not limit themselves to the trading or production of tropical crops in the habitat where they found them. Instead they brought about an extensive exchange of economic plants between the three great regions of the tropics; so that today, with few exceptions, the main production areas are not located in the area where the crop was found originally. Various commodities have seen several shifts of their centre of production in the course of the last five centuries. Both economic and historical geographers are concerned with the study of these shifts and the resulting changes in cultural landscapes. Such shifts of the centres of production may have been caused by changes of economic or social policy or they may have taken place during periods of international conflict or they may have become necessary because of the effects of destructive exploitation on the soil resources of an area. The effects of technological advancement upon the economy of tropical areas are well-known. They may be adverse, such as the ruining of the indigo culture of Java, India, and other tropical countries through the invention of aniline dyes, although this was partly counterbalanced by the fact that this development made land available for the production of food crops needed as a result of increasing local demand. On the other hand, the development of the margarine industry in the 1870's and of the tinplate industry in the 1890's created an ever increasing demand for tropical vegetable fats which became an important source of cash income for the peasant of the tropics.

Because of great differences in the modes of life, economic values, and techniques of the mid-latitude and low-latitude peoples, contact between them has had far-reaching and often tragic effects upon the social and economic life of the tropical peoples. The nature of the changes resulting from the contact differs from area to area and from period to period, depending upon such factors as the size and cultural level of the indigenous population, the physical-geographical character of the area, and above all, the economic and social policies of the metropolitan power at the time the region was brought under control, and the type of frontier that was developed, such as missionary's or trader's frontier, planter's or settler's frontier, miner's or strategic frontier.

The economic-political activity of the peoples of mid-latitudes set into motion great intercontinental, intertropical labour migrations, sometimes forced, sometimes voluntary, which have changed the geographical distribution of the races of mankind. Witness the migration of Negroes to the New World, of Indians to sections of the Asiatic tropics outside the Indian peninsula and to tropical sections of Africa and America, of Chinese to South-east Asia and to the islands of the Pacific, of Japanese to Pacific island groups and to the tropics of South America. At the same time European communities were established in highlands and in climatically favoured lowland areas, especially near the polarward fringe of the tropics.

A glance at the history of the relationship between Europe and the three great segments of the tropics reveals that in the seventeenth and eighteenth centuries it was the American tropics that dominated, with Africa serving as the labour reservoir. Then the abolition of slavery in the French and British West Indies and the end of the slave trade led to the rise of the Asiatic tropics as key economic regions. Today we are witnessing the shift of Europe's interest from the Asiatic to the African tropics, brought about by the flowering of nationalism in Asia. Great Britain withdrew from Burma, gave Dominion status to Pakistan, India, and Ceylon and is trying to reorganize the political structure of the Malay peninsula. The United States granted independence to the Philippines. France and the Netherlands, not willing to follow the British or American example in the Asiatic tropics, are at loggerheads with their subjects in Indonesia and Indochina.

Current plans of the European metropolitan powers regarding the economic development of the African tropics hold the possibility that the second half of the twentieth century may become the beginning of the century of the African tropics, in the way the period from 1840 to 1940 was the century of the Asiatic tropics. It remains, however, to be seen for how long the peoples of the African tropics will be willing to accept western political control. Out of the ranks of educated African youth may come the men destined to become as well-known as the present political leaders in the Philippines, Indonesia, India, or any other part of the Asiatic tropics.

The Boundary of the Tropics

Geographers have devoted a great deal of attention to the problem of the geographic boundaries of the tropics, but they are not anywhere near an agreement, except that they all find the mathematical-astronomical boundary, represented by the tropics of Cancer and Capricorn, to be unacceptable, because it cuts across regions of uniform climatic character. There is little agreement as to the elements characteristic of the tropics and there are as many polar limits of the tropics as there are climatic elements considered essential in the definition of the tropics.

Alexander Supan suggested the annual isotherm of 20° C. as the polar limit of the tropics, a line which more or less coincides with the polar limit of the trade wind belt and the palms. But since this boundary includes extensive areas which do not have high rainfall and high humidity, Supan's definition of the tropics is not acceptable to many geographers. Opinions vary greatly as to whether the boundary should be drawn on the basis of temperature or whether precipitation and evaporation should also be taken into consideration. Should the arid regions of low latitudes be considered a part of the tropics? Hettner, who regards the polar boundary of the trade winds as limits of the tropics, includes, like Supan, the arid regions of low latitudes in the tropics. Penck and Krebs, for example, exclude them.

Köppen's recommendation of the isotherm of 18° C. of the coolest month as the boundary of the humid tropics is well known. His definition excludes highlands, although their temperature regime shows slight seasonal variation, one of the main characteristics of low-latitude climate. Not only the *tierra caliente*, but also the *tierra templada* is a part of the tropics. The *tierra templada* produces a number of valuable perennial economic plants which are limited to low latitudes because of the high demands regarding temperature conditions.

The Tropics—A Panacea for the Troubles of the Middle Latitudes?

The peoples of Western Europe have for a long time considered the tropics as 'Ergänzungsräume'—as areas which supplement their own economy by supplying foodstuffs and industrial raw materials, by serving as outlets and markets for manufactured goods, and by providing possible areas of settlement.[1] Appreciation of the tremendous economic benefits derived from political or economic control of tropical areas found expression in the Dutch saying:

Indie verloren
Rampspoed geboren

—loss of the Indies would mean the birth of misery—and in the eighteenth century English doggerel:

If the slave trade had gone, there's an end to our lives
Beggars all must we be, our children and wives
No ships from our ports their proud sails would e'er spread
And our streets grow with grass where the cows might be fed.[2]

European interest in the tropics has reached new heights within the last few years as a result of such post-war problems as the critical shortage

[1] In 1940, when Germany expected to regain control over its former colonial territory, some twenty geographers contributed papers to a symposium primarily concerned with the tropics, published as *Lebensraumfragen Europäischer Völker*. Vol. II. *Europas Koloniale Ergänzungsräume*, edited by K. A. Dietzel, O. Schmieder, and H. Schmitthenner, Leipzig, 1941. In addition to this volume German scientists produced three other great compendia of studies on tropical areas and problems, primarily the African tropics, which no geographer can afford to overlook. (1) *Beiträge zur Kolonialforschung*, Vols. 1 to 6, 1942–4, and a supplement: Pfalz, R., *Hydrologie der deutschen Kolonien·in Afrika*, Berlin, 1944. (2) *Mitteilungen der Gruppe Deutscher Kolonialwirtschaftlicher Unternehmungen*, Vols. 1, 2, 4, 5, 6, 7, 9, Berlin, 1939–42. (3) *Afrika, Handbuch der praktischen Kolonialwissenschaften*, edited by E. Obst. This handbook, edited by a geographer, was to include 19 volumes of which 10 volumes were published between 1941 and 1944.

[2] As quoted by Hancock, W. K., *Survey of British Commonwealth Affairs*. London, 1942, Vol. 2, Part 2, p. 156.

of many industrial raw materials, food—especially fat, lack of foreign exchange, and the need of finding settlement areas for thousands of displaced persons. Political as well as professional and lay circles in Europe have great hopes that the African tropics may prove to be the panacea for many of the ills which harass Europe today. British expectations of the benefits that could be derived from the economic development of the African tropics were expressed by Sir Stafford Cripps at a conference of the Governors of British Colonies in Africa held in November 1947:

We have for a long time talked about the development of Africa, but I do not believe that we have realized how, from the point of view of world economy, that development is absolutely vital. . . . In Africa, indeed, is to be found a great potential for new strength and vigour in the Western European economy. . . . It is the urgency of the present situation and the need for the Sterling Group and Western Europe both of them to maintain their economic independence that makes it so essential that we should increase out of all recognition the tempo of African economic development. We must be prepared to change our outlook and our habits of Colonial development, and force the pace so that within the next two to five years we can get a really marked increase of production in coal, minerals, timber, raw materials of all kinds, and foodstuffs, and anything else that will save dollars or will sell in a dollar market.[1]

West-European interest in the economic development of the African tropics is shared by a group of Americans who have recently prepared plans to develop the natural resources of the State of Liberia. Edward R. Stettinius, Jr., chairman of the board of the Liberia Company declared: 'What we face, I believe, is nothing less than a whole new frontier of opportunity, a frontier waiting for further exploration, a frontier which holds out the promise of the richest kinds of rewards in social as well as economic terms.'

Again, Secretary of State George C. Marshall, speaking before the opening session of the Fourth International Congress on Tropical Medicine and Malaria, expressed the view that the tropical regions hold the key to a world of plenty, and tropical medicine holds the key to tropical regions.

Statements like these attest to the widespread interest in tropical development. In Great Britain, especially, there seems to exist the fervent hope and optimism that western European recovery will be aided by the natural and human resources of the African tropics. Leaders of the Labour Party declare that this cannot and must not take the form of eighteenth- and nineteenth-century destructive exploitation for the benefit of the 'Mother Country', but that the interests of the indigenous population have

[1] As quoted in the *Crown Colonist*, January 1948.

to be fully protected; some even go so far as to demand that they should come first. But, so runs the argument, the tropical areas are capable of extensive development which, while benefiting the colonial peoples, would also benefit the United Kingdom and the world at large. Furthermore the old concept of the tropics as an area of unlimited natural wealth and soil fertility has given way to the realization that the 'bonification' of the tropics entails great expense if the chains formed by environmental factors are to be broken. The tropics will need considerable investment in form of technical and scientific research, aid and guidance, and capital goods such as rails, locomotives, road-building equipment and trucks, without which crop surpluses cannot be produced or moved to the ports.

Probably the most ambitious plans to mobilize the potential resources of the tropics have been drawn up in Great Britain during recent years. The Colonial Development and Welfare Act of 1945 made available £120,000,000 for loans and grants for the improvement of social and other public services and utilities, which in turn are expected to promote economic development. A substantial part of the funds is devoted to research programmes, including such topics as agriculture, plant and animal diseases, health, nutrition, social services, fisheries, forestry, surveying, geology, and the like. Considerable attention is being given to the higher education and professional training of students from the colonies in Great Britain.[1]

This is not the place to examine the economic soundness of these plans, which place a great strain both on the economy of the metropolitan state, because of their demands for heavy capital investment as well as for scientific and managerial personnel, and on the social and economic structure of the tropical communities affected; but the following sections will take up several aspects of colonial tropical development that have important bearing on the problems confronting those who wish to undertake a large-scale settlement of the tropics, especially the African tropics.

The Labour Problem of the Tropics

One of the main problems of the Western entrepreneur in the tropics is that of labour. This problem goes as far back as the first contacts of Westerners with the peoples of the tropics. Wherever the prevailing form

[1] In the spring of 1948, the British Government set up two corporations, the Colonial Development Corporation and the Overseas Food Corporation. Between the two of them these corporations are authorized to borrow up to £150 million in order to increase production in British dependent territories. An outstanding project of the Overseas Food Corporation is the East African Groundnut Scheme.

of land use is that of shifting cultivation the population density is bound to be relatively low. What is more important, everybody has access to all the land that he requires for the production of subsistence crops; so that it is impossible to find people willing to work for wages regularly, unless new wants are created which cannot be satisfied by the traditional economy. The only areas where agricultural labour is readily forthcoming are densely populated ones which have long since passed from shifting to permanent agriculture, and where population pressure has become so great that it has created a landless agricultural proletariat accustomed to working for wages. Such areas are India, Java, Tonkin, Annam, and the two southern coastal provinces of China, Kwantung and Fukien. But when Western entrepreneurs came to the American and African tropics they learned that one cannot recruit free labourers among shifting cultivators. It is striking that the African tropics for centuries acted only as a supply area of slave labour, but did not attract capital for the development of plantations. A very important reason for this is the fact that it would have been impossible to operate large plantations with slave labour on the African continent because it would have been a hopeless task to prevent the escape of the slaves. The transfer of slaves at first to islands off the West African coast and then away from the African homeland across the Atlantic made control of the slaves considerably easier. From the point of view of effective control over the labour force the West African and West Indian islands could not be surpassed. The planters of Brazil and Guiana on the other hand frequently suffered losses because their slaves would run away and escape into the forests of the hinterland; where we still have communities of Negroes who are the descendants of escaped slaves.

The leadership of the American tropics during the seventeenth and eighteenth centuries depended upon the favourable geographic location of centres of plantation agriculture in relation to their markets in Europe and upon slave labour supplied by Africa. When the slave trade was suppressed and slavery abolished in the British and French colonies the planters found that free Negro labour was not available in sufficient strength, and they attempted to solve their labour problems by importing free labourers from Asia, but at no time were they able to obtain an adequate number. Instead, the centre of the plantation economy shifted to the Asiatic tropics. Here labour became the location factor, while the geographic location of the new plantation areas in relation to the European market was much less favourable than the American ones had been. The situation was not improved until 1869, when the opening of the Suez Canal greatly shortened the route between areas of production and consumption.

As labour-intensive enterprises, plantations depend upon densely populated regions, but because of their demand for extensive areas they show a preference for undeveloped regions. In South-east Asia the planters were able to obtain land in undeveloped tropical areas which were in proximity to densely populated ones. Assam, the mountain districts of Ceylon, Southern India, and Java draw their labourers from the ranks of the landless rural population of nearby areas, while the planters of Malaya and the east coast of Sumatra have to go farther and import their labourers from China, India, and Java.[1]

As Waibel has pointed out, continental tropical Africa did not see a development of western plantations and mining enterprises until the 1880's. Only the islands off the Guinea Coast, São Thomé and Principe, and the East African islands developed plantation agriculture prior to that date. As a matter of fact, as mentioned above, the plantations of the island of São Thomé preceded the plantations of the American tropics.[2]

Since the 1880's an evergrowing number of Africans have been seeking employment in plantations, mines, and other enterprises, usually seasonally. Why has free labour become available in Africa during the last sixty years, despite the fact that shifting cultivation is still the prevailing form of agriculture? The situation is a rather complex one, and the specific reasons which cause Africans to seek employment vary from area to area. There are forces at work that drive, and those that lure. The introduction of taxation in money seems to be one of the main reasons, probably the most important one. Beside the necessity to earn money in order to pay the annual taxes appears the desire to obtain money in order to satisfy new wants which cannot be fulfilled by the traditional tribal economy.[3] The development of a taste for such foodstuffs as sugar, tea, bread, and preserves, the adoption of western style clothing, the desire to possess modern implements and utensils and to equip houses with doors, windows, and corrugated iron roofs, all act as incentives to seek employment at least until the specific wants are fulfilled.[4]

---

[1] Pelzer, Karl J., *Die Arbeiterwanderungen in Südostasien*, Hamburg, 1935; and Pelzer, Karl J., 'Present day plantation labour migration in India', in *Comptes Rendus du Congrès International de Géographie Amsterdam 1938*, Leiden, 1938, Vol. 2, pp. 65–75.

[2] Waibel, Leo, *Die Rohstoffgebiete des Tropischen Afrika*, Leipzig, 1937; and Waibel, Leo, 'Die Wirtschaftsform des tropischen Plantagenbaus', in *Probleme der Landwirtschaftsgeographie*, Breslau, 1933.

[3] Some observers are of the opinion that the shopkeeper provides a far greater incentive to seek employment than the tax-collector, especially in communities which have been in contact with the outside world for some time. See Orde-Browne, G. St. J., *The African Labourer*, Oxford University Press, 1933, p. 32.

[4] Schapera, I., *Migrant Labour and Tribal Life*, Oxford University Press, 1947, pp. 121–3.

A driving force of special interest to the geographer is land shortage. This is a force especially in territories where native reserves have been set up for Africans that prove to be too small for the growing population and where large blocks of land have been occupied by European settlers and plantation companies. Land shortage is not, however, limited to areas where tribes are confined to reserves. Throughout tropical Africa the suppression of tribal warfare and the introduction of modern medical services have reduced the death rate while the birth rate has, on the whole, remained unchanged; so that the population is increasing at a faster rate than in previous centuries. In areas where the economy of the African is based on livestock, the fight against animal diseases has been so successful that herds have increased very rapidly. Hence extensive areas of grazing land are over-stocked and are seriously affected by soil erosion caused by over grazing. Cultivation for export of indigenous and exotic crops in excess of domestic requirements, combined with the traditional extensive forms of land use—migratory hoe culture, or shifting cultivation—has greatly increased the demand for land. All of these developments have brought about land shortage in many parts of Africa, which in turn compels thousands of Africans to undertake seasonal migrations to areas which are short of labour.

The search for short-term seasonal employment every year sets several hundred thousand Africans into motion in various parts of Africa, many of whom travel distances of several hundred miles on foot. The more developed areas have modern means of transport. The present day conditions under which many Africans migrate between their villages and the plantations or other places of employment remind one of the seasonal migrations between Madras and the plantation areas of the West Ghats and Ceylon during the first half of the nineteenth century. What a waste of time and energy and what deprivation and suffering, much of which could be eliminated by appropriate planning and a further development of rail and motor transport lines between major labour supply and demand areas. Frequently the labourers arrive in such a poor state of health that it requires several weeks of special care before they are physically fit to perform a day's work. This is especially true for labourers trekking from the Belgian Mandate of Ruanda-Urundi to Uganda, Kenya, or Tanganyika. In Ruanda-Urundi population pressure has reached such levels that thousands leave the area annually during the season of food shortage in order to seek food even more than wages.

Our knowledge of this important aspect of the human geography of the African tropics is still incomplete, despite the fact that a few geographers, anthropologists, and administrators have studied the phenomenon of labour migrations in a number of areas.[1] Future studies should cover population distribution and density, techniques of land utilization, land tenure, the effect of labour migration upon the economic and social life of the individual family and community, size and main routes of the migration, and finally the geographical distribution of the labour population in the areas employing large numbers of immigrant labourers. Such studies are necessary because on the whole labour is relatively scarce in Africa, as it is in large parts of the American and certain parts of the Asiatic tropics. Too large a migration of able-bodied men from any one area to plantations and mines will endanger the importance of that area as a source of manpower in the future owing to a lower birth rate and an increased death rate, the latter a result of the deterioration of indigenous agriculture and a reduction in the local food supply. The low wage rates prevailing in the tropics do not permit the migrant labourers to save enough money to compensate the village and the family for the men's absence.

The labour problem, which has been present since the first days of economic penetration of the low latitudes by Westerners, should be studied in all its aspects, especially in view of the current heightened interest in the development of the human and natural resources of Africa.

Peasant or Plantation Agriculture

As long as Westerners have been interested and active in the tropics they have been faced by the problem of organizing and making the resources of the tropics accessible to the consumer of the mid-latitudes. This is essentially a question of the comparative advantage of native peasant and western plantation agriculture.[2] The controversy between the champions of plantation production and the champions of peasant production is still going on. It is mirrored, for example, in the struggle between the great industrial combine of the Lever Brothers and the British Colonial Office over the question of how to organize the palm-oil production of West Africa.

[1] Kayser, K., 'Bevölkerungsdichte, Wanderarbeit und Europäischer Arbeitsbedarf in Ostafrika', in Comptes Rendus du Congrés International de Géographie Amsterdam 1938, Leiden, 1938, Vol. II, Sect. IIIc, pp. 441–57; Schapera, I., op. cit.; Orde-Browne, G. St. J., Labour Conditions in East Africa, London, 1946.

[2] See Credner, Wilhelm, 'Tendenzen in Aufbau Tropischer Landwirtschaft', in Lebensraumfragen Europäischer Völker. Vol. 2: Europas Koloniale Ergänzungsräume. Leipzig, 1941, pp. 111-130; Pim, Sir Alan, Colonial Agricultural Production. The Contribution made by Native Peasants and by Foreign Enterprise. London, New York. 1946.

The native peasant of the humid tropics was often rather slow in seeing the economic advantages and possibilities arising out of the contact with peoples of the mid-latitudes, and was not immediately ready to exert himself in order to satisfy the latter's demand for tropical products. The Westerner, who claims for climatic reasons not to be capable of doing hard physical labour in the humid tropical lowlands for prolonged periods, therefore, had to look for ways and means of organizing agricultural production in such a manner that he himself would not have to do the physical labour but could limit himself to management and supervision. The answer to this was the plantation, a type of economy not known in the tropics prior to the coming of the Europeans. Waibel has defined the plantation as a combined agricultural-industrial enterprise, usually managed by Westerners, which is both labour and capital intensive and produces agricultural commodities for the market, especially for the market of the mid-latitudes.[1] According to Waibel, this type of economy reached the tropics in the second half of the fifteenth century, when Portuguese entrepreneurs developed sugar plantations on West African islands.[2] From here plantation economy moved across the Atlantic.

However, these same Portuguese, who established plantations on the islands off the West African coast and, somewhat later, in the coastal areas of Brazil, did not build up plantations in South-east Asia, nor did the Dutch until the end of the nineteenth century, although they too had practised plantation economy in the American tropics. How is it that various European powers could satisfy their economic needs for more than three centuries in the Asiatic tropics without resorting to the economy of plantation agriculture? It is because the Westerner found in South-east Asia peoples who were accustomed to production for trade purposes. As a matter of fact, seafaring merchants from China and the Near East had already been competing with each other for centuries for spices and other products of South-east Asia. Furthermore, a large percentage of the peasantry of the Asiatic tropics had already advanced from shifting to permanent agriculture, were accustomed to intensive cultivation, and could easily be induced to cultivate exotic crops demanded by customers in distant markets. And, finally, the bulk of the peoples of the Asiatic tropics were subjects of politically advanced states, the rulers of which demanded tax payments in kind from their peasant subjects. The Western entrepreneur could therefore limit himself to trading and was not forced to organize agricultural production himself. In time the traders took over

[1] Waibel, Leo, 'The Tropical Plantation System', *Scientific Monthly*, Vol. LII, 1941, pp. 156–60.
[2] Waibel, Leo, 'Die Wirtschaftsform . . .' op. cit., p. 28.

the political control of the key economic regions and made even larger profits than before by demanding tribute. This development gave rise to the Forced Deliveries and Contingencies which played such an important role in the history of the Dutch East India Company. The logical sequence of this was the Forced Culture System, introduced in Java by Van den Bosch in 1831. Under this system the peasantry of Java had to plant one-fifth of the land under cultivation with crops stipulated by the government, especially sugar, coffee, and indigo, and to deliver the produce to government warehouses. The fulfilment of this demand took care of the taxes which the Netherland Indies government levied as legal successor of the Indonesian Rulers.

Thus, during the early phases of the economic penetration of the humid tropics the decision as to whether peasant or plantation agriculture would supply the demanded products depended upon the size and the cultural level of the autochthonous population that came into contact with the Western sojourner. It was a question of economic organization and utilization of the natural and human resources of a given area.

There are two fundamental differences between peasant and plantation agriculture. One is size. Plantations are large economic units, both labour and capital intensive, while peasant farms are small units requiring usually only family labour and scarcely any capital investment. The second difference is that most types of plantations maintain a factory to process the crop and prepare it for shipment to distant markets; whereas the peasant farm lacks such an industrial plant, although the peasant too is capable of preparing the product for shipment to distant markets. It is, however, true that today the technology of certain crops has reached levels which tend to take these crops out of the hands of small-scale peasant producers whose processed product, is no longer equal to that coming from the factory unit of the plantation. But the reverse trend can also be observed; sometimes a product, once a typical plantation product, becomes a typical peasant product, because the processing technology is so simple that it does not require expensive equipment and the services of a staff of technicians and scientists.

The cane-sugar and palm-oil industries are the best examples of the first-mentioned development. In the case of sugar the trend is practically completed. Because of the capital requirements of a modern sugar mill and because of the necessity of linking operations in the field as efficiently as possible with the operation of the factory, i.e. the sugar mill, many of the outstanding cane-sugar areas are plantation-type enterprises, which combine both the agricultural and processing phases of production under *one* management. But even in the sugar industry a compromise is possible, under which tropical peasant producers and Western entrepreneurs cooperate in such a way that the peasant raises the crop and sells it to the sugar mill outright or has it milled on a share basis. Such arrangements are known in Formosa, the Philippines, and Fiji.

In the palm-oil industry we have an original peasant commodity of the tropical rainforest areas of West Africa, which is experiencing ever-increasing competition from efficiently organized and scientifically managed plantations of the Belgian Congo and South-east Asia. The African peasant does not cultivate the palm tree, but collects the fruit under conditions coming closer to a gathering economy than to a horticultural economy. Furthermore, his methods of extraction are wasteful and inefficient and his product is of inferior quality, compared to the oil produced by a plantation. Since the African gathers the fruit slowly and does not process it immediately, fermentation sets in, causing a high free fatty-acid content and lowering the value of the extracted oil. The following table supplies the statistical evidence of the threat of plantation palm-oil to African peasant-produced palm-oil. Unless concentrated efforts are made by the Agricultural Service of Nigeria to modernize the peasant industry of the country the future of that industry is certainly dark.

Export of Palm-Oil
(in 1,000 metric tons)

Country	1909–13 average	1924–8 average	1930	1934	1936	1938
Indonesia	nil	2·9	9·6	121·3	172·3	220·7
Nigeria	176·3	249·1	262·8	113·0	163·7	111·3

On the other hand, in the economic history of the tropics there are numerous instances where a commodity once produced primarily on a large scale by a few plantations is now being produced by innumerable small peasants, each raising a small quantity for sale. A good example is cotton, which, in the tropics at least, is almost exclusively a peasant crop. Another is cacao, which in West Africa is a peasant crop, while in the American and Asiatic tropics it is produced by plantations as well as peasants.

South-east Asian rubber planters—who in the 1910's had completely ignored the Indonesian and Malayan gardens—became seriously concerned in the 1920's and 1930's over the remarkable growth of the peasant rubber production, since by that time peasant gardens were supplying about half of the world's rubber. Had it not been for the International

Rubber Agreement of 1934 the planters would have been in a desperate situation. There can be little doubt that the Asiatic peasant producers would have further increased their share of the world output at the cost of the plantations, many of which were forced to stop operations on account of high fixed overhead costs and low rubber prices. The raising of rubber is relatively easy and does not require much labour; the trees are practically free of plant diseases, have no dangerous insect pests, and are seldom subject to weather risks; the coagulation of latex and the preparation of smoked sheet rubber or crêpe rubber is so simple that it can be done by a peasant who has not more than a few buckets, a hand mangle, and a small smoking shed. So long as the market demands mainly smoked sheet rubber, rubber will remain an ideal peasant cash crop. Special types of rubber, such as creamed latex and sprayed rubber, however, will remain the domain of plantations, which have the technical installations needed for the processing of latex into such special types of rubber.

There is considerable evidence that official policy in both Malaya and Indonesia has favoured the plantations and has been definitely unfavourable to peasants, with the result that the trend leading towards a capture of the bulk of the natural rubber market by peasant producers was stopped.[1]

The table on page 325, giving the respective shares of peasant and plantation agriculture in the agricultural exports of Indonesia, is most interesting. It shows that commodities requiring a complex industrial apparatus for processing are produced by plantations, while other commodities are the domain of the small farmer.

In Indonesia, palm-oil, sugar, and tea are for all practical purposes plantation commodities, while nutmeg, kapok, coconut, and pepper are peasant commodities, in each instance more than 80 per cent of the production being supplied by one type of economy. Tobacco, gambier, rubber, coffee and essential oils are neither pre-eminently peasant or plantation products, but the two economies share more generally in the production. It must be kept in mind, however, that other parts of the tropics have a different division of labour between large-scale and small-scale production units.

The champions of plantation agriculture are too ready to pass condemning judgment on peasant agriculture, which they call inefficient and backward, in terms of yield, wasteful and destructive as far as the soil

[1] See Bauer, P. T., *The Rubber Industry. A Study in Competition and Monopoly*, Cambridge, 1948; Suchtelen, B. C. C. C. M. M. van, *Neerlands Nieuwe Eereschuld aan Indie*, Hilversum, 1939.

is concerned. Regarding the first point it may be said that the plantation yields began to exceed peasant yields only when the planters in their struggle to cut cost of production began to apply scientific research, especially of geneticists, chemists, and soil scientists; prior to this the yields were about the same. Scientific selection and plant breeding brought forth high-yielding strains, producing as much as several times the quantities that previously were considered satisfactory. The distribution among peasant producers of high-yielding plants raised in government nurseries should reduce markedly the difference between plantation and peasant yields. As far as the second point is concerned, it should be kept in mind that in the plantation history of the tropics there are numerous instances where cultivation practices led to rapid depletion of the soil resources through accelerated erosion. Westerners, accustomed to clean cultivation and clean weeding in the temperate zone, carried this practice into the tropics, regarding the native practice of keeping the ground between their tree crops covered by weeds, which were occasionally slashed, as a sign of laziness and backwardness. The financial depression of the 1930's forced the rubber planters to reduce production costs; so that clean weeding was abolished. What was once considered a 'typical sign of Oriental laziness' is today considered a sound cultivation practice.

The Respective Share of Peasant and Plantation Agriculture on the Agricultural Exports of Indonesia (1938)[1]

Commodity	Peasant agriculture (per cent)	Plantation agriculture (per cent)
Palm-oil and kernels	nil	100
Sugar	1	99
Tea	18	82
Tobacco	30	70
Gambier	36	64
Rubber	48	52
Essential oils	57	43
Coffee	58	42
Nutmeg	80	20
Kapok	83	17
Coconut products	95	5
Pepper	99	1

In other instances the peasant of the tropics will do well to take over cultivation techniques from plantations. Coastal tribes of New Guinea

[1] 'The Export crops of the Netherlands Indies in 1938', *Bulletin of the Central Bureau of Statistics*, No. 175, Batavia, 1939, pp. 14–15.

imitate European planters and lay their coconut orchards more efficiently than in the old days.[1] Should the West African peasant clear the forest and plant young oil palms, the latter, not shaded by other trees, would not grow as tall as formerly, which makes harvesting both easier and safer. By planting high-yielding strains he would have at the same time a much higher harvest than before.

As Governor of Nigeria, Sir Hugh Clifford, who had long experience in Malaya, one of the leading plantation areas of the world, opposed Lord Leverhulme successfully in his attempt to establish Lever Brothers plantations in British West Africa. His views on the comparative advantage of peasant and plantation agriculture are expressed in the following statement made before the Legislative Council of Nigeria in 1920:

> Agricultural interests in tropical countries which are mainly, or exclusively, in the hands of the native peasantry (a) have a firmer root than similar enterprises when owned and managed by Europeans, because they are natural growths, not artificial creations, and are self-supporting, as regards labour, while European plantation can only be maintained by some system of organized immigration or by some form of compulsory labour; (b) are incomparably the cheapest instruments for the production of agricultural produce on a larger scale that has yet been devised; and (c) are capable of a rapidity of expansion and a progressive increase of output that beggared every record of the past, and are altogether unparalleled in all the long history of European agricultural enterprises in the Tropics.[2]

Sir Hugh Clifford's opponents, the palm-oil planters, proved that scientifically managed plantations can produce more cheaply than peasants. Gilbert Burk in a recent issue of *Fortune* states: 'Total cost has been cheaper than the price paid for native produce in all except the depression years. And today the finest palm-oil can be produced for another half of the £25 a ton that the inferior native product brings.'[3] Sir Hugh's other two points still stand today. From a social point of view a peasant economy is no doubt preferable to a plantation economy. Elspeth Huxley recently entered the controversy after having visited the Groundnut Projects of East Africa, and her argument should please the Directors of Unilever, who conceived the scheme in 1946.

The basic trouble [with peasant agriculture] is that it can reach so far and no farther. The fortunate and industrious peasant may achieve a reasonable standard

[1] Reed, St. W., 'The Making of Modern New Guinea', *Memoirs of the American Philosophical Society*, Vol. XVIII, p. 255.

[2] Address to Nigerian Legislative Council 1920; quoted in Lord Hailey, *An African Survey*, New York, 1938, p. 962.

[3] Burk, G., 'Unilever's Africa', *Fortune*, Vol. 37, Jan. 1948, p. 136.

for himself, but he can scarcely ever produce a surplus for others, and for the enrichment of his country, large enough to support the elaborate machinery and social services of a modern state. Therefore, if you want an efficient Government, full of experienced experts, as you do nowadays, with all the benefits of schools, hospitals, welfare services and the rest, you must build on a more productive system. For instance, you must mechanise agriculture. The woman with a hoe must give way to the man with a tractor, who can do perhaps twenty times as much in a day. . . . What is now increasingly obvious is that it is not European but African peasant farming that is uneconomic, and that if these territories are to avoid disaster, the African must somehow learn to emulate the European— and abandon a way of farming which is inexorably and quite rapidly destroying the fertility of the land.[1]

Those familiar with tropical agriculture will readily see that this statement goes much too far. How many of the tropical export crops, for example, lend themselves to mechanization? Certainly none of the perennial tree crops do; instead they require individual care, attention, and handling. Peanuts can, of course, be produced efficiently with the help of agricultural machinery, and large surpluses will become available. Practically all the land of a large mechanized farm can produce for export, since little is required for the raising of food crops consumed by the small labour force of such a mechanized peanut farm.

The geographer is interested not only in the economic aspects of the controversy but also in the effect of the respective systems upon the cultural landscape of a region, in the physiognomy that these economies create, in types of land use and land tenure that they develop, in the effect on population distribution and racial composition where the plantation system prevails. We frequently observe the growth of a 'plural' society, consisting of a colonial aristocracy of Western stock, a group which German geographers call 'Koloniale Oberschicht', as well as a sizeable population group formed by non-native, non-western labourers, together with artisans, shopkeepers, and traders, and, finally, the local population, which usually represents the bulk of the population—although in Malaya the immigrant element actually outnumbers the Malay. Such a population structure becomes a source of friction and conflict as political consciousness grows.

Territories with a strong peasant economy follow a different pattern. The population remains homogeneous, which has a beneficial effect. Modern education, improvement in diet and health conditions, and improvement in production and trading bring about an uplift in the standard

[1] Huxley, Elspeth, 'Some Impressions of East Africa Today', *African Affairs*, Vol. 46, 1947, pp. 201, 202, 203.

22

of living, which affects probably a larger part of the population than is the case in plantation areas. Out of the ranks of the people come forth a group of educated men anxious to take over the government affairs of their native land.

Settlement Possibilities in the Tropics

In humid low latitudes contrast between highly developed, densely populated areas and areas which are either only partially developed or completely forest-covered is striking and thought-provoking. It is not surprising that geographers have frequently envisaged a great expansion of population and agricultural production in the tropics. Alexander von Humboldt pictured teeming cities in the Amazon Valley. Albrecht Penck was of the opinion that the humid tropics of America and Africa were capable of supporting 200 persons per square kilometre provided the agricultural techniques of the Asiatic tropics were carried over into America and Africa.[1] Sauer has pointed out that the New World 'tropical forests seem to have far fewer peoples than they did at the first coming of the white man . . .' and that therefore with modern hygiene it might be possible to repeople the American tropical forest areas.[2]

Although there is general agreement that, despite all specific limitations, the tropics do offer extensive possibilities for future settlement, there is no agreement as to who should fill these tropical lands. Most Westerners are inclined to look at the tropics from a Western point of view and to examine them as potential areas of white settlement. This becomes quite apparent when one compares the abundance of literature on white settlement in the tropics with the scant quantity on pioneering of tropical peoples or of mid-latitude Asiatics, such as Chinese and Japanese.

The problems of settlement and acclimatization of white settlers in the humid tropics has occupied geographers as well as scientists in other fields for a long time. But so far no conclusive answer has been found to the question whether white settlement and acclimatization in the humid tropics is possible. Instead we are confronted by confusion and many contradictory observations.[3]

[1] Penck, Albrecht, 'Die Tragfähigkeit der Erde', in *Lebensraumfragen Europäischer Völker*, Vol. I, *Europa*, Leipzig, 1941, p. 27.

[2] Sauer, Carl O., 'The Prospects for Redistribution of Population', in *Limits of Land Settlement*, prepared under the direction of Isaiah Bowman, New York, 1937, p. 20.

[3] The most comprehensive survey of the problem is found in Price, A. Grenfell, *White Settlers in the Tropics*, New York, 1939. See also Trewartha, Glenn T., 'Recent

The confusion is partly due to a lack of common understanding of what is meant by 'successful white settlement in the tropics'. It should not include government officials, missionaries, businessmen, planters, and soldiers who spend only a part of their life in the tropics, who have frequent furloughs in mid-latitudes, and who send their children for their education to non-tropical countries. These are tropical sojourners. The term should apply only to white colonists permanently settled in the tropics who carry on all types of activity, including manual labour, maintain standards of health, of physical strength, of mental energy, and of culture which correspond favourably to those of the parent stock in the homeland, and whose descendants in successive generations show no signs of either physical, moral, or cultural degeneration.

Again, many of the contradictory observations may be attributed to the fact that the climate of the low latitudes is far from being uniform. Instead we find numerous types, depending upon such factors as latitude, elevation, geographical location in relation to oceans, amount and seasonal distribution of rainfall, and prevailing atmospheric circulation. This lack of climatic uniformity in the tropics is, however, not the only obstacle that confronts us. It is practically impossible in historic studies of white tropical settlement to separate such factors as disease, dietary habits, social and economic conditions, influences of the indigenous population, and physiological effects of tropical climate upon white settlers.

Today we have two main schools of thought on the problem of white settlement in the humid tropics:

(1) There are those who hold that the tropical climate as such is no obstacle to white settlement, that in the past white settlers have failed so often mainly because of tropical diseases, poor dietary and sanitary habits, and the contact with an indigenous population of a lower culture.[1] This group regards the future with optimism because of the advancement of technology and above all of medical science. (2) There are those who maintain that, notwithstanding successful individual acclimatization of white sojourners, permanent white settlement in the humid tropics is not possible because of the inability of white peoples as a group to become

Thought on the Problem of White Acclimatization in the Wet Tropics', *Geographical Review*, Vol. 16, 1926, pp. 467–78. The agenda of the International Geographical Congress at Amsterdam in 1938 included a section on white settlement in the tropics. Some 42 papers were published in *Comptes Rendus du Congrès International de Géographie, Amsterdam 1938*, Leiden, 1938, Vol. 2, Section IIIc. See also the report on these papers by Verkade-Cartier van Dissel, E. F., in the same series, Vol. 2, *Rapports*, pp. 123–48.

[1] See Gourou, Pierre, *Les Pays Tropicaux, Principes d'une Géographie Humaine et Economique*, Paris, 1947, pp. 137–8.

acclimatized. They believe that tropical sunlight, heat, humidity, and the absence of pronounced seasonal variation have an adverse effect upon the white man's body and lead to general debility and degeneration.

In the past the rainy equatorial lowlands have been an area of activity for white sojourners, but they have been avoided by white settlers. White settlement has been undertaken either near the outer fringes of the tropics, such as northern Queensland or Espiritu Santo, or in highland areas, such as Costa Rica where the mean annual temperature is below 70° F. Many observers believe that even the more moderate temperatures of tropical highlands do not make such areas safe for permanent white settlement.

Only further research by physicians, physiologists, climatologists and geographers may give us the final answer to the problem of white settlement in the tropics. The elimination of the factor of tropical disease is a very important aid in this direction.

The main problem of white settlement in the tropics is that of acclimatization, and closely related to this is the question of whether white settlers are able to perform manual labour in the tropics. This problem either does not seem to exist or at least is not as serious for southern Chinese and Japanese.[1] Both groups have shown greater ability to settle in the tropics and greater readiness to perform manual labour there than have Westerners.

The settlement of Europeans in tropical regions seems invariably to have brought great disadvantages to aboriginal peoples who were politically weaker and who had a simpler material culture, because the interests of the two groups are diametrically opposed. It deprived the indigenous population of either a part or all of its land, or at least of that part of the land which was not yet used regularly but was needed as a reserve for future growth; it led, in some instances, to confinement on reserves; and it exposed the native inhabitants to a great pressure to work for the incoming white settlers. Too often these settlers have the attitude that it is the native's prescribed place in world order to be an inferior working class. They rationalize, moreover, that since the peoples of the tropics are not accustomed to steady labour eight hours a day six days a week they will benefit greatly from developing this Western habit, and that they also will gain from learning the agricultural techniques of the Westerner. Actually the average Westerner has little or nothing new to offer which would improve indigenous agricultural methods, and, as I have mentioned, there has frequently occurred a deterioration in native agriculture and a reduction of food supply as a result of the prolonged absence of a

[1] See Pelzer, Karl J., 'Japanese Migration and Colonization', in *Limits of Land Settlement*, op. cit., pp. 155-94.

large part of the able-bodied men while they are working in plantations or mines.

If, however, the indigenous peoples do take up the raising of cash crops and become competitors, the settlers often turn around and look for ways and means to reduce or even to eliminate this new competition. They ask the government for special considerations such as subsidies, reduction of railway rates, and they may even go so far as to request special legislation against native production of export crops which compete with their own crops. To give an example, the settlers of Kenya were strongly opposed to the raising of coffee by Africans for reasons of competition, but they supported their opposition by such arguments as that the carelessness of the African peasant represented a constant threat to the European coffee grower because pests might spread to European-owned coffee gardens, and that the inferior African production would lower the value of Kenya coffee on the world market. White settlers not only frown upon the development of indigenous export agriculture because of the competition that it creates, but also because it may deprive them of their labour force, without which they cannot operate. Today many students of colonial policy hold that the future economic prospects of tropical areas depend more upon a strong development of native agriculture and other native economic activities than on the economic success of a handful of Western plantation companies, small bands of white settlers, or a few white traders.

For such reasons it seems desirable to restrict the migration of white settlers as far as possible to those parts of the tropics which for all practical purposes do not already have a coloured population. I have come to this conclusion, although I participated for several years in studies of white settlement possibilities in the tropics, because of an increasing awareness of the fact that large-scale white settlement among indigenous peoples seems nearly always to create racial segregation, and to have many adverse effects upon the economic and political development of tropical peoples.

Furthermore, there is the vital consideration that tropical peoples themselves need pioneering areas for their growing population. In many parts of the humid low latitudes the population density has reached such levels that nothing should be left undone that may contribute to a lowering of population pressure and to a reduction of the ratio between farming population and cultivated land. Migration to agricultural pioneering areas is, no doubt, not as effective as industrialization or a lowering of the birth rate, but it should not be ignored. Pioneering of white settlers in the tropics is a costly matter, whereas pioneering of natives of the tropics can be undertaken at much lower cost. The difference in cost is due to the difference in standards of living and demands made by the two groups. The standard of living of tropical peoples in congested areas is so low that a migration of landless peasants to a pioneering region and their uplift into the category of landowners will bring about a marked improvement in the economic status of the pioneer within a short time. Provided the settler is given enough land he will produce more than he needs for his subsistence. It is an easy matter for agricultural instructors to foster the raising of export crops if this fits into the programme of the government sponsoring the agricultural colonization.

A comparative study of government-sponsored agricultural colonization programmes in the Philippines and Indonesia, which I made shortly prior to World War II, showed some striking differences.[1] The Filipino settler was given from six to twelve hectares of land, which permitted him to raise commercial crops in addition to his subsistence crops. The government encouraged him to raise crops which were in demand on the domestic market and were being imported from abroad. The Indonesian settler, on the other hand, was allowed only a subsistence farm of one hectare, since there the government was already harassed by the problem of marketing the country's production of commercial crops and was only anxious to relieve Java's population pressure by settling as many landless Javanese in the islands around Java as possible.

In the 1930's the Dutch, after three decades of experimentation, developed a technique of selecting pioneer districts which deserves careful study by other countries that face a need for agricultural colonization. Each area considered for colonization was subjected to careful surveys by legal experts, soil scientists, and agricultural and irrigation engineers. The various phases of investigation were undertaken in the order of the costs involved, starting with the least costly, so that unsuited districts could be eliminated with a minimum of expenditure.

The first survey investigated the question whether the land was free from any legal claims. The next phase of investigation was a reconnaissance survey by agricultural and soil specialists. The field workers collected data on topography, geology, soils, climate, vegetation, drainage, transportation facilities, local agricultural practices, planting seasons, yields, distribution and density of population—in short on all questions related to the suitability of the land for settlement. Since irrigation was considered essential for successful settlement of Javanese, the possibility of bringing

[1] See Pelzer, Karl J., *Pioneer Settlement in the Asiatic Tropics*, New York, 1945, for a comparative study of government-sponsored pioneer settlement projects in the Philippines and Indonesia.

the land under irrigation was carefully studied. If the reconnaissance surveys showed that the area seemed promising in this respect, the soil was then mapped, and soil samples as well as water and silt samples of the rivers were analysed in order to determine the suitability of soil and irrigation water for the cultivation of wet rice. The final phase involved detailed planning of the irrigation systems, the lay-out of the future rice fields, the location of future villages, and the network of roads. These various surveys required at least two years of intensive work before an area could be thrown open for colonization. Once the area began to receive migrants work progressed rapidly, however, since all important steps had been planned and all vital decisions had already been made by qualified technicians.

The failure of the Philippine Government to allow sufficient time for the preparation of colonization projects may be understandable in the light of political considerations, but the lack of detailed working plans and surveys did hamper the colonization projects in the initial stages.

Shifting and Permanent Cultivation

The striking disparity in population density between different parts of the tropics usually reflects differences in physical factors that have a bearing upon the carrying capacity of the land as well as differences in culture.[1] Wherever we find a heavy concentration of peoples we are bound to meet advanced agriculture, characterized by well tended permanent fields which are used in the most intensive manner year after year or even for the raising of two crops per year. This type of agriculture is called permanent-field, or permanent, cultivation.

Areas of low population density are usually inhabited by peoples whose agricultural technique is less advanced. Instead of maintaining the fertility of their land by intensive cultivation, they clear small forest patches, raise one or two crops and then abandon the plot for a new one, leaving the old one to lie fallow for many years. During this long fallow period the abandoned land usually reverts to forest. This type of land use is known as shifting-field, or shifting, cultivation.

Shifting cultivation is a sound agricultural technique only so long as

[1] The correlation between population density and mode of land use was discussed at the International Geographical Congress in Amsterdam in 1938. See Coulter, John W., 'Le rapport entre la densite de la population et le mode d'utilisation du sol dans les regions coloniales', in *Comptes Rendus du Congrès International de Géographie Amsterdam 1938*, Leiden, 1938, Vol. 2, *Rapports*, pp. 149–62. (Text in English.)

the population density is so low that each field can lie fallow sufficiently long to revert to forest and regain its former fertility. In many parts of the tropics, especially in the African tropics, shifting cultivation has, however, become a source of difficulties because there is no longer enough forest land available to permit a sufficiently long fallow period. This may be the result of population growth, development of indigenous export agriculture creating a greatly increased demand for land, or extensive alienation of land to European settlers or plantations, and confinement of the African population on reserves. Whatever the specific reasons, the effect is always the same: extensive deforestation and serious soil erosion threatening the future of the population.

When such a situation arises, it becomes necessary to replace shifting cultivation by permanent cultivation.[1] Permanent agriculture of the Western type depends either upon a rotation which includes a legume to replace nitrogen losses, and upon keeping livestock in stables so that the manure can be accumulated and applied to the land, or upon application of commercial fertilizers. Since the use of commercial fertilizers in indigenous agriculture is not feasible for economic reasons, other methods have been used. In West Africa, agricultural instructors have succeeded in teaching African shifting cultivators the use of cattle and ploughs and in developing mixed farming. The peasant learned to preserve the animal manure and to apply it regularly to the land in order to keep up the fertility which formerly was restored only through long forest fallow.

Where the development of mixed farming is not possible, the solution may be found in green manuring with a leguminous crop, although it must be kept in mind that this technique has to be carefully adjusted to climatic conditions, otherwise it is a failure. A technique that may be better suited for the African cultivator is the composting method—highly developed by Chinese and Japanese—as modified by Sir Albert Howard at the Institute of Plant Industry in Indore, India. The principle of the composting method is to use fungi and bacteria to break down mixtures of vegetable and animal waste in order, in a relatively short time, to produce a humus that is rich in plant nutrients. The 'Indore process' was modified and simplified in Kenya to meet African conditions, where labour is not as plentiful as in India. Tropical agriculture would benefit greatly if composting of vegetable waste products and animal and human excrement were generally adopted. In the early stages of the composting process—when properly handled—the temperature rises sufficiently high to destroy both helminths and dangerous bacteria in the excrement; so

[1] See Pelzer, Karl J., *Pioneer Settlement*, op. cit., Chaps. 2 and 3.

that from a sanitary point of view no objection can be raised to the addition of excrement to the compost pits.[1]

The key problem for large parts of the tropics is to intensify indigenous agriculture by changing over from shifting to permanent cultivation. This requires such methods as mixed farming, use of cover crops, crop rotation, green manuring, composting of vegetable waste and excrement, terracing, irrigation, and drainage. A combination of several techniques is usually required in order to maintain the fertility of tropical soils which are subject to heavy leaching and oxidation, or decomposition, of the humus at a speed which is much higher than in mid-latitudes, where temperature is lower and light is not so abundant.

The Anthropogeographical Significance of Tropical Diseases

Geographers who have followed the research of their colleagues in the fields of entomology, public health, and tropical medicine have been benefited greatly in their studies of geographical problems of the tropics, since health conditions are an important factor in the human geography of the tropics. There exists a close relationship between certain types of diseases and natural as well as cultural environment. Such environmental factors are topography, temperature, amount and seasonal distribution of rainfall, fauna, flora, house types, cultivation practices of the farmers, sanitary habits, location of settlements, and such activities as raising live-stock and raising fish in fresh- and salt-water ponds. Among the insect-borne diseases, malaria, trypanosomiasis, and yellow-fever play a vital role in the distribution and size of the population in the tropics; of much lesser importance are such insect-borne diseases as plague, typhus, and dengue. Among the intestinal diseases, dysentery is important. Anky-lostomiasis, or hook-worm disease, affects probably more people than any other of the helminthic diseases. Considerations of space make it necessary that I limit myself to the first two diseases mentioned.

Malaria

Malaria, which is responsible for more sickness than any other disease in the world, is especially prevalent in the tropics. In 1880 Laveran dis-covered that malaria is caused by a parasite, and did away with the old concept of malaria being caused by germs emanating from the soil and floating in the air. Sir Donald Ross cleared up the mystery of how the

[1] See Hall, Sir Daniel, *The Improvement of Native Agriculture in Relation to Population and Public Health*, London, 1936, pp. 33–9.

parasite reaches the human body and how it passes from one human being to the other. He discovered in 1897 that the malaria parasite is not transferred mechanically by being sucked up from one person and injected into another one, but that the parasite breeds in the stomach wall of the *anopheles*, and that only its offspring are injected into another person. In 1898 Grassi made the further discovery that only the *anopheles* mosquito carries the parasite of malaria. Early efforts to control malaria by preventing the breeding of *anopheles* through clearing, filling, and draining were sometimes crowned with success, but in other instances these measures actually increased the incidence of malaria greatly.

Today we know that although in a laboratory all *anopheles* can be infected, in nature only a few *anopheles* carry malaria. Of the sixty-five varieties and species of *anopheles* in Indonesia only a dozen are malaria carriers. In India there are some forty *anopheles* species, but only a few act as vectors; in Malaya only three species out of thirty are vectors. It is not necessary, therefore, to combat all varieties and species of *anopheles*, but only those which are dangerous. These dangerous species have widely varying habits and demands so far as habitat is concerned. All *anopheles* need water in which to breed, but whereas some breed only in fresh water, others demand a certain degree of salinity; some prefer well-shaded water, others, water exposed to sunshine; some seek stagnant pools, while others require fast-flowing water. Again, there are *anopheles* that prefer animal blood to human blood. These are but a sample of the many idiosyncrasies encountered among *anopheles*. To make matters still more complicated, a species may act as a vector in one geographical area but not in others. From this it is clear that measures taken against one species with success may only improve the environment for another and make it more dangerous for the inhabitants. Recognition of all these facts has led to what is known as 'species sanitation' in anti-malaria work. This was first conceived by Sir Malcolm Watson in Malaya in 1909.

Malaria is not a single disease, but is manifested in two common types and one rare one caused by different species of *Plasmodium*, the malaria parasite. There is the benign tertian form caused by *Pl. vivax*, widespread far beyond the boundaries of the humid tropics, which is not responsible for any great rate of mortality despite the high fever that characterizes it. The sub-tertian, malignant type, caused by *Pl. falciparum*, is essentially tropical in distribution; it is responsible for widespread infant as well as adult mortality, and brings blackwater fever in its wake. Quartan malaria is less common and relatively mild; it is caused by *Pl. malariae*.

Repeated infections of malaria may result in an acquired immunity in areas where malaria is constantly present; but where transmission of malaria is seasonal, immunity is only partial.

In areas where malaria is endemic infants become infected with the disease and many die as a result, but those who survive the first infection and recurring bouts of fever may finally reach the stage in which the parasite continues to live and reproduce in the blood without causing attacks of fever. Endemic malaria is believed to reduce the fertility of women and increase the number of miscarriages.

Laymen generally are of the opinion that flooded rice fields must contribute greatly to the incidence rate of malaria by providing breeding areas for *anopheles*. Actually we have a variety of situations: (1) rice fields and irrigation channels may be completely free of any malaria vector, in which case wet-rice cultivation is completely harmless; (2) rice fields may be harmless, but the irrigation channels may be the source of danger if the area has an *anopheles* vector which prefers the latter; (3) rice fields may be breeding ground only for a part of the season, (4) rice fields may be dangerous throughout the growing season.[1] In other words, wet-rice cultivation may be malariagenic or may be completely harmless. Everything depends upon the habits of the *anopheles* found in a region.

Geographers do not sufficiently appreciate the fact that the flooded rice fields of the plains of the Philippines, Indochina, Siam, Burma, and Assam are practically free of malaria; while the foothills and uplands are hyperendemic malaria areas because of the presence of *A. minimus*, one of the most dangerous malaria carriers known.[2] This culprit prefers clear, unpolluted, slowly-moving streams and brooks with grassy edges; stagnant water, on the other hand, it avoids. *A. maculatus*, which also prefers a hilly or mountainous environment and quiet waters well exposed to sunshine, frequently appears together with *A. minimus*.[3] It is the presence of these two species that has made the upland regions of the Philippines,

[1] Russel, Paul F., Knipe, Fred W., and Rao, H. Ramanatha, 'On Agricultural Malaria and its control with special reference to South India', *India Medical Gazette*, Vol. LXXVII, 1942, pp. 744 ff.

[2] My studies of pioneer settlement regions in the Philippines made me aware of malaria as a serious obstacle of pioneering in areas above the coastal plains but below 2,000 to 3,000 feet. See Pelzer, Karl J., *Pioneer Settlement*, op. cit., p. 113.

[3] In the foothills of the Himalayas the planting of rhododendron and privet hedges along the banks of small streams has suppressed these two *anopheles* species. In Java they have been successfully combated by the planting of such shade-providing plants as *Tithonia diversifolia* and the New World plants *Ochroma lagopes*, or balsa tree, and *Cassia alata*, or 'kimanila', also known as 'katepeng manila'. (The name of the latter shows that the Indonesian is aware of the introduction of this American plant via the galleon route from Acapulco to Manila. In the Philippines it is known as 'acapulco'.)

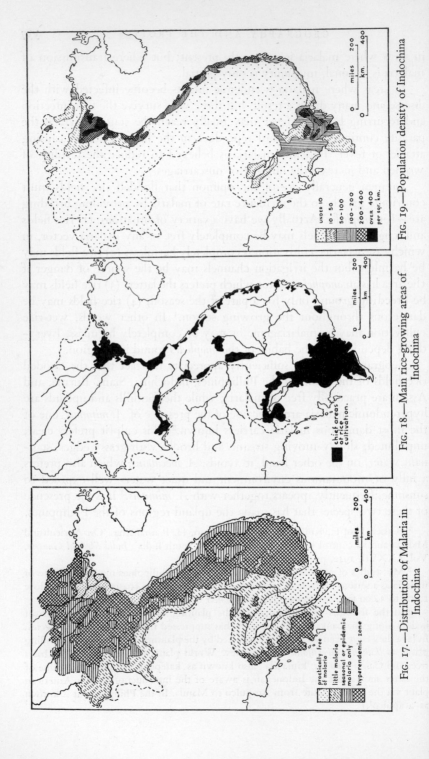

FIG. 19.—Population density of Indochina

UNDER 10
10 - 50
50-100
100-200
200-400
over 400 per sqr. km.

0   200   400
km.
0   200   400
miles

FIG. 18.—Main rice-growing areas of Indochina

chief areas of rice cultivation.

0   200   400
km.
0   200   400
miles

FIG. 17.—Distribution of Malaria in Indochina

practically free of malaria
little malaria
seasonal or epidemic malaria only
hyperendemic zone

0   200   400
km.
0   200   400
miles

Indochina, Siam, Burma, and other parts of India so feared by the peoples of the lowlands, who have not acquired immunity because they live in areas where malaria is rare. This lack of immunity on the part of the plains people, and the presence of a dangerous and effective malaria vector in the uplands among hill tribes infected with malaria parasites, make pioneer settlement in these areas so dangerous an undertaking. The hill people themselves have acquired immunity as a result of repeated infections in childhood. Nevertheless, infant mortality rate resulting from malaria is high among hill tribes since not all infants have the strength to acquire immunity. This fact acts as an effective check against rapid population growth in hyperendemic malaria regions.

The three maps of Indochina clearly show the correlation between the distribution of effective malaria vectors, rice cultivation, and population density. Gourou has suggested that man's activity, that is, the conversion of the alluvial plains from a natural to a cultural landscape has rid these lowlands of malaria vectors.[1] It seems more likely, however, that these plains were fortunate in never having really dangerous and aggressive vectors of the type which benefit from agricultural development, and which make other lowlands in the tropics so unhealthful that any attempt of pre-scientific man to settle them has been condemned to failure. In the delta of the Red River are found *A. vagus* and *A. hyrcanus* var. *sinensis*, which breed in swamps, irrigation canals that are badly kept up, and rice fields which do not completely dry up during the fallow period. These two potential vectors prefer animal to human blood and are therefore not considered dangerous; malaria is no problem in the delta of the Red River.[2] In the delta of Song Ca malaria epidemics occur during the time of the winter monsoon when *A. ludlowi*, which breeds in brackish water near the coast, is blown into areas far removed from its breeding grounds. Except for such special instances, the plains of Indochina are free of vectors which would benefit from the prevailing agricultural practice of the Annamese.

In Indonesia we find a different situation, resulting from the presence of a larger variety of vectors. Coastal cities of Java and Sumatra, such as Batavia, Surabaya, Sibolga, or Belawan Deli, were notorious for their malaria. It has been recognized that *A. ludlowi* var. *sundaicus* is the culprit. This species breeds in brackish water open to the sun, for instance where the mangrove belt has been cut and where we have lagoons and salt-water fish-ponds. It prefers to breed among long-fibred floating algae

[1] Gourou, Pierre, *Les Pays Tropicaux*, op. cit., p. 122.

[2] In the Javanese pioneering areas of South Sumatra *A. hyrcanus* causes regular epidemics of malaria, as I learned during my stay in the area in 1940.

which provide protection against larviparous enemies. Once it became known that this mosquito is always dangerous, since it attacks man readily, various techniques were developed to combat it.[1] Since salt-water fish-ponds play a very important role in the economy of the Indonesians, methods had to be found which do not reduce the production of the ponds but free them of this *anopheles*. Monthly drying out of the ponds eliminate the algae that provide *anopheles* larvae with hiding places against *Haplochilus panchax*, a fish that feeds on them. During the time that the pond is being dried the fish take refuge in a ditch dug along the margin of each pond. This relatively simple method makes the fish-ponds harmless.

More difficult is the sanitation of lagoons closed from the sea by sand-bars. We find these above all along the west coast of Sumatra, the north coast of Java, and the north coast of Madura. During a visit to Madura I saw that small jetties had been built which prevent the lagoons from being shut off from the sea. So long as the lagoons are kept open *A. ludlowi* finds no possibility to breed in them.

The construction of technical irrigation systems which make year-round rice cultivation possible may improve living conditions for *A. aconitus*, as became apparent in the plains of the Tjihea River of West Java. The plains of this river are irrigated by means of large-scale irrigation works, constructed between 1891 and 1904. As a result of continuous flooding of the rice fields the number of *A. aconitus* increased greatly and with it malaria, so that many peasants fled from the region. Finally in 1919 a method was devised to combat this mosquito successfully. The drainage system was improved, so that the rice fields now dry out completely after the rice harvest; all fields are planted at the same time and the irrigation and drainage canals are kept clean of all vegetation. These measures had a spectacular result. The average splenic index dropped from 88 per cent in 1919 to 72 per cent in 1922, 20·4 per cent in 1931, and, 12·5 per cent in 1935. The annual death-rate decreased from 33 per thousand in 1919 to 15 per thousand in 1935.

When *anopheles* mosquitoes breed during the growing season in rice fields which have an efficient irrigation and drainage system, they can be eliminated by the relatively simple method of periodically draining all water so that the rice field lies dry for twenty-four to forty-eight hours every six to nine days. The intervals at which the water is drained off depends upon the biology of the vector one wishes to eliminate, while the length of the drying period depends upon the type of soil one wishes to

---

[1] When one considers the amount of havoc that *A. ludlowi* has caused in Indonesia, one realizes how fortunate the Philippines are to be free of this dangerous vector, as salt-water fish-ponds play an important economic role there.

dry. This technique causes the death of all mosquito larvae, without interfering with the cultivation of rice.

In Indonesia malaria caused by *A. maculatus, A. minimus,* and *A. hyrcanus* is often man-made and results from an activity which unwittingly improves the environment of these mosquitoes.[1] Since such a large proportion of malaria in rural regions of the tropics is man-made, it is essential to survey carefully the *anopheles* population of a potential colonization area, to determine the species, and to study their breeding habits in order to avoid improving the habitat of the *anopheles* mosquitoes which are known to carry the disease.

There is, of course, also the problem that a dangerous carrier may be introduced into a new geographical area. *A. gambiae* was introduced from Africa into north-eastern Brazil, where it was first reported in 1930. Since this mosquito caused an appalling death-rate and since it steadily spread beyond Nata, large sums were spent to stop its expansion and to eradicate it completely before it was too late. The last *A. gambiae* was found in north-eastern Brazil in September 1940; but constant vigilance is necessary, otherwise *A. gambiae* will be brought again into the New World.[2] This invasion of Brazil by *A. gambiae* is one example of what may happen when modern transportation lines between different parts of the tropics enable dangerous disease-carrying insects to expand their geographical area, and establish themselves in new territory which has favourable environmental conditions.

In times of war we may free a limited area of malaria by exterminating all anopheline mosquitoes, but under normal peace time circumstances such an approach to the malaria problem seems to be unfeasible. The line of attack which is generally considered the most economical and promising is the one which tries to destroy the species known to act as a carrier without going to the expense of killing all mosquitoes. On account of the specialization of the *anopheles* it is often possible to do without insecticides and other chemicals, but to devise a natural control method such as shading of breeding areas; in some instances it is necessary to seek the aid of a biological agent, such as a fish that will feed on the larvae.

Trypanosomiasis

Trypanosomiasis, in both its human and animal forms, is carried by various species of the tsetse fly, or *Glossina*. Both forms of the disease are

[1] Pelzer, Karl J., 'Tanah Sabrang and Java's Population Problem', *Far Eastern Quarterly*, Vol. 5, 1946, pp. 140–1.

[2] Coggeshall, L. T., 'Anopheles gambiae in Brazil, 1930 to 1940', *Geographical Review*, Vol. 34, 1944, pp. 308–10.

generally fatal. They are one of the most serious obstacles to settlement in fly-infested areas and have in the past destroyed the life of uncounted numbers of both men and animals. A distinct correlation exists between tsetse fly density and population density.

Human trypanosomiasis, or sleeping sickness, is caused by one of two species of trypanosome, *T. gambiense* or *T. rhodesiense*. The former is carried by *Glossina palpalis* and the latter by G. *morsitans* or G. *swynnertoni*. Animal trypanosomiasis, or nagana, is caused by *T. brucei*, *T. congolense*, and *T. vivax*, which are transmitted by a number of species of the tsetse fly.

Various species of tsetse fly are widely distributed throughout Central Africa, but not all tsetse-infested areas are infected with trypanosomiasis. Infected areas are found in West African colonies, such as the Gold Coast and Southern Nigeria, the Belgian Congo, East Africa, and as far south as Rhodesia and Angola. Trypanosomiasis is known to have been spread from disease-infected regions into non-infected tsetse areas as a result of the opening of new communication routes and labour migrations.

The eradication of animal trypanosomiasis, or nagana, is difficult since wild game is immune to the disease but carries the parasite; so that wild game represents a reservoir of nagana against which domesticated live-stock has no immunity. Nagana-infected tsetse areas are consequently prohibitive for cattle.[1] Prior to the machine age all field work as well as transport had to be carried on by human beings unaided by work animals. The tsetse fly is one of several reasons why such a large part of the African population is still practising shifting cultivation. Because of the fly these people cannot practise mixed agriculture.

In recent years considerable progress has been made in the fight against trypanosomiasis. Two lines have been followed: treatment of the victims and action against the fly. The medical treatment of suffering men and beast has been greatly advanced. Prophylactics have also been found. Intravenous injection of Bayer 205, or Germanin, provides immunity against sleeping sickness at least for a brief period. Similarly, temporary immunization of cattle is possible, but, so far as I know, not permanent immunization.

As in the case of malaria most observers hold the view that it is impossible to eradicate the tsetse fly menace completely, since insecticides cannot be applied to territories extending over thousands of square miles.

[1] The correlation between distribution of tsetse fly and cattle in Northern Rhodesia is clearly shown by Ogilvie, Alan G., 'Co-operative Research in Geography: With an African Example', *Scottish Geographical Magazine*, Vol. 50, 1934, pp. 370–3.

They believe that the use of insecticides must be limited to critical areas. However, during the Fourth International Congress on Tropical Medicine and Malaria held in Washington, aerial spraying was demonstrated and it was maintained that new spraying and dusting equipment could cover as much as 10,000 acres of land in a day. Provided the costs are not prohibitive, such a development could contribute greatly to the expansion of human settlement and agricultural production in Africa, where 4,500,000 square miles are estimated to be infested by the tsetse fly.

Conclusion

Those who are of the opinion that the tropics will, at short notice, prove to be a panacea for the ills of the European parts of the mid-latitudes by supplying foodstuffs and raw materials which are lacking, by absorbing a greater share of industrial production than at present, and by offering settlement outlets for a large number of Europeans, are bound to be disappointed. They do not seem to realize that the settlement of tropical areas is beset with a great many obstacles inherent in the physical and cultural environment. Doubtlessly many parts of the tropics are capable of absorbing an additional population and of supplying greater quantities of food and industrial raw materials; but this will require a great deal of time, the one thing which those who are desperately seeking to bring about a rapid bonification of undeveloped tropical areas are not willing to grant. It remains to be seen, for example, whether it will be possible, at short notice, to turn an African shifting cultivator, who heretofore worked mainly with a hoe, into a permanent cultivator tilling the land with tractor-drawn implements. Would this not be too revolutionary a break with the accustomed economy and cultivation practices? It does not grow out of the African's own needs, but is something wished upon him in order to alleviate the economic distress of a far-distant people. There is danger that African leaders may arouse their followers to opposition if an attempt is made to speed the pace by enforcing more intensive cultivation practices, erosion control measures, pest control, and a reduction in the number of livestock. These reforms are needed, but unless the African peasant is willing to accept these changes and is ready to co-operate, it will be extremely difficult to obtain permanent results.

Above all, the development of tropical regions will require careful planning in order to forestall faulty or poor investment of capital. A sound knowledge, on the part of the planners, of the physical and cultural setting, and of the complex interrelation between man and his environment is essential. It would be ideal to obtain the co-operation of scientists

23

representing such disciplines as geology, geomorphology, soil science, hydrology, climatology, ecology, parasitology, medicine, agronomy, cultural geography, and anthropology.[1]

Aerial photography provides us with a very useful tool for speedy investigation of such topics as geology, soils, vegetation, extent of currently utilized area, and extent of damage caused by erosion.[2] But investigation on the ground must supply basic information about distribution of population, relationship between population and resources, seasonal demand for labour within the native economy, extent and effect of labour migration to Western-owned enterprises, types of land use in relation to topography, conditions of land tenure—especially the effect of contact with the Western world—upon indigenous concepts of land tenure, and cognate questions.

It is the task of the geographer to furnish a synthesis by integrating his own data and observations with those supplied by scientists in neighbouring fields as well as by non-professional observers familiar with certain regions.[3] Co-operative research of scientists concerned with the various tropical problems will give us the data necessary for planning a sound development of the natural and human resources of the tropics.

---

[1] The U.S. Economic Survey of Micronesia, organized in 1946 by the U.S. Commercial Company at the request of the United States Navy, is an example of such a co-operative research programme.

[2] See Troll, Carl, 'Koloniale Raumplanung in Afrika', *Zeitschrift der Gesellschaft für Erdkunde zu Berlin*, 1941, pp. 1–41, and 'Die wissenschaftliche Luftbildforschung als Wegbereiterin kolonialer Erschliessung', *Beiträge zur Kolonialforschung*, Vol. 1, pp. 11–26. See also Sisam, J. W. B., 'The Use of Aerial Survey in Forestry and Agriculture', *Imperial Agric. Bureaux Joint Publ.* No. 9, Oxford, 1947.

[3] The Committee of the British Association on the Human Geography of Inter-Tropical Africa, formed in 1926, sent out a pamphlet to government officials and missionaries containing two model essays on the relation of African tribes to their environment together with nineteen questions. It hoped to obtain a mass of data which, once integrated, would contribute to the understanding of the human geography of the various African colonies. (*The Human Geography of Inter-Tropical Africa: The Need For Investigation.* 1930.) The most comprehensive response came from Northern Rhodesia. A synthesis of the Northern Rhodesian reports was presented by Professor Alan G. Ogilvie in his presidential address to the geography section of the Aberdeen Meeting of the British Association for the Advancement of Science. (Ogilvie, Alan G., 'Co-operative Research in Geography: With an African Example', *Scottish Geographical Magazine*, Vol. 50, 1934, pp. 353–78.)

CHAPTER XV

GEOGRAPHY AND REGIONALISM

E. W. GILBERT, B.LITT., M.A.

E. W. Gilbert is Reader in Human Geography in the University of Oxford. Before 1936 Mr. Gilbert taught in the Universities of London and Reading. He is the author of The Exploration of Western America *(1933); he contributed to* An Historical Geography of England *(1936), ed. H. C. Darby, and to* A Survey of the Social Services in the Oxford District, 2 vols. *(1938 and 1940).*

Introduction

THERE is no State whose sovereignty extends over only one geographical region. The State is an artificial contrivance by which several, or perhaps many, geographical regions, some natural, some man-made, are welded into one working unit. Nevertheless, if only for the purposes of administration, even the most highly centralized States are split into numerous sub-divisions. An examination of the political map shows that France is divided into departments, Britain into counties, Spain into provinces, Poland into *powiats*, and that all countries have some such system. It is essential that a State should be divided in this way, but the political divisions adopted may or may not coincide with geographical regions.

Most of the modern States of Europe have come into being as the result of the union of previously independent political areas, and it has frequently happened that these older and smaller units are real geographical regions. This process can be studied in the history of France, Spain, and Britain for earlier centuries, and in that of Germany and Italy in more recent periods. During the last hundred years a reverse process has occurred. The regions, of which the large nation-states are composed, have been clamouring for some form of local independence, and sometimes for complete separation.

Regionalism is a word with many meanings. It can be used merely to imply the way in which a centralized State decentralizes its administration. On the other hand a separatist movement, whose leaders demand the complete severance of their region from the existing State, is also a form of regionalism. Again regionalism may mean the spiritual and intellectual activities by which a region tries to oppose the standardizing efforts of the capital. Somewhere between the extremes lies a mode of regionalism

345

that implies the grant of considerable powers of local government to a region, which still remains a part of the larger unit, the State. Regions can be regarded as the separate limbs of the body politic: regional diversity need not be a danger and it can strengthen the unity of the State.

There is no doubt that in many States the boundaries of the existing political sub-divisions are no longer suited to the needs of modern society; they do not contain the areas which really matter, the regions. It is quite as difficult to define the word region as to give a precise meaning to regionalism.

A region has been described by Professor E. G. R. Taylor as 'a unit area of the Earth's surface'. The unifying factor which makes mere space into a region may be natural or it may have been stamped on the area by man; the Sahara is a case of the former, the Black Country of the latter. Professor Taylor has also explained that regions can possess intrinsic 'wholeness' and social unity.

As Mr. F. W. Morgan has shown so admirably, the study of regionalism and regions has not been undertaken solely by professional geographers.[1] The politicians and practical administrators have been compelled to examine regions and regionalism through sheer necessity. Very often they have translated geographical theories into action in a haphazard fashion and with little understanding of the geographical facts involved. A third group, the regional poets and novelists, have been far more effective and influential than either politicians or geographers. The great writers who created the schools of regional novels, which have sprung up in so many countries of Europe, have exerted a powerful influence in fostering the growth of regionalism. The novelists discovered the regional personality of diverse regions in many lands, and have been able to illuminate the unity of place and people that gives spirit and vitality to a region. The novelists have made the people understand regionalism and the region more effectively than the geographers. In many countries in Europe the novelists and poets have stimulated those who dwell in a region to realize its existence as a provincial unit, distinct from the State; sometimes their writings have inflamed regional discontent against the State.

The study of regionalism and the region has awakened geography from the deep slumber into which it had fallen. It is through the region that new life has been given to the dead bones of geography. In the view of the writer, geography is the art of recognizing and describing the personalities of regions. It is soon realized that regions, like human individuals, have very different characters, and moreover, the characters

[1] F. W. Morgan, 'Three Aspects of Regional Consciousness', *Sociological Review*, XXXI (1939).

both of individuals and of regions are constantly changing and developing. The art of describing regions is, therefore, quite as difficult as the art of describing the characters of human individuals; in neither case is it possible to hope for complete success. There is no scientific formula by which perfection in either art can be attained. In the present century the geographers of many countries have devoted themselves to the task of delineating and describing regions. Thus the day-to-day work of the geographer may be of great value to the politician, if the latter wishes to make reforms in the internal boundaries of the State. Nevertheless, although the geographers have developed a technique for studying geographical material, the influence of their work on politicians has been comparatively slight, partly because they have seldom troubled to clothe their humane study with the graces of literary art. Geographers have much to learn from the novelists and poets.

The following account of regionalism is mainly concerned with some of the States of Western Europe. Summary descriptions of regionalism in France, Germany, Spain, and Portugal are followed by a lengthier discussion of the same problem in Great Britain. An attempt has been made to define the regions that would be, for geographical reasons, the best for planning England. The chapter concludes with some very brief references to regionalism in the United States of America and in Australia. As these countries have continental dimensions their problems of regionalism cannot be compared directly with those of Europe. One American or Australian region may be comparable in size to the whole of one European country like France. Throughout the chapter the work of geographers is placed in relation to that of politicians and administrators.

France

Administrative centralization has long been more highly developed in France than in any other modern state. Ever since the time of Richelieu the process of centralization had continued, although the old provinces were not abolished by the French monarchy. At the time of the outbreak of the French Revolution of 1789 France was still divided into forty 'provinces' called 'military governments', and most of these areas possessed real geographical individuality. In 1790 these historic units were wiped off the map of France and replaced by eighty-three departments. The departments are approximately equal in size and took their names from the mountains, rivers, and maritime features of France. The majority of the departments are very artificial as they were chosen with the set purpose of destroying the old areas of local unity.

The system of government by departments has been lasting and there are now ninety such divisions. Nevertheless a strong sentimental attachment to the old provinces has persisted in spite of 150 years of administration by departments. Excessive administrative centralization in Paris did not completely suppress the cultural regionalism of the provinces. Although the political tendency was to make 'all France a suburban extension of Paris', cultural regionalism remained strong in Provence, Brittany, the Basque Country, Flemish France, and Alsace-Lorraine. All these regions are remote from Paris and all have their own language or dialect. In all of them powerful regionalist movements grew up during the nineteenth century to combat the cultural standardization of the whole country by the capital.

Among the many exponents of regionalism was Vidal de la Blache (1845–1918) who founded the modern school of geographical thought in France. His geographical work enabled him to appreciate and to describe the division of France into natural regions, each with a well marked character; he saw that these regions were not used for the purposes of administration. He also observed that the provincial towns of France wielded considerable economic influence over the country which surrounded them; and that as France's economic development had proceeded, so the attractive power of the major provincial centres had increased. He described these towns as 'noeuds'—the nodes of economic concentration in France. By balancing the natural regions with the nodes, he produced in 1910 a scheme of seventeen administrative regions (Fig. 20). He argued that, with the improvement in means of communication, the departments had become too small and that a return to some form of the old provinces was essential. It is worth noticing on Fig. 20, which also shows the boundaries of the departments, that Vidal de la Blache's, proposals did not cut across the departmental boundaries, except in a few instances, but formed regions out of groups of four or five departments.

The war of 1914–18 made regional organization in France a necessity. The invasion of the country by the German armies and the possibility of Paris falling into the hands of the enemy revealed the dangers of excessive centralization. The war of 1939–45 was to show Britain precisely the same danger and it was met in the same way, by decentralization of the administrative machinery into the regions. Many French wartime problems were dealt with on a regional basis. Before 1914 France had been divided into twenty army areas for the purpose of rapid mobilization. The areas selected were chosen because they had roughly the same population and because they possessed a convenient central or nodal town in the network of railway communications. The army areas were adopted by France in

1915 for use as economic regions, and their functions were in fact very similar to those of the British Civil Defence regions in the Second World War.

Between the two wars the economic regions of France continued in being and were used for many peace-time purposes. Eventually twenty such areas were created; and although their boundaries were changed

FIG. 20.—Regions proposed by Vidal de la Blache

several times, the division of the country into economic regions corresponded in a general way to the theoretical division proposed by Vidal de la Blache. The economic regions grouped the Chambers of Commerce of several towns and each region was centred on the Chamber of Commerce of one large city. Although the economic regions had comparatively little power, they performed a useful function; and in particular they were the means of carrying out research which was of great value in the economic planning of France.

Germany

The problem of regionalism was carefully studied in Germany between
the two wars and the German literature on the subject has been analysed
in Dr. R. E. Dickinson's *The Regions of Germany* (1945). In Germany the
political framework, a legacy from the past, was exceptionally complicated and cannot be explained in a few sentences. In 1933 there were
seventeen *Länder* or Free States, in addition to Prussia which consisted of
fourteen separate divisions. These States and provinces had many outliers

FIG. 21.—Nazi Planning Regions of Germany, 1936

and inliers which added to the complications of the political system. The
great predominance of Prussia over the other States made regionalism a
more involved and difficult problem than in France or Britain.

At the same time the rapid changes, which the growth of industrialism
had brought to Germany in the last hundred years, had made the old
internal political boundaries out of date. The economic regions of reality
did not coincide with the political system. In Germany the aim of regionalists has not been to lessen the effects of centralization, but rather to
recast the boundaries of Germany on a new economic or geographical

basis. The object of many regionalists has been to prepare the way for a unified state.

There were many theoretical schemes, which are fully described by Dr. R. E. Dickinson. In 1918 Professor Hugo Preuss prepared a new set of political divisions for the Weimar Republic. Germany was to consist of a federal state of sixteen free states of roughly equal size, but his scheme failed like many others which succeeded it.

The Nazis laid great stress on the importance of a plan for national and regional development, and in 1935 they set up a National Planning Board to plan the whole German Reich. Germany was divided into twenty-three Planning Regions which broadly corresponded with the provinces of Prussia and the Länder (Fig. 21). The Ruhr, Berlin, and Hamburg were retained as separate regions. Side by side with this regional organization the Nazis set up a system of party districts of which the main unit was the *Gau*. Thus the Nazis endeavoured to root out the features of the political framework which they considered to be out of date, and to set up new regions which should function more efficiently.

Centralization became very marked under the Nazis, who deprived the old *Länder* of real self-government and made them mere administrative cogs in the machine of the Nazi state. Nazi regionalism was merely a device by which greater administrative efficiency was to be achieved.

Spain and Portugal

In both countries of the Iberian Peninsula regionalism has marked vitality although the Spanish form differs from the Portuguese variety. Spain is sharply divided by nature into separate regions each with a pronounced individuality; her King was known not as King of Spain, but as King of the *Spains*. The ancient provinces of Spain had once been kingdoms, and they were gradually united one with another. The whole country was arbitrarily divided into forty-nine so-called 'provinces' in 1833 on the model of the French system of departments. These modern provinces are not the traditional divisions of the country; they were created with the express purpose of diminishing the spirit of regionalism which was such a powerful force in the fourteen ancient 'kingdoms'.

But Spanish local spirit was far too strong to be killed by an artificial system of boundaries; and its active manifestations in Catalonia, in Galicia, and in the Basque country have sometimes savoured of nationalism rather than of regionalism. In particular, Catalan regionalism has been so clearly a movement for separation from Spain that it merits comparison with the more successful struggle of Ireland to break away from Great

Britain. Both Catalonia and Ireland desired rather more than regional home-rule. Catalonia gained a large measure of autonomy under the Spanish Republic in 1932 but this was lost in 1939. The Basque claim for autonomy was also granted by the Republic in 1936, but was not recognized by the Government of General Franco. Galicia had also asked for a Statute of Regional autonomy after a plebiscite in 1936, but no further steps have been taken to implement this since the Civil War. Only Navarra now enjoys a limited form of autonomy.

Although many geographical arguments can be brought forward to explain the political separation of Portugal from the rest of the Peninsula, none of them are entirely satisfactory. Portugal must be considered as one region of the Peninsula; and for a variety of reasons, not all geographical, it is the one region which has achieved and maintained its independence from the others. Regionalism within Portugal is not a question of independence, but one of creating convenient units for decentralization. The six ancient provinces of Portugal were divided in 1835 into seventeen districts on the French departmental model; an additional district named after Setúbal was created in 1926. These eighteen districts are not homogeneous and divide natural regions whose unity could have been preserved (Fig. 22).

A Commission of University Professors was given the task of examining the whole question in 1930. They were asked to group areas which presented marked affinities of climate, of landscape, of economic conditions, of population, of communications and means of access, and from a study of these factors to produce administrative areas which possessed natural and social unity. The Commission eventually produced a scheme by which Portugal was divided into eleven provinces (Fig. 23) and these were recognized in the new Constitution of 1933. The outer boundaries of these new units generally coincided with those of the old districts, but in most cases several districts were grouped into one province.

In the fashioning of these new provinces, Professor A. de Amorim Girão, Professor of Geography in the University of Coimbra, played a leading part. His well-known work Esbôço duma Carta Regional de Portugal, based on earlier articles, was first published as a book in 1930. His proposal for a network of thirteen regions is set out in his book and was largely adopted in a new division of Portugal into agricultural regions which was put into force in 1930.

By the Administrative Code of 1936 the Portuguese Government is committed to the new provinces, which are described as 'areas with geographic, economic, and social affinities'. It is clear that, in the case of

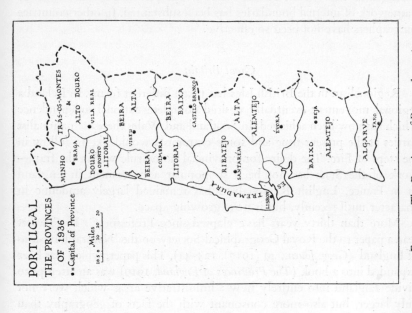

FIG. 23.—The Provinces of Portugal, 1936

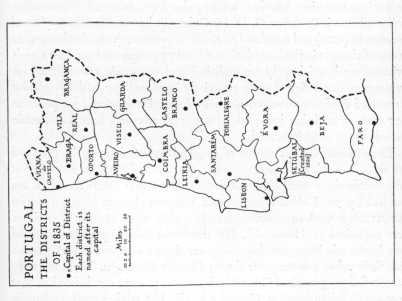

FIG. 22.—The Districts of Portugal, 1835

Portugal, the influence of a Professor of Geography on the revision of the framework of internal boundaries has been substantial. In other countries geographers have not been so effective.

Great Britain

Regionalism in the British Isles has taken different forms. In Ireland a regional movement eventually desired complete national independence which has now been achieved; in Scotland and Wales there are nationalist parties at the present time and some extremists would like to follow in the steps of Eire. The desire for provincial home rule within the framework of the State has not been so popular a movement in England as in France. English Regionalism has remained largely academic in character until recently, but is now growing apace.

More than thirty years have elapsed since Professor C. B. Fawcett read a paper to the Royal Geographical Society on the 'Natural Divisions of England' (*Geog. Journ.*, 49 (1917), 125–44). This paper, which was later expanded into a book (*The Provinces of England*, 1919) was an attempt to divide England into entirely new administrative areas which were not only larger, but also more consonant with the facts of geography than the ancient counties. Another writer who has advocated a somewhat similar scheme is Professor G. D. H. Cole. His books *The Future of Local Government* (1921) and *Local and Regional Government* (1947) both argue in favour of changes in the boundaries of local government. Professor Cole's divisions are based largely on political and economic reasons and his divisions are not designed to be so strictly in accordance with geography as those of Professor Fawcett. Since Professor Fawcett read his paper in 1917 some remarkable but rather haphazard advances have been made towards the goal he indicated.

The administrative divisions of England and Wales may be grouped into three 'orders'. First there are over 14,000 Civil Parishes, the smallest units, while the second-class consists of 475 Rural Districts which are matched by 572 Urban Districts and 309 non-County Boroughs. The districts are a modern creation, but in earlier times groups of parishes were organized as 'Hundreds'. The third and most important group of units in the administrative hierarchy are the 62 administrative Counties with their urban counterparts the 83 County Boroughs. There are only 52 co-called geographical Counties, but some of these are divided so that there are 62 administrative Counties in all. This triple system of Parish, District, County and Borough is a very ancient one and it has become unsatisfactory in several ways, but chiefly because it divorces the rural areas from the large boroughs and cities. Further, the boundaries of the counties in many cases have remained unaltered for the past thousand years, and have received only slight modifications in spite of the immense changes in the distribution of population that have taken place since the Industrial Revolution. The counties, for purposes of administration, consist of those portions of their geographical areas that remain after the County Boroughs have taken over very important parts of the county's original extent. For the counties there remain the rural areas, the smaller towns and the suburban districts that grew up immediately outside the boundaries of large towns.

It has become more and more apparent in Britain, as in so many other countries, that a new type of administrative unit is required, one that is generally larger than the existing divisions and intermediate between the local authority on the one hand and the State on the other. These regional areas are very necessary if plans of any kind are to be made for town and countryside at one and the same time. Such large units have not been unknown in English history, By the end of the period of the Roman occupation, Britain had been divided into five provinces of the Roman Empire. Between the seventh and ninth centuries, Anglo-Saxon England was divided into several independent kingdoms which included Wessex, Mercia, East Anglia, and Northumbria, and although these units of the Heptarchy have long disappeared, they left a mark on English life which has never been quite obliterated by the county divisions. Later examples of this kind are provided by Cromwell's division of England and Wales into eleven districts in 1656, and by the creation of twelve military districts in 1803 when Napoleon was expected to attempt an invasion. During both of the world wars England and Wales were divided into large areas for several purposes. For example, in the war of 1914-18 a system of eight principal divisions was adopted by the Ministries of National Service, Labour, and Munitions. During the war of 1939-45 England and Wales were divided into eleven Civil Defence regions.

The Effect of Broadcasting

It is clear that a very great stimulus to the development of regionalism in Britain between the two wars was provided by broadcasting. The establishment of regional broadcasting stations for the service of large provinces of England has given a considerable impetus to the growth of a regional consciousness, quite distinct from the old county spirit. The North Regional, Midland Regional, London Regional, West of England Regional, and Welsh Regional stations have probably done more than any other agency to foster the growth of what may be called a new heptarchy in England and Wales. In the words of a former director of the North Regional Station, Mr. E. G. D. Living, 'a new accentuation has been given to British life, in the sense that the B.B.C.'s scheme of regionalism has not only emphasized culturally the national entities of Scotland, Wales, and Northern Ireland, but has also marked out more definitely than ever before the somewhat vague entities of the English provinces themselves'. In the same speech Mr. Living also claimed that the B.B.C. had restored to 'the English provinces that distinctness of boundary and character that has been more apparent in some of the larger continental countries built upon a collection of neighbouring States'.

The early policy of the B.B.C. was to establish numerous small stations, each serving a city and its immediate neighbourhood. In 1926 the B.B.C. decided to build a number of stations of high power to serve large regions. The first of these was set up in 1927 at Daventry, as an experiment, with the object of serving the Midlands. The other regional stations followed, London for the Metropolitan region, a Northern station for industrial Lancashire and Yorkshire, a station for the thickly populated lowlands of Scotland, and one which was to serve Wales and the West Country jointly. In 1937 the Welsh and West of England Regions, which had previously had a composite programme, were divided.

By means of the wireless the country has become increasingly aware of the broad provincial differences which exist within it, but the B.B.C. cannot demarcate its regional system with exact boundaries. A greater amount of precision is given by the broadcasting and publication in the newspapers of daily weather forecasts. These are prepared with reference to a regional division of England and Wales into ten districts that has been adopted by the Meteorological Office of the Air Ministry.

In 1946 a proposal made by the Government to amalgamate the West Region of the B.B.C. with the Midland Region and to place the headquarters at Birmingham was received with indignation in the West Country. The case for the retention of the West of England Region was put so strongly that the Government gave way. The Member of Parliament for Taunton stated that a separate West Region was necessary to preserve the special cultural, civic, agricultural, and religious characteristics of the West Country. This controversy showed the great influence that the B.B.C. is able to wield in fostering regionalism. Among the other cultural influences which have stimulated a spirit of regional consciousness, the regional newspapers, the provincial universities, and the regional novels have been the most important.

The Four Kinds of Regional Areas

The purposes for which England and Wales are at present divided by defined boundaries into regional areas are of four kinds. In the first place there are the divisions made for *statistical* purposes of one kind or another. Secondly there are *administrative* regions organized by the State for some special purpose, while a third class consists of regions which are devised by *private* organizations for their own needs. A fourth group consists of regional schemes that have been made for purposes of *military* and civil defence. It is only very rarely that the boundaries used by these numerous and distinct bodies coincide with one another. The statistical regions seldom have any administrative reality; they are merely a convenience for the statistician and those who use statistics. Figures are provided for large regional areas, generally but not always consisting of groups of counties. The compilation of statistical material by large regions is a much more satisfactory way of presenting many classes of facts than the method of using the old county divisions.

The most important and most widely used of these schemes is that devised for the Census, by which England and Wales are divided into twelve regions. This division is said to have been designed in the light of the economic and other characteristics of the country. The nomenclature adopted in this scheme is highly unimaginative, as the regional names adopted for the northern parts of England are North I, North II, North III, North IV. The Board of Trade prepared another division of England and Wales into thirteen areas to show the regional distribution of industry. Agricultural statistics have long been prepared by regions as well as by counties; ten regions are now used. An American writer, Professor E. G. Mears, has called attention to the difficulty of interpreting and comparing British statistical information, because of the lack of uniformity in the regions used by the different Government departments (*Geogr. Rev.*, 29 (1939), 241). Not only do the regional boundaries differ as between one department and another, but one department may make changes in its own boundaries as between one census and another. These changes are of considerable inconvenience to those who use the statistics and wish to compare the figures of one year with those of another.

The second purpose for which regional divisions are used may be described as administrative. England and Wales are divided into regional areas for many different branches of public administration. The work of the High Court of Justice has been regionalized for centuries. In each of the eight 'circuits' into which the country is divided there are between four and ten assize towns, and the fact that a town is chosen as a seat for the judges gives it considerable prestige and importance in its region. In the same way the work of the Ministry of Labour is divided by means of large territorial units.

Some of the great public utilities are organized on a regional basis. In 1933 a system of ten 'scheme areas' was adopted for the work of the Central Electricity Board. Ten 'Traffic Areas' were set up to deal with road transport in 1930. Since the advent to power of the Labour Government in 1945 and the consequent nationalization of industry, the process has proceeded apace. In 1947 the nationalized coal industry was reorganized in eight regions. In 1948 a Regional system of administration was adopted for British Railways and for the electric power industry, both now under national control. A scheme of eleven regions was adopted by the nationalized gas industry and will no doubt come into force soon. The Hospital system of England and Wales is also being reorganized on a regional basis.

Between the two wars the British Post Office was regionalized. Seven Post Office regions named North Western, North Eastern, Welsh and Border Counties, Midland, South Western, Home Counties, and London were established. At the same time telephone areas, smaller in size than the regions, were created. These forty-six areas are in fact sub-divisions of the Post Office regions, and much research was carried out to ensure that the boundaries might be co-terminous. These sub-divisions and their capitals, or area headquarters, are of considerable interest to geographers, as they approximate in size to the old counties, but are more in accordance with the geographical conditions of the present day. In 1933 England and Wales were divided into the eleven regions of the Milk Marketing Board. The nomenclature adopted almost recalls America, and it will interest geographers to learn of the existence of a Mid-Western region and a Far-Western region in Britain. The Mid-Western region lies directly south of the West Midland region!

The third class of regional division is one set up by some private organizations and not in any way controlled by the State. The Automobile Association, a union of British motorists, divided England and Wales into twelve areas 'each in charge of a secretary who is a practical motorist, fully conversant with motoring conditions in the area'. Many business firms with national distributions adopt a similar policy of decentralization and divide the country into sales areas purely for their own purposes. For example, one well-known chocolate firm uses sixteen regions, each with a headquarters.

GEOGRAPHY AND REGIONALISM 359

Regions for Defence

The fourth type of regional division, namely that made for purposes of defence, has always been important and was especially significant during the last war. Both in past centuries and in the recent war a division of England and Wales into about a dozen regions has proved to be a more useful means of organization for defence than one based on the fifty-two geographical counties. In 1656 Cromwell divided the country into eleven districts, each governed by a major-general. This method of regional government, which was concerned with defence against enemies within the State rather than against foreign foes without, was exceedingly un-popular and involved many serious encroachments on the constitution. The system was in reality a new form of local government by which special taxes were collected and Puritan morals were promoted. In November 1803, according to a map published at that date by J. Fairburn, England and Wales were again divided into military districts, this time twelve in number. An invasion by the forces of Napoleon was anxiously awaited, and a regional organization was adopted to meet any emergency. The nomenclature adopted for the regions is attractive, including as it does the 'North Inland', 'South Inland', and 'Severn' districts. The latter was presumably designed with the object of combating the use of the Severn estuary by an invading enemy.

In February 1939 Sir John Anderson announced in the House of Commons that England and Wales would be divided into eleven Civil Defence regions, in the eventuality of war, and that Scotland would form a twelfth region. This system came into force in the same year and each region was put in charge of a Regional Commissioner. As in 1655 and in 1803, so in 1939 London was treated as a separate region. 'Its boundaries', said Sir John Anderson, 'will be those of the Metropolitan Police Area. Such a complex and densely populated area has many problems which require special treatment, and the machinery of a typical region would not meet the case.' The proposed system received much criticism before the war and Sir John Anderson answered the critics in the following words: 'The purpose of the regional organization which is being planned for war-time is simply to guard against a contingency, which it would be utter folly to ignore, of communications between various parts of the country and the headquarters of government being interrupted by war operations. It had seemed to the Government necessary, in order to guard effectively against that contingency, to make provision for the setting up in convenient centres of an organization which could, if necessary, and to the extent necessary, replace His Majesty's Government

24

for the purpose of giving effective decisions in matters of immediate urgency.' The Civil Defence regions are of much geographical interest. A Southern region with its capital at Reading was created, and it should be remembered that a Southern region or a Wessex had been previously proposed in the theoretical schemes of C. B. Fawcett and G. D. H. Cole. It seems strange that a region of this type had been disregarded in most of the earlier systems which were actually put into practice.

The Civil Defence scheme of regionalization was devised to meet the threat of invasion. If communications between a region and London had been severed by enemy forces the Civil Defence Commissioner would have taken the place of the central government in his region. Invasion did not take place, but the Civil Defence Commissioners did their utmost to co-ordinate the regional plans of the central departments in London, that were concerned with Civil Defence, with the work of the local authorities. All the central departments with the exception of those concerned with Trade, Education, and Agriculture adopted war-time administrative areas, which coincided with those of the Civil Defence regions. As a result of this, what were called 'miniature Whitehalls' sprang up in a dozen provincial centres to meet the emergencies of aerial bombardment and of possible invasion. The Ministry of Health was of especial importance in the regional hierarchy as it had the primary responsibility for rest centres, evacuation and billeting, health hostels and housing, hospitals, first-aid posts, sanitation, and water supply.

From the first, even before the war, the system of Regional Commissioners was not popular with the existing local authorities. The twelve Regional Commissioners were unfairly described as 'dictators' and the unpleasant comparison with Cromwell's major-generals was made. The number of the 'dictators' for England and Wales was the same in 1939 as in 1656, namely eleven. As the war proceeded some local authorities became very suspicious of Civil Defence regionalism and began to feel that the Central Government was plotting to force a form of bureaucratic dictatorship on the provinces. This feeling was particularly strong in Birmingham, where the Lord Mayor was reported to have said that the one great danger to democracy was the suggestion from certain quarters that local government should be superseded by dictators, imposed from above, without popular consent. When the war ended the Civil Defence Regional system and the office of Regional Commissioner were soon liquidated.

Regional Capitals in Britain

An important issue which arises from a study of regionalism is the influence of the regional capital. In the United States the significance of what has been called 'Metropolitan Regionalism' has been clearly recognized, and it is realized that certain American cities are gradually gaining more control over the immense regions which surround them. In the above account of the development of regional administrative organization in England and Wales, attention has been called to the fact that in many of the schemes a regional headquarters has been selected for each area. The regions differ in number and in their boundaries for each scheme, and the capitals chosen also show a certain amount of variation. Nevertheless certain towns appear in nearly every scheme and it is clear that the process of 'Metropolitan Regionalism' which has been observed in the United States, an area of continental dimensions, has also taken place in the far smaller political unit of England and Wales.

London, Birmingham, Manchester, Leeds, Bristol, and Cardiff appear in every official regional scheme and Newcastle in all save that devised by the Post Office. Thus these seven towns are clearly admitted to be the metropolitan centres of a new heptarchy—the regions of Greater London, the Midlands, Lancastria, Yorkshire, the West Country, Wales, and the North-East. When Cardiff had been selected as the capital of the Civil Defence region of Wales Sir John Anderson was asked, in the House of Commons, whether he would 'consider the geographical difficulties of administration in Wales from a headquarters in Cardiff', and replied that certain government departments would open sub-regional offices at Caernarvon, in order to simplify the administration. The difficulty of finding a suitable capital for Wales has always existed, and it has been facetiously suggested that the most suitable alternatives are Shrewsbury and the Paddington Hotel which adjoins the Great Western Railway terminus station in London! Shrewsbury was, in actual fact, the headquarters of Cromwell's major-general, James Berry, who ruled Wales with the four counties of Shropshire, Hereford, Worcester, and Monmouth.

Nottingham is nearly always used as a regional capital and can be regarded as the capital of the East Midlands, when such a sub-division of the Midlands is considered necessary. The great cities of Liverpool and Sheffield do not appear in the administrative schemes of the State, as they are too close to the obviously more central capitals of Manchester and Leeds respectively. Jealousy of Leeds which is often displayed by Sheffield was shown in a Sheffield newspaper, which once described the regional policy of the central government as a policy of 'Leeds über alles'. Sheffield was chosen by Professor C. B. Fawcett as the capital of a separate region which he named 'Peakdon' in his second theoretical scheme for a division of England. But no region of this kind has ever been officially adopted. Nevertheless the great size and the industrial importance of Liverpool and Sheffield sometimes compel a business organization to use them as headquarters and they are both headquarters of the sales areas of many firms.

The eight towns which are generally used as regional capitals may be described as centres of what are (with the exception of the West Country) primarily industrial areas. The division of the remainder of England which is less densely populated and whose interests are more agricultural, is difficult. The regions chosen in the various administrative and theoretical schemes differ very considerably, and the towns selected as capitals also vary. The most clearly marked region is East Anglia, which appears, admittedly in slightly varying forms, in nearly every scheme. The obvious capital of this area would seem, at first sight, to be Norwich, a city which proudly regards itself as the 'heart of East Anglia'; and yet the much smaller town of Cambridge is more frequently adopted. Cambridge was used as a capital of the Eastern Civil Defence region during the war. It had been selected by Professor Fawcett in 1917 and by Professor Cole in 1921 as a theoretical capital. In 1919 Professor Fawcett moved the capital of this region from Cambridge to Norwich and kept it there in his modified scheme of 1942. In the discussion, after Professor Fawcett's paper on the subject had been read to the Royal Geographical Society in 1917, Mr. A. R. Hinks, the Secretary of the Society, had remarked that Norwich is a 'sounder capital than Cambridge could possibly be for the province of East Anglia'.

The south-west, which is usually chosen as one region with Bristol as its capital, is unduly large, and if a sub-division is attempted with Devon and Cornwall combined as a separate region, then Plymouth or Exeter is generally used as a capital. The south-east of England is generally grouped with London, but if it is given a separate regional existence it is exceedingly difficult to name a capital. Brighton is the largest town, but has more of the nature of a seaside suburban outlier of London than that of a regional capital. Professor Fawcett was unable to name a suitable capital, but during the war Tunbridge Wells was chosen as the centre of the South-East Civil Defence region. The reason for its selection may have been the fact that it was already the centre of one of the telephone areas.

It is strange to find that a Central England, with a capital at Oxford, as designed by Professor Fawcett, is not used by any form of administration.

This is very surprising, as the area has considerable coherence and is sometimes known to geographers as the South-East Midlands, and its regional capital of Oxford possesses a remarkable degree of nodality in the network of roads and railways of England. This natural nodality has facilitated its recent growth. The city is situated at about the same distance (60–70 miles) from the three ports of London, Bristol, and Southampton, and from the industrial area of Birmingham. The central position of Oxford, not only in the Upper Thames basin, but also in the south in England as a whole, made it a possible alternative to London as a national capital, as it was in the Civil War.

Planning Regions for England and Wales

There are at least three ways of considering the problem of dividing England and Wales into Planning Regions. The first is to accept the Civil Defence regions as they stand, and to use them for the purpose of planning Britain. Although these regions were only constituted in February 1939 they have become firmly established in the official mind as the best areas for regional decentralization of the work of the central government. They are now used, with slight difference of boundary, by many Ministries and they are used by the Ministry of Town and Country Planning's Regional Organization. Unfortunately the Town and County Planning Act of 1947 makes the County Councils of the 62 administrative counties and the Councils of the 83 County Boroughs the planning authorities of their respective areas. There are, therefore, no less than 145 separate planning authorities and there is no provision for Planning Councils of large regions.

As long ago as 1915, Professor Patrick Geddes, after describing seven of the most densely populated areas in England and Wales, said that 'a new Heptarchy' had grown up 'naturally yet almost unconsciously to politicians' beneath the existing political and administrative network. He claimed that a new form of organization would be built up to meet these problems, which could not be left entirely in the hands of town and county councils. But no democratically elected regional councils have yet been set up for these dozen or so great regions of Britain.

The Civil Defence regions may have been the ideal divisions in war-time, but that does not mean that they are also the best possible areas for planning in time of peace. The distribution of hospital accommodation in the regions was probably a principal factor in drawing the Civil Defence boundaries, but the exigencies of military defence may have partly accounted for some of the divisions.

A second way of dealing with the problem is to construct Planning Regions regardless of the existing administrative boundaries, but after careful consideration of all geographical factors. Such a map was prepared by Professor E. G. R. Taylor (Fig. 24); but it is difficult to persuade British non-geographers that her scheme could be used in actual practice for local administration, as it pays no regard to the county boundaries. Fierce

FIG. 24.—Regions proposed by E. G. R. Taylor

opposition to this, or any other scheme which disregards the county divisions, comes from the partisans of the ancient counties. There is, in fact, a dead weight of opinion in favour of the retention of the counties, singly, or in groups, as administrative areas. England and Wales are tied up in the existing boundaries; the counties are entrenched with the inch, the pound weight, and the pound sterling, and they will not be taken by the assaults of any geographers, any more than the English weights and measures can be slaughtered by the supporters of the decimal system.

The third way of approaching the problem is to compromise, and it is as well to remember that the Civil Defence regions generally consist of groups of counties, but that in a few vital cases this Civil Defence system actually infringed the county network. Therefore the only system which

PLANNING REGIONS
BASED ON GROUPS OF COUNTIES
PROPOSED BY
E.W.GILBERT
1941
• Regional Capital
····· Sub-divisions of Wales
--- Regional boundaries
not coinciding with County
boundaries

Fig. 25.—Planning Regions proposed for England and Wales by E.W. Gilbert, 1941

is at all practicable at the present time is to devise a sounder grouping of the counties into regions than that of Civil Defence, and at the same time to rationalize the counties by dividing them in certain cases, where it is virtually inevitable.

In the regional scheme set out in the accompanying map (Fig. 25) the changes in county boundary have been reduced to a minimum, and have been adopted only where, in the opinion of the writer, they would greatly help to produce more rational areas. There are fifteen regions in the theoretical scheme proposed as against the eleven regions of Civil Defence (Fig. 26).

The reasons for the writer's choice of groups of counties as regions and some comparisons with the Civil Defence regions are given below.

FIG. 26.—Civil Defence Regions in England, 1939–45

(1) *Northumbria.* The Civil Defence region called Northern extends too far south by taking in the whole of the North Riding of Yorkshire. The name 'Northern' is also most unsuitable as the heart of the region is always known as the North-East. The writer has marked out a region called Northumbria, consisting of the counties of Northumberland and Durham, and of Tees-side and Tees-Dale, which can be cut off from Yorkshire.

(2) *Cumbria* should form a separate region. The region could be more effectively administered from Newcastle than from Manchester, which was its capital in Civil Defence, but it would probably be best to make a separate region of Cumbria with a capital at Carlisle or possibly at Penrith. This region has its own peculiar problems, notably with regard to its industrial area, one of the parts of Britain called 'distressed' before the war, and also with the proposed National Park in the Lake District.

(3) *Yorkshire*, or at any rate the great bulk of the county, is left intact by the writer (a Yorkshireman himself), and is promoted to the status of a region with York as its obvious capital. The wholly inappropriate name of North-Eastern given to the two Ridings of Yorkshire by Civil Defence is thus avoided.

(4) *Lancastria*. The North-Western region of Civil Defence becomes Lancastria with a capital at Manchester. It has been thought proper to add the northern part of Staffordshire (north of Stone) which contains the Potteries, to Lancastria, as the Potteries are more connected with Manchester than with Birmingham. The small section of Derbyshire formerly included in the region under the Civil Defence scheme should also be added to Lancastria.

(5) *Midland*. The Midland region with Birmingham as capital is the same as the Civil Defence region. It might be worth considering the possibility of detaching the greater part of Shropshire and Herefordshire from the Midland region and adding a part of Wales to these two counties, in order to create a Welsh Border region with a centre at Shrewsbury. This might involve too much changing of county boundaries to be practicable, but a smaller Midland region would result.

(6) *East Midland*. The North Midland Civil Defence region remains with Nottingham as capital, but its strange name is altered to the more usual and more accurate title of East Midland; and it is to lose the counties called Soke of Peterborough and parts of Holland of Lincolnshire to a new region called Fen Country.

(7) *Wales*. The Civil Defence region of Wales with Cardiff as capital remains unchanged. It would be well to sub-divide this region into three 'areas' of North Wales, Mid-Wales, and South Wales, with Caernarvon and Aberystwyth as their centres, but the problem of finding a satisfactory division of Wales by county boundaries is difficult, and several alternatives are possible.

The country south of a line joining the Wash to the Severn estuary is not well divided by Civil Defence for peace-time planning, and needs considerable readjustment and alteration.

(8) *London*. The salient feature of what Sir Halford Mackinder called

Metropolitan England is the enormous agglomeration of London, which overrules all other geographical factors. It is suggested that the Civil Defence region (virtually the Metropolitan Police Area) should remain a sort of 'inner' London. But the planning of this region must be constantly related to the far wider area of 'outer' London which may be called the Home Counties region.

(9) *Home Counties*. The two regions of London and the Home Counties must consider many of their problems in common, although there are some which are peculiar to each. The Home Counties region, as designed by the writer, includes a large part of Civil Defence's Eastern, the whole of its South-Eastern, and a small part of its Southern regions. The headquarters of 'Home Counties' and of 'London' would both be in London, and its planners would often sit together.

(10) *East Anglia*. The writer's East Anglia is smaller than Civil Defence's Eastern, as it is reduced to the area covered by the two counties of Norfolk and Suffolk. It thus has a more workable size and becomes more of an agricultural unit than the Civil Defence region.

(11) *Fen Country*. A new region to be called Fen Country, with its capital at Cambridge, can be easily carved out without much interference with county boundaries, and it is an area which needs uniform treatment as a whole in any planning scheme.

The remaining Civil Defence regions are Southern and South-Western. The former is a very inconvenient shape for administration while the latter is far too large. Bristol, the capital of Civil Defence's South-Western region, is not placed in a central position for this elongated division.

Both Southern and South-Western possesses little unity from any aspect and each should be divided into two. Southern can be divided into Upper Thames with its new capital at Oxford, and Wessex with its capital at Winchester.

(12) *Upper Thames* consists of Oxfordshire, most of Berkshire, and two-thirds of Buckinghamshire. It is in many respects a convenient unit and its natural centre is Oxford.

(13) *Wessex* in this scheme includes Hampshire, Dorset, and the southern half of Wiltshire. This region has real unity from a physical and from an agricultural point of view, as a study of the Land Utilization Maps shows clearly. South Wiltshire includes Salisbury and the valleys which lead to that city, but the ancient capital city of Winchester would probably be a better regional capital for Wessex than Salisbury.

(14 and 15) *Severn and South-West*. The South-Western Civil Defence region has been divided into *Severn* with its capital at Bristol and *South-*

West with its capital at Plymouth. The former consists of Gloucestershire, North Wiltshire, and Somerset without Exmoor. The latter consists of Devon and Cornwall with Exmoor. The problems of the last two counties include the question of National Parks and it would be as well to include the whole of Exmoor in South-West for that reason. The selection of Launceston as a capital is a possibility and would give pleasure to Cornishmen, but the more obvious choice is Plymouth.

Thus, with very few deviations from the existing county boundaries, a grouping of counties different from that of the Civil Defence scheme, but one more closely coinciding with geographical realities has been achieved. This might prove to be a more satisfactory basis for planning. It is a mistake to accept the Civil Defence regions as the last word on the subject.

United States of America and Australia

It is impossible to describe the development of regionalism in these immense areas within the limits imposed by this chapter; as the United States is about three-quarters of the size of Europe, its regions like New England and the South are comparable with France or Spain in magnitude. It is also unnecessary because H. W. Odum and H. E. Moore's *American Regionalism* (1938) and J. Macdonald Holmes' *Geographical basis of Government specially applied to New South Wales* (1944) have covered this ground in their respective fields. But it is worth pointing out here that the regionalism of the United States cannot be compared directly with that of Europe. Professor F. J. Turner recognized the importance of what he called the 'sectionalism' of American life. 'The United States', he wrote, 'has the problem of the clash of economic interests closely associated with regional geography on a huge scale. Over areas equal to all France or to all Germany, either the agricultural or the manufacturing types are here in decided ascendancy. Economic interests are sectionalized.'

In recent years there has been an increased effort to conserve the resources of America by planning both by States and by regions. Of the federal regional schemes the Tennessee Valley Authority is the most famous. The United States has felt the same fever for regional planning which has infected so many countries of Europe. At the same time the growing economic and social influence of large cities in the United States has made the existing arbitrary network of boundaries between the States out of date. As in European countries, so in the United States the need has been felt for new political units, large and small, more consonant with the facts of social and economic geography. 'Metropolitan Regionalism', by which the great cities of the U.S.A. obviously possess spheres of influence, regardless of State boundaries, has been thought by some to provide the basis for a sounder political division.

In Australia the same tendencies can be observed. Regionalism was so strong in Western Australia that a serious but unsuccessful attempt was made by that State to break away from the Commonwealth by means of the courts in London. In New South Wales a Regional Boundaries Committee has been at work to advise the government on a regional division of the State to facilitate a survey of its economic resources with a view to planned development. Professor J. Macdonald Holmes, Professor of Geography in the University of Sydney, has taken a leading part in this work.

Conclusion

The regional parts of the body politic are dependent on each other. If the whole is to function properly the political sub-divisions must be carefully chosen for their geographical unity. Although a State consists of an amalgam of diverse regions, it is not necessary to maim any one region by artificial internal boundaries. It is unfortunately true that the results of geographical research are still not sufficiently used by administrators in many countries. Nevertheless, in preparing the way for the construction of regional boundaries which accord more closely with natural population units than do the existing divisions, the geographers of the twentieth century are performing a valuable task. As a result of this pioneer work, geographical knowledge can be applied directly to the service of society and of the State and will enrich the life of both.

SELECT BIBLIOGRAPHY

1. R. E. Dickinson, *City, Region and Regionalism* (London, 1947). This is not an easy book to read, but it is the best geographical account of the whole subject. Contains numerous references.

France

2. Vidal de la Blache, 'Régions Françaises', *Revue de Paris*, XVII (1910), 821–49.
3. H. Hauser, *Le Problème du Régionalisme* (Paris, 1924). Describes the formation of the economic regions.
4. F. Prevet, *Le Régionalisme Économique* (Paris, 1929). An account of the working of the economic regions.

Germany

5. R. E. Dickinson, *The Regions of Germany* (London, 1945). A valuable geographical description of the regions of Germany.

Portugal

6. A de Amorim Girão, *Esbôço duma Carta Regional de Portugal*, second edition (Coimbra, 1933).

Professor Girão's account of the new administrative regions of Portugal can be found in *Comptes Rendus du Congrès International de Géographie, Amsterdam 1938*, Tome II, Section IIIa, 277–81.

Great Britain

7. C. B. Fawcett, *Provinces of England* (London, 1919). Still has great value, but has become out of date in certain respects.

8. E. W. Gilbert, 'Practical Regionalism in England and Wales', *Geogr. Journ.*, XCIV (1939), 29–44. This contains 25 maps of the regional frameworks into which England and Wales have been divided.

9. E. G. R. Taylor, G. D. H. Cole, E. W. Gilbert, and others, 'Discussion on the Geographical aspects of Planning', *Geogr. Journ.*, XCIX (1942), 61–80.

E. W. Gilbert's two contributions to the *Geographical Journal* quoted above have been reproduced in part, in this chapter, by kind permission of the Editor.

10. G. D. H. Cole, *Local and Regional Government* (London, 1947). A recent account of the position in England.

11. E. W. Gilbert, 'The Boundaries of Local Government Areas', *Geogr. Journ.*, CXI (1948), 172–206. This article contains 33 maps of the regional framework in England since 1945.

U.S.A.

12. National Resources Committee, *Regional Factors in National Planning and Development* (Washington, 1935). This book contains a valuable set of maps showing the different regions into which the U.S.A. has been divided by geographers, sociologists, administrators, and others.

13. H. W. Odum and H. E. Moore, *American Regionalism* (New York, 1938). Described in its sub-title as 'a cultural-historical approach to national integration'.

CHAPTER XVI

LAND USE SURVEYS WITH SPECIAL REFERENCE TO BRITAIN

L. DUDLEY STAMP, C.B.E., B.A., D.SC.

Dr. Stamp is Professor of Geography in the University of London at The London School of Economics. He organized the Land Utilisation Survey of Britain and has been its Director since its foundation in 1930. Since 1942 he has been Chief Adviser in Rural Land Use to the British Government (Ministry of Agriculture and Fisheries). In addition to numerous works dealing especially with Human and Economic Geography he has specialized in the study of British Geography and is the author of The British Isles: A Geographic and Economic Survey *with S. H. Beaver, M.A.,* Britain's Structure and Scenery, *and has recently summarized the whole work of The Land Utilisation Survey in the volume entitled* The Land of Britain: Its Use and Misuse, *Longmans, 1948.*

Introductory

IN recent years the status of geography has undergone a great change in Britain. The pioneer work of such outstanding figures as the late Sir Halford Mackinder, the late Professor H. J. Herbertson, as well as the solid foundation laid by G. G. Chisholm. L. W. Lyde, and Marion Newbigin, had resulted in the recognition of geography as a subject worthy of University study in London, Oxford, and Edinburgh amongst the Universities of the British Isles. It was the First World War, with its clear lessons of the rapidly approaching unity of the world, which underlined the widespread ignorance of the world and its peoples amongst those who by ability and education had risen to positions of leadership. Within a few years of 1918 University Schools of Geography, usually of an Honours standard, had been established in nearly every British University. Even so the majority of those who read geography in the Universities did so as part of their training as prospective teachers.

In the First World War geographers had been employed in the collection of material for the Intelligence Branches of the Fighting Services, including the production of Regional Handbooks, but it is scarcely too much to say that it was not until the Second World War that there came a fuller realization of the advantages of a geographical training in many spheres of activity. As a result, both during and after the Second World War geographers were fully employed not only in the collection and collation of material for the Fighting Services but also on those basic investigations so essential in the development of planned economies

372

which circumstances necessitated in so many European countries. In the ten years which preceded the outbreak of the Second World War there was abundant evidence of changing world conditions which were slowly appreciated in Britain.

The growth of economic nationalism in so many countries of the world, with the consequent abandonment of free trade between the nations, had obvious repercussions in Britain. Britain had grown great on the development of her overseas trade and commerce, there was an automatic flow into the country of abundant raw materials and foodstuffs as payment for services rendered, and as interest on foreign investments as well as in exchange for the outward flow of manufactured goods. The position had been reached that nine Britons out of ten lived in towns, the outlook of the people was predominantly urban, their concern with industry and trade. It was almost a natural consequence that home production of foodstuffs and raw materials was seriously neglected. Farming was a depressed industry and the land was only producing enough to feed the people two and a half days out of seven. There were many who clung to a rural life not because of the material gain but rather because of an innate love of the land and of the farming way of life. Thus the number of farmers changed but little from 1870 to 1939, whereas the farm workers in the same period dropped in numbers from about 1¼ million to about 500,000. To dispense with hired labour is always the farmer's easiest means of 'economizing' in times of difficulty. His other main costs—rents, seeds, manure, and general running expenses—tend to be incapable of more than small adjustments.

The neglect of the countryside was apparent to the discerning traveller throughout the length and breadth of the land. Where the land itself was marginal in quality, as on the edges of the great moorland stretches of Wales or Scotland, land formerly cultivated or improved had been abandoned, and the moorland edge descended to overwhelm with its growth of semi-natural vegetation the erstwhile farmlands. Even on the better lands outlying fields were left unused. Hedges grew ragged and unkempt through lack of attention. Field drains and ditches became choked and the fields water-logged, with a consequent growth of reeds and rushes. Farm buildings were frequently in obvious need of immediate repair.

Another aspect of the picture was the way in which agricultural land, irrespective of character and quality, was passing to other uses or, what was still worse, lying idle whilst awaiting sale or development for building purposes. It was apparent that one of the great national resources of Britain, the land, was being seriously neglected and allowed to deteriorate.

The Land Utilisation Survey of Britain

It was in these circumstances that the Land Utilisation Survey of Britain was established in the Fall of 1930. Its object was a national stock-taking of land resources, using the methods familiar to all geographers, relying essentially on field work and direct observation. The immediate aim of the Survey was to record the then existing use of every acre of England, Wales, and Scotland. The Survey was purely objective. It was not carried out with any ulterior aim: its purpose was to find out the facts, irrespective of what use might afterwards be made of its findings. It may truthfully be said that the organizers of the Survey had not the faintest dreams of the use which, within ten years, would be made of their work in the fields of national land-use planning and in the prosecution of the war effort towards greater production.

The whole story of the Survey, from its foundation, through its early difficulties, its organization and the eventual completion and analysing of the work, has now been told in detail, and is available for study by those interested.[1]

The Survey relied on funds collected by the Director from various sources, including the grant from the Rockefeller Foundation made for research purposes to the London School of Economics, and the Pilgrim Trust, but the whole of the field work was carried out by unpaid volunteers, drawn almost entirely from Universities, Colleges, and schools. The work was organized on a county basis, with a voluntary Director of the field work in each of the counties, and elaborate precautions were taken to ensure the accuracy of the work.

Britain is fortunate in having a magnificent series of base maps for use in such work. The whole country is covered by maps on the scale of 6 inches to one mile (1 : 10,560) and these maps are usually issued in so-called 'quarter sheets', each covering an area three miles from west to east and two miles from north to south. Some idea of the magnitude of the task may be gained when it is said that there are about 22,000 such sheets required to cover England, Wales, and Scotland, and the task of the Survey was to find 22,000 volunteers, each willing to undertake the survey of the six square miles of the home area.

The information provided by these basic six-inch sheets (which are published officially by the Ordnance Survey, the Government map-making and surveying organization which operates under the Minister of

[1] L. Dudley Stamp, *The Land of Britain: Its Use and Misuse*, Longmans, 1948. Short summary in *The Land of Britain and How it is Used*, published for the British Council, 1947.

Agriculture and Fisheries) includes all fields, with field boundaries, as well as all buildings, so that the apparently simple task of the surveyors was to identify each field or plot of land and to record its use. Although it was the intention of the Ordnance Survey that the whole country should be revised every twenty years, with the result that the average age of the sheets would be not more than ten years, in fact the revision programme had fallen far behind schedule. The L.U.S. volunteers in many areas found themselves working on maps forty and even fifty years old. Not only had much building taken place in the meantime, but in many cases field boundaries had been so changed that much work was entailed in recording first of all the new topographical details.

Despite these numerous difficulties the field work progressed rapidly. A very large part of England was surveyed in 1931 and major parts of Wales and Scotland were completed by the end of 1932. Thus it may be said that in general the Survey refers to the years 1931–3, only comparatively small areas were left for completion later and the whole country had been covered before the outbreak of war. Thus the Survey presents a picture of Britain at a time which one hopes will mark the nadir of British agriculture, in the nineteen-thirties.

When the field sheets were received they were carefully checked for agreement along the margins, and numerous journeys undertaken for purposes of checking to ensure further meticulous accuracy. The results were then reduced by a staff of specially trained cartographers to the scale of one inch to one mile in colour, and the work of publishing the one-inch maps was undertaken. The first two sheets for England were issued on 1 January 1933, and publication went on steadily until the whole of England and Wales had been covered in 140 sheets, despite such incidental interruptions as the destruction of the Survey's office and all its current work in one of the big air-raids on London. Owing to the huge areas of the Highlands of Scotland occupied simply by moorland or rough grazing and virtually uninhabited, only those one-inch sheets covering the more populous parts of Scotland have been published. Information concerning the remainder of that country is contained on the general map on the scale of 1 : 625,000, or approximately ten miles to one inch.[1]

It was of course apparent at a very early stage that the maps themselves could not tell the whole story, and that the findings of the Survey

[1] One-inch maps are obtainable from Messrs. Edward Stanford Ltd., 12–14 Long Acre, London, W.C.2, England, but unfortunately many of the earlier sheets are out of print owing to the destruction of both plates and stock by enemy action. Complete sets of maps may be studied in those Universities and Libraries which are listed in the Appendix to the *Land of Britain: Its Use and Misuse.*

25

needed to be analysed and explained. This has been done in a series of Reports, one for each county, published between 1937 and 1947 under the title of *The Land of Britain*. There are ninety-two parts to the Report, bound up into nine volumes, and covering the whole of England, Wales, and Scotland, together with the Isle of Man.

The Recording of Land-Use

The reader may feel that this elaborate work of recording the use of every parcel of land in Britain is a wasted effort in that the use made of the land is liable to change fundamentally and radically with changing economic conditions. This is a natural point of view for anyone who is accustomed to thinking in terms of one of the newer countries of the world, where the natural vegetation, be it virgin prairie or primitive forest, has been cleared and utilized within living memory over vast areas. The position in Britain, as in the whole of Western Europe and in many other parts of the old world, is entirely different. Leaving on one side the activities in cultivation of the pre-Roman inhabitants of the British Isles, the island settlers we know as the Anglo-Saxons were pioneers over the greater part of the lowlands of the country. The villages and towns which they established, added to the existing framework of Roman and British settlers, provide the essential rural pattern which has changed but comparatively little over the last 1,500 years. The counties of England owe their establishment and to a very large degree their present boundaries to the work of King Alfred (871–901), who established these units as the most convenient in the organization of the control and defence of the country. Thus, because Britain has been settled and farmed for many centuries, in practically all parts for more than 1,000 years and many parts for over 2,000, the present-day land-use which is a result of a very long process of trial and error, has a far deeper meaning and a far greater significance than land-use in one of the newly-settled countries. This is a fact which must be stressed. It means that the understanding of the land-use pattern of Britain is of absolutely fundamental importance in the determination and elucidation of those factors which continue to operate, and which must be taken into account by those concerned with land-use planning and development.

The types of land-use which were recorded by the Land Utilisation Survey are as follows:

(1) *Arable* (symbol A, colour brown)

It might be thought that the recording simply of arable, or ploughed, land is too simple a task. Over a large part of the country the crops being

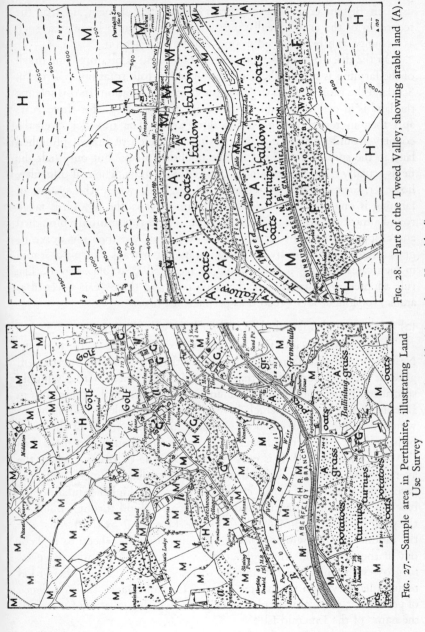

FIG. 28.—Part of the Tweed Valley, showing arable land (A).

(A, arable; M, meadow; H, scrubland)

FIG. 27.—Sample area in Perthshire, illustrating Land Use Survey

grown at the time were noted, but in the intensive system of farming usual in Britain crop rotation forms an essential element, so that the recording of the crop is really only of interest where a large area, such as a county, can be surveyed in one and the same season.

On the drier side of Britain where arable land is predominant much of the farming is still on the four-course or Norfolk rotation, whereas in Scotland the more usual is the Scottish six-course rotation. In this scheme the land is in ordinary arable crops—oats, roots, barley—for three years and then in temporary grass for three years. The traveller over the country would thus see not the continuous stretch of brown ploughed land in the spring, suggested by the published maps, but only half the fields actually thus, the remainder covered with grass. The real difficulty, however, arises in the wetter west of England, where the system of farming is one of long leys.[1] Whilst in many cases the plough is taken round almost the whole farm, an individual field is commonly ploughed and cropped for two or three years in succession and then put down to grass for anything from five to fifteen years. It is always difficult to know in such cases whether a field should be recorded as arable or grass. The rule adopted was that for leys between two and three years—record as arable; for longer leys—record as permanent grass.

(2) *Permanent Grass* (symbol M, colour light green)

The greatest difficulty in attempting to explain to the visitor from the New World British farming is to explain the importance of permanent grass. It must be emphasized that grassland management is a very highly specialized branch of farming technique. Thus some of the finest soils in Britain, especially those which have a high water-table, or are liable to winter flooding, are devoted to grassland. Similarly many of the tracts of heavy clay soils carry a larger proportion of permanent grassland than they do of arable land. It is only on the drier side of Britain, where the average annual rainfall drops below 30 inches, that summer conditions favour the ripening of cereal crops. Elsewhere the higher rainfall, combined with a high humidity and prevalence of cloud through much of the year, renders the climate practically ideal for the growth of grass, and the mildness of the winter not only permits cattle and sheep to be kept out in the open fields throughout the year but even permits the grass to grow sufficiently for the animals to find a major part of their food requirements even in the winter months. It is, of course, the prevalence of permanent grass, always pleasingly green, which has earned for Ireland the name of the Emerald Isle.

[1] Ley is pasture worked in rotation.

The concept that permanent grassland is land not good enough to plough is thus totally false. Permanent grassland is not only carefully manured, but is also managed by a system of carefully controlled grazing. If too many animals are turned out to grass they will damage the pasture by eating too near to the roots and preventing the re-growth of the sward. On the other hand if a field is understocked the animals naturally eat the palatable grasses first, whilst such coarse-growing weeds as thistles gain the upper hand, and may eventually ruin the pasture. There is therefore an exact balance to be maintained between the number of 'stock units' and the area of the pasture, varying with the quality of the grassland. Such controlled grazing is only possible in small field units and this is a primary reason why grassland fields in Britain do not normally exceed in area ten acres, a size of field which may look ridiculously small to a New World arable farmer.

British agricultural statistics published officially draw a distinction between permanent grass used for hay and permanent grass not used for hay. In some parts of the country the word 'meadow' is used indiscriminately, in other parts it is used to signify a field which is cut for hay in contradistinction from pasture which is used for the feeding or pasture of animals. This distinction was not possible in the Land Utilisation Survey.

(3) *Heathland, Moorland, and Rough Grazing* (symbol H, colour yellow)

A very large proportion of the sub-marginal land of Britain is covered with various forms of semi-natural vegetation which affords pasture for a limited number of animals, especially sheep belonging to the various hill sheep breeds. Sometimes the principal vegetation is of the famous shrubby plant, the heather (*Calluna vulgaris*), the purple flowers of which in the early weeks of August give a colour to whole hillsides associated particularly with the eastern parts of the Highlands of Scotland—the 'bonny purple heather'. Over the rainier parts of Britain the dominant plants on these moorlands are coarse grasses, *Nardus* in the drier parts passing to *Molinia* in the wetter, and giving place in still wetter areas to great stretches of cotton grass (*Eriophorum*), deer grass (*Scirpus*), or rush (*Juncus squarrosus*). The extreme is reached in bogs consisting almost entirely of *Sphagnum* moss.

Such tracts of moorland or rough grazing are not restricted to the hills and mountains—they reappear on the lower tracts in the drier east, where the soils are very coarse and sandy; in the wetter west, where surface drainage is deficient. Such sub-marginal land occupies more than two-thirds of the whole surface of Scotland and a third of Wales; and taking Britain as a whole, approximately one-quarter is thus accounted for by land which has a limited use from the farmer's point of view.

(4) *Forest and Woodland* (symbol F, colour dark green)

Despite the fact that the whole of Britain enjoys a type of climate which is essentially a forest or woodland climate, Britain has a lower proportion of its surface covered with woodland at the present day than is found in any other important country in Europe. The total is only between 5 and 6 per cent of the surface, and only a part of that total can be described as forest or woodland of economic importance. Owing to the early separation of Britain from the Continent of Europe after the Great Ice Age, the forest flora is poor in comparison with countries on the Continent. Britain has only one indigenous tree conifer—the Scots fir—though many others have been introduced.

In Roman and pre-Roman times it is broadly true to say that the whole of the lowland of Britain was occupied by a woodland in which oak (*Quercus*) dominated, where calcareous soils were indicated by an increase in the proportion of ash (*Fraxinus*), and where woodland of alder flourished along river-courses. On poor sandy soils and at higher elevations the oak woodland gave place to pine forests of Scots fir (*Pinus sylvestris*), but the upper limit of forest was found between 1,000 and 1,500 feet above sea-level, beyond which were the various types of moorland vegetation, not very different from those found at the present day.

Over practically the whole of the lowland, forest has been cleared to make room for farming; and the apparently well-wooded appearance of much of lowland Britain is due less to the small patches of woodland still remaining, and still providing fencing sticks and poles for farming use, than to the abundance of isolated trees in the hedgerows and parklands. It was not until the acute difficulties in the supply of essential timber during the First World War that Britain began to pay serious attention to afforestation, or re-afforestation; and in 1919 the Forestry Commission was set up with the task of planting $1\frac{3}{4}$ million acreas with trees, a task which was far from completed when the emergency of the Second World War further depleted stands of timber.

(5) *Orchards* (symbol O, colour purple ruling)

It was possible to show separately on the Land Utilisation Maps fruit orchards, which tend to be found in certain favoured parts of the country and are virtually absent in the wetter regions of the west or the colder regions of the north.

(6) *Houses with Gardens* (symbol G, colour purple)

If one can judge by the various investigations which have been undertaken, it is the great ambition, or frequently the declared ambition, of between 90 and 95 per cent of the people of Britain to live in a single detached house with a garden of its own. Generally the British, whatever the level of society or the family income, dislike living in blocks of apartments, or 'flats'. The terrace house (one of a row) is better, provided it has a yard of its own. Still better is the semi-detached, with its plot of garden—best of all the detached, standing in its own piece of ground enclosed by a hedge or fence.

Where the home has little or no land attached to it, a very common British practice is for the breadwinner to rent (at a very nominal cost, usually from the Local Authority) a small piece of land, or allotment, which he cultivates as he would a garden. Thus the Survey distinguished a category of houses-with-gardens, including allotments, the criterion being that the patch of land must be sufficiently large to be capable of producing some fruit, vegetables or flowers. In practice this means a density of not more than ten or twelve houses to the acre. In total the wartime production from these gardens, worked almost entirely by hand labour, added very considerably to the national food supply; and advertisement-hoardings were emblazoned with placards urging the people to 'dig for victory', and every effort was made to encourage by distribution of seeds, and so on, this small-scale production. There is no doubt that gardening is a very permanent feature of British life; and one result is the ever-increasing demand of land for housing purposes, because the obsolete housing of the Victorian industrial towns was often of the density of 64 houses to the acre compared with the modern standard of about ten or twelve.

(7) *Land Agriculturally Unproductive* (symbol W, colour red)

Land thus classified included not only the parts so closely covered with buildings as to be agriculturally unproductive, but also tracts of definitely waste land, such as the spoil banks, or tip heaps, from collieries, cemeteries, and so on.

On the completion of the survey calculations were made of the proportion of the surface covered by each of these categories of land use. The results for England, Wales and Scotland and Great Britain as a whole are given in the table on page 382.

LAND CLASSIFICATION *

	England		Wales		Isle of Man		Scotland		Great Britain	
	Acres	%	Acres	%	Acres	%	Acres	%	Acres	%
Arable	8,339,400	26·0	535,900	10·5	65,500	46·5	3,128,600	16·4	12,069,400	21·4
Permanent Grass	15,238,400	47·7	2,167,800	42·5	19,900	14·2	1,471,400	7·7	18,897,500	33·5
Orchards	257,100	0·8	3,400	0·1	—	—	800	—	261,300	0·5
Forest and Woodland	1,827,900	5·7	294,200	5·8	2,800	2·0	1,094,300	5·8	3,219,200	5·7
Rough Grazing	3,812,700	11·9	1,906,400	37·4	44,800	31·6	13,011,300	68·2	18,775,200	33·3
Houses with Gardens	1,487,500	4·6	73,300	1·4	3,800	2·7	155,300	0·8	1,719,900	3·1
Land Agriculturally Unproductive	1,069,600	3·3	117,700	2·3	4,200	3·0	207,700	1·1	1,399,200	2·5
Total Area	32,032,600		5,098,700		141,000		19,069,400		56,341,700	

* It is important to notice that this refers to conditions as they were before the outbreak of the Second World War, and before the intensive ploughing-up campaign, which greatly altered the proportion of arable and permanent grass.

The Interpretation of the Land-Use Pattern

It matters little what sheet one takes of the published land-use map—almost any one will illustrate the surprising complexity of the land-use pattern. This pattern varies greatly, however, from one part of the country to another; and if one attempts to analyse the general picture presented by the generalized map of the whole country it is clear that the physical or geographical factors are those of the greatest importance. One sees the huge tracts of yellow, indicating heathland and moorland, coinciding with the upland or mountainous areas, or those rendered of little value by excessive moisture. One sees the dominance of the brown, for arable, on the drier eastern side of the country, with patches of cultivated land elsewhere indicative of more local conditions conducive to arable farming such as locally lower rainfall, or stretches of good loamy soils. Elsewhere over the bulk of the lower land of the country the light green indicates the widespread dominance of that carefully managed permanent grass; notably where there are extensive stretches of heavier soil, difficult to plough, and where the rainfall can be described as moderate, between 30 and 60 inches a year.

The few tracts of dark green, for forest, seem incidental. On the whole they are on the margins of the moorland masses, where the land is too poor for farming but not at such an elevation as to prevent tree growth; though one notices that the extensive woodlands seem to avoid the wettest and most exposed places of the west, where the dominant south-westerly winds are inimicable to tree growth. Some of the larger patches of woodland in the lowland areas seem to call for explanation. For the most part they will be found to coincide with tracts of poor, light soil, as in the New Forest and the Breckland of East Anglia, or the Sherwood Forest of Nottinghamshire; but it is in studying the distribution of woodland that we are brought up against another of the great groups of factors which have helped in the shaping of the land-use pattern. These are the historical factors, including what may sometimes be called accidents of land ownership. Thus the Royal Forests, which were demarcated by William the Conqueror (1066–81) and his successors, the great land barons of medieval times, for their own enjoyment in hunting, tend to occupy always the poorer tracts of land, but they do in many cases, notably in the case of the New Forest, owe their preservation to the present day to the laws which protected them from spoliation.

It is interesting that the larger stretches of woodland in Britain are either very ancient or very modern, representing in the latter case the work carried out by the Forestry Commission since 1919. With the incidence of direct taxation in the form of death duties, or inheritance tax, it is no longer an attractive proposition for land-owners to undertake the long-term investment involved in afforestation, and the bulk of the present-day planting is that undertaken by the State.

The investigations of the Land Utilisation Survey definitely confirm a truth which is not always fully appreciated. There is very little land indeed in Britain which is 'waste' in the parks and estates of the nobility and the landed gentry. The old land-owners of the Middle Ages were far too wise to waste good land on their parks and mansions, so that the 'stately homes' of Britain are usually located on the poorest tracts of land in the neighbourhood. It was only in the late eighteenth and nineteenth centuries when those who had made fortunes in the manufacturing towns decided to establish great country residences for themselves, and forgot the countryman's view of land quality and laid out their parks on some of the better land of the country. Thus, in the West Riding of Yorkshire, where there are many mansions built from industrial profits, these tend to waste good, productive farmland.

These are but some of the historical factors which have gone to the shaping of the intricate land-use pattern. Examined in still greater detail we find the incidence of the more purely economic factors. By studying changes in land-use, especially over the last hundred years, the Survey found that fluctuations in agricultural prices had resulted in changes of land-use most marked on land of intermediate quality. The very best lands were discovered and cultivated by the farmers of the Middle Ages, and survived all the vicissitudes of economic conditions and did remain in arable cultivation right up to 1939. Similarly there has been very little change of land-use on the poorest lands. It did not pay the medieval farmer to attempt to tame and use either the poorer moorland tracts or the lowland sandy heaths. It certainly did not pay the farmer in late Victorian and twentieth-century times to attempt the task, and so they remain to the present day. Cobbett, writing 120 to 150 years ago, commonly refers to land which it pays to plough 'in dear-corn times'. This is the land of intermediate quality, under crops when prices are good, allowed to revert to grass or even rough grazing when prices drop. Much of this land was lying idle in the inter-War years.

Where the Economic Factors cause the Greatest Change

One sees the general truth of these statements in the alterations to the land-use pattern which have taken place, in 1939 to 1945, under the stress of wartime needs. There has been very little increase in the ploughed land in the predominantly arable eastern counties, whereas in the Midlands huge areas of permanent grass have been ploughed and cropped. It is the heavy clay lands which have yielded the greatest crops of wheat, and the greatest changes apparent to the eye are in the huge stretches of downland with their thin light soils, formerly sheep pasture, capable of producing reasonable crops of barley and oats.

The Wartime Effort and the Future

The achievements of the British Fighting Services on land, sea, and in the air during the Second World War have become part of history, but far less is known and understood of the victories on the home front. Amongst these the achievement of the British farmers, with a sadly depleted male labour force, though augmented by 80,000 volunteers of the Women's Land Army, must take a very high place. Emphasis was laid on the conversion of much of the permanent grassland to ploughland. The reason for this plough-up campaign was not only the increased production, albeit at a higher cost, from ploughland, but also the greater flexibility this introduced. Human beings cannot eat grass, but they can and do eat and sustain life on potatoes, turnips and swedes, and these crops can be used either for human consumption or food for animals. Thus during the war years the ploughed acreage in Britain returned approximately to the figure of the eighteen-seventies, in the high days of arable farming. Production in the case of many crops was more than doubled, and from a production of about 35 per cent of the food consumed in the country Britain was able to feed herself to the extent of nearly 60 per cent. Admittedly much of this was regardless of money costs. The former reliance on imported feeding stuffs for animals was almost wholly replaced by self-sufficient farming, each farmer growing the bulk of the foodstuffs he required for his animals. The emphasis was on milk, and the farming programme was dictated by the Ministry of Food, which laid down an essential, balanced diet required to maintain the national life. The achievements in farming are discussed in detail elsewhere.[1]

We turn now to consider the relationship between such land-use surveys as those carried out in Britain and the future. It seems inevitable that the countries of Europe, including Britain, should make the utmost use of their home resources, including the productivity of their land. In the years immediately following the cessation of hostilities Britain continued her efforts to secure maximum production from her own lands,

[1] L. Dudley Stamp, op. cit. See also 'Wartime Changes in British Agriculture', *Geographical Journal*, Vol. CIX, Nos. 1–3, 1947.

consistent with the re-establishment of overseas trade with those countries which had normally supplied her with foodstuffs. The British climate is not primarily suited for the ripening of cereal crops, and the wartime emphasis on wheat for the national loaf should naturally give place to a concentration on other foods less easily transported and stored. Thus amongst the objectives of the home production drive, milk and meat and vegetables take a high place.

Under peacetime conditions it is clear that the farmer needs certain conditions before he can play his full part in this national drive towards maximum efficiency. It was felt that the old concept of piecemeal subsidies had the effect of upsetting the balance of farming; and so the Agriculture Act of 1947 provided twin pillars of a guaranteed market for the total of the farmer's production together with prices fixed in advance by agreement, which would afford a reasonable return for expenditure and effort. Thus British agriculture is geared to a national nutrition policy.

One other thing the farmer needs, and that is security of tenure. The age-old system of farming in Britain is landlord, tenant, and farm worker; and although there has been a considerable increase in the number of owner-occupiers amongst the farmers this has not necessarily been to the advantage of agriculture. A farmer whose capital is locked up in his land often has insufficient to spare for the adequate running of his holding, so that in Britain it is not the shiftless farmer who is the tenant but often the better man. Tenant farmers do not move any more rapidly than owner occupiers, and it was found that the average length of time which the tenant farmer or his family had occupied a holding, taking England and Wales as a whole, was fifteen years.[1]

The danger to security of tenure is not from the landlord. It comes from the demand for land for non-agricultural purposes. The total area of England and Wales, i.e. excluding Scotland, is about 37 million acres; and of this total no less than three-quarters of a million acres—more than the area of the whole of the fertile county of the East Riding of Yorkshire —passed in the ten years 1929–38 out of agricultural use for industry, housing, airfields, and other purposes. Tragically much of this land lost to production was of the highest possible agricultural quality, because the best agricultural land is naturally well drained and either flat or gently undulating and hence most easily 'developed' whether for industry or housing. For so long oblivious to the importance of food production, the Government of the day (1939) was thoroughly alarmed at what had been happening. A declaration of policy was made in both Houses of

[1] *Summary Report of Farm Survey 1940–1941*, H.M. Stationery Office, 1946.

Parliament that the Government would 'seek to avoid the use of good agricultural land for housing development where other and less valuable land could be appropriately used', and a Committee was set up on Land Utilisation in Rural Areas, under the Chairmanship of Lord Justice Scott, and of which the present writer was the Vice-Chairman. This Committee produced a Report, popularly known as the Scott Report,[1] which not only attracted wide interest, but which has laid the foundation in the general policy of land-use now put into execution by the setting up of the Ministry of Town and Country Planning in 1943, and which underlies the work envisaged in the Town and Country Planning Act of 1947. Britain is definitely committed to a policy of planned land-use.

The Classification of Land for Land-Use Planning

When the Government declared that good agricultural land should not be used for housing and industry when other, poorer land equally suitable on other grounds was available, a number of difficulties were at once apparent. What is good agricultural land, and where is it found? It may be true that from an academic standpoint various definitions of good land have been attempted, but not in terms which could be interpreted by the town planner, trained primarily as an architect, and out of contact with rural practices. In any case no attempt had been made to map such land. Rather naturally the attempt to fill this serious gap fell to the lot of the geographers of Britain attached to the Land Utilisation Survey. It is easy to talk about the 'best agricultural land' until one asks, 'Best for what?' The light, easily-worked loams, producing the best crops of such vegetables as carrots, asparagus, and celery, are very different from the firm clay-loams which will carry the heaviest crops of wheat, or from the well-watered alluvial tracts which support the best spring growth of grass for fattening of cattle. So the Land Utilisation Survey, after some two years of discussion with experts in various fields, drew up a simple classification of the land into ten types. Whilst the first four of the types are regarded as constituting the Good Agricultural Lands, and Types 5 and 6 the Medium Quality, and Types 7 to 10 the Poor Quality agricultural lands, it is not true to say that there is a steady change in quality from No. 1 the best to No. 10 the poorest. For certain purposes No. 1 is the best, for others No. 3 or even No. 4. The Land Utilisation Survey took into account all the relevant factors, and their method of approach is described in detail in *The Land of Britain: Its Use and Misuse*,

[1] *Report of the Committee on Land Utilization in Rural Areas*, H.M. Stationery Office, 1943.

so that their findings differ in some respects from those resulting from the work of the soil surveyors attached to the Soil Survey of England and Wales, who consider only soil and site.

The ten types distinguished by the Land Utilisation Survey are defined as follows:

Major Category I—Good Quality Land

Land in this category has a site which is not too elevated, is level or gently sloping or undulating, and a favourable aspect, together with soils which are deep with favourable water conditions, actual or potential, and a soil texture embracing mostly loams but including some peats, sands, silts and clays.

(1) *First Class Land* capable of intensive cultivation, especially of foodstuffs for human consumption; has soils which are deep and in texture are mainly loams; the drainage is free but not excessive; soils are not excessively stony and can be worked freely at all seasons.

(2) *Good General Purpose Farmland.* This land is similar to the first, but has a restricted range of usefulness due to:

(a) less depth of soil, or

(b) presence of stones, or

(c) occasional liability to drought or wetness, or

(d) some limitation of seasons when the soil works easily.

It is possible to distinguish (A) suitable for ploughing, (AG) suitable for crops or permanent grass, as when associated with high rainfall.

(3) *First Class Land* but with restricted use owing to a high permanent water table or liability to winter or occasional flooding or somewhat heavier soils. Such land is usually unsuitable or less suitable to arable cultivation, though it may frequently be converted to Category I by drainage operations.

(4) *Good but Heavy Land.* Although such land has soil of a good depth and the natural fertility is often high, the soils are heavy loams with the result that both the period of working and the range of possible crops are restricted.

Major Category II—Medium Quality Land

This is land of only medium productivity even when under good management, the productivity being limited by reason of the unfavourable operation of one or more of the factors of site or soil character. These unfavourable factors include:

(a) high elevation,   (b) steepness of slope,

(c) unfavourable aspect,   (d) shallowness of soil,

(e) defective water conditions.

(5) *Medium Quality Light Land.* This is land defective by reason of lightness and usually shallowness of soil. Some such land can be ploughed (usually shallow ploughing) but in other cases, particularly on lime-stones, the occurrence of rock near the surface or of rocky outcrops renders it unsuitable for ploughing, though affording excellent permanent grass.

(6) *Medium Quality General Purpose Farmland.* This is land defective primarily by reason of relief-land broken up by steep slopes with patches of considerable elevation with varied aspect and varied water conditions. In consequence the soils are varied, often deficient by reason of stoniness, heaviness, or in other ways. When a tract of country of this general character is studied in detail it is usually possible to resolve it into a mosaic of small tracts or patches—it may be only a part of a field in size—of land varying from Categories 1 to 10.

Major Category III—Poor Quality Land

This is land of low productivity by reason of the extreme operation of one or more factors of site and soil.

(7) *Poor Quality Heavy Land.* This is land suffering from extreme heaviness or wetness of soil, and includes the more intractable clay lands and low-lying areas needing extensive drainage works before they can be rendered agriculturally useful.

(8) *Poor Quality Mountain and Moorland.* This is land rendered poor by extreme elevation or ruggedness of relief, usually combined with shallow-ness of soil, or occurrence of peat.

(9) *Poor Quality Light Land.* This is land rendered poor by extreme lightness of soil, with attendant over-drainage resulting in drought and poverty in nutrient materials and is the land described by the farmer as 'hungry'. It usually coincides with the outcrop of coarse sands or porous gravels.

(10) *Poorest Land.* This is land where several factors combine to render the land agriculturally useless or almost so. It may be very diverse, including shingle beaches, moving sand dunes, and salt marshes, and in some cases reclamation is possible.

Calculations have been made of the area occupied by each of these main types. The table on page 390 gives a summary:

It will be seen that the comparatively small areas of really good land must be regarded as very precious indeed, and must be protected from other uses as far as possible, if Britain is to maintain a large output of home-grown foodstuffs.

GEOGRAPHY IN THE TWENTIETH CENTURY

DETAILED LAND CLASSIFICATION *

	England and Wales		Scotland		Great Britain	
	Acres	%	Acres	%	Acres	%
Major Category I—Good	17,846,300	47·9	3,546,700	17·5	21,393,000	37·9
1. First Class	1,962,900	5·2	368,100	1·9	2,331,000	4·1
2. Good General Purpose Farmland						
2(A) suitable for ploughing	7,065,800	19·0	1,500,800	7·7	8,566,600	15·2
2(AG) crops or grass	2,636,700	7·1	211,000	1·2	2,847,700	5·0
3. First Class, restricted use unsuitable for ploughing	1,235,200	3·3	7,600	0·0	1,242,800	2·2
4. Good but heavy land	4,945,700	13·3	1,459,200	7·7	6,404,900	11·4
Major Category II—Medium	11,933,700	32·0	1,910,800	10·1	13,844,500	24·6
5. Medium Light Land						
5(A) suitable for ploughing	2,402,200	6·4	84,600	0·5	2,486,800	4·4
5(G) unsuitable for ploughing	220,300	0·6	1,000	0·0	221,300	0·4
6. Medium General Purpose Farmland	9,311,200	25·0	1,825,200	9·6	11,136,400	19·8
Major Category III—Poor	6,350,400	17·0	13,493,100	70·8	19,843,500	35·2
7. Poor Heavy Land	825,500	2·2	75,400	0·4	900,900	1·6
8. Poor Mountain and Moorland	4,516,500	12·1	13,371,300	70·1	17,887,800	31·7
9. Poor Light Land	811,300	2·2	46,400	0·3	857,700	1·5
10. Poorest Land	197,100	0·5	—		197,100	0·4
Residue—Closely Built Over	1,141,900	3·1	118,800	0·6	1,260,700	2·3
Total	37,272,300		19,069,400		56,341,700	

* The figures for England and Wales include the Isle of Man.

This table differs slightly in totals from the one published in pp. 482–4 of *The Land of Britain: Its Use and Misuse*, since it is based on a final recount of areas, county by county.

Principles of Land-Use

From the preceding paragraphs it follows that land-use planning must be based upon certain principles. The first can be called the principle of Optimum Use, that it should be possible to determine the optimum use in the national interest of any given tract of land. Despite the importance of keeping in agricultural production the best quality lands, there are obviously occasions when other national needs transcend even this consideration. Such was the case when the finest remaining market-garden lands in the vicinity of London had to be sacrificed in the decision to establish Heathrow as an international airport. Elsewhere considerations of national defence may be the most important. But it is often possible in the detailed planning of the expansion of a town or the siting of a new one for development to be directed to the poorer tracts of land, saving the better for food production. This is the principle now followed daily in the work of the Ministry of Town and Country Planning, operating in close junction with the Land Use Division of the Ministry of Agriculture, with similar arrangements operating in Scotland.

There is secondly the principle of the Multiple Use of land. In Britain as a whole there are only $1\frac{1}{4}$ acres of land of all types per head of population, even including the virtually uninhabited moorlands of Scotland. Taking England and Wales the land available is less than one acre per head of population. Amongst the needs of the people which must be satisfied are work, which suggests location of industry as a prior consideration; housing, which involves the use of very large areas to meet modern standards; food and raw materials, which involve the function of agriculture in the national economy; recreation, which brings into the picture not only public access to land, but also the overdue creation of National Parks as well as a further provision of playing fields and urban parks; free communication, which involves use of land for improvement of the existing road-network and the provision of main motor-highways; and defence, or security, which brings into the picture the very large demands of the Fighting Services for training grounds.

With so many demands on her limited land resources, Britain faces the problem of Multiple Use. There is no reason, for example, why many tracts of moorland should not only be available for access and recreation of an urban population, while at the same time they are providing feeding grounds for mountain sheep and gathering grounds for the water supply of neighbouring towns. Unfortunately the greatest offenders in restricting such multiple use of land have been Government Departments and such public corporations as Water Supply Authorities. They have

26

been greater offenders than some land-owners who have sought for purposes of sport to close their land to access by any others than their own friends.

We might enunciate other principles such as Maximum Production, which introduces the work of the recently reorganized National Advisory Service for farmers, and the gearing of production with the national policy.

Sufficient has been said to indicate in this brief essay the way in which geographers, starting from the well-worn paths of local survey, have become deeply involved in the work of physical planning, and also it is clear that many basic problems still await further investigation and it is in these fields that the technique of geographical survey and analysis has undoubtedly an important part to play.

Postscript: Since this article was written a Commission appointed by the International Geographical Union has drawn up a scheme for a World Land Use Survey recommending the preparation of a series of maps on the scale of 1 : 1 million with explanatory memoirs. The scheme, with suitable modification, follows closely that discussed above for Britain.

PART III

SPECIAL FIELDS OF GEOGRAPHY

For as Geography without History seemeth a Carkasse without motion, So History without Geography wandreth as a Vagrant without a certain habitation.

JOHN SMITH of Virginia

CHAPTER XVII

GEOGRAPHY IS A PRACTICAL SUBJECT

D. F. PUTNAM

GEOGRAPHY is pre-eminently a practical subject despite the tendency of geographers to fall back upon abstruse theoretical arguments to justify its existence. The conclusion of a group of students at a recent geography summer school are very much to the point. Discussing the age-old problem of a definition for geography these students finally stated that 'Geography is what geographers do'. This somewhat quizzical definition is probably as near the truth as statements that geography is human ecology, or the science which relates man to his environment, or many others of the same ilk.

If geography is what geographers do, it is, for the most part, what they have been taught to do by precept and example during their student days. It is the purpose of this brief study to examine these techniques in order to see whether they are adequate or whether they are in need of revision and enlargement.

University instruction, traditionally, developed by the lecture method. Even geography was and, unfortunately, often still is, presented only in this way. With the rise of medicine and the natural sciences, demonstration and experiment became, after a long struggle, recognized methods of instruction in the university.

Modern geography too, has felt the urge to become more than a series of recitations on the description of the earth and includes, albeit sometimes rather reluctantly, so-called practical work in its curriculum.

The systematic sciences of botany, zoology, entomology, geology, &c., have a distinct advantage in that plants, animals, insects, and rocks may be brought into the laboratory for the detailed study. Geography, which deals in landscapes and areas of the earth's surface, is under a handicap in that the concrete natural objects of its study cannot be treated in this way. The student is, perforce, obliged to journey into the field for his observation; or to use in the classroom the results of other people's investigations in the form of maps, charts, photographs, &c. Practical work in geography can therefore logically be discussed under two headings: (a) Field Techniques, and (b) Maps and Map interpretation. Study guides such as often form part of regional geography courses and even elementary courses can hardly be termed practical work. Especially is this true of the type which advises the student to read pages 93–7, and then answer such questions as 'Account for the development of podzols in coniferous forest lands', 'Account for the productivity of chernozems', &c. The similarity to public school seatwork in history or English literature is entirely too close, and the net effect upon the acquisition of geographical knowledge just about the same.

PART I. FIELD STUDY

Geographers often point out that they derive much of their factual material from the writings of other scientists and proceed to mould it, through the geographical approach, into the textual material of geography. This is true, for the geographer is often able to supply correlations which escape the single-minded 'pure scientist.' Geography, however, is more than a book study or an academic discipline. It is more also than a mere rearrangement of facts drawn from the observations of others.

Geography is primarily a field study dealing with the surface of the earth and the features and phenomena which are associated with it. Such a study involves three principal processes: *observation*, *recording*, and *interpretation*. The ways in which these are carried out vary greatly depending upon the type of area involved, the objectives and purposes to be served by the study, the equipment, and personnel available to do the work.

Fundamentally, there are three types of areas with which a geographer must deal:

1. The *natural* area, unmodified by any effect of human occupance.

2. *Rural* areas, which have a low to moderate density of human population, and in which the works of man do not entirely obliterate the work of nature even though a considerable degree of modification and control is exercised. Such areas may vary in the scale of land utilization all the way from nomadic pastoralism to intensive market-gardening. They may include also areas in which the adjustments of man are not pastoral or agricultural but instead those of mining, forestry or other type of resource exploitation.

3. *Urban* or agglomerated settlement areas. These also may vary according to a scale expressed in terms of hamlet, village, town, and city. In addition there is, especially near the larger cities that rather vague zone known as the 'rural-urban fringe'. This is the area in which rural and urban phenomena grade into one another and in which, for this very reason, many geographers find a very interesting field of work.

The objectives of geographical field study may also be of various sorts. The mere gathering of factual material in the hope that it might be informative and useful is in itself a worthy objective. The writer cannot help but be impressed with the number of information and publicity bureaus in operation throughout the United States and Canada. Much of the information which they dispense is, or should be, geographical. The fact that, unfortunately, much of it is not, is a record of two failures; first, that of the publicity executive in the understanding of his true function, and second, that of the geographer in demonstrating the excellence of the geographical method. However, information for the sake of information is about the lowest point in the scale of geographical objectives. There are many higher ones. Particularly in recent years the aid of geographical information is found of value in areal and regional planning projects. In fact it might well be said that all regional planning is in essence applied geography, although far too many plans are proposed which fly directly in the face of geographical principles. Particularly is this so in the case of plans based on single factor analysis without the benefit of multiple cor-relations involving consideration of all the important regional phenomena. That is not to indicate, at all, that the compilation of a single factor map is not a worthy objective, but it would be a pity if geographical ambition were to stop there.

The equipment of a working geographer is apt to be as varied as his objectives. While the efforts of a geographer are often very largely directed towards making maps, the first items in his equipment should be the map records of all the work previously done in the area. Par-ticularly is it advisable to have a good topographic map as a base for recording data—providing one exists. There are still many areas, even in North America, for which accurate maps do not exist. It was still possible in 1948, for example, for a party of geographers from the University of Toronto to discover an unmapped river in Northern Canada having a flow volume equal to one-quarter that of Niagara. Where maps do not exist, then, the geographer perforce must make his own.

Whittlesey[1] suggests that all pertinent material—maps, statistics, &c. be taken into the field. After that he lists the following items of equipment:

> Note-book, containing plain, cross-section and tracing paper;
> Pencils of a dozen different colours, as well as hard black pencils fitted with erasers;
> Compass, plane table, ruler alidade, and ruler protractor;
> Soil auger, soiltex (or some other simple acidity test);
> Camera and tripod.

[1] Whittlesey, D. S. (1927), 'Devices for Accumulation of Geographic Data in the Field', *Annals of the Association of American Geographers*, XVII, 72–8.

Whittlesey wrote, of course, before the present great wealth of aerial photographs was available, and they are not mentioned. They should certainly be given first place on the list. One is somewhat surprised that the list contains no instrument for measuring elevation or slope. The aneroid barometer, Abney level, hand level, and even sometimes a surveyor's level come in very handy in some types of geographical field work. If much attention is to be paid to soil, a good spade or short-handled shovel should be included. A small miner's pick is decidedly useful. Fairly large holes have to be dug occasionally in order to get a proper understanding of the soil. No one has yet photographed a profile down an auger-hole! A bottle of dilute hydrochloric acid is, in the experience of the writer, at least twice as useful as the acidity indicator, but, of course, both should be included in the equipment.

The geographer must have some means of transportation. True, much of the work is finally done on foot, but getting to the point of action fully equipped is somewhat of a problem. A car or light truck is useful. Since the last war, the jeep has been much in evidence for field work of all kinds, and is able to go through many terrain conditions where modern automobiles cannot be taken. It is, however, surprising where a geographer with skill, ingenuity, and sheer pertinacity can take a car—and bring it back!

Perhaps the reader wonders why the word *personnel* was mentioned since, presumably, geographical field work is always done by geographers. It is perhaps more correct to accept the fact that geographical data may be gathered by any scientific worker, and that for many types of work auxiliary training in botany, zoology, soils, geology, &c. is just as valuable as training in geography. In fact, field geography has, very largely, been created by men who had background training in one or more of the sciences mentioned. It seems logical therefore that geographical work parties might still include some auxiliary scientists whose specialized training would enable them to add significant detail from their own fields. However, every geographer should have a field knowledge of at least one of the natural sciences in addition to his geographical training.

This background of training is immediately brought into focus when we proceed to discuss the primary process in the gathering of geographical knowledge, namely, observation. What is a geographer supposed to see? The categorical answer, of course, is *everything*—every feature of the natural physical fundament and every man-made modification or amendment to it. This all-inclusive assignment is quite clearly stated in the outline of the content of geography as given by V. C. Finch and G. T. Trewartha[1] and in the briefer outline of the content of the landscape as given by James.[2]

While, presumably, every geographer must subscribe to this concept as an article of faith in the same way that every Presbyterian must accept the doctrine of predestination, it is too difficult a goal with which to present the neophyte on his first approach to the subject. Such an all-inclusive purpose would perhaps be better kept in the background and presented at the end of the volumes in question. Quite obviously something simpler should be cited as a first objective.

Let us consider first the atmospheric or climatic factor. Obviously it is of highest geographical importance, but one cannot see a climate, it is deduced from a study of meteorological data extending over many years. A short field trip or even a field season is inadequate for a comprehensive study, and if records are available from nearby meteorological stations such instrumental routine is unnecessary. In unexplored areas, however, any data on temperature and rainfall is welcome. The effects of drought, excess rainfall, frost, &c., should be observed as well as the general behaviour of the weather.

Much more can be observed concerning the land form of a region. Geomorphology, or physiography as it was often called, has held a recognized place in geography for a long time. The shapes of hills and valleys, the degree and frequency of slopes, the development of drainage patterns and the nature of the material exposed in all available sections should be noted. So also should all the details of soil development as seen in exposed profiles. The associated vegetation, be it grass or forest in the uncultivated state, conveys a great deal of information about the condition of both soil and climate, even though it can no longer be considered as even remotely resembling the primeval condition. The whole cultural pattern should be observed, including settlement patterns, farms, fields, crops, livestock, industries such as grist-mills, quarries and manufacturing plants of all kinds. Like the Indian tracker, the geographer must be reading signs all the way. It is a pity that the educational value of the geographical approach is not appreciated and used to a greater degree in modern education. The value of having school children learn to observe the patterns of their own environment cannot be overestimated—yet under our present system we have very few teachers with the training or inclination—and practically none who are permitted the time to take a class into the field. We hear the same cry from our friends in natural

---

[1] Finch, V. C., and G. T. Trewartha (1942), *Elements of Geography*, McGraw Hill Book Company. See pp. 2–3.

[2] James, Preston (1943), *An Outline of Geography*, Ginn & Co. See p. 11.

sciences such as botany and zoology—education has been imprisoned in the classroom with a resultant neglect of the environment.

We have answered the question 'What do we record?' We now pass on to consider how this should be done. Again we face a choice depending upon objectives and types of survey. If at all possible, the true geographer's choice is a map. If no base map is available he will make one as he goes along. Only in case of dire necessity under duress of limited time will he

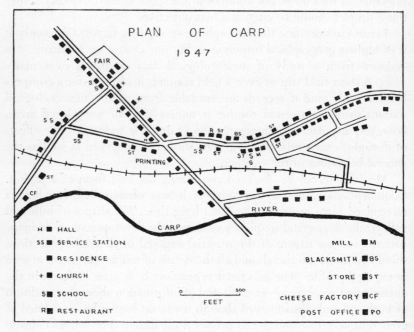

FIG. 29.—The plan of a small village, drawn from a quickly-made survey of Carp, near Ottawa, Ontario. (*Survey by L. G. Reeds*)

resort to serial notes apart from a map. However, in a rapid traverse along a railroad or a highway, notations of mileage and observed phenomena may later be used to reconstruct the geography of the route.

Perhaps the first technique which the geographer should learn is that of the pace-and-compass survey. This was brought home to the writer early in his career when he was turned loose on a land utilization survey in a region where property is delimited by metes and bounds. Actual details and areas were required and no air photographs were available, hence it was necessary to sketch land-use in the field, and later tie it into a base map enlarged from a scale of one inch to four miles. The plane table would have been more accurate but infinitely more time-consuming. An example of a geographer's field map is given in Fig. 29.

The traverse is the simplest form of field investigation and is usually a preliminary to more intensive study. It is, undoubtedly the thing which a student should learn to do first. Traversing may be done from any sort of vehicle or even on foot, but where passable roads are available the most satisfactory traverse is that done from a motor-car. From personal experience of many thousands of miles of traverse it may be stated that without using excessive speed, and with numerous stops for closer observation and checking and the occasional brief interview with local inhabitants, a road distance of 50 to 100 miles may be covered in an eight-hour day.

Traverse workers should always work in pairs, with one man spending his full time following the map, the countryside and recording notes. The driver should concentrate primarily on driving, but he should be ready to add his own comments and to draw attention to points of interest on his side of the road which might otherwise be missed. In the case of a car full of students, all except the driver should be busy keeping a record of the traverse. It will probably simplify the procedure if each student keeps a record of certain assigned phenomena only, so that together they have a complete record. Stops should be made whenever any particularly revealing view of the landscape is noted so that a full examination may be made. Roadside exposures in which soil profiles may be studied and stream-cuts showing the underlying geological strata should be carefully observed.

In unsettled areas the record will consist largely of land-forms and material, soils and vegetation. In the cultural landscape, or the area affected by human settlement, on the other hand, the details of land use will occupy much of the attention of the geographer. In order to record them on an inch-to-the-mile map, it will be necessary to adopt some kind of a system of symbols. One of the most satisfactory methods is the use of coloured pencils. These may be obtained in sets of twelve or twenty-four in a box which may be attached in some way to the instrument board of the car so as to be available at all times. Almost as good a record may be made, however, by using a hard lead pencil, kept sharpened so as to make small clearly legible symbols on the map. In this way six or eight entries per mile may be made on either side of the line of traverse without becoming too crowded. This is usually sufficient in a general farming region. In areas where specialization occurs and small fields are prevalent, it is probably easier to keep the traverse in a notebook on a scale of four inches to the mile (or more if necessary). One does not cover one hundred miles of such traverse in a day, however. While, of course, the records of such traverses will not be strictly accurate, they may, if faithfully kept, be used to make a rough statistical analysis of land-use in the area.

For detailed work, either on sample areas or in complete studies, no other medium is as good as the vertical air-photograph carried into the field. It can be held on a stiff board back by a couple of elastic bands and the entries made directly upon it, field by field as the geographical surveyor goes over the area. Such photographs are usually obtainable in scales of one inch to one thousand feet, more or less, and with the use of a full code of symbols a very complete record may be written on each field.

In recent years a number of field-record codes have been devised such as those used by the Tennessee Valley Authority, the United States Soil Conservation Service and many other land classification services.[1]

An early example of such a code was used by V. C. Finch[2] in a study of the Montfort area of South-western Wisconsin. In the form of a fraction, it had three symbols in the numerator, which represented land-use, and three in the denominator, indicating land characteristics.

Numerator

First digit: major use type; tilled land, permanent grass, timber, idle land.
Second digit: specific crop or use type.
Third digit: condition of crop.

Denominator

First digit: slope class; level, rolling, rough, steep.
Second digit: soil type.
Third digit: drainage condition.

The following example of a fractional symbol, $\frac{221}{15X}$, means permanent grass pasture with scattered trees or brush, good quality, on level land, Wabash silt loam soil, poorly drained.

The number of digits used may be greatly increased if desired; very long fractional codes were used by the land-use surveyors of the Tennessee Valley Authority. The same technique of the fractional code may be used to record the use, structure and condition of buildings, roads, bridges, &c. An amazing amount of geographic detail may thus be recorded upon a photograph or map of similar scale.

[1] *Land Classification in the United States*, National Resources Planning Board (1941), Washington, D.C.

[2] Finch, Vernon C., and Robert S. Platt (1933), 'Geographic Surveys', *The Geographic Society of Chicago Bulletin No. 9*, pp. i–xiii, 3–75.

Maps and notes, however, do not constitute a full geographic record, they should be supplemented by pictures illustrating specific landscapes or important details. 'Any fool can use a camera', but it is a particularly foolish geographer who neglects to take plenty of illustrative photographs. These should include the common and more or less monotonous features of the area under study as well as the most striking features which, in all probability, are not typical of the area as a whole. By all means, take more pictures than you think you need for you may not be back again. It is easy to discard unneeded pictures, while a neglected opportunity may result in lasting regret.

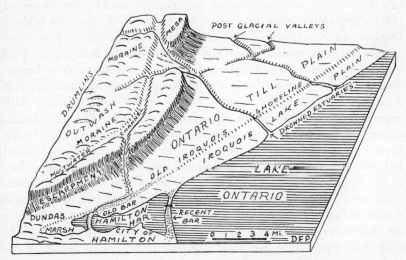

Fig. 30.—Block diagram to illustrate some of the physiographic features along the Niagara Escarpment near Hamilton, Ontario

The field geographer should also cultivate the art of sketching (see Fig. 30). Often the camera shows too much, and the wealth of detail in the landscape obscures the geographical relationships. At other times the camera record shows too little. In both cases a good field sketch would be much more valuable. It takes time but is usually worth it. Good geographic sketches may also be made from photographs. Some of the published reports of the various land-use surveys of Britain publish both the photograph of the landscape and an interpretative sketch made therefrom.[1]

The field worker should make line sketches. Shading and colour take

[1] *English County—A Planning survey of Hertfordshire* (1946), Faber & Faber, London.

too much time and are difficult to reproduce. Practically anything of value in a landscape can be shown by lines anyway.

Having made observations and completed our records, what then? It may, of course, be that we are baffled. Our scattered observations may appear as separate pieces of a jig-saw puzzle which have no discernible relationship one to another. If so, we do not essay an interpretation, but present our record; and leave it for other men to explain the relationships and to obtain a closer approach to reality after more data have been secured.

'Geography tells what is where, why and what of it', according to a definition attributable to Isaiah Bowman. While we should be wary of any deterministic snap judgements, geographers should relate cause and effect where such relationships are clearly visible. In the drumlin fields of Ontario and New York one observes many hillsides left in permanent grass, whereas the rounded crests and flat inter-drumlin areas are occupied by cultivated fields. This distribution of land-uses is the result of human choice, but does anyone doubt that the simple environmental factor of slope has determined that choice? Not if he has been a farmer with experience on a hillside farm. One further example. The settled agricultural area of southern Ontario is separated from the region to the north by a transition so abrupt that it may be represented on all small scale maps as a single line. That line coincides with the geological boundary of the Canadian Shield. The farmlands are on the till-covered plains underlain by Paleozoic sedimentary rocks, the rugged hills of the Shield remain in forest. Does anyone doubt the causal relationship underlying the differences in land-use? Only a confirmed mugwump would be content to report only that there appeared to be a high degree of co-variation when he has a specific answer to the question, 'why?'

Geographical phenomena are, however, by no means environmentally determined in all cases. In southern Ontario at the beginning of the twentieth century a whole series of small towns were dotted along the railway between Toronto and Kingston. They are still there, only one or two of them have grown to have more than 10,000 inhabitants.

There is one exception—the city of Oshawa, which in 1901 had a population of 4,394 and now contains over 30,000 people. There is, so far as one can see, no reason why Oshawa should be the second ranking Canadian city in the manufacturing of automobiles. The industry might just as well have developed from a carriage factory located in either Bowmanville or Port Hope. It would, in all probability, have been located more logically in either Toronto or Hamilton. The factor of human choice, expressed as business initiative, located the industry in Oshawa and the city developed forthwith. The existence of the city, itself, is now the strongest factor in the immediate environment, and the geographer finds himself reporting its influence upon its own inhabitants and upon those of the surrounding countryside.

What of it! On the basis of his interpretation may the geographer peep into the future to predict future environments and future human activity? Just as surely as the weather man predicts tomorrow's rain. The accuracy of his predictions varies with the time factor, but so does that of the meteorologist whose probabilities become possibilities when extended beyond a twenty-four hour period.

The geographer reports conditions as he finds them regardless of whether his facts lie in the realm of the natural or the social sciences; and in so far as he can he establishes correlations and chart trends, knowing full well that the will of man or the vagaries of nature may invalidate many of his predictions. On the basis of his observations he is able, at least to hazard an educated guess. Better still, he has in hand the basic information necessary in the formulation of plans for future development. Instead of 'what of it?' we may ask 'what can we make of it?' and preface an answer with reasonable assurance.

PART II. LABORATORY STUDIES

All geographical field work is done through the use of maps and all geographical reporting is done in large measure through the medium of maps. In fact there are geographers who say 'If it isn't mapped, it isn't geography.' Hartshorne[1] asks: 'If the geographer has any specific technique, what is it. . . ?' and a few lines later answers his own question thus, 'Surely it is the technique of cartographical presentation, the one technique which geographers have developed in a great variety of rich detail.' There is no denying the importance of the map, consequently the study of geography, either by geographers or by others, must begin by obtaining a working knowledge of maps.

Geography deals with landscapes just as geology deals with rocks and botany with plants. The geologist and botanist are able to bring small samples of their materials into the laboratory for detailed study. The geographer cannot break off part of the landscape, the only way in which he is able to bring the landscape into the classroom is through the medium of the map. Thus through the medium of a series of carefully selected, representative maps, the student of geography may become familiar with the details of many landscapes which he is unable, personally, to visit for

[1] Hartshorne, Richard (1939), 'The Nature of Geography', *Annals of the Association of American Geographers*, Vol. XXIX.

the purpose of study. On the basis of his familiarity with the actual landscapes of a few areas and their map images the student, and, in fact, any intelligent layman, is able from the map images of other areas to reconstruct an intelligent approximation of their geographic realities. The available maps may be of many types; but the most useful is the large scale detailed *topographic map*; often known as the military map because of its extensive use by armed forces, and from the fact that in many countries, including Canada and the United Kingdom, they are produced by the geographic sections of the military establishments. In the United States they are issued by the Geological Survey. Such maps on a scale of 1 : 50,000 to 1 : 100,000 show, by means of various map symbols, the relief, drainage, vegetation, settlements, and communications of the area in question. Even to a non-geographer, these maps impart a great deal of information. To a man trained in geographic interpretation they speak volumes.

The most important of the physical factors shown on the topographic map is surface relief. So great is this importance that in English-speaking countries the word *topography* has come to mean relief to most people, rather than its original connotation, namely, the detailed description of small areas.

The problem of representing relief on a map is, of course, the problem of showing three-dimensional objects in two dimensions. Older maps show relief in symbols or hachures, that is by means of a multitude of fine lines showing the general direction of the slopes. Others do it by plastic shading of the hills, the hill-shading usually being drawn as though the light comes from a constant direction. Some very beautiful and very carefully drawn maps using hachures and hill-shading have been produced, especially fine are those of the Italian and Swiss cartographers showing the relief of the Alps. However, though the overall effect is very pleasing, there is so much ink on these maps that it is a difficult task to read them, moreover, topographic detail is not always as accurate as could be desired.

The Study of Contours

Of all the methods in use, contouring is the most accurate and most desirable. It is necessary, of course, to have accurate data before they can be drawn. A map contour is a line joining points which have been determined to have the same elevation, the greater the number of points determined, the greater the ensuing accuracy of the map which may be produced. Such lines are usually shown at standard vertical intervals; 20 feet in the case of U.S. maps, 25 feet on Canadian maps. In very rugged or mountainous areas, 100-foot or even 500-foot intervals may be used, depending upon the scale of the map. Contour lines are usually printed in some shade of red or brown, and are thus much less obstructive of the other map detail. The geographer is trained in both drawing and interpreting contours. He also receives training in the topographic surveying, plane-tabling, and levelling which must be done in order to obtain the data from which the map is drawn.

Map contours tell much more than the story of relief, the differences in height above sea-level. To the trained eye of the geographer and geologist they also tell the story of the way in which this relief was developed. So important has this become that a separate science, *geomorphology*, the study of land-forms, has grown up to occupy a middle ground between the two older earth sciences. Training in geomorphology has always been considered as part of geographic training, because a good deal of the early work was done by men who called themselves physical geographers; and because, for the most part, the geographically significant phase of relief is not so much elevation above sea-level as it is the actual shape of the surface itself. This is particularly true in all areas with an elevation of less than one thousand feet above sea-level.

Geomorphology is not a laboratory science, it is a field science; and observations upon land-forms have already been cited as about the first and most important observations which a geographer can make. However, when maps must be substituted for landscapes beyond immediate reach, the land-forms must be interpreted.

Actual land-forms are the results of the interaction at the surface of the earth of geological and climatic forces. The earth's crust is not static, it is subject to movement. Tectonic forces may cause buckling of the rocks so that great folds are raised many thousands of feet in the air. Corresponding great depressions are also formed. The simplest and most fundamental law of earth sculpture is that which states that water runs downhill. In doing so it usually carries some of the material from the hill along with it and eventually a valley is formed. As soon as rock masses are raised they are attacked by running water which carries the particles into the great water-filled depressions of the earth. A mountain range or any upraised mass of land carries on its face the record of this war between the uplifting forces and those which seek to bring all land to a uniform level. All stages of this process may be seen from young recently uplifted mountain ranges of great height to old worn-down surfaces practically at sea-level. To the great American physical geographer William Morris Davis[1] the credit must be given for having most

[1] Davis, W. M. (1909), *Geographical Essays*, Ginn & Co.

27

clearly set forth this concept of the cycle of erosion, or 'geographical cycle' as he called it.

According to the cyclic concept land-forms and, in particular, river valleys could be classified by age groups. Young valleys have steep gradients and are V-shaped in cross-section; old valleys have low gradients, or have 'reached grade' as he termed it, they also have wide flaring valleys with gentle slopes and flat flood plains. Eventually, of course, all uplands are worn away leaving a monotonous low-level surface which he termed a *peneplane*, meaning almost a plain. Since the cycle is usually incomplete, having been interrupted by renewed earth movements, some remnants of the former upland remain while the present rivers are busily carving new relief in the old erosion surface. Thus it is that in any mountainous area and, in particular, in the Pennsylvania mountains where Davis conducted his investigations, the land-forms are the present expression of a long history of uplift and denudation. The science of land-forms is a fascinating one to which many men, inspired by Davis, have devoted the best parts of their lives.

Not all the surface features of the earth owe their form to river sculpture. There is a cycle in the desert where there are no rivers and where wind is a powerful agency. Even in the 'arid cycle', however, water in the form of infrequent sudden showers does much of the work. Another sequence caused by subterranean solution of limestone rock is known as the 'Karst cycle'. There is also a cycle of shoreline erosion due to wave action. High mountains show the results of cycles of glacial erosion while vast areas in Canada and Northern Eurasia have had their land-forms determined by continental glaciation.

The topographic map, by its patterns of contours, makes clear not only the form but the developmental history of the physical landscape or, at least, gives enough information so that the geographer may be reasonably sure of those areas which he cannot visit. Even for those areas in which he intends to do field work the relief map is indispensable, for it gives the geographer powerful suggestions as to what to look for. The checking of map-born theories in the field is one of the most interesting phases of physical geography.

Many geographers contend that we should accept earth forms as they are, name them, describe them and show how they affect the activities of mankind without worrying about their origins. From personal experience the present writer is unable to accept such a philosophy; but would wholeheartedly accept the statement of Wooldridge and Morgan[1] that 'by

[1] Wooldridge, S. W., and R. S. Morgan (1937), *The Physical Basis of Geography*, Longmans Green & Co.

study of origins we are led to the most accurate conception of the nature of relief forms, and thereby equipped to approach the immediately practical problems of representing and "using" relief in the geographic synthesis'. If the geographer surrenders physical geography he has left himself no ground upon which to stand.

Block Diagrams and Models

There are several devices by which the nature of relief can be taught and appreciated in the geographical laboratory. The interpretation of the contour map is made much clearer to students by the construction of profiles, block diagrams, and solid relief models. After such practice he is much more able to visualize the map relief.

The first problem which must be solved is that of the vertical scale. Only in mountainous country can relief be shown satisfactorily with no vertical exaggeration. In plains where river valleys less than one hundred feet deep are important, the vertical scale may have to be at least ten times that of the horizontal while, in ordinary uplands with a relief of 500 to 1,000 feet the exaggeration may be only four times or perhaps less. The drawing to scale of the profiles of river valleys, hills and mountain ranges will soon give the student a sense of feeling for the significance of the placing of contours. The nuances of concave and convex slopes and changes in slope which indicate old erosion surfaces then become familiar.

The block diagram is an even better but, of course, more difficult technique. Done to scale, it involves either the drawing of a series of closely spaced profiles upon a skewed base or the drawing of raised contours as a step in the reconstruction of the surface. Once this is done the surface forms themselves are then sketched in by simple line hachures. Plastic shading is of little use to the beginner. The drawing of block diagrams was early developed by W. M. Davis.[1]

The modern exponent of the technique is A. K. Lobeck[2,3,4] whose books should be consulted both by those who desire to acquire graphic skill, and those who wish merely to reach a proficiency in the interpretation of relief (see Fig. 31).

Most satisfactory in the end, but most tedious to construct, is the solid

[1] Davis, W. M. (1901), *Physical Geography*, Ginn & Co., Boston.
[2] Lobeck, A. K. (1924), *Block Diagrams and other Graphic Methods used in Geology and Geography*, John Wiley & Sons, Inc.
[3] Lobeck, A. K. (1939), *Geomorphology*, McGraw Hill Book Co.
[4] Lobeck, A. K., and W. J. Tellington (1944), *Military Maps and Air Photographs*, McGraw Hill Book Co.

relief model, yet there are good arguments for requiring students to do it as part of their geographical training. There are various methods of construction. In the Department of Geography at the University of Toronto map contours are traced upon sheets of cardboard of the required thickness.[1] These are cut out and nailed one upon the other to build the framework. The final surface form is supplied by a coating of putty upon which other topographical detail may be painted. In the Toronto School of Applied Science a machine was built which through an adaptation of the principle of the pantagraph enabled the operator to cut the contours directly on a block of plaster with an electrically driven drill. These have

FIG. 31.—A quickly-made field-sketch

Although not accurate as to detail, the above sketch depicts the geographical essentials of a notch in the Niagara Escarpment, north-west of Toronto. The young valley, the stratified rocks, the waterfall, power house, coniferous vegetation, and the two railways in the pass, are all represented

been left unsmoothed because of the needs of engineering students to visualize exact contour levels. By whatever method models are built they serve the purpose of an instructive experience for those who build them and they provide excellent teaching material in the faculties where they are built. With the recent introduction of cheap plastic map models such as those of the Aero Corporation of Philadelphia the necessity of home made models has greatly lessened. They should not, however, be entirely abandoned.

Graphic aid to visualization of surface features on a smaller scale is also necessary for large areas. Satisfactory models can be made, although

[1] See Griffith Taylor, *Geographical Laboratory*, Toronto, 1945. Here also are described new techniques for teaching Navigation, Correlation Coefficients, &c.

with rather great vertical exaggeration, on the scale of 1 : 1,000,000. Scale block diagrams, however, of continental areas are practically impossible. In these cases the earth scientist falls back upon the physiographic diagrams. This is a technique whereby land-forms are symbolically shown on small-scale maps drawn on one of the usual projections. A. K. Lobeck has produced many excellent examples in this field, a notable collection of which appears in his *Airways of America*.[1] Another acknowledged master is Erwin Raisz, whose illustrations of the land-forms of the United States show great wealth of detail.[2] A bold style is exhibited by Griffith Taylor, who illustrates his own books.[3]

From these and from many others the budding geographer may hope to acquire points of style and technique which will stand him in good stead, while the merely interested reader will have cause to marvel at the skill and patience with which these examples of pictorial cartography have been produced. Incidentally, a great number of ideas concerning the relief of many parts of the world will be encountered.

Cultural Patterns

Map interpretation is not all concerned with physical relief because the topographic map contains records of cultural patterns also which, to the geographer, are no less interesting than the land-forms.

In a settled country perhaps the first detail which strikes the eye is the location of town sites. Why do towns develop at certain points and not at others? Study of the map will often provide the answer. Many have grown up at river-sites of one kind or another such as fords, bridges, power-sites, stream confluences, the head of navigation or other advantageous points. A whole series of cities in eastern U.S.A. are located at the *fall-line* where the rivers leave the Piedmont and enter the flat coastal plain. Other cities are seaports, located at the points providing the best landing-places. In hilly lands many small settlements arise along the 'spring-line' because of the necessity for drinking water. Desert towns arise in *oases* for the same reason. Many cities grow up because of their convenience to some route of travel such as a mountain pass. Many others are *cross-roads* towns

[1] Lobeck, A. K. (1933) *Airways of America* (Guidebook No. 1, The United States Airlines), The Geographical Press, Columbia University, New York.

[2] See text figures and folded map in Atwood, W. W. (1940), *The Physiographic Provinces of North America*, Ginn & Co., Boston. See also Raisz, E. (1938), *General Cartography*, McGraw Hill Book Co. Inc., New York.

[3] See for examples: *Environment, Race and Migration*, The University of Toronto Press (3rd edition, 1949). *Our Evolving Civilization*, The University of Toronto Press, 1946. *Urban Geography* (Methuen, London), 1949.

located where two routes meet; they may be either land or water routes or land and water routes. The city of Montreal, for instance, is the greatest place of meeting for transportation routes in Canada. Since the development of railways many towns have arisen at junctions, divisional points, river crossings, and other strategically placed railway stations. In western North America, very often, the sole reason for existence of a nucleated settlement is the railway station which furnishes a base of supply and a shipping point for the farmer's grain. In the Canadian Shield and in the Rocky Mountains, to mention just two areas in the New World, there are many mining towns. Sawmills and pulp mills also attract settlement. Many towns are located under the influence of several important factors and the map reader should not be too hasty in passing an opinion but should look for all the clues.

The location of transportation routes are also to be interpreted as being under the influence of geographical factors. Railways often run from one city to another by routes which are far from the most direct. The search for low gradients is often a controlling reason. Thus many railways, and highways too, follow river valleys. The Mohawk Valley in New York State, uniting the interior of the continent with the port of New York, carries one of the greatest concentrations of transport facilities in the world.

Agricultural settlement is also shown on the topographic map by appropriate symbols. In older countries many factors of the natural environment can be seen to control the location of farm villages and isolated farmsteads. Water supply is always an important factor. In areas of varied relief we find it reflected strongly in the location of cultivated fields, vineyards, and orchards. Blue ditch-lines indicate the reclaimed marsh lands as well as irrigation projects, but there is seldom any reason for mistaking one for the other. In North America, except in the Atlantic coastal regions, farm distributions are under strong control of the surveyor's line and many of the natural factors are ignored. Even so, the location of houses, fields, and other features are found often to be located with respect to water supply, drainage, shelter from wind, or other factors of the immediate site.

It is impossible here to catalogue all the interpretations of the topographic map. A good map reader can reconstruct a very detailed geography from map interpretation if the map details are present. A geographer can even read between the symbols and supply items of information which are not actually present on the map but which are missing links in the chain of interpretive reasoning. There is great controversy as to whether this should be done by teachers of map interpretation. The purist school maintain that the reader has no right to any information which he cannot deduce from the map, whereas most geographers maintain that personal knowledge of geographic association should also be used if most value is to be obtained from the study.

Geological maps are of great value to the geographer. They give specific and accurate information about rock formations which are, perhaps, only suggested on the topographic map. With both maps in hand the map reader has a greater wealth of fact at his disposal.

There are many other types of maps with which a geographer must become familiar both as a reader and interpreter and as a craftsman and user. Part of the geographer's job is to design maps which will present his facts more clearly than words can do. There is a great deal of truth in the words which Hartshorne quotes from Hettner: 'In consequence of the development of cartographical methods of presentation, verbal description has lost its original importance and serves now only to complete and explain the maps.'[1] A great deal of cartographic technique has been developed in the forty years since Hettner wrote these words.

Climatic Maps

The geographer spends some time in getting a mastery of climatic maps and diagrams. Rainfall and temperature distribution maps for various countries and for the world have been available for many years. They are in need of revision and are constantly being revised as new data become available. The technique of the weather map has undergone a complete transformation within the past decade. Whereas only isobaric lines used to appear, the map now bears symbols for different types of fronts, air masses, upper air conditions, and a whole collection of data in the detailed station model showing local conditions. National meteorological services now issue guides to weather maps for the use of the public, as for example, the one issued by the Canadian Department of Transport.[2] It is issued in conjunction with a selected series of weather maps to illustrate the cyclonic sequence of Canadian weather.

Climatology is part of the regular content of geography and climatic description and classification consists in the synthesis of weather data from all parts of the world. Practice in transforming statistics into climatic maps and diagrams should certainly be part of the training of every geographer. The standard rainfall and temperature chart appears in every

[1] Hartshorne, Richard, op. cit., p. 248.

[2] Clark, W. Gilmour (1946), *A Guide to the Weather Map*, Series for High Schools, Meteorological Division, Department of Transport, Canada.

textbook in geography and climatology and needs no further reference. There are special techniques such as the *hythergraph* devised by Griffith Taylor[1] which are valuable. Very similiar is the climograph favoured by Huntington.[2] On them one can show precise ranges of raininess, dryness, and other climatic conditions.

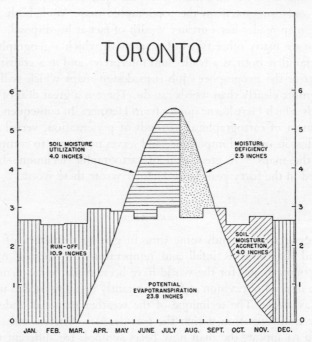

TORONTO

SOIL MOISTURE
UTILIZATION
4.0 INCHES

MOISTURE
DEFICIENCY
2.5 INCHES

RUN-OFF
10.9 INCHES

SOIL
MOISTURE
ACCRETION
4.0 INCHES

POTENTIAL
EVAPOTRANSPIRATION
23.8 INCHES

JAN. FEB. MAR. APR. MAY JUNE JULY AUG. SEPT. OCT. NOV. DEC.

FIG. 32.—Moisture relations of the Toronto climate according to the Thornthwaite formula. Toronto receives 32·2 inches of precipitation per annum, has an actual evapo-transpiration of 21·3 inches, a run-off of 10·9 inches and late-season moisture deficiency of 2·5 inches. (*Data supplied by M. Sanderson*)

A complete new system of climatic classification is being developed by Thornthwaite[3] based upon the evaporation factor and he has devised a diagram which shows a combination of moisture factors including rainfall, evaporation—both potential and actual—run-off, and moisture deficiency (see Fig. 32). He has not invented a name for his diagram but

[1] Taylor, Griffith (1947), *Canada*, Methuen (see p. 127).
[2] Huntington, Ellsworth (1940), *Principles of Economic Geography*, John Wiley & Sons.
[3] Thornthwaite, C. W. (1948), 'An Approach Toward a Rational Classification of Climate', *Geographical Review*, XXXVIII, 55–94.

it is certainly a special type of climograph, and most useful for putting the emphasis upon some neglected and sometimes obscure phases of climatology.

Dot Maps and Isopleth Maps

Among the many useful maps which the geographer learns to use are those which show the geographical distribution of statistical data such as the results of a population census. Apple trees or acres of wheat may be treated in the same way. The census is compiled on the basis of the township or other minor subdivision, these are grouped into counties or major subdivision and finally into states or, in Canada, provinces. The problem is to portray the density of population and it may be done in a variety of ways. The simplest type to make is the *unit dot map* in which each dot is made to represent a convenient number of people and the appropriate number of dots are evenly distributed on the map area of the subdivision. With the help of a topographic map the dots may be placed more accurately, thus they will tend to be placed in the valleys rather than on the ridge tops. Where there are many towns it is impossible to use the unit dot system satisfactorily and a multiple dot system is used with a series of dots of different sizes to represent population clusters.[1] Other maps have densities represented by different shadings ranging from very light for the least occupied area to black or almost black for the most densely occupied. Such shadings are usually applied to the whole area enclosed by a civil boundary. This has its drawbacks because on a population map of North America, on a small scale, Ontario would be shown as having uniformly a density of less than 10 people per square mile. Actually a number of areas in Southern Ontario have well over 100 persons per square mile. Even on a county basis a distorted picture would be presented because Ontario has several counties which lie across the boundary of the Shield. However the *choropleth* map, as this is called, is often used because once the calculations are made it is easy to construct on the ordinary base map showing census divisions.

Another method of showing population, and like-behaving densities, is the isopleth map. The principle employed here is exactly the same as that used in constructing the physical contour map and it can be very accurate if the data can be computed for small areas. For areas like Ontario where township densities can be plotted it is quite satisfactory. On a small scale an isopleth map of population densities for a large

[1] For many of these mapping techniques see E. Raisz (1938), *General Cartography*, McGraw Hill Book Co.

country like Canada shows a much closer approach to reality than does the density shading or choropleth method.

The geographer must eventually become familiar with the whole array of land-use maps which have become available in recent years. The Land-Use Survey of Britain about which Professor Stamp writes in this volume has provided many interesting examples. The soil conservation service, the Tennessee Valley Authority and various land-use surveys such as those of New York, Michigan, and Wisconsin, to name just a few, have produced types of land classification maps which the geographer can use and also learn to make. The laboratory and drafting phases of this work must have been preceded by field work in order to provide the raw data, hence a land-use project may often prove to be an ideal student project, permitting him to get an integrated concept of geographical work.

Map Projections and Aerial Photographs

Last to be mentioned here, but nevertheless usually given considerable emphasis in the geographical laboratory, the geographer needs an understanding of the principles behind the construction of map projections. In most books on maps[1] a chapter is devoted to projections. There are also books devoted wholly to map projections such as those of Steers[2] and Deetz and Adams[3] to mention only two. From these the student may learn the construction of the Mercator, Mollweide, Orthographic, Stereographic, and other methods for projecting a round surface on to flat paper. In actual practice he will probably never have to construct his own grid since world maps on all sorts of scales exist already, and he merely has to choose one to fit his need. Other projections which should be studied are the conic projections, particularly Lambert's Conformal projection which is used in so much mid-latitude topographical mapping. The budding geographer should construct a few projections for himself and plot maps thereon. He should also study carefully the properties of all commonly used projections to enable him to choose intelligently the type of map adaptable to any special purpose which he might have in mind.

In recent years air-photography has become a powerful agency in the production of maps. It was particularly useful during wartime, but many

[1] See for example David Greenhood (1944), *Mapping for Everybody*, Holiday House, New York.

[2] Steers, J. A. (1937), *An Introduction to the Study of Map Projections*, London University Press.

[3] Deetz, C. H., and O. S. Adams (1938), *Elements of Map Projection*, U. S. Dept. of Commerce, Spec. Pub. 68.

countries have put it to extensive peacetime use also. All Canadian topographic maps produced during the past twenty years carry the phrase 'with aerial photography by R.C.A.F.' Many other agencies such as Departments of Lands and Forests, Mines, Highways, Planning, and Conservation make extensive use of aerial photography in order to obtain exact data on terrain conditions. While photogrammetry is a long and exacting process it is well to have some parts of it learned by the geographer and a number of good books exist.[1,2] The geographer, however, is most interested in what he can get directly from the photographs themselves, and should certainly master the technique of the stereoscope as an aid to their interpretation. Air photographs are fascinating in the details of land-form and human occupancy which they contain, and they are absolutely without peer as the source of geographical information.

It has not been the intention of the writer to lay down herein the detailed programme of practical work in geography. Institutions and geographers differ greatly as to the emphasis which is put upon the different phases of the work. That does not greatly matter. The objective will be served if the geographer is reminded and the general reader informed as to the wealth of practical methods which are available. It should hardly be necessary to repeat, 'Geography is a practical subject.'

Editor's Note: It is thought that a few notes on the technique of lecturing as practised at Toronto may be of interest. For a dozen years the editor has used coated glass-slides to replace blackboard and wall maps; indeed, he uses such slides for all notes which it is desirable for the students to copy in detail. A quick-drying solution of Canada Balsam (3 per cent in xylol) is used to prepare lantern-slide covers so as to be suitable for drawing sketches and maps. A dozen or so of these slides are always on one's desk, and any maps which may be needed are traced in simple form for each lecture. With a fine mapping pen and various coloured inks, one can produce maps, which are ideal for lecture purposes, in a few minutes. Five lanterns are in constant use at Toronto, and with modern lanterns it is easy to keep the room quite light so that full notes may be taken. The lecturer stands at the lantern and uses a thin wire pointer, inserted close to the slide, to indicate the features he is discussing.

---

[1] Smith, H. T. U. (1943), *Aerial Photographs and their Applications*, D. Appleton—Century Co.

[2] Eardley, A. J. (1942), *Aerial Photographs, their use and interpretation*, Harper & Brothers, New York and London.

CHAPTER XVIII

GEOGRAPHY AND EMPIRE

CHARLES B. FAWCETT

Professor Fawcett graduated at Nottingham and Oxford. He was a member of the staffs of Southampton and Leeds Universities before he was appointed Professor of Geography at University College, London University. He is Professor Emeritus since 1949. He is well known for his books on Political Geography; and has published Frontiers, Provinces of England, Political Geography of the British Empire, Bases of a World Commonwealth.

Introduction

MANY writers on geography and on history, from Herodotus to the present day, have made some references to relations between these subjects, including those related to the political aspects of both. But, so far as I know, the first modern attempt at a systematic treatment of Political Geography was in the works of Friedrich Ratzel, particularly in his *Politische Geographie* (1897). This work had a considerable influence on later thought, especially in its concepts of the influence of space relations on the growth of states and its foreshadowing of the concept of *lebensraum* and the need for an expanding state to acquire sufficient *lebensraum* for its growth. An application of these ideas may be seen in Friedrich Naumann's *Mitteleuropa* (1915, English translation 1916). More objective studies came from French geographers, including Camille Vallaux's introductory work on Political Geography and Albert Demangeon's *L'Empire Britannique.*

After *ca.* 1930 the German studies degenerated into *Geopolitik.* During the inter-war period there were some useful preliminary studies by British and American geographers, and the very valuable series of factual studies in Isaiah Bowman's *New World* (1912 and later editions). But the systematic treatise on Political Geography is still to be written. The subject is necessarily very closely linked with Historical Geography, a branch of the science that is also still in a very early stage of its development.

The idea of the development of the nation and state in its nuclear area, or metropolitan region, was adumbrated by Mackinder in some of his lectures, and in studies of history and geography. He also introduced the concept of the complementary and conflicting roles of the Heartland and the marginal regions. This was most fully set out in his *Democratic Ideals and Reality* (1919), and was more recently discussed by the present writer in the Herbertson Lecture of 1946.[1]

This present essay follows on from these works; but it is concerned with only one part of Political Geography, as indicated by its title.

GEOGRAPHY AND EMPIRE

Medieval Empires

The word *Empire* has denoted many different states in the world. In Western civilization we think first of the Roman Empire, the typical Universal State of Toynbee's classification. But this, like other universal states, dominated a whole civilization and a major geographical region. The medieval Holy Roman Empire of the German nation claimed, but never attained, the same status for Western Christendom. Since the break-up of the Roman Empire there has been no 'Empire', in this comprehensive sense of the word, in our Western civilization.

The Modern Age was inaugurated by the Age of Discovery—of the open sea-ways to the older worlds of India and Cathay and to the New World—in the last decades of the fifteenth century. This made possible the overseas expansion of the Atlantic States of Europe and the establishment of partial empires of a new kind. No one of these has ever been able to dominate the whole of the civilized world. But it is of these incomplete and temporary empires that we must think in discussing the relations of geographical facts to imperial problems today—with perhaps a glance at possibilities of a real empire, in Toynbee's sense of a universal state, which now must be a World State.

Every empire has at its heart a geographical base, a nuclear area, or metropolitan region. This region supplied the human and natural resources and the ability to use them, the men, the material, and the organization, for the building of the original state and its expansion to an empire. In Mackinder's term this nuclear area was the geographical base of the manpower and the munition-power.

Imperial power is fundamentally dependent on the possession of a base of this type—a base at once adequate to the demands on it, secure from hostile invasion, and in control of communications with the areas where the imperial power is to be exerted. In this sense the island of Great Britain is the base from which the British Empire was built, and that Empire depended on British use of the sea-ways.

[1] 'Marginal and Interior Lands of the Old World', *Geography*, March 1947, and in *New Compass of the World*, 1949.

Spain built up a great empire in Latin America during the sixteenth and seventeenth centuries. That empire was built by manpower from the base in Spain, and its essential communications were across the Atlantic Ocean. At the same time the Spanish Monarchy was involved in European power-politics and dominated by the tradition of the Roman Empire as the universal state of Christendom. This led to the first of the series of great wars of the Modern Age. The resources of Spain and her dependencies proved insufficient for the re-establishment of that universal empire.

France is a far more fertile and populous land. In it the French State had grown from its nuclear area of the Paris Basin, a greater base than any in the Iberian peninsula. By the end of the seventeenth century France was the richest and most populous state in Europe; and again there was a series of great wars. In these the French Monarchy failed to conquer Europe. None-the-less France remained for another century the strongest Power; and at the end of the eighteenth century the armies of France, armed on this occasion with new ideals, overran most of Europe, till the third of the series of great wars of the Modern Age ended at Waterloo.

Before the Industrial Revolution France was the richest available geographical base in Western Christendom. Its nuclear area of the Paris Basin is near to the maximum size of a strongly knit cultural and political unit of the age of horse-and-foot travel, before the development of printing. It is a very productive agricultural region; so it was capable of maintaining a larger population than rival areas. Also the Paris Basin was, and is, well placed to dominate, unite, and finally absorb into its cultural sphere, the smaller surrounding areas which are united with it to form the France of today.

The chief alternative nuclear region in Western Europe seems to be the lowland to the north of the Paris Basin in the Low Countries and the Rhineland, between the Rhine Highlands and the North Sea. This is, in its natural resources, perhaps the richest of the few well-marked geographical regions of Europe which appear to have been possible nuclear areas for a Great Power. But in the Modern Age it has never been politically united; and its history illustrates a failure to develop a human unity in a well-marked natural unit area. Perhaps the main causes may be found in (1) the presence during the Medieval Age of ecclesiastical states, in Cologne, Münster, Liège, and Trier, which prevented any political union of the region by a secular state until after the Protestant Reformation; and (2) the fact that it is in the border lands of the French and German peoples and states, whose rivalries have been sufficient to prevent any such union since then. Yet this Lower Rhine Lowland is the natural geographical focal area of Western Europe.

The nuclear areas in western continental Europe had both landward and seaward frontiers. And for all of them the problems of the land frontier were the more urgent ones. Spain and France made their great oversea colonial and imperial expansions with only a small part of their resources, and with only spasmodic efforts from their Governments. Always the chief and lasting preoccupations of the rulers of those countries were those concerned with neighbouring lands and states.

Britain

Britain is detached from Europe. The physical separation is only that of the Narrow Seas. But there have been periods when Britain could hold aloof from Europe and its troubles in a 'Splendid Isolation'; though these periods have never been of long duration. Before the Age of Discovery the peoples and States of Britain were continuously entangled with those of Western Europe. From the end of the Dark Ages and the Angle and Saxon colonization of the eastern and southern lowlands England was linked with continental holdings. The reign of Danish kings over both sides of the North Sea was short-lived; but the Norman Conquest of 1066 started a period of five centuries during which the Kings of England were also rulers of territories in France. That conquest was the last of a long series of successful invasions of the island from the continent.

In Britain the English Lowland is the dominant nuclear area. It is comparable to the Paris Basin and the Lower Rhine Lowland in extent and resources; though its more northerly and maritime position makes it less fertile and so agriculturally less productive. But it has no rival in Great Britain. It extends from the east coast to the Welsh Highland, reaching the west coast at the Severn Sea and in Lancashire. It extends from the south coast to the Central Highlands of Britain, half of which is in the political area of England. Beyond these Central Highlands is the much smaller Scottish Lowland, the nuclear area of the smaller Scottish nation. But the English Lowland occupies more than a third of the total area of Great Britain. It is larger than all the other lowlands of that island taken together; and also, because it is the south-eastern third of the island, it is the most favoured part in climate, in soils, and in its relations to the continent and to the sea-ways.

Early in the Modern Age Britain had two pieces of historic good fortune. (1) In 1558 England lost Calais, the last of her continental territories. Since then Britain has never attempted to hold any near-by part of the continent. (2) The dying out of the Tudors, the Welsh dynasty which had completed the union of England and Wales, left the Scottish king heir to the Crown of England. Though the full union of the kingdoms did not come for another century (1707) the union of the Crowns in 1603 left Britain free for overseas expansion. Also the Tudors had established the English navy, and its traditions were well founded in the conflict with Spain which culminated in the defeat of the Spanish Armada in 1588. Britain was only half as large, and much less than half as populous, as France; but she started the modern age of expansion with the great advantages of a secure home base and a realization of the facts that both the security of the homeland and all possibility of overseas expansion depended on her seapower.

So the stage was set for the building up of the modern empires which were the Great Powers of the Modern Age till the World Wars of this twentieth century.

Portuguese and Spanish Empires

The Portuguese were the first of the Empire-builders among the Atlantic States of Europe. Their incursion into the Indian Ocean in the first decades of the sixteenth century brought them into contact with Arabs and Indians and Malays, none of whom then possessed ships or armaments or skill in navigation equal to their own. So the Portuguese had for a short while an effective naval dominance of the Indian Ocean; and this, guided by the abilities of their great viceroy Albuquerque, enabled them to build a tenuous empire of trading stations on its coasts. That empire never extended over any large land area, and it lasted in effect for barely one generation. The homeland of Portugal was too small to supply enough men to maintain the fleets and hold all these far-flung stations. When other European adventurers reached the East Indies the Portuguese Empire faded out with hardly a struggle. But in the course of early voyages to the Indies their sailors discovered Brazil. Here there was no indigenous people and culture able to yield wealth to conquer or trader, only a fertile land which could be colonized and cultivated. Here Portuguese colonies grew into the major part of her empire. Brazil is now far more populous than the original homeland, and is the chief area of Portuguese language and traditions.

In Spain the marriage of Isabella of Castile to Ferdinand of Aragon had recently united the central and eastern parts of the Iberian peninsula. (It is interesting to speculate on what might have happened had Isabella married the rival suitor from Portugal and so united the central and western kingdoms.) Early in 1492 this united kingdom had completed the expulsion of the Muslims. It was faced with the problem of dealing with a nobility and army which had been for seven centuries engaged in the patriotic crusade against the infidel, and whose men were neither fitted for, nor inclined to settle down to, a quiet life.

The proposals of Columbus attracted Queen Isabella. His success opened a vista of infinite possibilities. And the surplus adventurers of Spain found a new outlet for their energies in the conquest and conversion of the new Indies in the west.

But it should not be forgotten that Aragon had possessions and ambitions to the east. The new Spanish kingdom was thereby involved in wars in Italy and against the Turk, wars which led it into central Europe and to conflict with France and absorbed the larger part of its energies. The Spanish Monarchy expanded over a large part of Italy and the Netherlands, and Charles V was Holy Roman Emperor as well as King of Spain. The Spanish conquest of most of Latin America was a minor part of the expansion, though it has had far more lasting results than the gains by marriage and conquest in Europe. Spanish America is now the chief area of the language and culture of Spain.

Very early in their expansion Spain and Portugal had agreed on different spheres of influence, and the Pope had divided the non-Christian lands of the world between them along the line defined in the Treaty of Tordesillas (1494). The 'line' is still traceable in the division between Spanish and Portuguese states of South America.

When Columbus discovered land beyond the Atlantic (1492) and Vasco da Gama reached India (1498) England was just in the beginning of the Tudor reorganization and consolation. This was made necessary by the suicidal Wars of the Roses (1454–85) in which the feudal nobility had almost exterminated itself. The country needed rest; and, though it was, like all the rest of Western Europe, thrilled to its marrow by the reports of new access to the fabulous wealth of the Indies and Cathay and of a New World to the west, England was not then prepared to challenge Spain's claim to a monopoly of the New World.

The new realization of the globe, and its study, led to the search for shorter sea-ways to the Indies, far from Spain. The first English expeditions went north-west, and found Newfoundland and the barren coasts of Labrador. Next they tried for a north-east passage, and made the first effective contact of Western Europe with Muscovy by way of Archangel. But also they found that both North-east and North-west passages were blocked by the Arctic ice. No way to wealth or empire lay along those routes.

The Low Countries came into the newly opened trade because they had fallen to the Spanish Monarchy by marriage, and so were inside the

28

Spanish monopoly area. They are far more favourably located than Spain, and Antwerp became the first centre of a world-wide commerce. But the Protestant Reformation cut across the Low Countries. Under Philip II Spain became the leader in the military crusades to conquer and re-convert the heretics; and the sack of Antwerp ended that first concentration of transoceanic trade.

The Protestant Dutch succeeded in their War of Independence, largely because they were partly insulated from the armies of Spain by their ability to flood their lowlying polder lands; and because England prevented Spain from using the Channel as a safe highway for her armies and their supplies. The Dutch were formally excluded from trade with the Indies; but in fact their ships forced a way through and Holland entered the scramble for wealth and empire.

England was for a time neutralized by the marriage of Queen Mary to Philip of Spain and the temporary success of the counter-Reformation here in that reign. Later the cautious diplomacy of Elizabeth played off rival French and Spanish suitors and gained time for internal growth and consolidation; while it also ended the Scottish wars by ensuring the succession of the King of Scots to the Crown of England.

But Elizabeth was unable, perhaps she did not try very hard, to prevent English adventurers from sailing to the Spanish Main and attempting to trade. There they were violating the monopoly claimed by Spain and were liable to be treated as pirates. So their voyages became warlike enterprises. The stormy northern seas had fostered the development of handier ships and better sailors than those of the zones of sub-tropical and tropical calms and steady breezes: and English seamen soon found that they could outsail and outmanœuvre the clumsy galleons of Spain. While they always retained a real respect for the courage of the Spaniard they developed contempt for his seamanship. In this maritime guerilla warfare the English seamen grew to a great sea power.

But the Spanish Monarchy was still the strongest Power in Christendom; though it failed to conquer France, its chief rival in Europe. And when Philip incorporated Portugal and its overseas possessions into his empire (1580), he took up a war of conquest which was also a crusade for the extermination of the Protestant heresies. He massed his armies in what is now Belgium, under the watchful and suspicious eyes of Dutch and French, and gathered in Cadiz and Lisbon the fleet which his courtiers styled the Invincible Armada. The preparations were harried in their harbours by English raids; but at last, in 1588, the Armada sailed to the English Channel. It came, it saw, it was broken and scattered.

That defeat ended Spain's attempts to reach England. It clenched the independence of Holland. It helped France in her struggles against the power of Spain. It effectively ended Spain's attempt to dominate Europe. It left England secure in her home base, with her sailors free to range all the oceans.

So it opened to England the career of expansion which built up two successive British Empires, and has made English the most widely spoken of the languages of Western civilization.

Dutch and French Empires

The defeat of the Armada left England, France, and Holland as the active expansionist Powers in Western Europe. The home bases of these three are almost as strongly contrasted in their geographical resources and positions as is possible for nuclear areas which are all in one major natural region.

France was then, and remained till well into the nineteenth century, larger in area and population than Britain and Holland combined. Until the Industrial Revolution transformed Britain, France had far greater available natural resources than the other two could command. But France was, and is, primarily a continental power. The chief aims of her expansion policies were always in Europe. The dangers threatening her were also in Europe. In her two attempts to establish hegemony in Europe she was fighting land wars; and, though Britain in both cases threw her weight against France, including the small British armies led by Marlborough and Wellington, Britain did not attempt to rival France on land. So France never gave more than the lesser part of her men and her resources to her oversea expansion and her naval development.

Holland was, and is, much the smallest of the three. It was probably her small area and population which removed any temptation to attempt conquest in Europe. But the exposed land frontier absorbed much of her energies and even, during the Revolutionary War, enabled France to incorporate her in Napoleon's Empire. England and Holland came into conflict in their rivalry in the Indies. But always their conflict was restricted by consciousness of the fact that they needed each other to maintain their independence in the homelands. Their alliance against France was more important to each of them than their rivalry. Also England alone, and after the Union still more Britain, was far larger and stronger than Holland. So after their first flush of expansionism in the seventeenth century they have been friends and often allies.

England was thus the chief of the expanding powers looking overseas.

After her defeat of the Armada her seamen ranged the oceans. Within twenty years her first successful colony was founded at Jamestown; and the 'Old Dominion' of Virginia dates from 1607. A little earlier the East India Company was formed and its ships had reached India to begin the connexion which led to the British Indian Empire. Within the same generation the Pilgrim Fathers had settled in New England.

France versus England

The chief contest for overseas empire after 1600 was between Britain and France. During all these wars Britain's home base remained inviolate; but France was compelled to maintain strong armies. So Britain usually prevailed on the seas. The contest for India was decided by the defeat of French fleets at sea, which cut off French communications with oversea territories. The same victories enabled a British force to take Quebec, to which France could send no reinforcement or succour. This capture of Canada released New England from fear of French attacks from the north, and so allowed the differences between Britain and the growing American colonies to develop into conflict.

The successful revolt of the American colonies, after a civil war in which neither British nor Americans were unanimous, ended the first British Empire. In 1781 a French-Spanish fleet for a time dominated the Channel, and roused Britain to unity. Before the end of the war she had recovered her seapower; and the loss of the Thirteen Colonies left Britain still the strongest of the colonial powers of Europe. That loss also led directly to the Loyalist migrations to Canada and to the peopling of Australia; and so to the beginning of the growth of the overseas Dominions and the second British Empire.

A still greater change occurred in the same generation as the American War of Independence. The successful smelting of iron ore with coal and the invention of the first effective steam engine, both in England, inaugurated the Industrial Revolution. Of the leading states Britain was by far the best placed to take advantage of these developments. Her natural resources in accessible beds of coal and iron ore, and the exhaustion of Europe in the Napoleonic wars, enabled her to be the first to make use of, and to profit by, the new powers and to be the leading Industrial Power for nearly a hundred years. In the new era her natural resources were greater than those of France; and she still had all the advantages of an island base. In 1805 British naval supremacy was fully established, to last unchallenged till the close of the nineteenth century.

During this century of dominance on the seas and in manufacturing industry Britain's population increased fourfold, and British emigrants were more numerous than those from any continental country. Most of them went to the U.S.A. where they strengthened the hold of English speech and traditions, till that country is now the major part of the English-speaking world. Others built up the newer Dominions.

The maintenance of her seaborne communications was a chief policy of Britain from the beginnings of her expansion. Spain lies near the seaway to the south and east. Hence Britain sought to renew and maintain the old English alliance with Portugal. From this alliance Britain obtained the use of well placed harbours in friendly hands, of which Lisbon is the chief; and Portugal the support of a Great Power in the maintenance of her independence and her overseas possessions, most successfully during the Napoleonic Wars and in the late nineteenth century Partition of Africa.

In the conquest of India British forces, supplied with men and munitions from Britain, but mainly composed of Indians and maintained by India, built up the greatest dependent Empire which has ever been held by an external Power. It was made from the remnants of the collapsing Mogul Empire; and for nearly two centuries it petrified and stabilized the anarchic political geography of India in that collapse. Also this Indian Empire, its defence and the maintenance of communications with it, dominated the external and military policies of Britain.

Napoleon's attempt to control the short inland-sea-way to India by the conquest of Egypt led a British fleet into the eastern Mediterranean, and to the annexation of Malta and entanglements in the Near and Middle East. When French armies conquered Holland the same policy led Britain to take Cape Town and other stations on the open-sea-way to India, as well as the French and Dutch stations in the East and West Indies. By the end of those wars in 1815 Britain, and her allies, were in possession of almost all the overseas colonies of Europe. At its close most of them were returned to their former owners; but the outstanding strategic importance of the Cape as the great turning-point on the open-sea-way to India decided Britain to keep that territory. The comparable importance of the Malay peninsula on the sea-way between India and China led to the purchase of Singapore island in 1819. Britain also opposed, successfully, the projects of the Holy Alliance for the reconquest of Spanish America.

The Industrial Age

Meanwhile technical developments of the Industrial Age in Britain were changing the relative values and accessibility of the geographical bases, and so the sites of economic and political power. The application of steampower to transport produced the railway and the steamship, and made possible regular and cheap long-distance transport on land and sea. Accompanying developments widened the needs of the industrial powers for materials and by now have destroyed all possibility of self-sufficiency for any civilized country. New metals, greater quantities of fibres, and such products as rubber and vegetable oils have become vital to modern industry. Hence came the nineteenth-century scramble for Africa, and other unappropriated intertropical lands. In this stage of imperialism the one important newcomer was Germany which, after the consolidation of the German Empire, had become one of the (then) three Industrial Powers.

But the nineteenth-century development of transport had an even greater effect on political geography by the change of scale which it produced. In all previous ages land transport had been limited by the speed and carrying power of men-on-foot and their beasts of burden. The earlier part of the Modern Age, from the sixteenth century on, saw the development of wheeled transport, and a great extension of roads fit for it, in Europe. This, however, did not seriously increase the speed of travel; though it did carry a far greater bulk of goods. It improved on earlier land transport in the same way as the sailing ships of those centuries improved on earlier sea transport; and it allowed a small extension of the effective reach, and so of the unifying and consolidating power, of governments and great cities.

The railway, however, revolutionized land transport. Before it the effective reach of a government was limited. The nuclear regions of the Paris Basin and the English Lowland were near to the maximum area which could be thoroughly organized from a single centre. In the hundred years which preceded the first public railway (the Stockton and Darlington Railway 1825), each of the larger countries of Western Europe, Britain, France and Spain, and also the U.S.A., experienced secession movements in areas more than 200 miles from the national capital. But now the reach of the government was suddenly, and enormously, extended. With, and shortly after, the railway came the telegraph and the ocean-going steamship. It has been said, with much truth, that the U.S.A. is a product of the railway and the modern British Empire a product of the steamship. It became possible to organize the human and natural resources of far larger geographical bases. In the early part of the nineteenth century the larger states of Western Europe, which had been formed and developed into Nation-States earlier, were still the Great Powers. By the latter half of that century the world had entered the age of the Giant States. The British Empire spread inland, from its former coastal colonies and trading stations, over vast sub-continental areas in Canada, Australia, India and Africa. The U.S.A. extended from its original states, all within 300 miles of the Atlantic, westwards to the Pacific.

The Giant States

In the vast interior lands of the Old World the Russians had spread eastward, from 1537 onwards, through the forested zone of Siberia to the Pacific, in the same way as the British fur-traders of the Hudson Bay Company spread over the corresponding zone of Canada. But before the mid-nineteenth century the Russian expansion was only a thin sprinkling, of fur-traders, mineral prospectors, and political exiles, in the northern forests. The southward push came later: it reached the River Amur in 1858, and central Asia twenty years later still. The effective control of, and settlement in, north and central Asia is as much a result of the railway as is that of the mid-west of Canada and the U.S.A.

Today the smaller states are completely outweighed in both natural and human resources by the Giant States. Britain, with less than 100,000 square miles of land and about fifty million people, on a territory rich in natural resources and very favoured in its geographical location, is one of the strongest of the lesser Powers. The States of the British Commonwealth as a whole have the extent and resources of a Giant Power; but they are separated by the oceans and can act together only so long as they can use the sea-ways freely. No one of them alone has sufficient resources to be a Great Power.

The two Giant Powers which are so far developed that their resources can be used, and their power is or can be effective, are the U.S.A. and the U.S.S.R. The only region which is comparable to them in developed resources—human and natural—is Western Europe, with its dependencies to the south. But this third region is still a political anarchy of separate independent sovereign states. Unless these can unite its power will remain ineffective, and they themselves merely buffer states between America and Russia.

The real geographical base of the U.S.A. is the north-eastern quadrant of its home territory, the lands east of the Mississippi and north of about latitude 35° N. Here is by far the greater part of its developed industry and its population, as well as a very large proportion of its fertile land. The corresponding base of the U.S.S.R. is the south-western corner, on less than an eighth of its territory, south of the upper Volga and 60° N., and west of the lower Volga. This Russian base is somewhat larger than that of the U.S.A.; and it has been recently expanded by the territories which the Soviet Union has gained since 1939. Its backing in sub-arctic lands to the north and north-east, and in arid and semi-arid lands to the east, is probably less than that of the American base in the similar areas of North America.

These two bases of the Giant Powers are separated by the width of Western Europe and the North Atlantic; and the routes of effective communications between them lie there. The trans-Arctic air routes can be used for stunt flights and possible raids; but not for reliable regular communications. The trans-Pacific routes are far longer, and involve also the crossing of the semi-arid and mountainous half of North America, and the whole length of Siberia. It seems clear that if the two Giant Powers fight the battle grounds must be in Europe.

In the nineteenth century there were periods of tension between the British and Russian Powers. Some observers then asked 'Can the elephant fight the whale?' In fact the land-locked bases of Russia could not be injured by naval power, and the seapower of Britain kept its island base equally safe from any Russian attack. Today the developments of airpower have removed that simple insurance against a great war between ocean and inland Powers. The range of aircraft and of guided missiles makes it possible for either Russia or America to raid the other's homeland. But unless one of them secures possession of the intervening lands of Europe they can hardly do more than that.

Hence Western Europe is at present the key region in world politics; and the hope of peace in the world of today depends on whether its peoples and states can, and will be allowed to, unite for the maintenance of their own economic and political security and freedom. Without such union the States of Western Europe cannot hope to maintain their independence, or to hold their dependencies, except under the protection of one of the Giant Powers. Yet today the addition of Western Europe with all its human and natural resources to either of the Giant Powers would give that one a decisive superiority which could lead to one World State.

Other Possibilities

For the near future there is also a third geographical base for a Giant Power. The populous lands of East Asia are sufficient in extent and in agricultural and mineral resources; their peoples are equally civilized and fully capable of adopting and developing the technology of Western Civilization, which they have begun to apply. China, as a populous region, is separated from the populous lands of Russia by the zone of the Midworld Deserts, which has kept East and West apart during all the growth of their distinctive civilizations. Despite all improvements in transport this wide zone of arid and semi-arid lands keeps the main populous areas, i.e. the vital geographical bases of China and Russia, as far apart from one another as are the east and west shores of the North Atlantic Ocean.

At present China is under Communist rule. It may become a dependency of Russia, like the communist satellite states of Eastern Europe. But the inclusion in the communist world of two such distinct and widely separated geographical bases as China and Russia, at opposite ends of that world, seems more likely to lead to the emergence of rival communist Powers. Such a development is made more probable by the facts that Chinese civilization is older, and perhaps stronger, than that of Russia; and that a communism modified by Chinese traditions may well differ widely from that which has been influenced by the Byzantine Orthodox traditions of Tsarist Russia. Even in the nearer lands of Europe there is evidence that not all communist States are content to submit to Russian imperialism. There are precedents for such a division, in the growth of rival eastern and western Powers in the medieval worlds of both Islam and Christendom.

What of the fourth really populous civilized region, the sub-continent of India? This is now associated with the British Commonwealth, and so with the Western democratic states. Its natural resources, particularly for industrial development, are far less than those of either Western Europe or China. Yet they are perhaps greater than those of any other comparable region; while its population is more numerous than those of either of the present Giant Powers, or of Western Europe. But India is divided within itself by the long-standing enmity between Hindu and Muslim. It does not seem likely that it can, in any near future, become one of the Giant Powers. India is bounded to north and north-east by the greatest mountain barriers on the earth; so that along the effective communication routes it is roughly equidistant from China, from Russia and from Europe.

At present it is still true that Western Europe is the principal region of pressure in the 'cold war' between the Giant Powers, and the key region of world politics. But the development of China into an effective, instead of only a potential, base may alter the pattern of power distribution within a few years.

BRIEF BIBLIOGRAPHY

1. A. J. Toynbee, *A Study of History* (6 volumes), Oxford Univ. Press.
2. D. C. Somervell, Abridgement of Vols. I–VI of Toynbee's *Study of History*, Oxford Univ. Press, 1947. This is a good statement of Toynbee's argument: but gives only a few well-chosen examples from his almost exhaustive series of particular cases.
3. H. J. Mackinder, *Democratic Ideals and Reality*, Constable, 1919.
4. V. Cornish, *The Great Capitals*.
5. I. Bowman, *The New World*.

CHAPTER XIX

RACIAL GEOGRAPHY

GRIFFITH TAYLOR

A. THE DEVELOPMENT OF MODERN THEORY

GEOGRAPHY is concerned primarily with distributions, and of these distributions none is more important than the distribution of man himself. Anthropology is of course a discipline quite distinct in many ways from geography, but there is a common ground in the pattern displayed by the distribution of the main divisions of man over the face of the earth. We geographers must learn from the anthropologists what are the characteristics of the various types of man, but in return we can plot these characteristics, and by using a technique which the writer has ventured to call 'Evolution from the map' we can make valuable deductions as to the evolution and classification of man, which would not be in the least apparent to a student who did not chart his data. Furthermore, our knowledge of the immemorial corridors used by primitive man is much more complete now than it was a few decades ago, and this also gives us the key to the meaning of various race-distributions as exhibited on the map.

Let us, however, traverse very rapidly the history of race-science, using the authoritative study by von Eickstedt (*Zeitschrift für Rassenkunde*, 1937, Stuttgart). We owe to Linnaeus in 1758 a classification based on the continents, which has been slavishly followed by most writers ever since. His divisions were: American, European, Asiatic, and African. Blumenbach in 1806 changed the names somewhat, but not the distribution of the main classes. He used the terms, Caucasian, Mongolian, Ethiopian, American, and Malay. He split Eur-Asia approximately along the Ural-Himalaya axis, and thus linked the folk of South-west Asia with the Europeans. Here we can I think see the effect of history and linguistics on what should be a totally distinct field of biological research, that of race-science (i.e. ethnology).

Cuvier in 1817 referred back to the biblical classes of Shem, Ham, and Japhet; and so utilized only three races—European, Negro, and Mongolian. Prichard about 1840 increased the number to seven, including European, Mongolian, American, Hottentot, Negro, Papuan, and Australian; thus adding various recently discovered peoples in lands south of

433

Eurasia to earlier classes. In 1870 Huxley was one of the earlier scientists to use biological criteria instead of mere habitat. He adopted five classes, including Negroid, Mongoloid, Australoid from older schemes, but divided the European types into two according to their skin-colour. Thus we find *Xantho-chroide* for the blonde northern folk of Europe, and *Melano-chroide* for the brunette folk, who extend from Ireland to India.

Topinard in 1878 made use of the character of the hair as the main criterion; and this classification is still accepted as quite important. His *Straight-haired* race included Eskimo, Amerinds, and Mongols; the *Wavy-haired* were Europeans, Australians, and North African tribes; while the *Frizzy-haired* were negroes, negritoes, and Papuans. However, in 1885 he produced another much less satisfactory classification based essentially on nose-breadth and skin-colour. Here again there were three classes as follows: *White*, Narrow-nosed, mostly European; *Yellow*, medium-nosed, Eskimo, Polynesians, Eastern Asiatics, and many Amerinds; and finally *Black*, broad-nosed, including Australians, Melanesians, and negritoes.

Deniker in 1889 supported the classification by hair, and used much the same classes as in Topinard's first essay. He split the European peoples into many sub-races, such as the Littoral, Iberian, Occidental, Dinaric, Northern, and Eastern types. Sergi in 1908 formed a group called *Eura-fricus* which included such diverse types as Nordics and Mediterraneans from Europe, *africanus* from North Africa, *dravidicus* from India, *poly-nesianus*, *toda-ainu*, *Australianus*, and *pygmeus*. His scheme is worthy of note, for he threw overboard the classification by continents, which had obsessed most of his predecessors, and linked far-distant tribes, which in some cases agree with classes propounded quite recently.

The Italian Biasutti in 1912 produced a valuable study of the races of man, since he adopted a geographical approach, and charted many of the data in separate world-charts. Thus head-index, face-index, nasal breadth, hair-colour, &c. were given for the whole world. However, in spite of these maps he still adhered to a continental classification; for his five main groups were African, Asiatic, American, European, and Oceanic (Malay, Papuan, Polynesian, and Ainu).

Ripley in 1900 brought out the first edition of his *Races of Europe*, one of the most remarkable scientific texts ever written. In this volume he gave us a most satisfactory discussion of the spread of man and his differentiation in various regions. His book discussed areas far beyond Europe, and was fully illustrated with detailed maps of most of the main factors used by anthropologists in their work. It is indeed a book to be followed in other continents as soon as the data are as well known as

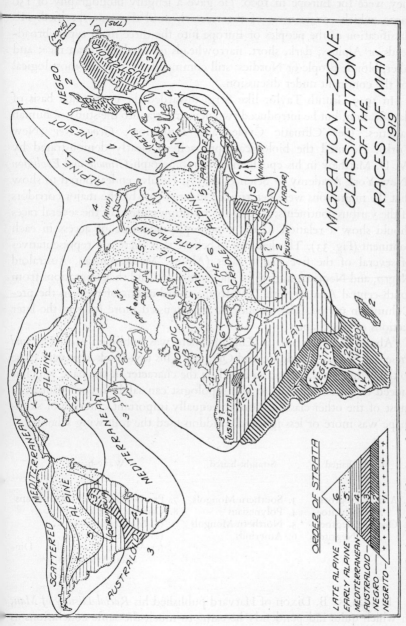

Fig. 33.—The logical classification of the Races of Man, based on racial history and ecological principles as well as on head index, hair, &c. The five major races about A.D. o had spread all over the world. Ecology gives the clue to their common cradle land and order of evolution. (Revised 1919 map from *Environment, Race and Migration*, Oxford, 1937)

they were for Europe in 1900. He gave a lengthy bibliography of 150 pages, which covers most of the research until the year specified. His classification of the peoples of Europe into the three main types: broadheads or Alpines; dark, short, narrowheads or Mediterranean race; and taller, blonde people or Nordics; still commends itself as the most logical for the continent under discussion.

In 1919 Griffith Taylor like Sergi discarded the continental basis of classification; but he introduced two new criteria into the study of human varieties. (See 'Climatic Cycles and Evolution', *Geog. Rev.* New York). He used the biological approach so clearly demonstrated by W. D. Matthew in his epoch-making monograph *Climate and Evolution* (New York Academy of Sciences, 1915). He also endeavoured to show that the migrations were determined in large part by the major corridors of the various continents; so that the resulting pattern of the several races should show a relation to the topography and ease of access in each continent (Fig. 33). This led him to believe that there are representatives of several of the five major races (Alpine, Mediterranean, Australoid Negro, and Negrito) in each of the continents; and that migrations from south-central Asia were the key to the distributions of races in the pre-Columbian period. These concepts are discussed more fully in the later sections of this chapter.

About the same time in England there was published *Man, Past and Present*, by Keane, Haddon, and Quiggin. This text-book kept very close to the orthodox classification based on the character of the hair, which is indeed the criterion that no anthropologist can safely ignore. But as in most of the other classifications the equally important criterion of skull-shape was more or less ignored. Haddon used the following scheme.

Woolly-haired	Straight-haired	Wavy-haired

1. African Negroes
   ,, Negritoes
2. Oceanic Negroes
   ,, Negritoes
	3. Southern Mongols
	4. Polynesians
	5. Northern Mongols
	6. Amerinds
		7. Pre-Dravidians and Australians
		8. Caucasic peoples
		   (*a*) Mediterraneans
		   (*b*) Nordics, Afghans
		   (*c*) Alpines, Cevenoles, Dinarics, Armenians

In 1923 R. B. Dixon of Harvard published his *Racial History of Man*, in which quite independently he came to much the same conclusions as Taylor with regard to the wide spread of the major types of human races. He made use of three main criteria; head-breadth, head-height, and nasal index; though he ignores head-height in his main maps. These were combined so as to characterize eight racial classes which may be summarized as follows:

	Narrow-nose		Broad-nose	
	High skull	Low skull	High skull	Low skull
Narrowheads	1. Caspian	Mediterranean	3. Proto-Negroid	Proto-Australoid
Broadheads	2. Alpine	Ural	4. Palae-Alpine	Mongoloid

Regardless of corridors of migration or of the zones of race, which might be assumed to develop if the races moved out from a common centre, he plotted the habitats of all the skulls (whose data were available in 1923) on maps of the world. He found, as did Taylor, the clearest

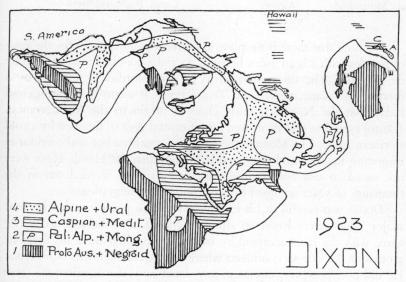

FIG. 34.—Habitats of Dixon's four major classes of race, compiled from his data

evidence of widespread migrations (of the eight sub-types of his classification) into all parts of the world. Again we see that the older classification by continents is likely to be extremely misleading.

It will be worthwhile to dwell on the distributions established by Dixon for his (somewhat arbitrarily chosen) racial types. Some of the main features of this distribution are shown in the following table:

Dixon class	Usual name	Localities
1a. Caspian	Mediterranean in part	Russia, Eskimo, Sardinia, Japan
1b. Mediterranean	ditto	Egypt, California, England, India
2a. Alpine	Alpine in part	Swiss, Hawaiians, Araucanians, Czechs, Armenians
2b. Ural	ditto	Swiss, Kalmuck, Basque, Venezuelan
3a. Proto-Negroid	Negro	Gaboon, Iroquois, Papua, Brazil
3b. Proto-Australoid	Australoid	Australia, California, Sicily, Ostiak
4a. Palae-Alpine	Negrito	Philippines, Burmese, Valais
4b. Mongoloid	Alpine	Lapps, Bushmen, Swiss

We note that there is no place in Dixon's major groups for the zone of peoples with a head index between 73 and 82, a place usually filled by the Nordics. The oft-quoted purity of the Nordics is replaced by a mixture of Asiatic, negro, and 'Dago' types. It seems to be recognized today that the Nordic is fairly close in origin to the Mediterranean (Dago) type, but that he moved out of central Asia to the west by a cold northern route. The Mediterraneans used a southern hot arid corridor in migrating from central Asia; and it is likely that the blonde types were not suited to this hot environment, and so were weeded out in the thousands of years occupied by these prehistoric migrations.

Dixon was careful in his lengthy volume to point out that his four major 'types' were based on arbitrary criteria, and did not necessarily agree with the races accepted by other anthropologists. In his maps he plotted on the various continents where there were majorities of his types. He did not, however, discuss in any detail how the distributions came about, or how they were linked with major corridors or with changes of topography and climate. However, the generalized diagram given as Fig. 34 shows approximately where the main representatives of his four main types were to be found. The map is collated from Dixon's separate maps, but the isopleths (i.e. distribution lines) are added by the writer.

It may be pointed out that his conclusions are very like those put forward four years earlier in the *Geographic Review* (December 1919) by

Taylor. In the Old World we see the Negroid types relegated to the hot southern borders of the continents in South Africa, in India, and in Australia (Fig. 33). Within this broken zone of Negroids is a fairly continuous belt of Caspian and Mediterranean peoples in Western Europe, the Mediterranean areas, and in western India. Within this again is the central 'core' of broadheaded Alpine types. In the New World we find the same general distribution, with the Negroids pushed to the farthest eastern limits (in North and also in South America) from the universal line of entry at the Bering Straits. It is very significant that Dixon postulated a strong resemblance between Negroid and Iroquois skulls, and farther south between many Brazilian and negro skulls. In the New World, as in the Old, there is the same distribution of broadheaded Alpines along the major corridors of the continents. The reason for this will be made clear in a later paragraph (p. 452).

Before discussing in some detail the various classifications so far summarized, two other important books may be referred to. The first was published in Stuttgart in 1934 by E. von Eickstedt, and is a large volume entitled *Rassenkunde und Rassengeschichte*. It is the best detailed account known to the writer of the various ethnological groups of man; but its adherence to the ancient Blumenbachian classes shows that a number of biological and geographical principles have been ignored.

Von Eickstedt divides human beings into four main divisions, which he calls *Europide, Mongolide, Amerikanide*, and *Negride*. Thus on the whole he keeps to the old continental divisions, but in his book he gives plenty of instances of overlap. These four divisions are split into smaller groups, which he calls 'series'; while each series in turn is subdivided, giving a total of about sixty 'varieties'.

The four chief classes, as given by von Eickstedt, are shown in Fig. 35 in the main map. To the geographer the chief interest lies in the division between the *Europide* and the *Mongolide*; i.e. in the line labelled AB in the main map. This contravenes all the main principles based on mammalian diffusion and differentiation; for the great corridors of migration have always been from the centre (in an east–west direction) in the Old World. The main path of movement to the west has been along the Caspian–Ukraine corridor; while to the east it has been the Tarim–Jade Gate corridor around the north of the Tibetan plateau. The writer has endeavoured to demonstrate this in the four small maps given at the foot of Fig. 35. Here each of four major anthropological criteria shows isopleths (lines of equal distribution) running *concentric* to the coast, rather than in accord with the major line AB as charted by von Eickstedt.

Another important blemish is that the world-map is divided at the

29

Bering Straits rather than at Iceland—as is far preferable. All the migrations into America have entered by the Bering Corridor, so that the Amerinds are to be considered expansions of the tribes of Eastern Asia. This concept is clearly rather ignored, when Asia is placed at one side of the map, and America at the other. Finally a careful study of the physical anthropology of the Amerinds (American Indians) shows that they also should be subdivided by lines parallel to the major (north–south) coasts, as is indicated in Fig. 33. All these points will be discussed at greater length in the second part of this chapter.

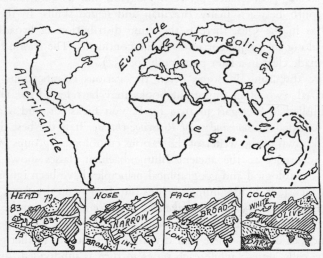

FIG. 35.—The upper map shows Von Eickstedt's four main races, which are unsatisfactory, especially the division AB. The four lower maps show the *concentric* isopleths (determining racial groups in the Old World) based on Biasutti

The last volume which space-limits permit us to discuss is that published by C. W. Coon entitled *The Races of Europe* (New York, 1939). It covers to some extent the same field as Ripley's *Races of Europe* (1900), but there is no similarity in treatment, and considerable difference in many of the conclusions. Ripley's book is very much easier to read, because it deals with races in the simpler fashion current in 1900. In some small degree Coon's valuable treatise illustrates the natural swing of the second-generation student away from early theories towards something new. Many more data have been discovered in the thirty odd years since Ripley's book, but the present writer (perhaps himself one of the older generation) seems to see illustrated by some recent books the adage that 'they can't see the forest for the trees'.

Coon's volume is replete with anthropometric discussions and tables, while a remarkable series of more than 500 photographs of the various types adds greatly to its value. It might be described as an 'anthropological Baedecker' for every region in Europe. Since it is my firm belief that each continent contains numerous representatives of *several* of the major races; it follows that the technique employed by Coon for Europe will later be used in the other continents to elucidate *their* anthropological problems. Hence it may well be discussed in some detail—even if it seems to consider only one small corner of the lands of the world.

His main thesis is that the peoples of Europe are descended from two major racial groups. One of these includes the primitive 'Paleolithic Hunters', who lived in Europe in the last Ice Age. He calls these the *Neandertal-sapiens* hybrids. Coon believes that they are the chief components of the Alpine, Brunn, Borreby, Ladogan, and Lappish folk of today. The second great division is descended from *Mediterranean* folk without any Neandertal blood; and they first brought agricultural and stock animals into Europe. From these '*Food-Producers*' are derived the modern Mediterraneans, the Nordics, Dinarics, Armenoid, and the Irano-Afghan types which he allots to the Europe of today.

In Fig. 36 I have endeavoured to interpret Coon's data in a series of four maps, since he does not give in his book charts isolating his major racial divisions. I have inserted by means of heavy lines the racial divisions which I have used in my own studies; thus in A the northern limit of the Mediterranean race extends from Scotland through France to Palestine. Coon, however, divides these dark slender dokephs (narrow-heads) into shorter and taller groups, and he calls the southern taller group *Atlanto-Mediterranean*. He also shows extensions of these two types (naturally in less pure form), as suggested by the dots (shorter type) and dashes (taller type).

At B in Fig. 36 is shown my own boundary of the Nordics, which includes a wedge-shaped area around the North and Baltic Seas. In Coon's opinion very few pure Nordics are to be found in Germany; and the largest numbers occur in Britain, Sweden, and Lithuania. This finding should exercise the minds of those who support the 'Nordic Fetish'! He suggests that the German Nordics were largely killed off in the numerous wars of the Christian era. In the same map (B) are shown his Irano-Afghans, who are not far removed from Nordics; and an allied but less clearly defined Nordic type is present in central Russia (see dashes). A hybrid type with much Alpine blood he names 'Noric', and this is indicated as occupying the south-west of Germany in Fig. 36 at C.

At C in Fig. 36 are charted the main Alpine (brakeph or broadhead) affiliations. As before, a wedge-shaped area, extending from Central France to Anatolia, includes that region which in my opinion is to be labelled *Alpine*. However, only in the three regions of Brittany, Cevennes, and south Albania, does Coon find pure Alpines; though he remarks that there are large areas in central Asia with Alpine groups, such as the Tajiks of Persia. The distribution of the hybrid *Dinaric* and *Noric* types is charted also.

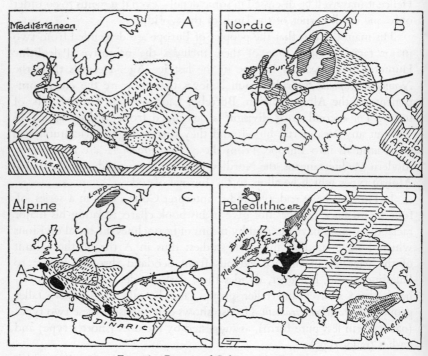

FIG. 36.—Races and Sub-races in Europe

The heavy lines show the generalized boundaries used in the writer's publications. In Fig. C the *black* patches show unmixed Alpines. In Fig. D the hybrid Neo-Danubians and Armenoids are also charted.   (*Mainly after C. S. Coon*)

At D I have endeavoured to chart other sub-types suggested by Coon. Centred near the Kiel Canal and the adjacent island of Fehmarn, but found chiefly in south-west Germany (and extending into England, Norway, and Denmark) are the big-headed *Borreby* type; and the somewhat allied *Brunn* folk of west Ireland and west Norway. Coon describes these folk as a re-emergence of the Palæolithic types around the North Sea. We are all familiar with the ancient 'nests' found in the Dordogne and in Wales. But Coon extends their habitats greatly, and finds them in huge areas in northern Germany and elsewhere, as cited. He traces these primitive survivals in part by their big heads; and gives it as his opinion that this Borreby 'Palæolithic survival' 'has become the most important single racial element in modern Germany'. Since these folk are relatively brakeph (broadheaded), it is difficult to class them as any brand of Nordic.

Many controversial questions are raised by this book, but we have only space to discuss two or three. Coon seems to have adopted the 'White Race' as a scientific entity, though his reasons are not clear to the present writer. Perhaps he felt that as he was dealing chiefly with Europe this controversy was a matter of little import. In view of Ripley's strong and logical opposition to this concept of a White (Caucasian) Race, this seems a serious omission. Secondly he does not seem to lay sufficient stress on the fact that numerous migrations (since Wurm Ice Age time) have poured into Europe along the Ukraine corridor from Central Asia. It is much more likely, in the present writer's opinion, that the brakephs of Europe today are descended from them rather than from the few brakeph Europeans of the Ice Age. Possibly the custom of cremation has destroyed much of the evidence of these later migrations. One admirable feature of Coon's research is the way he has tried to interpret the fossil strata in the different districts.

Another important feature is his discussion of the hybrid types. Coon calls this *Dinaricization* and discusses it in the light of his recent work on the Albanians. 'Dinarics' result from a cross of two parts of Mediterranean and one part of Alpine. The stable type resulting has the narrow face and the long nose of the Mediterranean, while the head-breadth derives from the Alpine. The Dinaric type is also rather tall. Armenoids (see D) are similar hybrids of Alpine and Irano-Afghan, while *Norics* are 'Iron-age Nordics, brachycephalized by Dinaric mixture'.

B. THE ECOLOGICAL BASIS OF RACE CLASSIFICATION[1]

Introduction

In 1919 the writer published a classification of human races which departed in a number of respects from current classifications. Perhaps his chief interest in science in recent years has been in the early history of the human races, especially in their differentiation and migration, and he is now even more sure in his belief that the somewhat new tools and methods then employed, if adopted more generally, would in considerable measure modify current classifications.

[1] This section is based on an article contributed to *Human Biology*, September, 1936.

Two quotations from authoritative books will emphasize his point of view. Kroeber (in his standard *Anthropology*) writes: 'The only classification that can claim to rest upon a true or natural basis is one which takes into consideration as many traits as possible . . . and weighs the more important more heavily than the unimportant features.' The present writer would like to see included under the word 'traits' such factors as ecological distribution and archæological strata. Another pertinent quotation is from E. B. Tylor (in the article on Anthropology in the *Encyclopædia Britannica*), as follows: 'The classification by Cuvier (about 1820) into Caucasian, Mongol and Negro corresponds in some measure with a division by mere complexion into white, yellow and black races . . . but cannot be regarded as separating the human types either justly or sufficiently.'

Strangely enough, the classification of Cuvier, made before anthropology was a science, still seems to be the basis of most modern classifications. It is surely unusual for pre-scientific classifications to remain orthodox for so long a period, and the present writer has been completely unorthodox in this respect ever since he commenced his research in anthropology over thirty years ago. It is the purpose of this section to draw attention to an ecologist's approach to the problem, to the confirmation to be derived from modern biological research, and to suggest a classification of the races which seems to him more in harmony with the history of the races concerned.

Few anthropologists have given much attention to the fact that the environment during the critical period of man's differentiation was very different from that obtaining today. His routes of migration are by no means to be understood by mere reference to present-day topography and climate. The forces that set him migrating are not in general in action today. In other words, among the factors to be considered in evaluating our problem the changing environment is by no means to be neglected —and can give us many clues if used in connexion with isopleths of present-day distribution.

The 'Zones and Strata' Theory, i.e. Evolution from the Map.

Perhaps owing to the fact that anthropology is now treated largely from the cultural point of view, there seems to be a tendency to separate the needs of primitive man too largely from those of the other higher mammals. For instance, certain modern books on the subject state that primitive man migrated in order to seek adventure, to make war, or to gain pearls and gold. Possibly some of these reasons dominated man during early historic times, but in the far distant days when man was evolving into the races which are distributed over the world today, the related factors of food, climate, and shelter were, in the writer's opinion, all-important, and the other 'urges' hardly existed. We may safely assume that the world was relatively empty of man in those distant days of the ice ages. If so, then 'pressure of population', 'trade incentives', and 'laws of trespass' may well have been unknown. On the other hand, it seems likely to the writer that primitive communities might be likely to stay in any environment which they found satisfactory; and that they dreaded the unfamiliar and were loath to leave their homelands, unless they were driven to do so. When migrations occurred, probably the weakest folk moved out first. Holding these opinions, the writer has for many years felt that primitive man offers exceptional advantages for testing the validity of the 'age and area' concept; or, as he prefers to put it, the 'Zones and Strata' concept. Speaking biologically, primitive man was a large mammal who left abundant traces of his presence in the form of artifacts, carvings, monuments, place-names, &c., of a type which are not available in aiding our studies of the distribution and evolution of other mammals.

The 'Zones and Strata' theory as applied to Man starts with the following premises, which are acceptable to most ethnologists.

1. The great land-masses of the world consist of a central continent (Asia) with three 'peninsulas', i.e. Europe-Africa, America, Malaya-Australia (Fig. 33).

2. Each 'peninsula' includes a similar series of nine zones of environment arranged according to latitude. From equator to pole these zones are: selva (forest), savanna, desert, steppe, Mediterranean evergreen forest, temperate forest, conifers, tundra, and ice cap.

3. The evolution and migrations of primitive man occurred during the last half million years.

4. The period was marked in the northern hemisphere (and probably in the southern also) by the great climatic variations known as the Four Great Ice Ages, and by later minor fluctuations.

5. It is easy to show that the vegetation zones (and therefore man's food supply) moved alternately south and north in accord with the waxing and waning of the ice ages.

It was his use on world maps of the isopleth method in charting the criteria of race, in conjunction with the findings in W. D. Matthew's memoir, *Evolution and Climate* (1915) (see bibliography at end), which led the writer to publish the Zones and Strata Classification of Races in 1919. The general principles of this concept are illustrated in Fig. 37. Here three parallel cases of evolution are considered. All anthropologists will agree as to the explanation of the block diagram on the left. Here we see zones of common *Methods of Transport* (ox-team, horse-bus, motor, aeroplane) arranged round the city of Sydney—the only settlement of note for sixty years in Australia—about the year 1920. The 'strata', resulting from this evolution in Sydney and gradual migration to the margin, are indicated on the vertical edge of the block diagram. Clearly there is a common cradleland, where commercial activity is greatest, in the centre of the zones—and the primitive types in later years (1920) occur precisely where they did not originate. With no other data but this diagram, we can deduce the cradleland and the order of evolution of these methods of transport.

Turning to Fig. 37, centre, we find the same process illustrated in the evolution of the artio-dactyls (or even-toed mammals) based on data given by Matthew. The antelopes are earliest and are displaced farthest

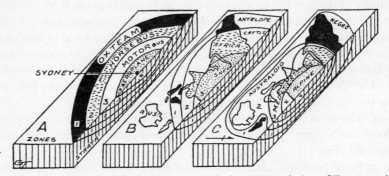

FIG. 37.—The 'Zones and Strata' Concept applied to (A) Evolution of Transport, i.e. Culture; (B) Evolution of Even-toed Mammals (based on data by Matthew); (C) Evolution of the Races of Man in the Old World

In each case the 'Cradleland' is at the centre of the Zones, and the earliest most primitive type (1) is pushed to the margin

from the centre. The sheep are latest and still characterize the common cradleland. The fossil strata are in accord, using the palæontologist's 'Law of Superposition'. No biologist doubts that the zones and strata in the case of these mammals indicate the order of migration and of evolution for the artio-dactyls.

The writer believes that primitive man was differentiated into the five major races long before the later races reached Western Europe. This evolution almost certainly took place in Asia and occurred before the last Ice Age. It certainly far antedated early Neolithic times. It is probable that the first Alpine broadheads reached France (Solutré, &c.) in Aurignacian times (*vide* A. Keith); and Koeppen dates this as far back as 74,000 years ago. Neolithic times in France were only 8,000 years ago. Hence early man of such a primitive type can surely be considered as obeying the same laws of migration as the higher mammals. If now the pre-Columbian distribution of the races be plotted in a block diagram (Fig. 37, right), we find a series of zones and strata closely resembling the two already charted. It is difficult to escape from the conclusion that the centre of Asia is the common cradleland where evolution progressed most actively in the case of primitive man—just as Matthew has shown it progressed most actively here to produce new types of the earlier mammals. Indeed, we can almost exactly parallel the spread of the Rhinoceros from Asia with the spread of the negroes, while the spread of the Pleistocene Equidæ is the same as that of Alpine man.

The centre of stimulus in Fig. 37, left, was the commercial progress in the city. In the case of the mammals and man it was the stimulating climate of south central Asia. I have in a number of books and papers (see bibliography) shown that this region in the past has been characterized to a marked degree by such climatic features, but lack of space prevents my covering this ground again.

It seems fair to state that the technique based on the 'Zones and Strata' is one of the geographer's chief contributions to the study of distributions. In a word, by its use we may 'deduce evolution from the map'. The following description of the concept is given in general terms, and shows how it can be used for races, languages and other culture facts, animals and plants.

> If there be a centre where evolution (whether of organic or inorganic type) is taking place ... then, after a reasonable lapse of time, the various differentiated classes will be found to be arranged in zones ... so that the most primitive is at the margins, and the most advanced at the centre of the series of zones. Thus the earliest class will have covered the greatest area in its migrations; but fossil evidence of this class will be found buried in the deepest stratum, under the later strata at the centre of evolution. This is the 'Zones and Strata' concept, which is less clearly called the 'Age and Area' concept by certain biologists.

The actual mechanism whereby the changing environment (especially the vegetation belts) led to the migrations of primitive man has been illustrated by the writer in his various publications. A series of four block-diagrams shows how the changes of climate (from 18,500 B.C. onward) in Scandinavia produced the shift of belts of trees at the rate of perhaps three miles a century. Neolithic Man, Bronze Age Man, and Iron Age Man show (by their artifacts) that they migrated here in accord with climatic change.

The five major races (see Fig. 33), as deduced from their zontal distribution—and from their anthropological 'strata' in so far as we can reconstruct them—are given in the following table.

TABLE

THE FIVE MAJOR RACES

Race	Criteria		Habitat
	Head index	Hair	
LATEST MIGRATIONS			
Late Alpine-Mongolian (ruled in Fig. 33)	88–83	Straight or wavy	Central zone and highest stratum. Extends from Swiss Alps to Manchuria (still in or near corridors of migration in Eurasia and America)
Early Alpine-Mongolian (Variants, Pareoean and Polynesian)	83–80	do.	Second zone and second stratum in cradleland. Covers most of Asia and Central Europe (widespread in America)
Mediterranean (Fig. 33) (Variants, Nordic, Nesiot)	80–77	Wavy to curly	Submarginal zone. North Africa, South Asia, fringe in North Eurasia (sporadic in the east of America), South-west Europe
Australoid (Fig. 33) (Variants, Pre-Dravidians, Veddah)	76–73	Wavy to curly	Marginal zone in 'peninsulas' of India and Australia. (Few reached America and Europe)
Negro (Fig. 33)	74–70	Frizzy	Marginal zone in southern Africa and in Melanesian Islands
Negrito (Fig. 33) EARLIEST MIGRATIONS	About 80 Aberrant	do.	Most marginal zone and lowest stratum. Inaccessible forests or deserts or small islands of Africa and South-east Asia, &c.

The Head Index

It will be noticed that in the above table the writer relies on head index and hair texture primarily. Charts by Biasutti will be found to demonstrate the reality of the racial zones which were, however, deduced by the writer several years before he knew of Biasutti's maps (1912). Unfortunately, there is a distinct tendency today to depreciate the value of the head index as a racial criterion. This is in large part due to the research of Boas (1911) on the changes which the children of European immigrants experience if they are born in the city of New York. Everyone has heard that the head-breadth of the brakeph[1] Jew children decreases, and that the head-breadth of the dokeph[1] Neapolitan children increases with the change of birth place. But it is not so clearly realized how slight is the change—what factors have produced the change —and finally that Boas himself issues a cautionary statement with his findings.

The average decrease in head-width in Hebrews merely amounts to 1·52 millimetres; which is just one per cent of the absolute width. (This would hardly affect the cephalic index by one unit.) In the case of the Neapolitans the increase is 0·48 millimetres—and the change (in some 140 mm.) is still slighter.[2] Moreover, Boas very properly points out that certain measurements of the parent immigrants (such as width of head and width of face) varied steadily from 1880 to 1910—which variation certainly affects the importance of the change in their progeny born in New York. Moreover, the writer would like to be sure that the age-factor does not enter into the problem. There is usually a slight change in the head index as a child grows up—quite independent of his race. Venn (1889) showed this years ago for undergraduates at Cambridge (England). Here there was an increase from 77·9 to 79·9 during the period from nineteen to twenty-three years old. On the other hand, A. Macalister (1897) states that there is in general a change towards brachycephaly as the child grows up. Since Boas is mainly dealing with young subjects (from birth to twenty-five), this is a vital point.

The present writer feels that the slight non-continuous variation noted by Boas do not affect the validity of the cephalic index.[2] How else can we account for the relative uniformity of the Alpine race (inhabiting high plateaux, hot plains, salty steppes, deserts, wet mountains, marshes, and fertile lowlands) which extends from the Himalayas to the Bay of Biscay?

As Ripley (1900) writes, 'The Galchas, Tadjiks and their fellows (of the Pamirs) are grey-eyed, dark-haired, stocky in build, with cephalic indices ranging above 86 for the most part. From this region a long chain of peoples of similar type extends uninterruptedly westward over Asia Minor and into Europe.'

[1] Convenient contractions for brachycephalic and dolichocephalic.

[2] Mathematical analyses of Boas data have been made by Morant and Samson in *Biometrika* (London, June 1936). They state that 'considerably larger divergences would have to be found to establish the fact that head-form is directly modified by environment. Boas' theory cannot be upheld.'

Corridors into the Continents

It is of considerable interest to use our knowledge of the relative accessibility of the various continents, and to see how it agrees with the Zones and Strata hypothesis.

Most anthropologists accept Asia as the cradleland of the Alpine, Mediterranean, and Australoid races. If we are to assume that the negroes or negritoes evolved in Africa, then we are faced with several cumbrous inconsistencies. Where did the negroes (and negritoes) of Melanesia and thereabouts come from? If Africa is suggested, the obvious reply is that it is far simpler to assume that both African and Melanesian negroes came from south Asia, i.e. the same centre of racial evolution as did the other races. Moreover, the Zones and Strata hypothesis leads us to believe (even if this be not actually proven) that primitive races persist in the marginal lands, precisely where they did not evolve. The same arguments apply to the negritoes, and lead us to accept an Asiatic cradleland.

What was the relation of Africa, Australasia, and America to the Eurasian land-mass during the later Ice Ages—when we may surely picture these earlier racial migrations as occurring? Surely something like this. The easiest of access was Africa, for only the Red Sea—probably much less of a barrier then—separated that region of deserts and savannas from the cradleland (Fig. 38).

Australasia was the next most accessible. During the Ice Ages no doubt the broad low area of Sunda Land with the almost dry Bali-Timor ridge led to the large low Sahul Land and so to Australia (see the writer's book, 1927). In the Interglacial period both Sunda Land and Sahul Land were drowned as the result of the filling of the oceans by the melting Ice Caps. Hence we may postulate that Australia and Melanesia were on the whole much harder to reach than was Africa in those early days.

As regards America, all migrations must pass via north-east Siberia. In the Ice Ages this was covered with an Ice Cap (Taylor, 1930) which would definitely discourage migrations. During interglacials the Behring route might be quite feasible—and doubtless during such a period a few tribes of Australoids or kindred folk reached America (Taylor, 1919). Possibly during the close of the Wurm Ice Age the Eskimo reached America while their congeners, late Palæolithic Man, were reaching Western Europe. The main migrations into America seem to have occurred in the warmer periods (say of the Achen retreat of the ice or between the Buhl and Schnitz minor advances of the ice in Europe) some ten to twenty thousand years ago.

Now assuming these geographical relations, what should we expect

FIG. 38.—Five stages in Racial Migrations in the Old World, each representing a separate Major Race

Black areas show present habitats. Dotted areas are probable early habitats. The lowest race in the diagram was the first differentiated, the highest was the latest to find? Primitive man was thrust out of south central Asia (primarily by climatic changes leading to greater cold or aridity) and would know nothing of the outlying areas. He would no doubt move off in several directions (to south, south-west, or south-east) more or less equally. Thus the greater proportion of the earliest migrations would inevitably reach Africa (the easiest outlet, on the whole), while a smaller number would reach Melanesia by circumventing the very difficult tangle of mountains in South-east Asia, crossing the 'stepping stones' of the East Indies; and, if fortunate enough, making use of the alternately open and drowned corridors of Sunda and Sahul Lands. This 'paired' dispersion to west and east is illustrated in Fig. 38.

As millenia passed the more accessible lands of Africa would fill up, and Australia would receive a much larger proportion of later (Australoid) migrations. Finally as the latest migrants were thrust from Asia, the American corridor became available in the warm periods succeeding the Ice Age—and this is why we find so large a proportion of the Alpine-Mongolian race in the New World. A glance at the arrangement of the Zones (Fig. 33) will show that this series of migrations is fully corroborated. The shift of the climatic belts, the changing topography, and their effect on the migration zones are discussed in the writer's two books *Environment, Race and Migration* (1946) and *Our Evolving Civilization* (1947).

The Negrito Zone

No feature of the classification adopted is entirely new, for the obvious reason that among the dozen latest classifications almost all reasonable methods have been suggested. But it is because the writer has applied a somewhat novel test—the ecological one—and finds that it lends support to one set of racial classes and not to the others that he adopts the former.

Let us consider the five classes in order of development (Fig. 38). Most anthropologists group the negritoes as a stunted variety of the negro, though Dixon has made them a variety of the Alpine. The writer's belief that they are relics of a very ancient type of man, contemporaneous with Neandertal man, cannot be claimed as proven, but seems to be more in accord with the facts than the other two suggestions. The writer has shown (1934) by means of his 'ethnographs' (which correlate five important physical criteria) that the brakeph negritoes of the Congo Forest have little in common with the surrounding dokeph negroes; and the same is true of the Tapiro negritoes of New Guinea and the surrounding negroes. Yet the two far-distant negrito types very closely resemble each other (Fig. 38 at A). The only link between negrito and Alpine is the rather broad head of the former. In no other respect are they alike, and the writer cannot see any evidence in the general plan of racial migration which would remove the negritoes so far from all Alpines— if they were really an off-shoot of the latter. Similarly in Luzon (and in the tip of India, if recent research is correct) we find numbers of negritoes with no adjacent negroes from which to derive them!

Negroes and Neandertals

All anthropologists adopt the negro as one of their major classes (Fig. 38 at B). It is almost the only point of general accord. But the present writer has been endeavouring for many years to develop a reasonable theory of negro origins. Are there any relics of the ancestors of the negroes? Has their hot environment any bearing on their evolution? It is logical to expect to find some clues to their ancestry in the 'strata' underlying the relics of the present negro races in Africa, or below the Mediterranean race in Europe, Africa, and Asia.

These occur even in Asia, for Guna and Basu (in *Anthropos*, 1932, p. 162) mention several 'inliers' of tribes where 'crepe' hair is to be observed among the Nagas in Assam and also in Cochin. Furthermore, Mansey has described 'Melanesoid' skulls from Tonkin (*vide* von Eickstedt).

Western Europe is the only region which has been moderately well investigated as regards Palæolithic times. Here we find an almost universal 'stratum' characterized by Neandertal man, followed by Cromagnon, Combe Capelle, and Grimaldi man. Not many years ago it was customary to state that Neandertal man had died out, and that no living races had descended from him. The writer believes that later evidence is disproving this statement. In the first place, Neandertal man seems to have been a distinctly variable person.

The skull from Ehringsdorf (1925), although dating from Pre-Wurm days, had a loftier vault, thinner walls and a more vertical forehead than many later Neandertal types. In Keith's words (1931) already he approached modern man in these respects. One of the most primitive skulls of all comes from Broken Hill, Rhodesia—yet Smith Woodward links it with the Australoids. At Predmost (Moravia) twenty skeletons of Aurignacian culture are described by Keith as having large heads, with palates rivalling the Australoid, and in their long high skulls reminding one of the 'negroid features of the Combe Capelle type'. The Galilee skull (Keith, 1931) also exhibits features linking Australoid and negro skulls to Neandertal, especially as regards the frontal bones and the height of the vault. Sarasin (1924) is emphatic that living negroes from New Caledonia as regards the orbit, jaw, nose, and humerus are more primitive than the Neandertal type (1924).

Von Eickstedt (1934) corroborates the view put forward by the writer in 1919. He states that the Aurignacians of Europe show a great similarity with recent Australoids, and the resemblance also obtains with Neandertal man, but to a less degree. In his opinion, the Aurignacians are somewhat less primitive than the Australoid, as regards prognathism, face, and skull-base, but are extraordinarily alike as regards body-shape, length of skull, shape of chin, &c. In Capetown in 1929 a skull was dug up from a depth of four metres which again links the European Aurignacian type with the Australoid in von Eickstedt's opinion.

Since so many writers have demonstrated that a series linking Cromagnon to Combe Capelle and to Neandertal is gradually being discovered (cf. von Eickstedt, p. 425), there seems no good reason to doubt that Neandertal man was physically as near to the ancestor of his successors as we could reasonably expect to find in a marginal region. An analogy with Greenland may make this clearer. Suppose anthropologists had only evidence of a marginal colony like Greenland to help them in their reconstruction of Scandinavian history. They would find skeletons and artifacts to help them to elucidate Scandinavian history from A.D. 1000 to A.D. 1400. Then right from 1400 to 1700 (when Egede made another settlement) there was an absence of Scandinavian man and culture in Greenland. The new culture after 1700 seemed entirely dissociated from that of the early Norsemen. But elsewhere, i.e. in the cradleland (here Norway), the sequence was unbroken. So also West Europe was a marginal land receiving interrupted migrations, and the *complete* picture of racial and cultural evolution of Neandertal man is obviously to be sought in southern Asia, not in Western Europe.

Let us once more return to the topic of living descendants of Neandertal man. Most convincing is the description of an Australoid woman who died only a few decades ago in Eastern Australia. Burkett and Hunter (1922) give fourteen Neandertaloid features in this skull. Indeed, in the regions of the torus and bregma they notice affinity to *Pithecanthropus*! The writer believes that it is precisely because the negro was thrust into the stagnant environment of the Tropics (of Africa and Melanesia) that he preserves so many primitive features. Of course he has evolved somewhat since his early arrival in the Tropics perhaps 100,000 years ago. But meanwhile in other stimulating areas racial evolution has been much more striking and has left him far behind. His 'paired' environments (in Africa and Melanesia) are indicated in Fig. 33 and Fig. 38.

The Australoid Zone

The writer in 1921 in a large coloured chart of nine maps (in the *Geographic Review*) showed his conclusions as to the evolution and migrations of races. The relative position of negroes and Australoids is a little difficult. In both there is a wide range of characters. Thus in Australia the writer has investigated most of the coastal regions, and here the aborigines in general are much less 'primitive' in appearance than those from the central deserts, made familiar by Spencer and Gillen's splendid photographs.

Apart from the hair, there is no very striking difference between the Australoids and negroes. But hair texture is universally admitted to be of great importance—and in the Australoids it is almost universally wavy rather than curly, and never frizzy. This places them biologically nearer the central racial zones (Mediterranean and Alpine). It is of interest that Sarasin (1924) records that the new-born New Caledonian negro has wavy hair which is replaced after the first week or so by the usual kinky negro hair. So that kinky hair is possibly a secondary character acquired by negroid peoples.

If we turn to the ecological evidence, then it seems clear that the Australoids migrated out of Asia much later than did the negroes. Thus Mitra (1927) writes: 'India shares with Africa Proto-negroid beginnings . . . and with south-east Asia the superimposition on them of Proto-Australoid elements.' There are now no negroes or negritoes on the mainland except in Perak (and perhaps in the tip of India). But there are millions of Australoids (the so-called Pre-Dravidian tribes) in the eastern hills of the Deccan in India and in Ceylon. So that we may surely say that their less marginal position agrees with the hair-character, and places the 'wavy' Australoids a little higher than the 'frizzy' negroes of Africa or Oceania.

My suggestion is that a Neandertaloid type lived in southern Asia and gave rise to the negroes far back in the Pleistocene—perhaps in the Gunz-Mindel Interglacial (Fig. 38). The Mindel Ice Age drove most of them to the south-east—whence later they reached Africa.[1] Fewer went to the south-east and so ultimately gained Papua and Melanesia. The Semang of Perak and possibly some tribes in Assam support this hypothesis. It is little use speculating as to change in hair character which probably now developed in the cradleland, but I picture the next

---

[1] Somewhat doubtful 'inliers' of negroid races have been described from Susa (Persia) and south-east Arabia (Taylor, 1921).

migration as consisting of Australoids—most of whom went into India or to the south-east and so reached Australia. Possibly their cradleland was farther to the east in Asia than was that of the negroes.

In Upper Tonkin seventeen skulls of Australoids akin to those found in the Aurignacian in Europe are mentioned by von Eickstedt (1934). Many of the people living in Western Europe about 20,000 B.C. were very like the Australoids (Taylor, 1933); and Sir Harry Johnston (1923) draws attention to the Australoid appearance of the Ushtettas still living in the mountains of Algeria. It seems likely that some Australoids reached America in one of the interglacials—probably the Riss-Wurm Interglacial. The Punin skull from Ecuador is described by Sullivan (1925) as showing a strong resemblance to Australian skulls. So also the rather numerous skulls from Lagoa Santa, Bogota, Coronel, and Patagonia, described by Verneau (1924) and others, probably represent descendants of the early Australoid migration. The Qurungua type described by Wegner (1931) from lower Bolivia is probably a living representative of this early migration.

The Mediterranean Zone

The next zone consists of the Mediterranean type with its variant, the Nordic (Fig. 38 at D). Buxton (1928) links together the Proto-Nordics of north Asia (Turkoman and Ainu) with the Australoids of India as forming one group—the Primitive Cymotrichous. While the present writer prefers to separate the Australoids as an earlier zone, he agrees that the Nordics could readily have evolved in central Asia from the Australoid type. Perhaps the Todas of India and Ainu of Japan are survivors of this peculiarly hairy, dokeph type—but with noses much more leptorhine than most Australoids. (The writer (1926) has, however, examined a number of full-blood aborigines in north-west Australia whose noses could fairly be described as leptorhine.)

Many writers since the time of Sergi (1901) have linked the Nordic and Mediterranean. Sergi considered the Nordics as 'bleached' Mediterraneans who had moved from Africa into the Baltic region. It seems, however, more likely that Siberia was their homeland (Taylor, 1921) in view of the kurgan relics and the similarity between the Nordic and Siberian cultures. I have long suggested that a dokeph race with wavy hair, developing (say) in Turkestan, might split into two migrations. One slowly passes through hot, arid lands to North Africa and this environment 'selects' a dark, slender type, the Mediterranean race proper. The northern migration halts for several millenia in Siberia and then slowly moves to the Baltic. This cold, dry environment picks out the blonder, hairy types, and ultimately the taller Nordic race is differentiated.

It is perhaps significant that the blood indices of the Nordics resemble those of the Mediterranean on the one hand and the Australoids on the other (Taylor, 1930), and are very different from those of the Alpine race or negroes. On the other hand, the Alpine and 'Mongolian' blood indices are much the same, thus supporting the writer's views as to their close kinship.

As regards the origin, status, and migrations of the Mediterranean group as a whole, there is little controversy. Their migrations can be traced back towards southern Asia; both from the European and African 'wings' on the west, and from the American and Indonesian wings on the east. There is no break in the centre, as in the case of the negro and Australoid zones, for India contains many representatives of this race. Indeed, it extends all round the margins of Asia, for there are many tribes of this type still surviving in the rugged ranges of South China where they have not yet been overwhelmed by the Alpine-Mongolian flood. The zone is more broken along the east coast of Eurasia than on the west —and the shattered tribes from this area are to be found in Micronesia, and constitute what Dixon calls the Caspian migration into Polynesia and America. Heine-Geldern (1932) places the cradleland of the allied Austronesian tribes in Yunnan whence they spread through the East Indies.

In India, as Mitra (1923) points out, there are clearly several distinct migrations of the Mediterranean race. First came the early Dravidian-speakers—probably tribes akin to the Ethiopians of north-east Africa. Their descendants are the Kurumbas of the south, and possibly the folk who built Mohenjo-daro. They may have been in control in India from 5000 B.C. to the invasion of the Aryan-speakers from the north-west. The latter were at first mainly Nordic and Mediterranean, and perhaps date as far back as 2500 B.C. Later came further invasions from the north-west which consisted largely of Alpine tribes, and these conquered the folk in the main river-corridors, i.e. down the Indus and Ganges (Taylor, 1927).

In 1919, disagreeing with Perry's deductions, I stated that these Mediterranean tribes 'migrated from the Arab-Persian region and erected Megalithic monuments in Turkestan, Persia, North Africa, North India, and the East Indies'. Mitra (in 1927) corroborates this view as follows: 'A migration from Central Asia brought about . . . an Indian-Erythrean complex which saw the rise of the huge countless funerary monuments in the Deccan as well as in Egypt.'

The Alpine-Mongolian Zone

The most popular classification of races as regards Eurasia seems to be indicated by a line AB running from Lapland to Burmah, which is given in Fig. 35. The writer cannot understand how this division between the so-called Caucasian and the so-called Mongolian has persisted so long, presumably from the time of Cuvier in 1820. Many authors (e.g. Ripley) object strongly to the term Caucasian; and to the writer the only common character of the nations living in the so-called Caucasian moiety of Eurasia is that they nearly all speak Indo-Aryan tongues. But this use of language as a primary guide to race has long been given up elsewhere.

Let us, however, use 'as many traits as possible', as Kroeber advises us (see Introduction). In Fig. 35 I show the main features as given in Biasutti's atlas of anthropological criteria. If we consider skin colour, we find that the isopleths of colour have nothing in common with the reputed major racial division (shown by the heavy AB line). The Olive complexion is equally common on both sides, as also is the next grade of colour, Light Brown. Head Index may be considered next, and here again the isopleths clearly run at right angles to the reputed race boundary —which to the ecologist means that they have little or nothing in common. Consider Facial Breadth (in the third map) and we see that Broad faces are characteristic of the Eurasian peoples as a whole—there is no division here either, along the reputed boundary. So also Stature gives us no data to support this division, and Nasal Index has little bearing on it, since Biasutti labels all the Eurasian region (except the south-east) as Leptorhine. Only in Biasutti's map of hair texture is there some justification for this division for the straight-haired folks are in general to the east of the reputed boundary and the wavy-haired to the west. (See the map of Nasal Index.) Kroeber, however, assigns all the straight-haired peoples of central Asia to the Caucasian,[1] while Ripley links Alpines and Mongols in his chart of Hair Distribution.

Another map (1936 paper) shows us that racial history lends little support to these Caucasian or Mongol subdivisions. Right through historic times peoples and cultures have passed freely between the east and west of central Asia as shown by the two long arrows. We may be sure that in prehistoric times—especially in the very long interglacial periods when the climates were neither so dry in summer nor so cold in winter —primitive peoples migrated even more freely between the Turkestan area and the regions east and west of it.

[1] Minor differences like 'shovel-teeth' and the 'epicanthic folds' are surely not important enough to isolate the Mongols as a major race.

Early Chinese history is an account of thrusts from the north-west. Indian history is the same story of thrusts from the north-west. Egyptian history records the major migrations as coming from the north-east. European history is mainly controlled by thrusts from the east. There can be little doubt that stresses and strains in the heart of Eurasia—one deduces in the area between the Caspian and the Pamirs—have set in movement racial migrations throughout the Ages. If this be so, then the main racial isopleths should be lines more or less concentric around the centre of disturbance—and cannot possibly run almost through the Pamirs as shown in Fig. 35.

For these reasons the present writer in 1919 adopted the term Alpine-Mongolian to indicate that the Mongol type was only a variant of the fairly homogeneous group of peoples which occupy the main bulk of Eurasia. The characters of the Alpines are indeed summed up in the set of four charts. They are all brakeph (80 to 90), almost all olive in colour, all broad face, of medium stature, and with leptorhine noses. The hair is on the whole wavy in the west and straight in the east, but is never curly—much less frizzy. They occupy the centre of the series of approximately concentric racial zones—and for reasons already given represent the latest development of the human race. Man has evolved in the common cradleland of most of the mammals—the heart of Eurasia —owing to the fact that the climatic stimulus right through later Tertiary times has been the most favourable for producing mammalian evolution. It does not seem to occur to most anthropologists that the cradleland of the higher mammals would *a priori* be the most likely place for the highest type of all (man) to originate and to continue evolving.

Races and Blood Groups

We shall do well to consider a new method of approach to the racial problem. Around 1900 Landsteiner investigated the differences in the bloods of normal individuals, and discovered the main groups. There are four types, which are identified somewhat as follows. If the red corpuscles of an individual are mixed with the serum of folk of the same 'blood group', the suspension remains unaffected. If, however, the serum belongs to another 'blood group', the red cells will come together in clumps. This is called agglutination. It depends on reactions between two substances, one in the cells and the other in the serum. These substances are probably complex proteins.

The four blood groups are known as A, B, AB, and O. The serum of A agglutinates the corpuscles of B, and vice versa. In the third group the cell suspension may be agglutinated by both sera, in which case the blood group being tested is AB. Lastly the corpuscles may be affected by neither serum A nor serum B, in which case they belong to group O.

In 1930 the writer published a map[1] showing that the blood groups of the Nordic and Mediterranean folk were somewhat alike, and differed very materially from those of folk occupying the central portion of the Old World, i.e. the Alpines. The problem has been studied by a number of human biologists in the last decade. In the recent book by F. Schiff and W. C. Boyd entitled *Blood Grouping Technic*[2] two maps are given showing the distribution of the A and B groups for the whole world.

The map representing the distribution of the B blood group is satisfactory from the point of view of the drawing of the isopleths; but the map for the A group seems to the writer to be unnecessarily complicated, even granting that the data are rather sporadic. The lines (isogenes) have therefore been redrawn in what seems to a geographer to be a legitimate reconstruction of the data given (on p. 204) in the book cited. This map appears as Fig. 23 in my book *Our Evolving Civilization*.

In both cases we see that there are two poles of distribution centred in Europe and Australia respectively. Thus the A groups are exceptionally numerous in these marginal areas; while the Indian Ocean bounds coasts with distinctly low values for A group folk. It is important to note that the main mass of Asia is inhabited by peoples with an intermediate number of A group folk; i.e. this group is neither very abundant nor very rare.

In the case of the B group there is a clear indication that among the peoples of central Asia (i.e. those called Alpines in the present book) there is emphatically a high percentage of the B type. The area with a strong preponderance of the B group suggests some characteristic especially common in the central Asiatic region and spreading along the Tarim Corridor into China, as well as extending down into Persia and the north of India. These are almost precisely the migrations of the later-evolved peoples of the Old World, if the thesis advanced previously is correct. As mentioned earlier there may be a real anthropological kinship between the primitive folk of Europe and the Australian aborigines, which is corroborated by the similarly low proportions of the B blood group in these two marginal areas. Further than this the writer is not disposed to go.

[1] 'Racial Migration Zones' (*Human Biology*, Vol. II. No. 1, 1930, p. 54).
[2] New York, 1942.

Changes in Classification

A glance at Fig. 39 will show how the writer's Zones and Strata classification differs from the more orthodox form, which is usually like that used by Keane and Haddon. The preceding discussion has shown that a major feature in the differentiation of races is their migration away from the centre of Eurasia, in effect, it is centrifugal. The racial history (as based on the zones and strata) is a very important feature in the classification, but head index, hair, and other features are made use of as criteria

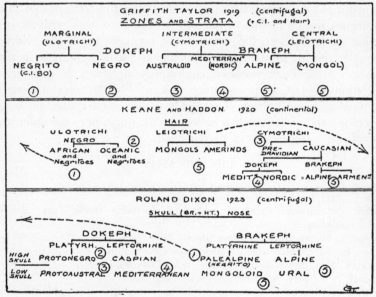

FIG. 39.—Comparative outlines of Racial Classifications, showing the main criteria adopted by Kean and Haddon, Roland Dixon and the present writer

also. As a result we obtain five races, of which Negro, Mediterranean, and Alpine are the most significant, while Negrito and Australoid are less so.

In Fig. 39 the five major races in the writer's classification are shown by the numerals. These are repeated in the two lower classifications. The broken lines show the major changes necessary to bring the latter into approximate agreement with the Zones and Strata classification.

In Keane and Haddon's classification we find still persisting the Caucasian, Mongol, and Negro groups of Cuvier. Hair is used as the major criterion. Head index is given no weight at all, for Mongols and

Amerinds are linked, as are Mediterranean and Alpine. These schemes do not explain why so many of the Polynesians and Amerinds should much more closely resemble the distant Western European peoples than the nearer Mongol-Alpines. Nor do Keane and his supporters state why the Caucasians should only reach eastward to Central Asia, the great breeding ground of peoples, and there change into a group apparently different enough to be considered a new race.

Dixon (1923) has discarded many of the earlier concepts and developed a scheme (based on head and nose indices) which in many ways corroborates the writer's deductions (Fig. 39). Indeed, he goes further, for he finds the major racial groups penetrating by centrifugal movement into all the continents. But his linking of the earliest or negrito stock with the latest Alpine stock seems to the writer to be contrary to all the evidence. Moreover, he, like most other anthropologists (excluding Ripley), perhaps does not lay enough stress on environmental factors in determining migrations. In fact, he is not much concerned with causes. The writer knows of no recent anthropologist but himself who has applied the lessons of ecology and of mammalian biology to the question of the differentiation of man—the greatest of the mammals.

BIBLIOGRAPHY

Biasutti, R., 1912, 'Antropogeografia Generale', Mem. Geog., Florence.

Boas, F., 1911, Changes in Bodily Form, Washington.

Burkitt and Hunter, 1922, 'Neandertaloid Australian skull', Journ. Anatomy, Cambridge.

Buxton, L. D., 1925, Peoples of Asia (Book), New York.

Dixon, R., 1923, Racial History of Man (Book), New York.

Keith, A., 1931, New Discoveries Relating to Man (Book), London.

Kroeber, A. L., 1923, Anthropology (Book), New York.

Matthew, W. D., 1915, 'Evolution and climate', Ann. Acad. Science, New York.

Mitra, P., 1927, Prehistoric India (Book), Calcutta.

Ripley, W. Z., 1900, Races of Europe (Book), London.

Taylor, Griffith, 1919, 'Climatic cycles and evolution', Geog. Review, New York.

    1924, 'Kamilaroi and white', Roy. Soc., Sydney, Australia.

    1927, Environment and Race (Book), Univ. of Oxford Press (Japanese edition, 1931).

    1930, 'Racial migration zones', Human Biology, Baltimore.

    1936, Environment and Nation (Book), Univ. of Toronto.

    1937, Environment, Race and Migration (Book), Univ. of Toronto.

    1945, Human Origins (Part of a Symposium), Univ. of Chicago.

    1947, Our Evolving Civilization (Book), Univ. of Toronto.

    1949, This is Race (Part of a Symposium), New York.

CHAPTER XX

THE SOCIOLOGICAL ASPECTS OF GEOGRAPHY

JAMES WREFORD WATSON

Professor Watson was born in China; educated Edinburgh; M.A. 1936; University of Sheffield; then McMaster University, Ontario; Ph.D. Toronto, 1945; head of the new Department of Geography at McMaster 1947; Director Geographical Branch, Dept. of Mines, Ottawa 1949. Has published articles and contributions to books on land-use, rural settlement, urban geography, and historical geography.

PART I. THEORETICAL CONSIDERATIONS

INTRODUCTION: EARLY GEOGRAPHICAL THOUGHT

GEOGRAPHY has always been interested in society, although their association has not always been clear. The early geographers, such as Strabo, contented themselves with describing different social conditions in different places. Their emphasis on the social contrasts between one area and another—usually between Europe and the outer darkness—while sometimes stressing the strange, to the exclusion of differences in day-to-day life, nevertheless created for geography the vital tradition of differentiating regions as much by their social content as by their physical character.

Gradually, this has been perceived as the chief function of social geography. Kant's interest in a moral geography which would describe the mores of people in different areas was along this line. Ritter stressed the concept by insisting that social factors were to be studied, in relationship to other human factors and to the earth, if the true character of the areas of the earth should emerge. Ratzel's bold use of the word 'anthropogeography' further emphasized geography's concern with racial, political, and social factors in the description of regions.

Unfortunately, the relationship of geography and society was looked at, by eighteenth-century materialism, as a means of explaining society by geography. Over-confident claims, sometimes bordering on the extravagant, were made by geographers, which led to a strong reaction on the part of historians and philosophers. When Montesquieu, who had attributed racial differentiation to climate, without unduly straining credulity, went so far as to explain human laws in similar terms—calling them bad if they favoured the 'vices of climate', or good, if they opposed

463

them, and also made climate responsible for drunkenness or temperance, suicide, polygamy, jealousy, and divorce—he went too far, and justly deserved the rebuke of Voltaire. 'On a peut-être attribué trop d'influence au climat. . . . La différence la plus réelle est celle qui existe entre les Européens et le reste du globe; et cette différence est l'ouvrage des Grecs. . . . Si Xerxès eut vaincu à Salamine, nous serions peut-être encore des barbares.'

THE CONTRIBUTION OF SOCIAL GEOGRAPHY

(1) *With Reference to Physical Geography*

The result of all this was the reaction on the part of some geographers to abandon social geography, and confine themselves to 'pure'; i.e. physical, geography. This attitude has been revived today because of the present situation in public-and-middle-school geography. Many Provinces in Canada, and States in the American Union, have a type of geography in their schools called 'Social Studies'. These studies are meant to embrace history, economics, and civics, together with geography, on the grounds that all are related to each other, and are dependent on each other. Yet few teachers could have equal training in geography, history, economics, and civics. Consequently the teacher is left to emphasize one of these components, over above the others, according to interest or education.

One is not entirely unsympathetic with them, when even academic geographers and historians are still unsure of themselves, and are unable to bring their two studies into a single focus. Meantime, the nebulous nature of the geographical part of social studies has led some teachers to demand a 'scientific' geography instead. But in doing so they simply re-echo the cry of over a century ago, when early nineteenth-century geographers in Germany turned to 'pure' geography,[1] or the study of the physical environment, as an escape from the somewhat amorphous, or less easily defined, social geography.

Many of these teachers are science masters, who find their sympathies with geology, biology, or physics. Their complaint is that 'social' geography is unscientific, and that therefore geography should withdraw its frontiers to the 'physical'—to the easily measurable factors of temperature and pressure, rocks, water, plants, and animals.

Yet in trying to be 'scientific' in this way, they are actually in danger of making geography less of a science, not more. If geography is the science of landscapes, or the science of environmental control, or the

[1] Hartshorne, Richard: 'The Nature of Geography', *Ann. Assoc. Amer. Geog.*, Lancaster, 1939, p. 48.

science of distributions, or the science of regional differentiation (and these seem to be the more common definitions) then it is unscientific to leave out the sociological aspects of geography, because these affect the landscape, they modify the environment, they change distributions, and they are a part of those areal complexes that help to differentiate one region from another. Thus the inclusion of social geography in the subject as a whole helps to make geography more scientific, not less, by helping it to present the whole picture of a place or of the earth.

This point of view has been vigorously expressed by Fairgrieve,[1] who urged teachers to realize that 'the very insistence on explanations of geographic facts in terms of natural science only, was profoundly unscientific'. Geography must be all humane as well as all scientific. In fact, it might be argued that, not only is human geography a good corrective for 'pure' physical geography, but it does much to justify the existence of geography as a separate subject. Leave out human geography, and other sciences can do the rest. If the human factor is left out, there is merely a collection of information on the natural environment derived from other sciences. But it is only by relating the different physical factors to each other, for the purpose of correlating them with man, and thus of giving a total description of the earth, that geography finds its *raison d'être*. Already, in not a few universities, departments of geology have taken over geomorphology; meteorology—climate; botany—plant geography; so that, if this process were extended, physical geography would have relatively little justification. In that case human and regional geography would become the chief reasons for the existence of geography as a separate discipline.

The fact is, social geography is needed because geography, if it is to be successful, must describe the total relationship of a place, in comparison with other places. Not least among those relationships are social ones. The French school of geographers perhaps grasp this more clearly than any other. Vidal de la Blache has made it a cardinal principle of his human geography, and worked for 'the conception of the earth as a whole, whose parts are co-ordinated, where phenomena follow a definite sequence and obey general laws'.[2] The environment is not merely a physical thing. It has long ceased to be that—if it ever was. It is a composite thing, 'grouping and holding together heterogeneous beings in mutual vital relationships'. The concept of terrestrial unity is fundamental to

[1] Fairgrieve, James: *Geography in School*, University of London Press, London, 1937, p. 16.

[2] Vidal de la Blache, Paul: *Principles of Human Geography*, Constable, London, 1926, p. 7.

modern geography, and includes in its orbit, not only nature, but man, and not only the physical aspects of man, but the ethereal as well.

Historians, and others, have done a lot to help us realize the fact. Thus, in dividing the world up on the basis of spatial as well as temporal factors, Toynbee reviews twenty-two civilizations, which rose and spread as the result of a complex of natural and human causes, of physical and ethereal forces. Professor Childe, in his stimulating book, *What Happened in History*, remarks that socially approved and sustained ideas must be treated as just as real as more substantial objects. 'In practice, ideas form as effective an element in the environment of any human society as do mountains, trees, animals, the weather and the rest of external nature. Societies behave as if they were reacting to a spiritual environment as well as to a material environment.'[1]

The closer understanding between geographers and other social scientists has led them to respect this spiritual environment, and to take it into account in their description of the total relationship of things in any area. Again Vidal de la Blache played an important role in this regard. In his *Personality of France* he remarks:

A geographical individuality does not result simply from geological and climatic conditions. . . . It is man who reveals a country's individuality by moulding it to his own use. He establishes a connexion between unrelated features, substituting for the random effects of local circumstances a systematic co-operation of forces. Only then does a country acquire a specific character, differentiating it from others, till at length it becomes, as it were, a medal struck in the likeness of a people.[2]

If this is the case, it is the human element, and in that, perhaps above all, the social constituent, that distinguishes one place from another, and gives character to a region.

THE CONTRIBUTION OF SOCIAL GEOGRAPHY

(2) *With Reference to Natural Regions*

Thus social geography is a needed corrective to the theory of the natural region, namely, that the earth is divided naturally into regions, and that it is the different action of these regions that produces social differentiation. The theory of natural regions, like that of 'pure' geography,

[1] Childe, Gordon: *What Happened in History*, Pelican Books, London, 1942, p. 14.

[2] Vidal de la Blache, Paul: *The Personality of France*, Christophers, London, 1928, p. 14.

has also been revived in our time. Unfortunately, some people who use it do so without the breadth of mind of its originator, Herbertson. Too many have stressed 'natural' in the sense of 'non-human', rather than in Herbertson's sense of 'not-artificial'. Now there may be 'natural' regions, in the sense of regions which appear to 'exist in nature', but these are not of interest to the geographer unless they are also geographic regions. The latter take account of all sorts of artificial areas, such as political tracts or spheres of influence, cultural spheres, the Bible Belt, T.V.A.'s and so forth. These may emphasize existing areal relationships that appear to be natural; or they may ignore them. The important thing in geography, as Crowe[1] indicates, is not to build up a synthetic picture of facts so as to reveal 'natural harmonies in all their splendour', but rather to face *all* the facts, which include other harmonies as well, and to know how they are all integrated—or even 'organized'—in an area. An area of unique organization perhaps best corresponds to a geographic regions.

Herbertson seems to have used 'natural' to distinguish those regions which, because of a certain natural homogeneity of physical *and* human relationships, were more or less self-evident, from regions, such as political ones, drawn by man. Yet, using vegetation, as he did, as a basis for his scheme of major natural regions, he appeared to stress the material rather than the social factor, and left himself open to the misinterpretation that a natural region is primarily physical. Of course, a relationship between natural regions and man was seen, or contemplated. But here again, having decided what a natural region was, largely on a material basis, it was assumed that it would influence man to such an extent as to make itself apparent in human affairs.[2] In other words, as Roxby once suggested, similar natural regions would tend to produce similar ultimate effects on human development.

This is far from the case. Social geography points to the contrary. There are many instances where similar environments, such as the Mediterranean and California, have 'produced' dissimilar societies. There are examples where the same environment, such as the St. Lawrence Valley, has been divided on social grounds, and, far from presenting a single aspect, may look like two or three different landscapes. As Stevens says, the physical region, based on physical homogeneity, may interest the topographer, or the climatologist but 'is an irrelevance in geography'.[3] Actually, the boundaries of geographical regions, including as they do a

[1] Crowe, P. R.: 'On Progress in Geography', *Scot. Geog. Mag.*, Jan. 1938, p. 10.
[2] Herbertson, A. J.: *Man and His Work*, A. & C. Black, London, 1911, p. 6.
[3] Stevens, A.: 'The Natural Geographical Region', *Scot. Geog. Mag.*, Nov. 1939, p. 308.

hanging together of social, political, economic, cultural, organic, and physical phenomena, 'may be indifferent to natural boundaries'.

The belief, therefore, re-established itself that, to quote Stevens again, in matters of geographic description, 'what is fundamental is relativity to man', since man is a potent factor in almost every environment, and by his intervention in the ecological processes, has changed the face of the earth.

THE CONTRIBUTION OF SOCIAL GEOGRAPHY

(3) *With Reference to the Cultural Landscape*

Perhaps no one has done more to insist on man's adaptation of nature than Bryan, who uses the concept of the cultural landscape as the basis for regional subdivision. He describes the earth essentially in terms of cultural areas, in which different societies, with different cultures, have made a unique use of the land. Undoubtedly this represents an advance on the idea of the natural region, and in so far as it does, stresses the value of social geography.

Yet it has an important drawback; it limits itself, more or less strictly, to the concrete forms or activities of human culture, as evidenced in the landscape, and thus does not, and indeed cannot, consider *all* the sociological aspects of geography. To quote Bryan,[1]

the cultural landscape presents a fourfold aspect. It has structural forms as in fields, mines, houses, and factories. It possesses moveable forms as in the cases of men and vehicles. It has activity expressed in the operations of seeding and harvesting, manufacturing processes, and the movement of vehicles. Lastly, it has the results of these activities in the form of crops, manufactured products, the transportation of goods and people, the production of health, good government, and amusement.

In other words, the cultural landscape is the concrete representation of man's adaptation of his environment.

But why stop at the concrete representation? If we are going to lay the emphasis, in geographical description, upon relativity to man (upon what man has done to change nature, rather than what nature has done to influence man), then it is impossible to stop at the concrete. The human factor is something more than the works-of-man. It includes ideologies, as well as technologies. And in not a few instances it is the immaterial force that is the really significant thing in the geography of a region, which gives that region its distinctive character, and separates it from others.

[1] Bryan, P. W.: *Man's Adaptation of Nature*, Henry Holt, New York, 1933, p. vi.

There may be no concrete evidence of this in the landscape; nevertheless, the interpreter of the region knows it is that which has made the region unique.[1]

Here again, the desire to make or to keep geography 'scientific' was probably what led to making it concrete. But every area sees an assembly of a great number of very heterogeneous things, and it may be necessary for the geographer to describe *all* of these, immaterial as well as material, in order to portray the essential character of the area. Actually, it seems to me unscientific not to do so, in the sense that we might leave out of the picture significant factors that give co-ordination to an otherwise inexplicable juxtaposition of things. Few geographers today, therefore, confine themselves to the material cultural landscape, although it is a valuable contribution to their studies. It is now seen that Brunhes' emphasis on a concrete geography—'Human geography, properly so called, must be first and above all the geography of material human works'[2]—was an over-emphasis. Students of cultural geography, such as Griffith Taylor, claim that *all* the factors needed to interpret and describe the personality of a region or country, must be brought into the ken of the geographer. According to him even 'religions and philosophies are amenable to study by the geographical approach'.[3] If that is so, if they can be studied geographically, they ought to be included, wherever relevant, in the description of places.

This is an important emphasis, especially for social geographers. All too few geographers have had any training in sociology, and, therefore, all too few feel competent to deal with the immaterial social factors in the geographic scene. Some would go so far as to say that these should be left out, since there is sufficient remaining anyway to the geographer to

---

[1] See how the characteristic forms and development of settlements along the west side of the Niagara River differ from those on the east side, very largely because of political and social differences. Here loyalism, as a social force, and the British connexion, as a political factor, are the real things which divide a region—the Western Peninsula of New York and the Niagara Peninsula—which is in every other way integrated. Cf. Watson, J. W., 'The Impact of the American Frontier on Niagara Settlements', *Geog. Rev.*, Jan. 1948. Also, cf. Watson, J. W., 'Rural Depopulation in S.W. Ontario', *Ann. Assoc. Amer. Geog.*, Sept. 1947, for the influence of social forces in the depopulation of S. Ontario as compared with that of 'natural' forces, such as deforestation, soil erosion, &c. In considering depopulation as a factor in regional differentiation, these social forces, though quite intangible, are very significant.

[2] Brunhes, Jean: *Human Geography*, Rand McNally, New York, 1920, p. 71.

[3] Taylor, Griffith: *Our Evolving Civilization*, University of Toronto Press, Toronto, 1947, p. 4.

make a worth-while study. Thus Granö[1] insists that, even although the material and immaterial phenomena of an area form a unity, geography must consider only the material facts, and leave the immaterial ones to sociology. But there may be, and are, cases where to leave the immaterial out of consideration would be to miss something of value to the interpretation of the region.

The geographer cannot afford to do that, without giving up his main claim to describe the earth, in terms of regional differentiation. And it should be noted here, although it will be discussed later, that if he does not stress the social character of regions, as they differ over the earth, no one else will. The sociologist does not do it. He is interested in processes rather than patterns; he discusses the sociological aspects of a region, not in order to bring out the personality of the region, but to understand the processes of social development there.

It was Sir Patrick Geddes who showed the essential necessity of including *all* the physical, biotic, and human elements in the study of society. Central to his thinking were life's fundamental categories, form (organism), function, and environment, in perpetual interaction.[2] He believed the unity which exists in any area consists of a trinity of relationships between Place, Work, and Folk. (These were, of course, in widened form, the Lieu, Travail, Famille of Le Play.) There is a constant series of reactions between these three, and what is more, they are multiple-way, not one-way, reactions. In some cases the reactions might stress the material power of PLACE, and the relative unimportance of folk; in others they might reveal the spiritual significance of FOLK as compared with place. The factor of WORK would in all cases be critical.[3]

Daryll Forde has qualified the idea somewhat in his book, *Habitat, Economy and Society*, by saying the relationship really depends on stage of cultural development.

Between the physical environment and human activity there is always a middle term, a collection of specific objectives and values, a body of knowledge and belief: in other words, a cultural pattern. That the culture is . . . adaptable and modifiable in relation to physical conditions, must not be allowed to obscure the fact that adaptation proceeds by discoveries and inventions, which are themselves in no sense inevitable. Equally important are the restrictions placed by social

[1] Granö, Johannes G.: 'Reine Geographie: eine methodologische studie beleuchtet mit Beispielen aus Finnland und Estland', *Acta Geographica*, 2, No. 2, Helsinki, 1929, p. 38.

[2] Geddes, P., and Thomson, J. A.: *Life*, Harper, New York, p. v.

[3] Geddes, P.: *Cities in Evolution*, Williams & Norgate, London, 1915, p. 286 f.

patterns and religious concepts on the utilization of resources or on adaptations to physical conditions.[1]

Thus the degree of cultural advance changes the degree of economic skill and of social organization and so constantly alters the influence of the habitat, or man's adaptation of it to his ideals.

THE CONTRIBUTION OF SOCIAL GEOGRAPHY

(4) *With Reference to Human Regions*

It seems to me the main trend of modern geography is to emphasize the importance of cultural and social factors in the geographic scene, and to set up branches of geography, such as cultural geography and social geography, specifically to study them. In Bowman's classic, *Geography in Relation to the Social Sciences*, he brings this out in a telling paragraph.[2]

It follows that the natural environment is always a different thing to different groups. Its potentialities are absolute but their realization is a relative matter, relative to what the particular man wants and what he can get with the instruments of power and the ideas at his command and the standard of living he demands or strives to attain.

One notes in this the emphasis on values, as well as objects, on the standards of living man *demands*, on the things he *wants*, and on the *ideas* at his command. These are all geographical, though they are all immaterial, because they help us understand the interrelationships between folk and place.

The emphasis on the human factor gave rise to the concept of human regions which Fleure presented in his *Human Geography in Western Europe*. Like all the great geographers Fleure has been fully impressed by 'the fount of idealism at the roots of personality' which makes it impossible to treat man as a creature of circumstance. The geographer who regards man as such not only does an injustice to man, but he does an injustice to geography. For if the geographer is to describe the earth's surface as it is, he must frequently record instances where environment fails to control man, but where, on the contrary, a difficult environment, in challenging man's idealism and his ingenuity, may stimulate far greater advances in human thought than an easy one.

[1] Forde, C. Daryll: *Habitat, Economy and Society*, Methuen, London, 1934, p. 463.

[2] Bowman, I.: *Geography in Relation to the Social Sciences*, Scribner's, New York, 1934, p. 115.

31

The ultimate thing that matters in man's relationship with his environment is surely his idealism, and his capacity to put it into effect. Therefore, Fleure chooses to 'look out upon the world as the field of expression, and especially of cumulative expression, of the human spirit'.[1] Looked at in this way the earth is the scene of man's endeavour; and is differentiated, not so much by continents and oceans, mountains and plains, climatic or edaphic regions, but by human regions; by areas on which different men have set their characteristic stamp. Such regions overleap oceans; top mountains; and go beyond climates.

However, human regions do not ignore the physical. After all, they are the result of human efforts to make the environment conform to ideals. Fleure's human regions are major areas of the earth where 'the essential character and the reward of man's effort'[2] give character to regions; that is, surcharge place with folk. In working these regions out, Fleure had to take into account the cumulative effects of effort, over long periods of time, from great numbers of people. In doing so, consideration was paid to the *social* characteristics of the areas involved. Actually, to amplify the concept, rather more attention will have to be paid to these characteristics; for, with changes in social organization, the character and the reward of effort: also change: the human regions will alter.

THE CONTRIBUTION OF SOCIAL GEOGRAPHY

(5) *With Reference to Functional Regions*

Another concept which the emphasis on sociological aspects of geography has sponsored, is the functional region. This is an area, dominated by a particular community of interest and activity, which functions in a characteristic way. As Stevens points out, a geographical region is the result of a synthesis of environmental and human factors. These factors are actually two aspects of the same thing. The geographer focuses attention on the synthesis in space—on the region: the sociologist on the synthesis in life—on the community. Since the community is a vital entity, it is dynamic, and has certain functions. Social geography studies the community in the region, and finds *function* and *form* more or less fused together in what he has come to call the functional region. It, too,

---

[1] Fleure, H. J.: *Human Geography in Western Europe*, Williams & Norgate, London, 1918, p. 1.
[2] Fleure, ibid., p. 29.

helps to stamp an area as individual, and thus assists the geographer in creating what Hettner has called a science of areal differentiation of the earth surface.[1]

It is perhaps at this point that geography and sociology come most closely together. The concept of the functional region was first of all a sociological one, and is now used in both disciplines. It was in 1915 that C. J. Galpin[2] produced his 'Social Anatomy of an Agricultural Community' in which he showed that each function in the community, whether banking, retail trade, education, or religion, had a characteristic pattern of its own. This pattern had a typical spatial distribution and institutional structure.

The early contributions of geographers to community studies were based rather on physical control, or economic and technological influence, or historical changes, than on functional regions. Certainly, all these have played an important part, both in themselves, and in the way in which they have been worked into the functional concept. However, the classical study of communities was not in terms of functions, and functional patterns, but of general morphology, in relation to site and situation. It had this to say for it, that it emphasized space relationship. But it confined itself to the obvious relationships of buildings and streets as they responded to regional situation and local site.

The advance to social geography was probably due to Le Play, more than anyone else. This amateur sociologist was interested primarily in the relations of society and industry in different places. With painstaking care he made a great number of statistical analyses of families in relation to their occupation and habitat.[3] From these he derived his famous formula, already mentioned, of Lieu, Travail, Famille. Family life and morals were found to be conditioned by the economic system and by settlement. Le Play was especially interested in the primary occupations, which could be more easily studied. He was one of the first to work out what Geddes called 'The Valley Section', that is, the differentiation of occupation (as of plants) with altitude. This, in itself, was an important contribution.

As Branford suggests,[4] if the student concentrates on the first aspect

[1] Hettner, Alfred: 'Die Entwicklung der Geographie in 19 Jahrhundert', *Geog. Ztschr.*, 4, 1898, p. 320.

[2] Galpin, C. J.: 'Social Anatomy of an Agricultural Community', University of Wisconsin Agricultural Experiment Station, *Research Bulletin No. 34*, Madison, 1915.

[3] Le Play, P. G. F.: *Les Ouvriers Européens*, Paris, 1855.

[4] Branford, Victor: 'Sociology', *Ency. Brit.*, 14th Ed., Vol. 20, p. 914.

of the Le Play formula, the spatial factor, the study becomes social geography, if he seeks to co-ordinate all three aspects, it becomes sociology. Actually, this is an oversimplification. In emphasizing spatial differentiation, the social geographer is also interested in the factors of work and folk.

Geddes widened the scope of Le Play's surveys by stressing all the social groups, not merely the family, in their relation to occupation and habitat. He developed the regional survey movement in Britain, with the idea that regions were syntheses of civics, industry and country. He was particularly interested in cities, which embodied for him the whole heritage of race, religion, nation, and civilization. In his descriptions of cities Geddes included site and situation, the influence of climate, economic relations, and the historic heritage, and approached a more functional interpretation.

Having done so he was impressed, not so much with the different patterns produced by topography and climate, or by the geographic setting, as with the patterns due to different stages in economic development. His classification of towns into palæo-technic and neo-technic types was thus a major advance in regional differentiation in relation to socio-economic characteristics.[1] Mumford's rather fuller scheme of eo-technic, palæo-technic, and neo-technic landscapes proceeds from this. His filling out of Geddes's six urban types, from Eopolis to Nekropolis, is more nearly a functional system of cities.[2]

Meantime, Fleure has urged the consideration of different historical traditions in interpreting city forms. In his *Spread of the City Idea*,[3] he refers to the Greek mercantile tradition, the Roman military and administrative traditions, the Franco-Roman synthesis of administration, religion, and pleasure, the Franco-Gothic ecclesiastical tradition, and the German bourgeois tradition as affecting the urban patterns of Western Europe. Here again, emphasis is laid on social institutions and their functions, expressed in city forms, as a means of understanding the personality of regions.

The functional concept embraces all of these ideas, and is, therefore, a composite one. It represents a dynamic synthesis which includes the patterns of streets moulded on topography, the types of institutions and buildings arising from economic activity and conditioned by cultural advance, and the contacts with different historical traditions made

[1] Geddes, P.: *Cities in Evolution*, pp. 60–108.

[2] Mumford, Lewis: *The Culture of Cities*, Harcourt-Brace, New York, 1938, pp. 284–92.

[3] Fleure, H. J.: in a private letter.

in the region. As a result the functional concept is now widely used by geographers in regional analysis, and the description of the earth.

It should be noted that the use of the concept is rather different in sociology and in geography; in sociology it is used to distinguish social structures in an area, in order to show how, or to what extent, the social forms of the community are developed out of the functional processes: in geography it is used to show how, thanks to differences in function, one region differs in form from other regions.

THE CONTRIBUTION OF SOCIAL GEOGRAPHY

(6) *With Reference to the Sociological Concept of the 'Natural Area'*

The divergence of outlook between social geographer and sociologist, leads to an interesting, but confusing, difference in terminology. The great, and proper, emphasis of the sociologist on the community has made him regard social structure or interaction as the basis for delimiting regions. Park[1] went so far as to describe a region in terms of the existence there of a type of social interaction, or a typical synthesis of social interactions. This, in brief, is his famous concept of the 'natural area'. In other words, he defines his natural area largely in terms of social interactions.

Certainly this would be a far cry from the geographer's natural region, were that thought of, as it sometimes is, in terms of a unit of the natural landscape, which influences man. Park all but ignores the landscape in his natural area. It is true that the landscape is a factor in the need for communication and the urge to competition which are found in every community, and which govern social interaction. But it is quite subordinate to the social forces involved.

All sociologists stress this. As Gillette[2] says, the development of culture has produced a 'cultural surplus'—which enables man to manipulate, exploit, and control nature. It is the degree of cultural surplus that is important. In Western civilization this surplus is so great that it effectively cushions man off from the natural environment. That being so, the social forces at work in most communities are more important than those of external nature. Consequently, communities are bounded by no other frontiers than by those where their particular association of daily

---

[1] Park, R. E., in Burgess, E. W., *The Urban Community*, Chicago, 1926, p. 12.
[2] Gillette, J. M., and Reinhardt, J. M.: *Problems of a Changing Social Order*, American Book Co., New York, 1942, pp. 46–7.

interactions comes to an end. The spatial pattern is, in the last analysis, a reflection of the moral order.

If this were so, and if geography was concerned primarily with human distributions, it might have to concern itself rather more with what Kant called moral geography than with geomorphology. But of course the question would then arise, could not the sociologist do a better job of describing these distributions, since they derive from man's reaction to man, and are more directly in his field? If society dominates nature, and social structures determine spatial patterns, then the sociologist is in the best position to discover and describe those patterns, and his natural area might well displace the geographer's region.

THE NATURE OF SOCIAL GEOGRAPHY

(1) *Is it the Distribution of Social Phenomena?*

This brings us to the problem of what is social geography, and what sort of service can it perform either to the geographer or the sociologist. Obviously, this can only be answered, if at all, within the general framework of what is geography, and what kind of service does it render to knowledge and to life.

Perhaps it would be easier to start off by saying what geography is *not*. Geography, I think it will be generally agreed, is not the mere account of distributions on the earth's surface: social geography is not simply the description of where the boundaries begin and end of different social systems. If that were all, the sociologist could readily take over, since it is a legitimate part of his study to concern himself with the distribution of social phenomena. In this sense, every sociologist (or every economist, historian, botanist, geologist, and zoologist for that matter) is a geographer. For distributions may help each of these sciences to come to significant conclusions about the systems or processes they are studying.

Would it be enough for the geographer simply to gather data on distributions? It is clear, if this were his chief function, that he could not go on to state what significance those distributions might have, say in social or in geological processes: because, by implication, he would not be primarily interested in processes. His only useful function, apparently, would be to relate the distributions to each other. Yet again, if his chief purpose were distribution and not relationship, then he could not proceed very far. A geography which is simply the Where of things is not enough: though the Where of things is essential to geography. Consequently, the social geographer must find some goal other than to map the distributions of social systems; and that is, to show how social systems differ in different parts of the world, and how they are related to a great number of other factors in their several regions.

That is to say, by focusing his attention on the region, rather than the community, the social geographer can bring to light the great variety of factors, over and above social ones, with which every community comes into contact in its area, and which give the area its distinctive personality. No sociologist will, or can, do this, even though he is able to, and does, plot the distributions of community activity or structure. His interest is not in the personality of areas, but in the structure and functions of communities. Geography, as a science of distributions, would always be nothing more than the hand-maiden of other sciences, and would have little relevance, in itself, for society. Social geography is not simply the spatial framework of sociology.

THE NATURE OF SOCIAL GEOGRAPHY

(2) *Is it the Social Adaptation of Areas?*

Conversely, it is not simply the social adaptation of areas—although, if it were, it would offer a more fruitful study than that of distributions. Because it would be a genetic study. It would imply a series of forces, behind the distributions, producing regions. It would further imply that these forces rose from a population united on the basis of symbiotic relationships. The study would be a causal, integrated account of the interactions in society which transform areas.

So far, so good. Yet by the very nature of this study, its emphasis would be on social interaction, taking place in an area (and making a certain use of that area), but it would not be on the area. This may seem a quibble, until carried through to its logical conclusions. Social geography, taken in this light, would begin by discussing group adjustments to each other in a specific environment. It would then discover certain social patterns. In analysing those patterns, as Quinn[1] points out, it would come to realize that the interrelations among groups were the really important part in determining the spatial patterns of the community. The analysis of the material environment would play a subordinate role to the struggles between social groups. The significant thing would be the interactions of those groups in competing for limited environmental resources, or controlling limited space, or developing new resources, or new means of organizing them.

[1] Quinn, J. A.: 'Community Research', *Amer. Soc. Rev.*, Apr. 1948, pp. 146-8.

It might be difficult to study these interactions without being more of a sociologist than a geographer. In describing social adaptations of areas one would have to emphasize the social forces of co-operation and competition, of aggregation, concentration, centralization, segregation, invasion, and succession which, presumably, produce the patterns concerned. This would mean a social interpretation of the use of space, such as social ecologists make.

In other words, distance and area would only have meaning in terms of the nature and interaction of social groups. These groups would be seen to compete for limited space so as to 'minimize the cost-distance of transporting men and material'—a fact involving technological and historical factors, together with the structures, functions, and aims of the respective groups.[1] What one would actually be studying, in this sort of geography, would be the spatial structure of society. And that is a very different thing from the social character of regions, as an index in the regional conspectus of the earth.

I think it is the fear that some geographers have that social geography might turn out to be merely the sociology of areas that has kept them away from it. Yet the interest in the subject is growing, and would seem to testify to its value.

THE NATURE OF SOCIAL GEOGRAPHY

(3) Is it the Geographic Basis of Society?

For some scholars, the interest in social geography has lain in the influence of the earth upon man. Geographers made a great advance when they examined this scientifically, and showed a causal connexion between many social forms and the environment. Their enthusiasm at having found an 'explanatory' method of describing the earth, started human geography off in this direction. Thus, in Reclus' L'Homme et la Terre he asserts that the inequalities of man are due to the inequalities in the external environment.[2]

Each period in the life of peoples [he writes] corresponds to a change in their environment. It is the inequalities of planetary traits that create the diversity in human history. Life corresponds to the environment. The earth, climate, habit of work, type of food, race, kinship, and the mode of social grouping—these are the fundamental facts which play their part in influencing the history of every man.

[1] Hatt, P.: 'The Concept of Natural Area', Amer. Soc. Rev., Aug. 1946, pp. 425, 427.

[2] Reclus, E.: L'Homme et la Terre, Paris, 1905, p. 42.

Now there are obvious inequalities related to the environment, but there are also economic, social, spiritual inequalities which have to do, not with the external environment, but with internal factors, such as economic ideology, social customs, and spiritual inspiration. The truth is, the material environment, while necessary to society, is no more basic than ideology or religion. Few geographers would claim it is, unless they happened to be thorough-going materialistic determinists. Nevertheless many geographers work *as if it were*. For them, this presumed relationship between the earth and man is the chief reason for the existence of geography. As social geographers, their chief study would be 'the geographic basis of society'. However, I think it is well to remember that there is another science, that of social ecology, which has made it a specific field of study to survey man's relations with his environment. It, too, concerns itself with the interactions of social forces and their reaction with their environment.

What is the division between the two subjects? Social ecologists are interested in what geography has to contribute to the understanding of society, but they cannot let geography explain society. In Harrison's reply[1] to Fitzgerald's correspondence on the question of Social Geography, he states that sociologists have become 'increasingly aware of the great importance of purely geographic factors . . . in shaping not only the social structure of the community, but also the life, outlook and interest of all its component individuals'. Nevertheless, he probably would not equate social geography with social ecology.[2] Then what is the difference?

It is possibly as much in the point of view as anything. The geographer is interested in the influence of environment on man, in order to understand certain differences from place to place, and so to build up his picture of the earth. But that is a different viewpoint from the sociologist's. Therefore, it seems to me, the geographer is really doing less than might be expected if he limits himself primarily to the factors of adaptation. These factors lie chiefly in the field of social ecology, as a division of sociology, because as Hollingshead remarks, sociology, is primarily interested in processes,[3] not in patterns. Adaptation to environment, while it produces patterns, is fundamentally a process. The geographer is

[1] Harrison, Tom: 'Correspondence, Geography and Its Components', *Geog. Jour.*, July–Sept. 1946, p. 126.

[2] Cf. Halecke's original definition of ecology in Haeckel, Ernst: *The History of Creation*, New York, 1876, Vol. 2, p. 354.

[3] Hollingshead, A. B.: 'Community Research', *Amer. Soc. Rev.*, Apr. 1948, p. 139.

interested in the patterns that come out of it, because, by those patterns, he is able to build up his picture of the world, and to compare and contrast differences from place to place. The way in which the patterns emerge should be subordinate to those patterns themselves, and to their relationship to other patterns within the region.

This is not to say that geography should not be an explanatory science. It should—for its own purposes. But its real aim is not the explanation of individual processes, so much as the integration of patterns, causally related to the earth. This, I take it, is why geography departments generally omit courses in geological processes, but nevertheless offer courses in land forms; or why many of them omit courses in dynamic meteorology, but none could do without climatology. Social geography is to social ecology what climatology is to meteorology: it is a chorological study in contrast to a systematic one. Social geography is not a systematic treatment of society in relation to its environment, but a genetic description of social differences as they are related to other factors and to differences in areas of the earth's surface.

I do not mean to imply that social geography is not interested in processes, but merely, that it cannot afford to make them its chief object of study. Actually, it should understand the social processes, just as much as the climatologist ought to know his meteorology. Perhaps more— because social geography must, by nature of its special field of interest, be a dynamic study. The spatial patterns which society forms are changed almost as soon as they arise. Perhaps only in primitive economies can socio-geographic patterns remain substantially unchanged over a long period of time. In civilized societies, in the present era, change is typical. Consequently, no patterns are static ones: and social geography cannot be a static subject.

Crowe has rightly said that, 'Only by a dynamical study of man's geographical reactions shall we approach the truth.'[1] Such a study emphasizes the differences that interrupt, replace, and create anew the scheme of existing things. It helps, better than any static type of geography can, to interpret areal differences, and to recognize the character of regions. Crowe felt that economic geography could perhaps present this dynamical view better than any other. Yet surely the factors which go to make up social geography—the mobility of population: emigration and immigration: ethnic invasion, conflict and succession; the decline or expansion of settlements; the rise, spread, decay, or rejuvenation of institutions; and the interplay of social groups—offer a highly successful method, if adequately handled, of representing the changing patterns of

[1] Crowe, P. R.: op. cit., p. 18.

the earth, or the changing organization of regions? If they do, and in so far as they do, they help geography to recognize the dynamic content of areas, and so they emphasize the chorological aspects of the subject.

THE NATURE OF SOCIAL GEOGRAPHY

(4) *Is it Regional Differentiation in terms of Social Characteristics?*

Let us refer to a suggested outline of what social geography is. In their article on Social Geography, Gilbert and Steel[1] agree that social geography has four branches. These are—the distribution of population, the distribution and form of rural settlement, the geographical study of towns and cities, and the distribution of social groups and their way of life in different environments. One might also refer to Huntington's concept, outlined in the text he wrote with Carlson. On the face of it, Gilbert's view does not differ much from Huntington's. Yet the stress is on the geographical expression of social differences, rather than on a geography of society. Huntington and Carlson consider geography to be a study (1) of 'the various environmental factors, considered from the point of view of their geographic influences; and (2) of human beings and their activities, considered in the light of their adaptation to the environmental factors and of the way in which they modify or make use of these elements in their environment'.[2] They regard social geography as the systematic treatment of man's adaptation to or of the environment. The one view is concerned with patterns; the other with processes.

May not the two views be fused? They are both representative of contemporary geography. Personally, it seems logical, as it is empirical, to start with the patterns seen in the landscape. Social geography, by its title, will obviously confine itself to the social patterns; that is, to those made by people coming together in groups; to the patterns of population, settlement, social institutions, and organizations.

Not all of these are immediately self-evident. They are not all expressed as material objects in the cultural landscape. But those which are; houses, barns, factories, villages, cities, communications, are first noted. Then perhaps the statistical data on population, race, language, and religion can be gathered, and fitted into the picture. Lastly, the study of social groups and their activities is made, and incorporated with the rest.

[1] Gilbert, E. W., and Steel, R. W.: 'Social Geography and its place in Colonial Studies', *Geog. Jour.*, Sept.–Oct. 1945, p. 118.

[2] Huntington, C. C., and Carlson, F. A.: *The Geographic Basis of Society*, Prentice Hall, New York, 1938, p. 6.

The several patterns studied by social geography, namely, settlement, population, and social organizations—have certain relationships with each other. A thorough study of patterns, and their mutual relationship, will show the basic factors in their development. These may be deduced, to a certain extent, from the forms observed. However, as Dickinson notes,[1] 'function and form are not necessarily in harmony'. Consequently, the functions underlying the patterns, will require study, and will show in what way the several patterns are related to each other, as they exist in the region under discussion. To understand more fully how the social groups function, and how they are related, and why they take the form they do, it will be necessary as Huntington maintained, to consider their adaptation to the environment, or their use of it. Finally, when this is done, comparisons should be made with other regions, so that the areal differentiation of the earth, in relation to social characteristics, may be fully interpreted. This would appear to be the chief contribution of social geography.

The really significant things in this study are not the phenomena in themselves, nor their interaction with each other, nor their reaction to the environment, but *the way in which they provide distinctive character to the regions which they fill*, and enable us, therefore, to build up our picture of the earth. As Taylor claims, geography is the correlative science; its function is to perceive those correlations between things which give areal differentiation to the surface of the earth. Geography attempts to analyse and synthesize, as Hartshorne[2] reminds us, 'not processes of phenomena, but the associations of phenomena as related in (areal) sections of reality'.

THE NATURE OF SOCIAL GEOGRAPHY

A Suggested Definition

We may define social geography, therefore, as the identification of different regions of the earth's surface according to associations of social phenomena related to the total environment.

This would entail distributions, social structures, functions, and processes, and their adaptation to and of the environment, but its chief emphasis would be on the regional differentiation of social characteristics. Thought of in this way social geography would continue to make a major contribution to geography as a whole. At the same time it would be

[1] Dickinson, R. E.: 'Landscape and Society', *Scot. Geog. Mag.*, 55, p. 14.
[2] Hartshorne, R.: *The Nature of Geography*, p. 460.

distinct from social ecology, and yet could contribute to that study as well, and so to sociology. But to do so it would have to emphasize spatial patterns in terms of regional differentiation.

Social Geography in Relation to Human Geography

There has been some discussion of the place of social geography in geography as a whole. It does not seem to me to be a happy idea to equate social geography with human geography, as Fitzgerald did.[1] 'I feel certain', he writes, 'that I should recommend replacing "Human Geography" by "Social Geography" as not only philologically sound but also the most suitable omnibus term for all our humanistic studies.' Apparently, he would have Social Geography include racial, cultural, political, economic, and historical geography.

It seems to me there are several valid objections to this. In the first place, I do not think it is feasible to retain all these separate facets of geography within one discipline. It would no doubt be convenient to have a Physical Geography, on the one hand, and a Human Geography, on the other. But specialization has long proceeded beyond that to establish political, economic, and historical geography—at the very least—as separate branches. And very healthy branches they are. There is less development in racial, cultural, or what I would call social, i.e. sociological, geography—but a good case could be made out for their separate contributions.

The matter is surely one of curriculum organization. A general introductory Human Geography might be taught in the first year of college, in which attention would be divided about equally between racial, cultural, historical, economic, political, and social geography. Thereafter, in subsequent years, specialization in some or all of these fields might be taken up, according to opportunity.

If that were the case, social geography would be a branch of human geography. I do not think the two are one and the same, or that they are equal. The word 'human' has a different and a wider connotation than 'social'. Surely 'human' is practically synonymous with mankind, and as such, should include 'social' along with 'economic', 'political', &c.

Moreover, the term 'human' geography has now become a traditional one—although there may still be a good deal of discussion about its exact meaning and content. Generations of geographers have now been brought up to use and revere the term. There would be considerable confusion

[1] Fitzgerald, W.: 'Correspondence, Geography and Its Components', *Geog. Jour.,* May–June 1946, pp. 272–3.

in replacing it with 'social' geography—especially now that that name has been associated, to some extent at any rate, with the sociological aspects of geography.

Finally, it should be pointed out that most social geographers work in closest association with social ecologists, and thus with sociologists. As a result, social geography has come to have a specific meaning outside of geography altogether, which could by no means be equated with human geography. (Similarly the worker in economic geography, who has close associations with economists, has created a specific meaning for his discipline outside of geography, which would be lost if it became simply part of a course in human (or social) geography.)

There seems to me, then, adequate reason for equating social geography with the sociological aspects of geography. It would thus embrace population (density, mobility, age and sex composition, and ethnic structure), settlement (rural and urban), social groups (home, work, play, worship groups), and social institutions and their function.

Social Geography and Geography as a Whole

Of course, it is not possible to go far in describing the relations of these phenomena to each other, or to the areas where they are studied, without having to bring in economic, historical, political, as well as physical aspects of geography. And in this respect, the social geographer would do well to remember that he is first and foremost a geographer, and that, while he may be emphasizing the sociological aspects of the subject, he can only do so after having considered the whole geography of the area concerned. It is worth while to recall that

geography is not so much a study or branch of study as an attitude to, a way of thinking about, certain phenomena in their relation to mankind or mankind in relation to these phenomena. The emphasis is placed sometimes on one aspect and sometimes on another, but the well-trained geographer does not neglect any aspect.[1]

PART II. THE SOCIAL GEOGRAPHY OF A CITY

The Environment of Hamilton

The city of Hamilton, with 175,000 people, is the second largest in Ontario. It lies at the head of Lake Ontario, on main connexions between the American and Canadian manufacturing belts. With an unusually high proportion of its wage earners engaged in industry, it is the most

[1] Handyside, W. L.: 'Correspondence', *Geog. Jour.*, Oct. 1947, p. 288.

highly industrialized city in Canada. It is the third in the Dominion in net value of production. Loyalist by origin, it is still predominantly British, but the foreign-born, of non-British stock, are increasing, and form a high percentage compared with most other cities. Rapid industrial expansion, and very unequal social conditions, have together left their mark on its character.

The local site consists of a large bay, between two bay-bars which enclose one of the finest natural harbours on the Lakes. The Niagara Escarpment approaches from north and south, and shelters the city from the intense cold suffered in more open locations. The great Dundas re-entrant breaches the scarp, to give access to continental land routes. In its wider situation, Hamilton is on or near two of the chief routes of immigration into the country, the Hudson-Mohawk route from New York,

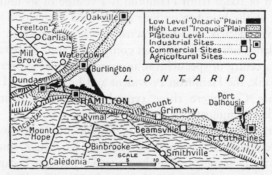

FIG. 40.—The district surrounding Hamilton, Ontario

and the St. Lawrence–Great Lakes route from Montreal. It lies between South-west and Central Ontario, and is the regional centre of the Niagara Peninsula and Grand River. (See Fig. 40.)

At the western entrance to the city stands the Battery of Burlington Heights, commanding the harbour from the upper bay-bar. As a relict of pioneer times, it recalls that Hamilton was then much less important than Niagara-on-the-Lake, now a small summer resort frequented by Hamiltonians. There being no roads or canals then, connexions between the Lakes were by river, and the Niagara River was the chief axis of the Niagara Peninsula. Niagara-on-the-Lake guarded the approaches to the frontier river sites from the Mohawk valley. Thus the early historical situation, and stage of technical development, by-passed what now appears, in Hamilton, to be the obvious centre of the Peninsula region, and made the Niagara Frontier important.

This was also the case during the period of domestic industry, which depended chiefly on water-power. Old mills in the vicinity of Hamilton are reminders that industry was scattered at the several waterfalls in the environs. Development was held back because mill-streams often ran dry in the summer droughts which afflicted the region. At St. Catharines, however, was a vastly superior, and more dependable, source of power deflected from the Welland Canal. Mills concentrated there in great numbers. Moreover, the canal became the chief route of the region, displacing the Niagara River, and also the pioneer roads radiating from Hamilton. Meantime the Niagara frontier had lost its critical political importance. Consequently, St. Catharines became the focus of the Peninsula in the mid-nineteenth century. It must have appeared the 'natural' centre of the region then, much as Hamilton does now.

Nevertheless, roads improved, and became more important. The radial pattern of roads from Hamilton is a vestige of its mid-nineteenth century role as the base for settling South-west Ontario. The character of the town, reflected in quays, warehouses, construction and bridge companies, land mortgage and loan companies, and wholesale agencies, was that of a centre of speculation, immigration, and general provision. The Gore Bank, the Hamilton Provident and Loan Co., and the Canada Life Insurance Co., were three typical influential institutions which served a wide community.

However, with the completion of settlement, South-west Ontario developed regional nuclei, such as London, Kitchener, and Windsor, which took away some of Hamilton's trade. London became the land mortgaging centre, and its main company, the Huron and Erie, swallowed up the Hamilton Provident. (The new H. & E. sign swings above the old P. & L. name embossed on the Hamilton office.) Meanwhile, the rise and spread of railways, 1853-85, led to growing competition from Montreal and Toronto. Immigrants no longer made their way up the St. Lawrence to the Head-of-the-Lake en route to 'Western Canada'—i.e. South-west Ontario and the Upper Lakes. The new West was opening up beyond Ontario, and tapped the St. Lawrence immigration route more directly from Montreal and Toronto. These cities became the chief banking, insurance, and outfitting centres: the Canadian Bank of Commerce (Montreal) absorbed the Gore Bank; the Canada Life moved its head office to Toronto. Many business families moved away, and Hamilton lost its character as a first-ranking commercial and wholesale community.

Yet railways tied Hamilton to the American Manufacturing Belt. A new international network was superimposed on the earlier inter-provincial (water) and regional (road) pattern. A new realization of Hamilton's position, close to American raw materials and other supplies, and midway in the field of Canadian distribution, led to the concentration of large-scale industry. For this, the city offered more space, a better harbour, and a more ramified road and railway system than any of its local rivals, and so, once the technological stage was set in its favour, surpassed them. In doing so it challenged St. Catharines and Brantford as the regional foci of the Niagara Peninsula and the Lower Grand Valley, respectively, and united these districts, together with the Head-of-the-Lake, in a new organization of industrial, trade, transportation, recreational, and cultural contacts. This area of organization bids fair to be called the Hamilton Region.

Consequently, although these other centres grew, they did not grow nearly as rapidly as Hamilton. The rapid expansion in size and in numbers gave Hamilton the industrial diversity and sort of labour force which developed an industrial momentum that has continued to attract more factories to it than to the Peninsula or Valley towns. In turn, this has produced a social momentum that attracts social, recreational, and cultural institutions: the city is today the centre for business, labour, and professional conferences, for sports rallies, for service gatherings and military displays, for regional industrial fairs, for musical eisteddfods, drama festivals, and the like. Significant, too, is the fact that the Bishop of Niagara (whose See originally centred in Niagara-on-the-Lake) now lives in Hamilton; and that, when the Niagara Peninsula agitated for a university, Hamilton became its university town. It is actually these social forces, more than industry, per se, that are welding the three once-separable districts of the Niagara Peninsula, Lower Grand Valley, and the Head-of-the-Lake, into a single region. Whatever their 'natural' distinctness (and they are really quite unlike each other physically), they have been given a social unity, through the attraction of Hamilton as an agent of regional organization. (Tests of this have been made on the basis of the proportion of business men coming to Hamilton for conferences, the number of church-members meeting in the city for conventions, the number of students from the region attending McMaster University, the circulation of Hamilton newspapers, and the location in Hamilton of regional head offices of government and business agencies covering the three districts concerned.)

The impact of expansion and regional concentration on the city has been tremendous. It can be measured by the many material signs of disorganization and reorganization of areas. Yet, since outward forms change more slowly than functions, it must also be measured by immaterial, but none the less factual, changes in the social reaction and interaction of groups. The patterns of changing areal structures and of changing

32

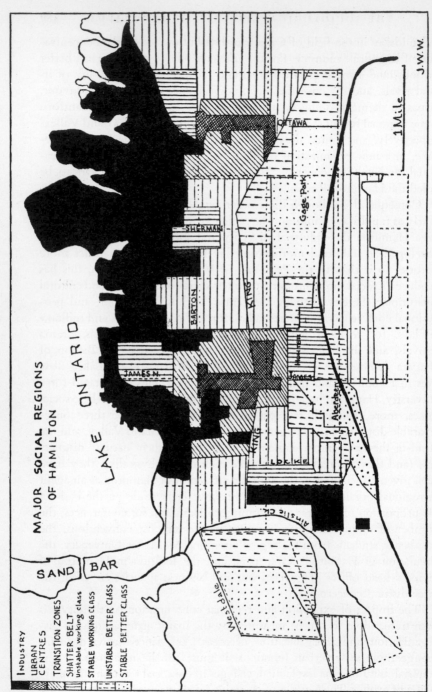

MAJOR SOCIAL REGIONS
OF HAMILTON

LAKE ONTARIO

SAND BAR

INDUSTRY
URBAN CENTRES
TRANSITION ZONES
SHATTER BELT
unstable working class
STABLE WORKING CLASS
UNSTABLE BETTER CLASS
STABLE BETTER CLASS

Westdale

Ainslie Ck.

King
Locke
James S.
Aberdeen
Hunter St.
King
Barton
James N.
Sherman
Ottawa
Gage Park

1 Mile

J.W.W.

Fig. 41.—The major Social Regions in Hamilton, Ontario

group interactions form the social geography of the city, and distinguish Hamilton from the other cities which it has displaced in the region, and from other regional centres. (See Fig. 41.)

The Industrial Factor

The major reliance of Hamilton on industry makes it clearly different from the neighbouring regional centres of London (commercial and transportation) and Toronto (financial-industrial and commercial-professional). Hamilton has a very high proportion of labourers, foremen, and industrial managers; but a significantly small class of financiers, business, administrative and professional men. This affects the whole social tenor of its life, which is distinctly different from that in either London or Toronto. It is hard to measure such a difference, yet it is one of the important things setting the Hamilton region off from the others.

For one thing, the lack of a larger business and professional class has widened the social distance between the working and managerial groups. In Toronto there is a gradation of levels of accommodation not found in Hamilton. In the latter city, the discordancy is actually greater even than it seems. Looking at the pattern of houses, as judged by size and outward appearance, there might seem to be a gradation, at least in the south-central part, between the dwellers in the fourth class districts and those in the first. But judging by social participation and interaction, the dichotomy is considerable (bearing in mind the relative size of the city).

The structure that the city shows is typical of any expanding industrial centre. It forms a balance between social ecology and topography. Growing population and the aggregation of lesser districts of settlement have produced an increasing concentration on Hamilton, as indicated by the density of routes there, by the increasing cluster of factories, and by the widening built-up area. This movement inwards is chiefly industrial— a concentration of factories at the site of greatest cost advantage. It has rapidly filled up available space along the harbour front, up western and eastern creeks (where land is cheap), and along the railway entrances. Large factories have attracted rings of satellites, that handle sub-contracts. Light industry has advanced in by road, and crowds toward the road-meetings of the city.

This inward concentration has increased the competition for space. Land values have gone up rapidly, particularly at the urban centre. The ability to pay the cost of contacting the main railway and road sites has controlled the distribution of factories, offices, and stores. They have segregated out on a basis of cost-distance from the road centre or railway terminal. The ability to pay is unequal, and therefore segregation is unequal. Specialization occurs to exploit these inequalities. (See Fig. 42.)

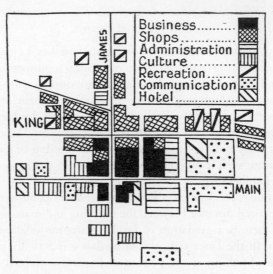

FIG. 42.—The urban centre in Hamilton

City Institutions

For example, while commercial and administrative institutions, as a whole, have segregated out at the meeting of four main roads, to form a business section, the detailed pattern is very uneven. Within this general business area there is a junction of the main municipal streetcar lines. Here multiple stores and fashion shops are found. Yet only a hundred yards south is a junction of regional bus lines. Here banks, land mortgage and trust companies, brokerages, and insurance agencies occur. These function for a wider area, and so choose the junction with regional rather than local significance. The hotels lie half-way between the railway terminals, which border the business section, but a little away from the chief offices and stores. They do not get the equivalent profit out of cubic building space and so avoid the costliest sites, and yet must be near to the main junctions and terminals. Town hall, post office, registry house, and county court are also at the fringes of the business sector. They must be central for administrative purposes, and yet cannot compete for the primary centres of traffic.

An interesting down-town distribution is that of recreational and cultural centres. All the major cinemas are in the north or east parts of the business sector; the library, art gallery, conservatories, metropolitan churches, and Y's are in the south and south-west. This can best explain itself by the fact that the bulk of the working-class population—indeed the bulk of the population—lives to north and east of the city centre, while most of the upper classes live to south or south-west.

Specialization, then, is not simply in terms of cost-distance, though that factor is dominant; but it also adjusts itself to the function which particular institutions have for special interests or groups. The distribution of commercialized recreation centres and of voluntarily organized recreation centres points this out, and bears an interesting relationship to the distribution of kinds of social participation. A separate survey of recreation has shown that the northern and north-eastern Wards of the city are exceptionally low in the numbers of children belonging to organized clubs. In some neighbourhoods as many as four-fifths of the children did not belong to any organizations. They got their recreation from the cinema mainly, or from gangs, or unorganized play. The mentality of such a population obviously is better exploited by the stadium, cinemas, and beverage rooms than by public library, conservatory, or Y's. Conversely, these last-named institutions exploit, and therefore build next to, neighbourhoods trained in organized associational recreation. The geography of recreational institutions then is very largely the social geography of the groups they serve.

Similarly the social service agencies segregate out to exploit special groups: the public relief office is towards the north—where unemployment is most prevalent; the Salvation Army in the north-west, near the worst slums; the children's aid society at the north centre, nearest to the proliferative working population whose children they most tend; and the family service bureau and local council of social agencies—with the most generalized services to offer—are more or less central to the whole city.

A closer examination, however, shows that many institutions owe their position to past conditions. The history of evolution must be taken into account. Their present distribution would not seem to bear out the sort of relationship to the groups using them as is suggested. For instance, next to the Conservatory of Music are stately grey-stone houses, in an Adam style, which once betokened a genteel neighbourhood that no doubt patronized the Duet Club, the Faculty Club, and so forth. Now most of those are offices, or rooming houses. The local residents no longer form the chief patrons of the Conservatory: but these are drawn from the wealthy suburbs to which gentility has retired. Similarly, just south of the

Library, rise two of Hamilton's finest grey-stone residences, surrounded by iron railings or stone walls. They are relics of a stately area whose cultured families once approved of, and supported, the neighbouring Library. But on the west side of the Library are two rows of the worst slums in Hamilton, where old homes first deteriorated into rooming houses, and were finally replaced by squalid brick tenements, whose present inhabitants rarely enter the Library, far from forming its chief patrons. The Library gets most of its readers today from the stable working-class areas and the upper-class suburbs, at some remove from itself.

Finally, let us look at the churches. Three outstanding churches at the centre of the city were founded by Scotch and English free-church families then living within half a mile of them. They were community churches. But as commercial and industrial interests pressed upon their precincts, the surrounding homes were overshadowed and at length driven out. The old families fled to the south, up the steep slopes of the Mountain, where railway and through-road were unknown, or to the vicinity of parks in the east and west, in sheltered interstices of the industrial web. Nevertheless, their strong loyalty to the churches built by their fathers kept them in continued association with them. Consequently, although the churches are in walking distance of many tenement dwellers in the downtown area, they do not receive their support, or cater to their interests, but still endure by serving the old families, long since fled from the neighbourhood. (One of them tries to make the best of two worlds by having a 'mission' for the local residents, while preserving the main church for its suburban followers.)

Of course the institutions described can carry on, in spite of being divorced from their earlier immediate clientele, because Hamilton is still small enough to allow the wealthier, cultured families, who have flown to the suburbs, to ride downtown by automobile in a matter of fifteen minutes. Measured in time-distance this is no further away than the few blocks they formerly walked from. One can understand why, then, the central institutions still receive considerable suburban support.

Social Contrasts

That they do not receive similar support from the populations now encroaching on their neighbourhood, and who are much nearer to them physically than the nearest suburbanites, is due to the fact that in the main they do not cater to the interests of the new populations. On the contrary, they are cut off from them by social distance, and are therefore further away from them socially than the remotest suburbanites. This is, in turn, due to the nature of the incoming population, and the circumstances under which they live. They are predominantly foreign born, poor, and with a limited education. They live in houses vacated by the old families and now turned into rooming houses; also in tenements which have replaced the gracious mansions of the past; and not a few are found in attics or cellars above or below business premises. They crowd into the central region because they must be near places of work, because they somehow bear living next to beverage rooms, terminals, offices, workshops, and stores, and because they are exploited by landlords who rent them cheap accommodation through crowding them into the available space. It is not surprising to find that they have little to do with the cultural institutions which they have surrounded. This fact explains why in closest juxtaposition to the region of the city with the highest number of social institutions, is the region in the city with the lowest social participation. (See Fig. 43.)

These striking social contrasts produce considerable disorganization. They result from the inward pressure of industry coming into conflict with the outward pressure of business. As industry gathers at the circumference, population grows and demands more services from business, which expands outward from the centre. It was actually the outward pressure of business rather than the impact of industry that led to the flight of the old families from what were once pleasant enough districts, near the urban nucleus, out to the present suburbs. The flight of these families has created zones of tension—of the uprooting or abandonment of established organizations, institutions, and associationships—which become regions of instability. Here an old-standing church is at length sold out, to become a furniture storage depot; an old masonic hall becomes a warehouse; a once-favoured ladies' college is replaced by shops; the Mechanics' Institute gives way to a Government block; and there is talk of uprooting the present Art Gallery to set it up at another site.

Meantime, the inward pressure of industry, invading more and more of what were working-class residential areas, has led to *zones of compression*. New industries buy up spare lots and cheap homes, invading residential streets. Yet they attract more people, who crowd into the remaining homes; young couples live with their in-laws; larger houses are subdivided into triplexes, smaller ones are converted into duplexes; and many change from family dwellings to rooming houses. Shops and places of amusement also want to crowd into the same areas, to take advantage of the dense population.

In Hamilton, the inward pressures of industry from the bay, and the outward pressures of business from the city centre have almost met. Their close approach is due largely to the topography, which makes southern expansion impracticable, because of the 'Mountain'. Consequently as industry moves south from the bay front, and business north from Main St., there is less and less room. This has had its physical effect in making industries plan a more efficient use of the space they possess, in making offices grow upward in skyscrapers, instead of outward along city blocks, and in making residences subdivide themselves into duplexes, or become converted to flats. The result is a region of stress and of change: a region of invasion, eviction, congestion, reorganization. The term

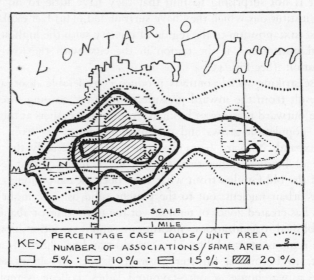

FIG. 43.—Social versus Geographical distance in Hamilton

usually applied, a region in transition, does not seem strong enough. I would prefer to see the term 'shatter belt' used of such a zone, whose stability has become shattered by the invading pressures, and in which the patterns of business, industrial, and residential uses of land are broken into many fragments, mixed with each other.

While the physical disorganization of the shatter belt is fairly evident to the trained geographer, the total change cannot be appreciated unless he plots the social disorganization present. I have found that the simplest method is to take the case loads of the Dept. of Relief, of the Unemployment Bureau, of the Juvenile Court, the Family Court, of the Children's Aid Society, and the Family Service Bureau and plot the incidence of cases. The result in Hamilton is to show a remarkable concentration of unemployment, neglect, desertion, and delinquency in the city's shatter zones. Other surveys, such as of overcrowding, residential mobility, recreation, &c. were more difficult to make, but show similar results.

Thus the character of Hamilton as a whole, and the character of its distinctive regions, take their nature in part from topographical influences of site and situation; in part from the ecological forces of concentration, segregation, specialization, expansion, and invasion at work in the area; and in part from the reactions of social groups to each other, as these forces bring them into competition for the sites or situation they want.

The social geographer makes his contribution in discovering how one major region differs from another, if at all, in social orientation and character; and how the region itself is made up of the interaction—in competition and yet in interdependence—of the many neighbourhoods whose social characteristics give them individuality.

In doing so his study will be genetic, explanatory, and dynamic, because his awareness of present pressures and tensions will lead him to take account of origins; it will lead him to explain the growth and spread of groups and institutions; and it will help him to perceive the constant flux of interaction between these groups as giving rise to dynamic changes in the organization of the region. I believe that by emphasizing pressures and tensions behind the ever-changing patterns, and tracing their connexion to changing functions of groups, and to their changing social ideals, the social geographer can help to describe the geography of places more fully than could be done on the basis of physical geography, or the geography of man-and-his-works.

In the case of Hamilton, its obvious dominance of the Head-of-the-Lake, of the Lower Grand Valley and of the Niagara Peninsula, which now appears so 'natural', is really due to the technological, economic, social, and political changes of the last forty years. Before that, there was no 'natural' unity in this area, but its different parts showed their differences through separate regional centres, only lately brought into Hamilton's orbit.

Stages in Development

Indeed, the area concerned has been a very different thing to different ages. In the frontier period, the Niagara Peninsula was the most important part, and the Lower Grand was wholly an Indian Reserve. Then the area was dominated, if by any one centre, by Niagara-on-the-Lake. But a change in the political, economic, and technological circumstances shifted the focus to St. Catharines; and so on. Thus a region may interpret its physical geography quite differently as its social geography changes. *Its character as a region depends not on the influence of natural material forces in the environment, but on social forces which re-adapt and reorganize the area, and give it a unique character.*

Much of this process of regional differentiation which is going on in the area, making it distinctive from other areas, can be measured by relics of historical change; by the aspect of the cultural landscape; and by functional subdivisions. These are all individual features of the total regional physiognomy. I have mentioned many relict features—the Battery, old mills, the mid-nineteenth-century orientation of roads, the institutions that once gave the region its commercial character (now bought out by stronger commercial rivals), and the central institutions evicted from the zones of tension or altered in form and function. The emphasis on relict features underlines the historical geography of the region, and is both a dynamic and genetic study of the present situation.

The cultural landscape includes these relics, and also the many other cultural features which give the region, and its central city, their typical appearance. An analysis of the cultural landscape shows the gradual agglomeration of routes, buildings, people, and goods at points in the region, such as Brantford, St. Catharines, and Hamilton, which are all interconnected. It shows the special concentration of these at Hamilton. Within Hamilton it reveals patterns of segregation into predominantly factory districts, business sectors, and different classes of residential areas. Yet it fails to give a truly dynamic or explanatory view of the region and its centre. It has nothing to say of the amount of traffic flowing into or out of Hamilton, the numbers of peoples moving in or out for the purpose of conferences, conventions, sports rallies, eisteddfods, and so forth, or the services radiating out from Hamilton in its radio coverage, newspaper circulation, advertisement and shopping services.

It cannot in itself explain the absences of other institutions and services which are concentrated instead at Toronto and Buffalo, and which draw people, for certain specialized interests, outside the Hamilton region. It fails to show that for the vast majority of people, within the Hamilton region, *these interests are simply omitted from their lives.* Nor can it, within the narrower confines of Hamilton, explain the specialized distribution of certain institutions, except by inference.

Obviously a study of functions will assist. How the Hamilton region mainly functions—as Canada's most purely industrial area, helps to explain a lot. How the separate institutions within Hamilton function, helps to explain their peculiar distribution. Examples are the recreational and cultural institutions. Space does not permit the explanation of the distribution of industrial concerns by the way they function, or by the nature of the work-force they exploit, or all the interests they serve.

Yet even functional areas do not seem to be enough to describe fully the geography of a region. This is because they do not take account of all the social interactions set up between functional areas, or even within them. Moreover, what areas or institutions function *for*, is the really important thing, since it decides, in itself, the nature and extent of the functional area. The discovery of the basic social forces at play between groups in an area, or between groups of different areas, is therefore of fundamental importance. This 'interactional geography', as it might be termed, is perhaps the chief contribution of the social geographer, and helps to explain how and why areas are different from each other.

The invasion of business upon the good residential areas immediately around the urban nucleus was offensive to the original residents, because it introduced noise, hurry and ugliness into their surroundings and also raised unduly the taxes on their property. As the invasion got under way it was joined by an ethnic attack, as poor, illiterate, foreign-speaking, and coloured people moved into old homes vacated by the old families and turned into rooming houses. The social effect of 'racial' conflict was to produce the rout of the remaining old English and Scottish families. No one can explain the changes in organization, and in ultimate appearance, of neighbourhoods without taking into account class and racial prejudices as geographical factors. The rout has been particularly noticeable from areas attacked by Italians, Jews, Chinese, and Negroes; but is far less noticeable from areas infiltrated by Germans or Scandinavians. These differences in degree of prejudice are therefore geographically important.

Yet the routed families have held to their down-town institutions, for the most part. Why have the *houses* fallen or changed out of all proportion to *institutions*—to old clubs, lodges, churches, and cultural associations? Partly because, as we have seen, the new-comers are of a class for whom these institutions have no relevant function. Partly because of social distance, which keeps these institutions *socially remote* from those who are *geographically near*, but *socially near* to those who have now become *geographically remote*. Social distance therefore qualifies geographical distance. On the flat plain of down-town Hamilton there is no geographical barrier at all to prevent the people who might appear to need these institutions most from taking advantage of them. But on the plain of social contact, there is a veritable Himalaya for them to cross. Unless the geographer takes account of these *social Himalayas* he cannot give an adequate, far less a full picture of the geography of a region; but when he tries to consider them then certain patterns become obvious, that would otherwise be obscure, while the connexions between patterns, and the explanations of their distributions, will be more evident.

Thus, when the region is seen in the light of its social characteristics, as well as of its other aspects, it becomes a more complete reality. To see it in this light is to be able to compare and contrast it with other regions, in a more significant way, and enables the geographer to get a truer picture of the earth as a whole.

SELECTED BIBLIOGRAPHY

(Arranged in order of publication)

Ritter, Carl: *Die Erdkunde*, &c., 19 vols., Berlin, 1822–59.

Ratzel, Friedrich: *Anthropogeographie*, Stuttgart, 1882–1912.

Demolins, E.: *Comment la route crée le type social*, Paris, 1901.

Herbertson, A. J.: 'The Major Natural Regions', *Geog. Jour.*, 25, 1905.

Hettner, Alfred: 'Die Geographie des Menschen', *Geog. Ztschr.*, 13, 1907.

Chisholm, G. G.: 'The Meaning and Scope of Geography', *Scot. Geog. Mag.*, 24, 1908.

Semple, Ellen C.: *Influences of Geographical Environment*, New York, 1911.

Vallaux, Camille: *Géographie Sociale, Le Sol et L'État*, Paris, 1911.

Vidal de la Blache: 'Les caractères distinctifs de la géographie', *Ann. de Géog.*, 22, 1913.

Gradmann, R.: 'Geographie und Landeskunde', *Geog. Ztschr.*, 21, 1915.

Fleure, H. J.: 'Human Regions', *Scot. Geog. Mag.*, 35, 1919.

Barrows, H. H.: 'Geography as Human Ecology', *Ann. Assoc. Amer. Geog.*, 13, 1923.

Gallois, L.: 'Géographie Humaine', *Ann. de Géog.*, 1922–23.

Passarge, S.: *Vergleichende Landschaftskunde*, Berlin, 1924.

Aurousseau, M.: 'Recent Contributions to Urban Geography', *Geog. Rev.*, 14, 1924.

Forde, C. D.: 'Values in Human Geography', *Geog. Teacher*, 13, 1925.

Park, R. E., Burgess, E. W., and McKenzie, R. D.: *The City*, Chicago, 1925.

McKenzie, R. D.: 'The Scope of Human Ecology', *Amer. Jour. Soc.*, 22, 1926.

Hettner, A.: *Die Geographie, ihre Geschichte, ihr Wesen und ihre Methoden*, Breslau, 1927.

Roxby, P. M.: 'The Scope and Aim of Human Geography', *Scot. Geog. Mag.*, 46, 1930.

Demangeon, A.: 'Le Paysage, miroir de la civilization', *Ann. de Géog.*, 1930–31.

Fleure, H. J.: 'The Geographical Study of Society and World Problems', *Scot. Geog. Mag.*, 1932.

Whitbeck, R. H., and Thomas, O. J.: *The Geographic Factor; Its Role in Life and Civilization*, New York, 1932.

Whittlesey, D., 'Environment and the Student of Human Geography', *Sci. Monthly*, 35, 1932.

Gist, N. P., and Halbert, L. A.: *Urban Sociology*, Crowell, New York, 1933.

Passarge, S.: 'Das Problem der Kulturgeographischen Raume', *Petermann's Mitt.*, 79, 1933.

Jones, Wellington D.: 'Procedures in Investigating Human Occupance of a Region', *Ann. Assoc. Amer. Geog.*, 24, 1934.

McKenzie, R. D.: 'The Field and Problems of Demography, Human Geography, and Human Ecology', in L. L. Bernard (ed.), *The Fields and Methods of Sociology*, New York, 1934.

Quinn, J. A.: 'Ecological versus Social Interaction', *Soc. & Soc. Research*, 18, 1934.

Taylor, G.: 'Geography the Correlative Science', *Can. Jour. Econ. and Pol. Sci.*, 1, 1935.

Park, R. E.: 'Human Ecology', *Amer. Jour. Soc.*, 42, 1936.

Davie, M. R.: *The Pattern of Urban Growth*, Studies in Science of Society, New Haven, 1937.

Hartshorne, R.: 'Human Geography', in *Man and Society*, (ed.) E. P. Schmidt, New York, 1937.

Moscheles, J.: 'Demographic, Social and Economic Regions of Greater Prague', *Geog. Rev.*, 27, 1937.

Alihan, M. A.: *Social Ecology*, New York, 1938.

Taylor, G.: 'Correlations and Culture: A Study in Technique', *Proc. Brit. Assoc. Adv. Sci.*, 1938.

Finch, V. C.: 'Geographical Science and Social Philosophy', *Ann. Assoc. Amer. Geog.*, 29, 1939.

Forde, C. D.: 'Human Geography, History and Sociology', *Scot. Geog. Mag.*, 55, 1939.

Gettys, W. E.: 'Human Ecology and Social Theory', *Social Forces*, 18, 1939.

Quinn, J. A.: 'The Nature of Human Ecology—Re-examination and Redefinition', *Social Forces*, 18, 1939.

Schmid, C. F.: 'The Ecological Method', in Pauline Young (ed.), *Scientific Social Surveys and Research*, New York, 1939.

Thornthwaite, C. W.: 'The Relation of Geography to Human Ecology', *Ecol. Monogs.*, 10, 1940.

Mackinder, Sir H. J.: 'Geography, an Art and a Philosophy', *Geog.*, 17, 1942.

Demangeon, A.: *Problèmes de Géographie Humaine*, Paris, 1943.

Fleure, H. J., Myres, J. L., and Mackinder, H. J., 'The Development of Geography', *Geog.*, 28, 1943.

Hawley, A. H.: 'Ecology and Human Ecology', *Social Forces*, 22, 1944.

Norwood, Sir C.: 'Geography—address to the Geographical Association', *Geog.*, 31, 1946.

Dickinson, R. E.: *City, Region and Regionalism, A Geographical Contribution to Human Ecology*, London, 1947.

Hollingshead, A. B.: 'A Re-examination of Ecological Theory', *Soc. and Soc. Research*, 31, 1947.

Sauer, C. O.: 'Cultural Geography', in E. C. Hayes (ed.), *Recent Development in the Social Sciences*, Philadelphia, 1947.

Fleure, H. J.: *Problems of Society and Environment*, London, 1948.

Platt, R. S.: 'Environmentalism versus Geography', *Amer. Jour. Soc.*, 53, 1948.

CHAPTER XXI

URBAN GEOGRAPHY

GRIFFITH TAYLOR

Introduction

PERHAPS the chief characteristic of our European type of civilization is the unmistakable shift from a rural to an urban way of life. Let us see what has happened in four of the chief nations of the world. In the United Kingdom it was natural that the change from rural to urban life should take place earlier than in most other countries. If we accept the proportion of 50 : 50 per cent as marking this change, then 1850 was the date when the United Kingdom crossed this 'Rubicon'. In Germany it took place about 1895, in the United States about 1918, while France is just entering the condition where the city dwellers equal the rural dwellers. These changes are illustrated in the graph which appears as Fig. 44. It is very significant that for many years Australia has been 'urbanized'. Although it is a young country it can no longer be termed pioneer, since for many years more than 60 per cent of Australians have lived in the large cities. Indeed today nearly 70 per cent are city dwellers, and in four of the States (Victoria, New South Wales, South Australia, and Western Australia) the capital city includes approximately half the people of the State.

Under these circumstances it is surprising that no lengthy study of the ramifications of Urban Geography[1] has so far appeared, though the urban aspects, of interest to the sociologist and to the town-planner, have resulted in many valuable general text-books. In English there are several works by geographers dealing with allied problems; for instance Geddes' *Cities in Evolution*, Ormsby's *Port of London*, and Van Cleef's *Trade Centers and Trade Routes* (New York, 1937). In German a small book by Hassert, *Die Stadt geographisch betrachtet*, appeared in Leipzig in 1907, while in French there is a modest volume by Lavedan, *Géographie des Villes* (Paris, 1936), which is a useful introduction to the subject. Primarily sociological and historical is Mumford's valuable study, *The Culture of Cities* (New York, 1936); but all geographers should read this volume, which contains many useful plans of towns and cities. R. E. Dickinson's study of region-

---

[1] See, however, *Urban Geography*, with 300 plans and diagrams, Methuen, London, 1949, by the present writer.

alism[1] has just appeared, and deals quite fully with certain aspects of city geography.

We owe to M. Aurousseau a valuable summary of the modern approach to Urban Geography (*Geographical Review*, New York, July 1924) from which I have borrowed a good deal in the next few paragraphs. As one might expect, the first modern papers on cities come from Germany, and deal with urban conditions in Dresden. They were published in 1903. However, on the whole, the French were most prolific in the field; and the numerous studies by Raoul Blanchard date back to 1911, when he published a valuable study of Grenoble. Rouen was

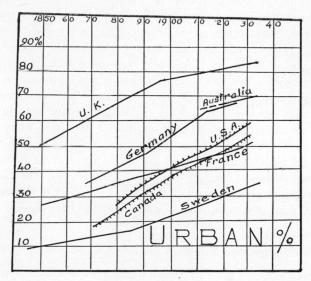

FIG. 44.—The rise in the percentage of urban dwellers in the last century in six leading countries

described two years later; and perhaps a lengthy paper by the writer, dealing with the choice and founding of Canberra about the same time, may be cited.[2]

In America Mark Jefferson was the pioneer, with such papers as that of 1909 which dealt with the 'Anthropogeography of some Great Cities'.[3] He

[1] *City, Region and Regionalism* (London, 1947). Valuable for town and country relations, and umlands.

[2] 'The Evolution of a Capital, a physiographic study of the Foundation of Canberra, Australia', *Geographical Journal*, London, April-May 1914.

[3] *American Geographical Society*, Vol. XVI, New York, pp. 537–66.

followed this by numerous other papers in 1913, 1916, 1917, and 1920, and these dealt with the distributions of Japanese, British, and American urban peoples. Those early voluminous writers, Ratzel in Germany and Reclus in France, gave many plans of cities in their publications; but they rarely gave much attention to the principles underlying urban agglomerations.

As Aurousseau has pointed out, recent geographical work has been more particular than general. Two of the most important studies, published in the *Scottish Geographical Magazine* in 1919 and 1921, dealt with the evolution of Edinburgh and Glasgow. The former is a particularly good example of a combination of historical, sociological, and geographical research, and it is plentifully illustrated by old charts, maps, and photographs. Scrive-Loyer in 1921 produced a similar study for the city of Lille in northern France. Geisler in 1923 completed an extensive study of Danzig, in which he dwelt especially on various difficulties which had been overcome in making Danzig the chief centre of the region.

In regard to the 'small town' the French again are in the lead. Caen, and especially towns in the vicinity of Grenoble, have been studied in detail by the students, trained mainly by Raoul Blanchard. In the United States progress in this field of geographic research has been general. Chicago has been treated very fully in various papers in the *Bulletin of the Geographical Society of Chicago* since as far back as 1913. Van Cleef produced an early study of Duluth (*Bull. Amer. Geog. Soc.*) in the same year, and many more American writers will be cited in later papers.

Prehistoric Settlements and Marginal Survivals

It would be out of place to devote much space to a discussion of early types of towns in this chapter, but some recent research may be mentioned. We can obtain a valuable picture of the progress of urban life by making use of the 'Zones and Strata' technique already explained in Chapter XIX. If we consider a small region like Britain, the archaeological strata give us a clear idea of the forms of settlement in prehistoric and early historic days. But we can obtain a somewhat parallel set of data by considering present-day methods of settlement in the distant *marginal* portions of the earth. In a general way, as we move outwards from Britain to the least cultured parts of the world, we pass through a series of zones which become more and more primitive the farther we move from the present centre of culture in Britain. This application of the Zones and Strata technique is epitomized in the following table, and also in Fig. 45 (from *Urban Geography*, 1949).

ANCIENT SITES AND MARGINAL SURVIVALS

Approximate date		'Strata' in Britain	Existing marginal examples
	B.C. 20000	Neandertal dwelling	Australian caves at Devon Downs, &c.
	15000	Aurignacian dwelling	Australian wurlies
Palaeolithic Age	10000	Magdalenian dwelling	
Mesolithic Age	6000	Maglemose dwelling	Eskimo hut
Neolithic Age	3000	Windmill Hill (Skara Brae)	
Bronze Age	1700	Beaker Man (Avebury)	Pit dwellings of Arizona
	800	Halstatt (Maiden Castle)	
Iron Age	100	La Tene (Glastonbury)	Colombian wattled huts
Roman Period	A.D. 43	Brythonic Speakers	Timgad in Algeria
Saxon Period	500		Roumanian barns
Plantagenet Times	1200	Medieval castles	Moroccan castles of today

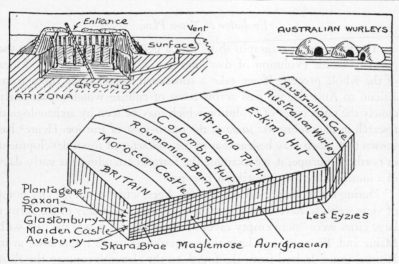

FIG. 45.—The evolution of settlements is shown by the zones (of today) on the surface, and the strata (of the past) on the front edge. Inset are sketches of primitive dwellings in Australia and Arizona. (From *Our Evolving Civilization*)

Readers will have a general knowledge of the types of dwellings present in the examples cited in the column labelled 'Strata' in the above table. There are few medieval castles in actual use in Britain today; but if we journey afield to the western Atlas mountains in Morocco[1] we can see

[1] Jules Blache in *Geographical Review*, October 1921 (p. 493).

33

medieval castles where the life and customs are still much as they were in Plantagenet times in Britain. The barns in common use in south-east Europe have much the same design as the ordinary houses of Saxon times in Britain. The Roman town, such as those of Britain, can be seen almost unchanged in the famous monument of Timgad in eastern Algeria. The wattled huts which have been identified at Glastonbury in Somersetshire are much like those I have visited in the Andes of Colombia. Reconstructions of the huts at Avebury remind us of the Pit Dwellings only lately abandoned by the Amerinds of Arizona, U.S.A. Sollas and others have shown that there is a structural resemblance between the Eskimo igloo and the huts of the Mesolithic Age in Britain. Quennell's reconstructions of Aurignacian dwellings remind us of the aboriginal wurlies that the writer has visited in outlying parts of Australia. Finally the famous shelter-caves of Les Eyzies (in the Dordogne in south-west France) have much in common with the shallow caves used not so long ago by the aborigines on the banks of the lower Murray River near Devon Downs.[1]

Evolution of Town Plans

The foregoing paragraphs show that a geographical approach to the problem of the evolution of dwellings can afford us a very good idea of the whole process. If we take a somewhat roundabout route from Britain to Australia we pass across *zones* of culture which repeat fairly closely the same types of evolution which may be seen by archaeological research in the prehistoric *strata* of the north-west of Europe. Fleure[2] has shown that much may be learnt as to the character of town development in northern Europe, if we examine the features attending the early days of a number of cities in northern Europe.

During the worst period of the Dark Ages, which from the city point of view seems to have been about the ninth century, many of the former large cities were 'mere empty caves of masonry'. Such was the case with Mainz and Trier, though later they acquired as much importance as in Roman times. Indeed from the fourth to the eleventh century the chief value of a town lay in its wall. In times of peril the peasants abandoned their hovels in the vicinity and fled within the walls until the enemy withdrew. About the end of the eleventh century 'guilds' grew up in the walled cities, and these may be described as an early form of trade union. In Flanders and Lombardy these new mercantile groups began to defy

---

[1] Sketches of these parallel types will be found in Chapter VI of the writer's recent volume on *Urban Geography* (London, 1949).

[2] *Geographical Review*, New York, December 1920.

their feudal lords; and this shift of power from the castle to the trading centre naturally greatly affected the pattern of the town.

Fleure points out that, as cities depend on trade, there must be a progressive change in the city types as we proceed from western France to eastern Russia, because conditions became stable first in the west, and did not develop in Russia until several centuries later. This change is illustrated in a somewhat general fashion in Fig. 46. In the south of France many of the towns, such as Arles, Nîmes, and Orange, seem to be built around a central *Forum*; and these towns go back to the time of Republican Rome. Northern France was settled in the days of Imperial Rome, when Christianity was a major factor in the development of the Roman Empire. In such cities as Chartres, we find that the magnificent *Cathedral* is the central point, while the Town Hall has a position rather south of

FIG. 46.—Zones across Northern Europe in the early Middle Ages. (*After H. Fleure*)

the centre. Paris of medieval times was also built around the nucleus of Notre Dame, which embellished an island in the middle of the River Seine.

As we move farther east we pass across the transition region of Flanders, where the Roman culture was not so deeply engrained as in France. Here we may perhaps say that *trade* was as important as Rome or as the Church, in the formative years of the Flemish peoples. Ghent may be taken as a typical early town of Flanders, and here the *Guild Halls* are perhaps more striking features of the city than the churches or forums. Crossing the Rhine we pass out of the region ruled by Rome, and enter the 'marches' where warfare was prevalent throughout early historic times. Here the *castle* is perhaps the most significant feature of the early city, and Heidelberg may be quoted as an example of Fleure's fourth 'city zone' (Fig. 46).

In much of Germany the towns were the creation of trade, i.e. places where folk congregated to exchange or sell the goods collected in the vicinity. The *Fairs* were very important in the medieval life; and Augsburg, being a great road centre, was noted for the annual Fairs. Fleure's two eastern zones (in Germany and Russia) are marked by many towns whose origin was of the *Acropolis* type. Prag and Moscow are described, in terms of their early growth, as centres of defence built around strong forts erected on eminences which could not readily be attacked.

Geography of Medieval Towns

The liaison between urban geography and town planning is obviously quite close, though the geographer is primarily interested in aspects of site, communications, and function; while the professional town-planner spreads farther afield into the disciplines of the architect and the sociologist. It is salutary to study the ideas and accomplishments of the ancient town-builders, for we then learn that many principles which are usually thought to belong only to modern civilization were recognized in early historic days. For instance the chequerboard plan of the American city exhibits much of the same pattern as the 'Terramare' settlements of the Bronze Age in the Lombard Plain. This in turn developed in a sense into the rectangular pattern of the Roman *castrum*, or temporary military camp. The latter is the basis of innumerable towns and cities in western and southern Europe, such as Chester or Colchester in England, Autun in France, and Cologne in Germany.

Vitruvius, who lived about the time of Augustus, left a number of treatises on architecture and planning which were much consulted during the Middle Ages.[1] His ideal city pattern embodied many of the best features of the 'cobweb' plan which is so marked a unit of modern planned cities such as Canberra. Many of the ancient Greek cities are of interest today, such as Selinus in western Sicily, for they show that the rectangular street pattern was prevalent some 500 years before the time of Christ. Syracuse and Thebes (north of Athens) show how shifts in trade and political control can ruin the prosperity of an ancient city. In both cases the modern settlement has only a tithe of the importance it possessed in classical times. A number of early classical towns were planned by builders who realized the importance of a 'processional way', much as the modern planner tries to place the major buildings where they can be seen to best advantage (e.g. Washington, D.C.).

[1] *The Art of Town Planning*, H. V. Lanchester, London, 1925. This is one of the best volumes from the geographer's point of view.

In medieval times as trade became of more and more importance the towns grew larger and their character changed. Even in this brief discussion some mention must be made of the important contribution of Lewis Mumford to Urban Geography. He points out in his *Culture of Cities* (New York, 1938) that a new technique developed in the eighteenth century which he calls the Baroque style. In these new plans, formal *geometric* designs replaced the crowded irregular streets of the earlier walled city. The 'avenue' became prevalent, and much wider streets were necessary with the increasing use of wheeled vehicles. A marked separation of the classes into rich and poor developed, and the segregation of mansions or of slums became noticeable. Karlsruhe, built as the capital of the Grand Duke of Baden about 1750, is a typical Baroque city. Many of the same Baroque features were incorporated by Major L'Enfant in the design of Washington, a few decades later.

The Industrial revolution may be said to have arisen as the result of Watt's invention of the practical steam engine about 1763. There were of course plenty of small factories before this date, which were usually clustered along rivers, especially near waterfalls. But with the spread of the steam engine we see for the first time the crowding of operatives in large factories, and this human shift was accompanied by the transfer of foodstuffs from regions far removed from the developing factory towns. To this type of town Mumford gave the name 'Palaeotechnic', by which he means that the city developed, without benefit of modern planning, mainly for the use of crowded factory hands. Owing to the steam engine being invented in Britain, and to the rich and easily won coal of the same region, we find that the industrial revolution is reflected in the population graph *earlier* in England than anywhere else. Fig. 47 shows that this critical period occurred about 1780 in London, about 1810 in Paris, and about 1840 in Vienna, Berlin, and New York.

From the smaller palaeotechnic town or city develops the Metropolis; and this in turn gives rise to the most characteristic of our town patterns of today, what Mumford calls '*Megalopolis*'. Another type of agglomeration develops when two cities grow into each other—as in the case of Liverpool and Manchester. This Geddes has called a '*Conurbation*', and one of the most striking examples is the ring-shaped cluster of towns in the Essen region of western Germany. Here we find streets of houses linking Krefeld on the Rhine, through Duisburg and Essen, to Dortmund far to the east. Along the Wupper valley somewhat south of this conurbation, a similar belt of factory towns is arising, linking Dusseldorf to Hagen in a similar fashion.

Mumford's conclusions as to the seeds of decay inherent in such a megalopolis should be read by all students of urban geography. He points out that the city rose as a special kind of environment favourable to nurture and education, because it was a *protected* environment. In the small city co-operative actions prevailed over the more predatory modes of life. But the 'giant city' (megalopolis) tends to produce many of the evils of 'crowd associations'. Most forms of crime are more prevalent. Many activities are only pursued vicariously, such as the games and boxing matches. In time of war the megalopolis is particularly vulnerable from

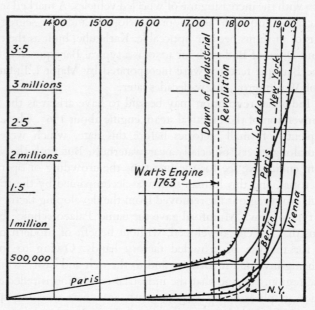

FIG. 47.—Changes in population due to the Industrial Revolution in five large cities.
(From Taylor, *Urban Geography*)

the air. Its huge populations are readily brought to the verge of starvation when outside supplies are merely interrupted. High land values and high costs of transport all increase with the congestion.

Mumford sees the end of this unhealthy growth in the cutting off of the supply of new citizens from the countryside or elsewhere. After a city grows beyond forty or fifty thousand it fails to produce the full quota of its citizens. The decline of the birth rate will cut down all immigration, and this is perhaps the chief reason why, in the next stage of our civilization, we shall see much smaller cities than today.

In the Middle Ages the prime consideration was defence; and this fact led to the strait-jacket type of town, enclosed in a circular wall at first, later in a rectangular wall, and last of all in the star-shaped walls of the military engineer Vauban. These last were very prevalent in the Baroque period towards the end of the eighteenth century. Walls were abandoned as means of defence with the growing power of artillery; so that a feature of the early nineteenth century was the destruction of the ancient 'bulwarks'. Their place was taken by broad streets which were given the allied name of 'boulevardes'. They gave 'lungs' and new arteries to many a congested city in western Europe about this period, as may be seen in Vienna, Paris, Cologne, &c.

After a period of chaos owing to the crowding due to the Industrial Revolution we find the dawn of a better system of city development. The gardens of the early nineteenth century, if they were anywhere near the new factories, were filled with slum dwellings; while in many cases the builders of the day, when they put up new houses, were chiefly concerned as to the largest number which could be placed within an acre of land.

Towns in the Nineteenth Century and Later

We may rapidly traverse some of the town plans developed during the nineteenth century. Washington, D.C. (1790–1800) incorporated some of the geometric ideas of earlier Baroque period, which had been demonstrated at Versailles.[1] Little towns such as Goderich and Guelph in southern Ontario were laid out around 1830 with some attempt to vary the monotony of the rectangular 'grid'. In both cases there was a central area which was approached by radial streets as well as by the conventional north-south, east-west streets, whose position was often determined by the direction of the magnetic compass! A very interesting example of better design is to be seen in Australia, where the city of Adelaide was planned in 1837 by Colonel Light.[2] He laid out two main centres, one on each side of the Torrens stream, and surrounded both portions with a broad belt of parks. In the main section, in addition to the central square, there were four smaller squares symmetrically arranged about the centre. We see the same pattern of four small squares in Charlottetown (Canada), which was laid out somewhat earlier.

Many of the larger cities of the United States departed to some extent from the conventional grid, as may be seen in Detroit, St. Louis and Indianapolis. But in general the grid was adopted as the main motif, and this was justified by stating that it fitted with chequerboard laying-out of

[1] *Outline of Town Planning*, T. Adams, New York, 1935. Very informative on early cities.

[2] *Foundation of South Australia*, A. G. Price, Adelaide, 1924.

farms, based on the ordinance of 1785. As C. M. Robinson has stated, this resulted in placing a huge chequerboard of survey lines all over miles of country north and west of the Ohio River, 'regardless of contours and relentless as fate'.

Around 1850 many communities were founded in the States by reformers (such as Robert Owen) at New Harmony (Indiana) or at Hopedale in Massachusetts. Other towns were built by manufacturers, such as Garden City on Long Island, or by Cheney Brothers as that near Hartford, Connecticut. Various large Exhibitions stressed the advisability of new designs for homes, villages, and towns; and a whole school of town-planners has grown up during the last fifty years, so that the towns of today are more aesthetic as well as more healthy and practical than most of those of the last century. Of especial note in U.S.A. has been the work of D. H. Burnham in regard to the development of Chicago and San Francisco or of Manilla and Baguio in the Philippine Islands.

To illustrate the recent developments in this century we may consider three small towns of considerable interest in three different continents. Letchworth is about thirty-four miles north of London (England), and here some 4,000 acres were purchased in 1903, and they have since seen the rise of a flourishing 'garden city'.[1] There is here no hint of a chequerboard pattern; but a straight avenue leads from the station to the town square, and is prolonged to the south-west. For the most part there are irregular segments of curved streets, with ample room for recreation in the form of large sports-grounds and commons. Minor industries such as printing, tool-making, &c. have been encouraged to develop in the east of the area. Each house has a fair-sized garden; and these gardens cannot become covered with slums, as happened so often to the pleasant towns of England when the Industrial Revolution overwhelmed them.

For our second example we may cite Prince Rupert on the coast of British Columbia.[2] Here the Grand Trunk railway of Canada had its western terminus on the Pacific; and it was hoped, early in the twentieth century, that the new port would soon rival Vancouver which had grown to 250,000 since its founding in 1885. Along the mountainous coast it was not easy to find a large area of fairly level ground suitable for a large town; especially as it must be near deep water, and yet be protected from Pacific storms. However, at Kaien Island, close to the mouth of the Skeena River, such a site was found; and a Boston firm was engaged to lay out the town plan (1914.)

A rocky ridge runs parallel to the coast with four 'steps' (Fig. 48).

[1] See T. Adams, loc. cit.
[2] 'British Columbia', *Geog. Rev.*, July 1942, New York, p. 381.

The shore platform has been broadened, and carries the railway to a power house, dock, and large fish-cannery. A small rocky step above this now accommodates the offices of the Canadian National Railway. The main road to the town rises by a ramp around this step. The second main 'step' is about 100 feet above sea-level, and carries the two chief streets of the little town, with the shops, hotels, and the post office. An imposing Court House terminates the street at the east. A steep rocky scarp rises about 60 feet higher to the main backbone of the ridge, along which three other streets have been laid out. In the south-west this ridge rises to a rounded knoll about 250 feet above the sea, on which is the large wooden Exhibi-

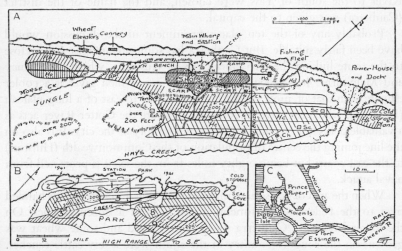

FIG. 48.—The Town plan of Prince Rupert, British Columbia. (From Taylor, *Urban Geography*)

tion Building. The town-planners designed nine different sections for the town, in each of which the curved streets were laid down in conformity with the hilly topography. But to date there are few houses outside of the three central sections, and second-growth trees are covering the once cleared sections labelled 2, 3, 4, 8, and 9.

A town which has been planned according to the best principles of the modern expert is that which is the capital of the Australian Commonwealth at Canberra.[1] The writer had made a study of the topography here, before the site was chosen for the capital, in 1908, and he was engaged in the geological survey of the adjacent districts at intervals during the next

[1] 'Environment, Village and City', *Ann. Assoc. Amer. Geog.*, March 1942, pp. 34-40.

decade. Some notes on the choice of the capital will be of interest to geographical students.

In 1900 it was decreed that the capital should be built in the state of New South Wales. But partly due to the jealousy of the other states it was ruled that the city should not be less than 100 miles from Sydney (the state capital). Since the western part of New South Wales is so hot and dry, it was clear that the new city would develop in the rather elevated and wetter areas in the east of the state. Various commissions visited suggested sites, so that at times Bombala, Albury, Tumut, and Dalgety were all selected as the probable site. However, in 1908 the plains on the Molonglo River to the south of Yass were chosen, and the name of the district (Canberra) was given to the capital.

Probably any of the ten places prominent in the discussion would have been fairly suitable. But Canberra has some advantages. It lies close to the route linking the two chief cities of Australia, which are Sydney and Melbourne. It is 1,900 feet above the sea, which gives it a cooler climate than that of most of the cities. It is just to east of a long plateau (Bimberi), which rises over 6,000 feet; and here the Cotter River acts as a valuable collecting ground for the water-supply of the city. It is also on the line joining the centre of population of the Commonwealth (Hillston) to the east coast; but being eighty miles from the sea it is protected from naval attack.

When the area of 900 square miles of the Capital Territory was handed over to the Federal Government, it consisted of a dozen ranches. On the lower lands near Canberra sheep were grazed and some wheat was grown; on the rougher country in the south were a few cattle ranches. The chief buildings on Acton station (ranche) became the centre of the new city, while Duntroon station to the east is now the Military College, and Yarralumla station to the west is the residence of the Governor General.

A world-wide competition resulted in the plans of W. B. Griffin of Chicago being chosen as a basis for the city pattern. A central avenue was laid down by Mr. Griffin, along the main flat valley between Black Mountain and Mount Ainslie. These conical hills rose about 600 feet above the wide plain of the Molonglo. Two main 'cobwebs' were laid out, and one to the north of the Molonglo River became the Civic Centre, while another cobweb to the south was where the Parliament House was erected. Other 'cobwebs' were arranged around the two main centres; and most of the area between the cobwebs is laid out as gardens or parks.

Clearly we have here a considerable departure from the plans of most cities of today. The experiment of splitting a small town of 15,000 people (its population around 1947) into civic and political units is very interesting; and the rather wide distance (some three miles) between the southern and northern clusters seems at present to waste a good deal of the citizens' time. But in Canberra the designer is commendably looking forward to a city of three or four times the present population. The radial streets, the wide park lands, the isolated units, the location of streets with respect to vistas, all of these are in accord with the ideas of the best planners of today.

The Site Factor in the Evolution of Towns

To the geographer no aspect of urban geography can be more important than the site. As I have stated elsewhere, the first question one should ask about any settlement is 'Why did man desire to establish himself there?' In the majority of cases the answer is 'Because he hoped to exploit Nature's resources in the vicinity.' The second question is 'Why that precise spot of all those available nearby?' The third question is 'What sort of a settlement developed there, and especially how did the topography control the ensuing pattern?' We may further investigate the lines of communication at any particular site, with a view to learning what part they play in deciding the continued growth of the settlement. All of these questions are closely linked with the topography.

In several memoirs the evolution of Sydney, Australia, has been discussed by the writer along the lines suggested above.[1] Here it is shown that Sydney possesses in Port Jackson the best harbour along the east coast of Australia. It is a deep *ria*, penetrating over twenty miles into the hinterland, yet receiving no river of note which might fill it with silts. The actual spot (within the branching ria) where the first settlers set up their tents and huts at Circular Quay was determined by the little Tank Stream. This has long vanished under the streets of the city, and is now only represented by storm-water sewers. The specific purpose of the settlement was unusual, since it was to gain a place for convict settlement, so far removed from the parent country that they could not return.

The north and south shores of the ria are rather different, for a fault or warp has given rise to a steep, rocky, northern shore to the ria, and a lower shale-covered southern shore. Hence the main settlement and the factories grew up on the smoother lower shore, while the rocky northern shore much later was crowned by bungalows and scattered residences, linked by steep and irregular streets. The ria extends far inland into a wide area of low plains, and this of course gave the young city a fair hinterland

[1] See pp. 129–35 in *Australia*, G. Taylor, London, 1940.

where farms have developed. But the environment is not by any means altogether favourable. Some fifty miles away from Sydney—whether we go north, west, or south—we find deeply dissected gorges in barren sandstone plateaux; so that the city is completely shut in by an adverse topography on every side but the east, where it fringes the Pacific Ocean.

Countless descriptions of the sort outlined above have been published by geographers, but my hope was that the reader would gain a clearer idea of the relation of site to city if one example were discussed in some detail. In the recent book by the writer on 'Urban Geography' a very large part of the volume is devoted to a discussion of the site-city problem. He has tried to describe enough examples of towns in a given topography to arrive at some generalizations as to the dependence of city on site. However, no very clear rules have resulted from this study, which is natural, since the whole research is still in an early pioneer stage.

Geological control is very obvious in some parts of the world, perhaps nowhere more so than in the South-east States. Here, along the 'Fall Line', the younger deposits of the coast cover the ancient Palaeozoic rocks of the Appalachians. From New York to the Mississippi valley is a string of famous cities, which arose near the falls on all the rivers flowing to the Atlantic. On a very much smaller scale we find the villages bordering various rocky plateaux near Rheims, where Aurousseau has described the relation of permeable rocks and springs to the villages in this area.[1]

The eroded 'dome' of the Weald in south-east England offers many examples of the control of town sites by the geological features. The main towns are in the broad vale cut out of the stiff blue clay called the Gault. Here are situated Sevenoaks, Dorking and Guildford. Another parallel set of towns developed below the famous Pilgrim's Way, which for the most part followed the northern slope of the Chalk. Here then we find Canterbury, Rochester, Dartford, and Croydon.[2]

Roderick Peattie in his book 'Mountain Geography' (Cambridge, 1936) has described the effects of *adret* and *ubach* in various valleys of the European Alps. He shows that in some cases there are more settlements on the shady (ubach) side than on the adret,[3] though as we shall see the contrary is the case at Davos in Switzerland. In the Sierra Nevada of Spain Peattie found that the villages reach up to 1,200 metres on the shady northern side, but only to 900 metres on the sunny southern side. The boundary seems to be determined by the presence or absence of sterile granite, much more than by the presence or absence of enduring sun-

---

[1] *Geog. Rev.*, Oct. 1921, New York.
[2] *Physical Basis of Geography*, Wooldridge and Morgan, pp. 240–8, London, 1937.
[3] 'Height limits of mountain economies', *Geog. Rev.*, July 1931.

shine. A valuable paper by H. M. Kendall[1] shows how villages and towns have arisen on a widespread fan extending over the slopes between Toulouse and Lourdes. On the plateau of Lannemezan at the head of this giant fan, the villages have developed on the flat tongues between the heads of the rivers. Elsewhere they cluster about the chateaux which were built on the isolated mesa-like outliers of the fan. Farther to the north, i.e. in the broader valleys, the roads follow the valleys, and the villages arise at cross-roads in these broad valleys.

A fairly complete study of the types of villages and towns in a great Alpine valley will be found in the paper by the writer entitled 'Trento to the Reschen Pass' (*Geog. Rev.*, April 1940). The highest permanent farm examined was just below the Ofen Pass at about 6,700 feet level. The little village of Roia (with a church) is at 6,600 feet near the Reschen Pass. The sites of the higher villages in the main glacial trough are largely determined by the presence of alluvial fans accumulating at the foot of steep tributary valleys, as in the case of Curon at 5,000 feet. Such small towns as Malles and Glorenza develop at the junction of side corridors with the main valley of the Adige. Of larger size are the great tourist centres of Merano and Bolzano, where again the importance of the alluvium of the fan is to be noted. The capital city of the Trentino is Trento, and this is a fine example of a medieval walled city spreading in modern times considerably beyond the walls, with an enclave in the centre of the city, where a new type of street and shop is developing in response to the tourist trade.

Cities on the Plains

North America affords examples of many villages, towns, and cities which have grown up on the great plains of the interior. Here there are obviously no topographic features of importance, and it is interesting to see what patterns of town life have developed. In Canada the sites of settlements were chosen in a very simple fashion. Many of the chief railways were built on the land-grant system, and in the northern prairies sidings for wheat were laid down at regular intervals of seven or eight miles all along the railway. At many of these sites a wheat elevator was built, and here farms naturally clustered as settlement became denser. In many cases the naming of the settlements was arbitrary, as for instance on the 600 miles between Portage (Manitoba) and Wainwright (Alberta). There are about 100 stations on this route, and the names run Arona, Bloom, Caye, Deer, &c.; the alphabet being traversed four times!

[1] 'The Central Pyrenean Piedmont of France', Ann Arbor, 1935.

The general procedure is much the same in all cases. A road is surveyed for a mile or so along the railway near the station. Usually the main street (named Main) runs at right angles to the railway from the site of the station. Blocks of land are surveyed on the basis of these two streets, usually with 200 to 600 feet a side. Lanes are laid out on the boundaries of these blocks as the village grows, always on a rectangular pattern, though not always square. The pattern of the city of the future is thus determined by the shape of the land blocks in the first survey. Until the town has a population of several thousand this 'grid' is not inconvenient,

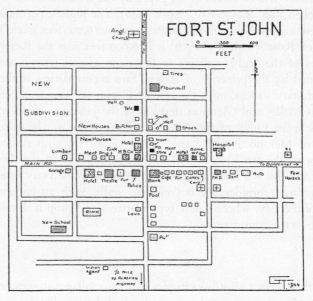

FIG. 49.—The plan of Fort St. John, a prairie town in the Peace River area

but it becomes a grave handicap as a large city develops. Most commuters wish to reach the centre of a city 300 times a year. On the gridiron plan, if they live in the 'corners' of the city area, they have to traverse *two sides* of a square, to reach the place they want. Thus the fundamental feature of most city-improvement schemes, is to lay out new diagonal streets to the centre cutting across the rectangular grid.

One of the best studies of towns of the plains is that by C. B. Odell entitled *Seven Villages of the Corn Belt*, and published by the University of Chicago in 1939. Here he discusses the evolution of a number of settlements about 100 miles to the south-west of Chicago. All are based on the grid pattern mentioned above, and they lie about five miles apart in the richest farm lands of the States. Odell discusses how the shift from rail to truck traffic has vitally affected the growth of these and neighbouring villages.

The present writer (in the volume cited on Urban Geography) has given fairly full studies of three little 'plain' towns which may be consulted. A typical new settlement in the Peace River area is Fort St. John, founded in its present position in 1928. As far as I could ascertain the site was determined as the point where four major 'township' blocks met (Fig. 49). Two main roads were laid out from this point along the edge of the townships, and lanes were surveyed to cut the adjacent land into blocks about 600 by 300 feet. In all these little prairie or plain towns, the shops are on the main street, while the churches and schools are nearly always on the margin of the settlement, at any rate until its population exceeds 500.

Another example discussed in the same place is Elbow, a small wheat town near a bend of the South Saskatchewan River in Saskatchewan. The town was laid out where the railway approached the ferry at the bend about 1909, and its pattern agrees very well with the usual type of railway town described above. A more interesting site is White River about 180 miles north-west of Sault St. Marie. Here a 'division town' has been in existence since the C.P.R. was built through the Shield around 1880. It has no roads linking it to the outside world; but it is an important railway station where engines are changed, and cattle watered, &c. on the chief transcontinental railway. It still has only four streets forming an incomplete grid, with about fifty houses, a school, and two churches.

Town Sites on Rivers

Many studies have been made of such sites both in Europe and in North America. The following may be consulted in the pages of the American *Geographical Review* for the years cited. G. T. Renner studies the Fall Line in U.S.A. in the number for April 1927; R. H. Brown described irrigation settlement in Colorado (Oct. 1928); P. E. James gives a full description of Vicksburg and the changes in the adjacent Mississippi (Oct. 1931); G. T. Trewartha describes a confluence site at Prairie du Chien in *Annals of American Geographers*, 1932; Carls and Ristow discuss Seneca Falls in *Economic Geography*, 1936.

Lavedan in his book on Town Geography points out that cities rarely develop equally on both banks of a large river. Thus Paris and Rouen are mainly on the right bank, while Mantes is on the left bank of the Seine. Similarly Orleans and Blois are on the right and Tours and Saumur on the left bank of the Loire. This is usually dependent on which bank is most subject to floods. Bern is on the narrow neck of an incised meander, and such a site is obviously an advantage for defence in troubled times. Cologne grew up on the west bank of the Rhine, because the Romans approached the river from the French side; but St. Louis and Omaha are on the farther side of the big rivers which flow near them.

Probably waterfalls exercise paramount influence in the settlement of hilly country, especially before the rise of the steam engine around 1800. A number of fall towns have been described in great detail, as for instance Miss M. T. Parker's study of the factory town of Lowell in Massachusetts, (New York 1940). The writer has described an interesting 'Company town' which has been built by the paper company at Grand Falls (in central Newfoundland) in his booklet on Newfoundland (Toronto, 1946). Here the power station was placed as far below the falls as convenient, while the paper mills were erected close by. The town was laid out by the company, on a low ridge nearby, and the houses for the staff and workmen were also erected by them. As a consequence we find a street pattern conforming to the topography, and there is a complete absence of the hateful 'grid'.

Rivière du Loup on the south side of the Gulf of St. Lawrence offers a good example of a French industrial town, built close to some sixty-foot falls on the river of the same name. Here the influence of the three parish churches is noteworthy; while the railways, entering the town rather late, have as usual exerted their control in the development of streets and housing. For a description of this town see *Canadian Geographical Journal* for June 1945. H. T. Straw has given us a study of the development of Battle Creek in Michigan as a result of the small falls on the Kalamazoo River.[1] Here the influence of a religious sect has been considerable, leading to the establishment of many special food factories, colleges, and other institutions. The shift from water power to steam is very evident here, since the industrial evolution has gone on long after the power supplied by the small falls became of negligible importance.

Site and Pattern in Sea-ports

Many valuable descriptions of ports have been published, and in this brief section we can only point out some of the salient characteristics. The topography of the shoreline is of course of much importance. In general we may say that shores are in a state of recent submergence, owing to the vast depth of water added to the oceans by the melting of

[1] *Michigan Academy of Science*, 1938.

the ice-caps. Sydney (Australia) probably owes its fine port to this factor, for here a deep juvenile valley has been drowned, as already described. Volcanic craters have been invaded by the sea, as in the port of Lyttelton in New Zealand; Pearl Harbour (near Honolulu) is a classic example of the opposite kind, where slight emergence seems to have killed the coral reefs and given rise to a fine naval base. Emergence in general ruins harbours, as is very evident in many of the ports in Finland on the Baltic Sea. Owing to the elevation of the crust, due to the removal of the load of ice since the Ice Ages, many ports are rather rapidly becoming too shallow for large vessels. The shift of the coast of Belgium to the north since Roman times is very pronounced; and Sluys, which was an important port at the famous naval battle of 1330, is now far inland.

A valuable paper by G. F. Deasy in *Economic Geography* (October 1942) gives notes on 88 harbours around the coast of Africa. He describes the various sites, somewhat as follows: 'Lagoon and Bar', as at Durban, Tunis, Bizerta, and Port Said; 'Drowned valleys' as at Douala, Mombasa and Lorenzo Marquez; 'Tidal inlet' at Lagos; 'Delta and bar' at Alexandria. Plans of these ports will be found in his paper. The well-known geographer de Geer gives a full account of Stockholm in his paper in the *Geographical Review* for October 1923. Strasbourg was discussed by Levainville in the same year in the *Geographical Review*. Malta will be found illustrated in the same journal for January 1924. Many useful maps of the famous Brazilian ports of Rio and San Paulo are discussed by P. E. James in the same journal for 1933. Van Cleef gives an account of the rise of the Polish port of Gdynia in the *Geographical Review* for January 1933. The silt problem in the port of Tientsin is described in 1935 by M. A. Hitch. In 1940 we find plans of Singapore by E. H. Dobby; and of Rangoon by O. H. Spate in the same journal for January 1942.

Few of these papers devote much time to the general features of ports, or compare them one with the other. The present writer has compared a dozen ports around the Gulf of St. Lawrence in a long article in the *Canadian Geographical Journal* for June 1945. Tadoussac dates back to 1599, and is perhaps the earliest settlement in Canada. It is shown that, owing to its sterile hinterland, the occupation by man has only spread a few miles inland in 350 years. (In the last century settlement in the plains of Alberta has spread through a belt of country some 600 miles wide.) Across the Gulf on the north Gaspé coast half a dozen small villages are described, which have developed to a much greater degree owing to the better fishing and the larger trees in the hinterland. Quebec is at the head of navigation for large sailing vessels; and so became the chief town until the rise of steam gave the advantage to Montreal, some distance farther

34

to the west in the narrow gulf. Quebec may be studied to advantage to show the effects of a horst topography on the growth of a city.

A series of settlements in Newfoundland have been described by the writer in a small book on that island (Toronto, 1946). In this work a good deal of attention is given to half a dozen villages and towns, and their development is shown to depend mainly on the topography and hinterland. Cupids, a village about 25 miles to the west of St. John's, was founded in 1610; but has not grown beyond a string of some sixty small two-storey houses around the bay in the long interval since. In Port aux Basques we find a port in the south-west corner, where passengers land coming from Nova Scotia, and here connect with the railway. There is no farming in the vicinity, but the railway and steamer traffic has built up a village of some 250 houses, though there is still no hotel in the place. Cornerbrook, though only twenty years old, has grown to a population of about 6,000, almost all dependent on the huge paper mill of the port. In winter the paper is shipped by rail to the ice-free Port aux Basques. St. John's early became the capital, and is the eastern terminus of the railway. It is a fine harbour, due to the sea breaching the side of one of the many parallel valleys, and now has a population of 55,000. There have developed three main streets parallel to the main shore, and the slopes are so steep that few streets lead up hill across these main streets. No grid has developed, but radial streets lead from the hinterland to the centre of the town on the harbour.

Finally in the same general region is Charlottetown, the capital of the tiny province of Prince Edward Island.[1] It was founded about 1768 and the island was fairly well occupied with farms by 1868. At this time the capital had a population of about 10,000, and it has changed very little in the last century. The pattern of this port may be described as 'crystallized'. George Street leads up from the wharves along the centre of a broad, low cape. Four parallel streets were laid down on each side of George Street, crossed by half a dozen west–east streets, thus forming a grid (Fig. 50). Four small parks were arranged symmetrically about George Street.

In the central Queen Square (on George Street) are the chief Government offices. Bordering these are the offices of lawyers and agents. Next comes a zone of brick shops, surrounded by a zone of smaller wooden shops. At a radius of about 800 feet from Queen Square is a zone containing most of the churches, while the schools are found in a belt farther from the centre of the city. Third-class houses crowd into the last zone and extend somewhat beyond it. The better houses are found in a crescent

[1] *Canadian Geographical Journal*, June 1945, pp. 272–5.

around the city about half a mile from the centre, but not on the southern or port side. Finally a belt of large public institutions, such as Infirmary, Gaol, Sanatorium, Hospital, and Government House are arranged still farther away from the centre of the city. During the last seven censuses

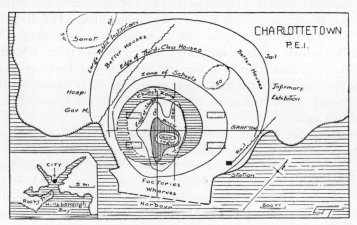

FIG. 50.—The cultural plan of Charlottetown (P.E.I.)

the population has been as follows: 1881, 11,500; 1891, 11,400; 1901, 12,100; 1911, 11,200; 1921, 12,200; 1931, 12,800; and 1941, 14,400. Hence it will be seen that this small provincial capital has not experienced the confusion of zones which usually arises in a growing city, as the good houses or shops of one generation become the slums of the next.

Mines and Resorts

The towns in this section due to the presence of valuable mineral resources, or to especial attractions in the way of scenery or because of some religious association with a place, are all likely to be built with little regard to those factors of fertility and ease of communications which generally control the situation of towns. The reader must refer to the volume *Urban Geography* for a number of studies of this kind which will only be listed in this present discussion.

Silver Peak in Nevada (about 100 miles east of Yosemite) is described at length by J. C. Weaver in *Economic Geography*, January 1939. Here agriculture is impossible, but a small town of about 100 folk has survived since 1863. Sudbury, about 260 miles west of Ottawa, is now an important town based largely on the great amount of nickel ore found in the vicinity. Kimberley in British Columbia in a corner of the Selkirk

Ranges is another mining town of about 4,000 people, which the writer has surveyed (*Geog. Rev.*, July 1942, pp. 392–5). Here no less than four small settlements have grown up, due to the distribution of the mines, mills, and concentrators. The pattern of the chief town is a very peculiar one, and seems to show a complete disregard of topography and drainage. Far away in arid New South Wales is the famous Broken Hill silver-lead-zinc field; and the geographic aspect of this cluster of mining folk is described at some length in the same volume. The coal fields of Sheffield, England, and their relation to adjacent towns is also described here; as is the environment of the steel works at Sydney, Nova Scotia, the Ruhr in Germany, and the oil towns of Norman Wells and Canol in the far north of Canada.

Some special patterns of settlement have developed owing to the religious convictions of the settlers. The most remarkable is that unusual city, the Vatican, the centre of the Catholic faith. This is described by U. Toschi in the *Geographical Review* for October 1931. Salt Lake City, the centre of Mormon religion, has been studied in great detail by Chauncey Harris in a special publication 'Salt Lake City' (University of Chicago, 1940). The desire of the Mormons to isolate themselves from the rest of the community played a considerable part in the choice of the site, while their religious administration also affected the plan of the streets. Further papers by Harris, and by A. L. Seeman (*Econ. Geog.*, 1938) may be consulted on this topic.

The socialist villages of Amana (in the state of Iowa, U.S.A.) are the subject of a study by D. H. Davis (*Econ. Geog.*, July 1936). In these villages community barns, factories, orchards, &c. are all laid out according to a uniform plan in the half-dozen little villages of the community. Somewhat similar Mennonite villages have grown up in southern Manitoba. Lourdes is perhaps the most striking example of the effect of a religious experience upon the growth of a town. It is stated that in 1858 the Virgin Mary appeared to a young girl in a grotto just west of the town; and today pilgrimages (totalling 600,000 annually) crowd into the town of Lourdes to visit the shrine. The many new churches, hospitals, hostels, avenues, parks, &c. have completely altered the pattern of the former town of Lourdes.

Some tourist resorts occupy unusual sites, as for instance Davos in the south-east corner of Switzerland. Here is the valley of the Land-wasser, about half-way between the upper Rhine and the upper Inn. One side of this broad glacial valley (*ubach*) is shaded most of the day; while the other or *adret* side is in brilliant sunshine for the most part. The pure air at this height of 5,000 feet, and the brilliant sunshine, are capitalized by hundreds of hotels and pensions. They cluster thickly on the north-west side of the valley, while only a few humble chalets engaged in grazing appear on the shaded *ubach* side.

The sport of ski-ing has grown to great proportions in the low mountains of the Shield behind Montreal. Here has developed an industry bringing in annually about 300,000 dollars to the railways, and 700,000 dollars to the habitant residents. The linking of the special ski resorts by long and costly ski-trails is an example of a new type of settlement of much interest. In the Rockies the alpine scenery has resulted in the development of three types of settlement which have been analysed by S. Jones (*Bull. Geog.*, Philadelphia; July 1936) somewhat as follows. In the first rank come places like Banff and Jasper, which he calls *Headquarter* resorts. Here are huge hotels and plenty of good roads, but usually no very striking features in the immediate neighbourhood; though they are surrounded by such at moderate distances. The second type of settlement he calls *Objective* resorts, of which Lake Louise, Emerald Lake, &c. are examples. Here there is usually only one road of access, and the superb scenery is concentrated nearby. Visitors do not as a rule make these places centres for tours as in the first case. Thirdly there are *Wayside* resorts, scattered along the main tourist roads to provide petrol, repairs, night lodgings, &c. Often these have no special scenic or tourist attraction, but are for the convenience of tourists who flock to all parts of the region.

The Earliest Stages of Settlement

Two important papers have appeared lately which show how the first stages of a settlement come about. A. Meyer gives a particularly well illustrated account of changes in the Kankakee Valley (about 50 miles south-east of Chicago) as the Indian tribes vanished and European settlers took their place.[1] The original terrain was a wide swamp with sandy islets. Here before 1840 the Pottawotamie Indians placed their huts. About this time pioneers built log huts, and exploited the marsh for fish, game, and timber. In the railway era much of the swamp was drained, but soon large numbers of wealthy folk from Chicago and elsewhere, who were interested in hunting, &c., built club houses in the larger patches of wild forest. In the fourth stage all the marsh has been drained, farms are wide-spread, and reclamation areas (supervised by the state) are being pro-claimed in the few small areas where farming is not profitable. Today there are a score of settlements, spread about six miles apart, around the edge of the former swamp; most of them containing 500 folk or less.

[1] 'The Kankakee Marsh', *Michigan Acad. of Science*, 1936.

Every geographer would be interested if a detailed survey by a competent geographer had been published of the settlements around the Gulf of St. Lawrence, say, in 1650. There is in North America another large river (the Mackenzie) along which are many settlements still in various 'infantile' stages of development. In 1944 the writer made a detailed study[1] of almost all the settlements along this great corridor, from Edmonton north across the Arctic Circle to Tuktoyaktuk near latitude 70° N.

Along the great river north of McMurray the settlements are usually spread at intervals of nearly 100 miles. These fur-trading posts were placed in the best positions to collect the fur, usually at the junction of the main tributaries (as in the case of Simpson and Norman) or below important rapids (as in the case of Fort Smith), or just above the same at the other end of the portage, as in the case of Fitzgerald. The sites of the last two settlements, where the river cuts across a corner of the great Pre-Cambrian Shield, are quite analogous to those of Montreal and Kingston. In the latter case the St. Lawrence cuts across the Frontenac Axis of Pre-Cambrian granite, which is an outlying part of the great Shield.

In the original paper a score of these settlements are studied, of which half may be described as 'Sub-infantile' and usually possess only one street and less than thirty houses. The other half are larger, with white populations ranging from 20 to 500, and with the beginnings of a grid in the street pattern. These may be termed 'Infantile'. There is little doubt that in the next century most of these settlements will develop into towns; as has taken place in Siberia along the Yenesei. Here Igarka is a town of 30,000 people, though it is not much older than Aklavik in the delta of the Mackenzie. The latter has much the same latitude and environment, but in 1944 had only 167 European inhabitants.

The Seven Ages of a Town

In an address to the Association of Geographers given in New York in 1941, the writer proposed a classification of towns based on the usual evolution of settlements throughout most of our industrialized occidental civilization. The scheme is based on the changes observed in the growth of Toronto, but it has been checked by comparison with many other modern towns, both in Europe and North America. A brief discussion of these stages will be found of interest. In the earliest stages of a settlement there is usually one street, and no differentiation into special areas of such shops as may be present amid the residences. Such a haphazard distribution of houses and shops may be cited as characteristic of the 'Sub-infantile' stage.

[1] 'A Mackenzie Domesday', *Canadian Journal of Economics*, Toronto, May 1945.

Many examples of this stage are to be seen along the Mackenzie, as at Wrigley, Good Hope, Macpherson, &c.

The second stage is the '*Infantile*' settlement, where the beginnings of a street-grid are to be seen; as at Providence, Simpson, Aklavik, and Fort Smith. In the '*Juvenile*' stage there is a fairly clear segregation of an extensive commercial quarter towards the centre of the town, including a number of streets without residences. The beginning of maturity is shown by a differentiation of the residences. The various types in this '*Adolescent*' stage are displaced outwards as the years move on, though naturally examples of the early houses survive in the expanding zones. When later the separation of the industrial portion of the city from the residential is fairly distinct, and when the residences themselves have segregated into four zones (ranging from mansions down to slums) then we have a '*Mature*' City. This usually occurs when the population has grown to twenty or thirty thousand; and somewhere about this figure is being accepted as about the 'optimum' for an industrial town.

It is difficult to classify the zones of growth in a town with more than 40,000 inhabitants. I have tentatively described a '*Late Mature*' stage, where some indications of modern town-planning in the form of new diagonal boulevardes, &c. are cut through the earlier grid. The last stage is '*Senile*' and is rarely met with in a prosperous young nation. In this stage considerable areas of the city are abandoned, and the remainder is stagnant. Many cities in the Old World (e.g. Nanking), however, show such a condition.

In the same memoir a method of drawing up a formula to express in one line the major features of a small town is put forward. This technique seems to me to be of considerable use in comparing the early stages of a city, but the formula of a city over 20,000 becomes too complicated to be of much use. However, we find extremely complicated formulæ for certain organic compounds in chemistry, and possibly later research may develop useful formulæ for our larger cities. An example for the little town of Port Credit, fourteen miles to the west of Toronto, will illustrate the technique (Fig. 51).

The indices for the formula are given in the form of an equation. On the left side the indices show the population, the stage of development, and the position and character of the nucleus of the town. On the right side of the equation, the character and position of the functional zones are indicated. In the case cited the population is 2,000. This would be represented by the figure 2 in the formula. The town was originally a lake port on a little river; and *with regard to the nucleus* (first house) the river is to the west, and the lake to the south-east. So our formula becomes

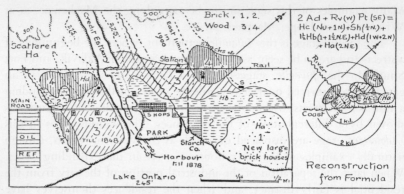

FIG. 51.—Plan of Port Credit, Ontario. The reconstruction of the plan from a formula is also indicated at the right

Rv(W.) Pt(SE.). The stage of development is what is called 'adolescent' in the preceding paragraphs, i.e. Ad. Thus the general portion of the formula (on the left side) is

$$2Ad + Rv(W.) Pt(SE.).$$

The particular functional zones are obtained as follows. The present shopping centre has been shifted from the nucleus about half a kilometre to the north. Thus the shop zone appears as Sh ($\frac{1}{2}$N.). The house zones are labelled Ha, Hb, Hc, Hd (from mansion to shack) and their position is shown in the same way. The complete formula is as follows:

$$2Ad + Rv(W.) Pt(SE.) = Sh(\tfrac{1}{2}N.) + Hb(1NE.)$$
$$+ Hc(Nu + 1N.) + Hd(1W. + 2N.) + Ha(2NE.)$$

It is also shown that—from this formula—it is quite feasible to reconstruct the plan of Port Credit. Further details may be read in the paper cited.

In concluding this brief account of Urban Geography some mention should be made of an alternative method of classifying towns, based upon their present *functions* rather than upon the stage of their development (as in the writer's classification). One of the best studies is that by Chauncey Harris (in the *Geographic Review*, 1943). Harris has studied the main functions of nearly 1,000 cities in U.S.A. and divides them into five major groups. *Manufacturing* towns are those where factories represent over 60 per cent of their commercial interests. *Diversified* cities are those where manufacturing, wholesale, and retail trade are respectively less than 60, 20 and 50 per cent. *Wholesaling* cities are where wholesaling constitutes at least 20 per cent of the whole; *Retailing* cities where this function concerns at least 50 per cent of the total; and finally *Transport* cities, where transport employs at least 11 per cent of the workers. On a map of eastern U.S.A. we see the Manufacturing towns occupying the north-east states, with a broad belt of 'Diversified' towns on the south-west side, and long tongues of towns devoted to Wholesaling, Retailing, and Transport, projecting into the region of the High Plains.

In the valuable article on the 'Distribution of Population' by Marcel Aurousseau (*Geog. Review*, Oct. 1921), he divides urban groups according to dominant *function* somewhat differently from Harris. He postulates eight major classes, as follows: *Administrative* (capital, revenue); *Defence* (fortress, garrison, naval); *Culture* (university, cathedral, art, pilgrimage, religious); *Production* (manufactures); *Collection* (mines, fish, forest, depot): *Transfer* (market, fall-line, break of bulk, bridge, tide, navigation-head); *Distribution* (export, import, supply); *Recreation* (health, tourist, holiday). Here again the evolution of the town; the stage at which it has arrived; and the dominant topographic features (as in the case of Harris's classification), are in general ignored.

BIBLIOGRAPHY

Burgess, E. W., *The Urban Community*, Chicago, 1926. (Sociological.)
Childe, G., *Prehistoric Communities*, London, 1940.
Dickinson, R. E., *City, Region and Regionalism*, London, 1947.
Geddes, P., *Cities in Evolution*.
Gist and Halberg, *Urban Society*, New York, 1938. (Sociological.)
Haverfield, F., *Ancient Town Planning*, Oxford, 1913.
Lanchester, H. V., *Town Planning*, London, 1925.
Lavedan, P., *Géographie des Villes*, Paris, 1936.
Mumford, L., *Culture of Cities*, New York, 1938. (Sociological.)
Taylor, Griffith, *Urban Geography*, London, 1949. (300 plans.)
Triggs, H. I., *Town Planning*, London, 1909.
Van Cleef, E., *Trade Centers and Trade Routes*, New York, 1937.

CHAPTER XXII

GEOGRAPHY AND AVIATION

ELLSWORTH HUNTINGTON

(Reprinted by kind permission of the Editor from *Air Affairs*, Vol. 2, No, 1, 1947)

Ellsworth Huntington was born in Galesburg, Illinois, in 1876. Before agreeing to supervise the present symposium the editor consulted his old friend, and was promised his help. His death shortly afterwards prevented his making a special contribution to this volume. But owing to the kindness of his widow (and of the editor of Air Affairs) *I was allowed to reprint the last article from his pen; so that this book, dealing with the new trends in geography, should not lack a sample of his work. Some of his earlier books, such as the* Pulse of Asia *(1907) and* Civilization and Climate *(1915), were major factors in deciding the research of a number of older geographers, including the present writer. Huntington has published over thirty volumes, which have been classified by S. S. Visher as follows: Text-books, 9; Regional Studies, 8; Climatic Studies, 9; Sociology and Eugenics, 9. For a sympathetic account of his life and work Visher's memoir (Annals Assoc. Amer. Geographers, March 1948) should be consulted.*

Introduction

THE development of aviation seems to promise contradictory results. In order to provide a basis for discussion, let us assume that within a few decades aeroplanes will average five hundred miles an hour on long trips, and helicopters, or some other craft that can hover in the air and land on a small space, will become practical for ordinary persons and will have a speed and cruising range similar to that of automobiles. If these assumptions are realized, we may reasonably expect that aviation will produce the following results:

It will promote the creation of one world, but it will lead to increasing contrasts between the parts of that world.

It will help to preserve the health of crops, animals, and man, but it will bring new hazards to all these forms of life.

It will diminish the population in some areas, and increase it in others.

After serving most terribly as an engine of war, it may become an equally powerful engine of peace.

Aviation is writing the final chapter in making the world smaller. Horses, wheeled vehicles, paved roads, railroads, and motor vehicles mark the stages of this progress on the land. Rafts, canoes, oared vessels, sailing ships, and ships driven by steam, oil, or motors, mark the stages on the water. Balloons, aeroplanes, and helicopters represent far shorter stages whereby the air has been conquered, the same craft has become able to travel over land or sea, and transportation has become far faster and more direct than ever before. For perhaps a million years man travelled on foot at the rate of only ten or fifteen miles in an ordinary day. Then, in some especially favoured regions, he doubled this speed to thirty or more miles by means of horses or camels. For 10,000 years that continued to be the normal speed until stage coaches, running by night as well as by day, led to a five-fold increase up to a speed of 150 miles in a day. Then, within the brief span of a century, locomotives, smooth roadbeds, and metal tracks produced an eight-fold increase, up to 1,200 miles. Now aeroplanes have suddenly brought a still greater increase, perhaps ten-fold, and we shall soon travel 12,000 miles in twenty-four hours.

This succession of more and more intense changes means that the size of the earth, as measured by day's journeys, has shrunk so much that the approximate time required to travel from Portland, Maine, to San Diego, California, may roughly be reckoned as follows: on foot, before the white man reached America, at least two years, for no one can travel every day and also find food; on horseback after about 1600 A.D., at least eight months if everything were unusually favourable; by stage coach and wagon in 1840, perhaps four months; by rail in 1910, about four days; today in a fast plane, ten hours.

Uncounted writers have elaborated on the way in which this almost incredible increase in speed will influence war, politics, trade, and travel. Almost every intelligent person knows that if war continues to be one of our customs, no part of the world is safe from atom bombs dropped by planes that can fly non-stop across continents or oceans. I am inclined to think, however, that this phase of aviation, vital as it may be, is no more important than other phases. The ease with which officials of the most remote countries can confer with one another face to face at short notice may in the long run do more than the fear of bombers to prevent war. The growing acquaintanceship and trade of the nations as a whole may be still more important. People who have travelled much, or have seen many foreigners in their own homes, are generally far more friendly to other countries and less suspicious of them than are those who always stay at home and see few strangers. Five or ten years from now, when peace and reasonable comfort return to war-weary Europe and Asia, international travel will doubtless increase greatly because aviation will make it so easy. Business men will hop back and forth to Europe, Asia, and South America as readily as they now move about at home. Trade will once more increase and in due time will be far greater than ever before.

People with only a two weeks' vacation will be able to spend ten days or so in almost any country. In a few years we shall have millions of people who know some foreign country personally. Helicopters, when they become practical, will do still more to increase travel. The study of foreign languages, including those like Russian and Chinese that are now little known among us, will be greatly stimulated. The acquaintanceship that thus arises through greater facilities for travel is only one item in the effect of aviation on international relations and war, but it should not be overlooked. Perhaps the deepest reason for our conflict with Russia is that so few of us really know the Russians, and so few of them know us. I spent a year in Russia long ago, and I thoroughly like the Russians as a people. It may temporarily be difficult to re-establish full and free fellowship with them, but the growth of aviation will assuredly help.

International Boundaries

The influence of aviation on international boundaries may be quite as effective as its influence on travel in impelling the nations to become one world. International boundaries are important largely in proportion to the difficulties imposed by man or nature in crossing them. The Pyrenees effectively separate France and Spain because they are hard to cross. Aviation makes such a barrier far less effective than ever before. Of much greater import, however, is the fact that aviation will have a deeply corrosive effect upon the human barriers that our outmoded political system sets up along international boundaries. When helicopters become efficient and numerous, our whole attitude towards international trade and migration may have to be altered. The resultant political effect may be profound. It will presumably not be long before a good helicopter, loaded with passengers, or with almost any kind of moderately light or small merchandise, can cross an international boundary at night with little chance of detection. It can deposit its load in some remote spot many miles from the border and get back undetected to its own country or to its mother ship at sea. In countries where helicopters have become so common that people pay little heed to them, a smuggling helicopter might readily keep on into the interior of a foreign country as far as it chose, and deposit its passengers and load almost anywhere.

There are two main ways of preventing such occurrences. One is for a nation to assume the almost unsupportable burden of watching every mile of its borders both by land and sea, and forcing every aircraft to land and be inspected. The other is to give up all attempts at collecting tariff duties on most if not all kinds of imports, and either permit free immigration or require identification cards which will be frequently inspected. The most probable course of events seems to be that at first the nations will try to maintain their old habits of closely guarding their frontiers. They will, perhaps, put rigid restrictions on the sale of diamonds, silks, expensive drugs, and other articles which can be most readily smuggled by air. They will probably find their task so difficult that the free list will grow rapidly. Then the nations that are really wise will accept the almost universal dictum of economists that free trade, is, in the long run, the most profitable method for all concerned. After a few generations aviation may lead to free trade practically everywhere. Restrictions on immigration will presumably last much longer than limitation of imports, but they can scarcely fail to be much modified by aviation.

It need scarcely be pointed out that such a weakening of international boundaries will have far-reaching effects on war. Unless war is dropped completely as a method of settling disputes, the full development of the helicopter will apparently put every nation almost entirely at the mercy of every other. This will be true even if some short-sighted government should totally ban the use of all save military aviation. In spite of such a ban, not even a Maginot Line of air defences around the borders of a country could prevent the helicopters of other countries from entering. Thus there seems to be practically no limit to the extent to which any nation can spread abroad its spies, its atom bombs, its virulent bacteria, and its other mechanisms for either slow or sudden mass destruction. It seems to me that in the long run aviation may do even more than atomic fission to bring world-wide peace. It will do this partly by creating peaceful friendship, and partly by making war so dangerous to everyone that it will have to be outlawed by some kind of strong federation of the nations.

Mountains and Aviation

This blurring and partial elimination of the effect of international boundaries will not have much effect on routes of travel, and it will increase rather than diminish the contrasts between regions of different geographic types. One of the most obvious geographic principles is that transportation is hampered by mountains, snow, ice, fog, and storms. Enthusiasts say that the aeroplane has overcome these natural barriers, and that we shall soon have regular service by air, not only across mountains, but also across the practically uninhabited forests, tundras, mountains, glaciers, and ice floes of northern Canada, Greenland, Alaska, northern Asia, and the Arctic Ocean. I do not share this idea. It seems to me to be out of harmony with the established principles of geography.

Mountains supply a simple illustration of how the principles work, and Arctic regions follow the same laws. Aircraft, both planes and helicopters, certainly make it easier than ever before to cross mountains. It is equally certain, however, that mountains will always be so much of a hazard that aviators will avoid them as far as possible. Many of our worst aeroplane crashes are due to the combination of a hilly or mountainous terrain and stormy weather with rain, fog, or clouds. Such accidents will doubtless become less numerous as time goes on. Nevertheless, pilots and mechanics will still be fallible, no matter how good their machines. Hence, rugged mountains combined with storms will always be more dangerous than level plains and clear air. Mountains and storms will be especially difficult for the helicopter because of violent winds and strong convectional air currents which there move upward or downward with bewildering irregularity. The clouds, which are a prevailing feature of mountains, will be especially dangerous for the helicopter because so many of the owners of such craft are likely to have the tourist type of mind. Travelling here and there for fun, as they surely will, they are bound to have far more than their fair share of accidents, just as do mountain climbers in comparison with the drabber people who stay in the lowlands. Even a perfectly safe landing by a helicopter in the mountains may be extremely unpleasant and dangerous, because a take-off may be impossible, and an escape on foot among clouds, crags, cold winds, and uncharted slopes may demand extraordinary intelligence and power of endurance. Thus, to the aviator, as to the pedestrian or any other kind of traveller, mountains offer a tempting challenge, but will always present difficulties and dangers greater than the gently sloping lowlands. Hence they will be areas where aviation will be comparatively scarce. As aviation becomes more perfect and speedy there will be more and more tendency for aircraft to cross mountains at very high levels or else spend a little extra time in going around them.

The Global Effect

The effect of mountains on aviation is emphasized here because it hammers home the idea that new inventions do not annul the principles of geography, but merely give them a new application. Another reason for such emphasis is that the public has become confused as to the significance of polar aviation. It has been led to believe that future airlines will criss-cross the Arctic wastes in large numbers and that huge sums must be spent for military landing fields in the far north. The extent to which these beliefs are justified depends partly on the simple geographic principle already mentioned as to the effect of mountains, storms, ice, and snow on transportation in general. It also depends on another principle: the world's main lines of transportation normally unite the largest centres of trade, but they rarely follow the shortest course between such cities. They deviate from that course because of the terrain and also in order to pass through subsidiary centres. The shortest railway route from New York to Boston runs via New Haven, Middletown, Williamantic, and Franklin, but no through train goes that way. A comparatively straight double-track road might readily have been built, but it would not have paid. Two longer routes are the ones that are worthwhile. Beyond New Haven one of these routes swings well south of the shortest route in order to tap New London and Providence. The other swings northward and is still longer, but it passes through Meriden, Hartford, Springfield, and Worcester. Both routes go out of the direct line in order to get local traffic that supplements the through traffic between New York and Boston.

Look now at a globe and see how Arctic routes are related to the principle that main routes diverge from the shortest line in order to pass through intermediate centres. By the short great-circle route, the distance from Chicago to Moscow is approximately 5,100 miles. This means a trip of about eleven and a half hours non-stop at 450 miles an hour. By way of New York, London, and Berlin the distance is 5,900 miles, a fourteen-hour journey if the plane again goes 450 miles an hour and stops twenty minutes at each of these three places. The gain by the great-circle route across the mountainous wilderness of Labrador, the vast ice sheet of Greenland, and the frozen sea north of Iceland is insignificant. In order to save two or three hours how many passengers will wait for an inevitably infrequent arctic plane, and run the risk of a stormy, dark, winter trip across ice and snow, where an accident means almost certain death? And how can any air transport company afford to maintain airfields in northern Labrador and Greenland for the few passengers and small amount of freight and mail that will choose the direct route?

From San Francisco to Moscow the great-circle route goes almost over the North Pole, and the gain in time is greater than from Chicago to Moscow. In order to pick up enough traffic, the direct San Francisco–Moscow route will naturally go first to Portland, Seattle, and Vancouver, about 800 miles. Then for 5,200 miles the plane will cross practically uninhabited forests and tundras, traverse the vast, lofty ice sheet of Greenland, and fly over a very stormy ocean and the forests of northern Russia to Leningrad and Moscow. Stops at the three Pacific coast cities and at Leningrad, will make the trip take about thirteen hours. Via

Chicago and New York the time will be increased by five hours. Reckoned in this same fashion, no Arctic route such as the one from New York to Shanghai will save more than a maximum of possibly six hours out of twenty-four. This saving can be effected only at the three-fold cost of (1) constructing and maintaining a considerable number of very expensive far northern airfields, (2) encountering all the discomforts, troubles, delays, dangers, and losses that arise from ice, snow, cold isolation, and prolonged winter darkness in the far north, and (3) foregoing the profit that comes from way-stations. Thus, the geographical principles that govern the location of routes of transportation seem to make it highly improbable that Arctic air routes will ever be of much importance. The main routes will presumably always follow the courses dictated by the location of the larger cities.

What has just been said does not apply to military aviation, for that is governed by a different set of principles which cannot here be considered. As a geographer, however, I am impressed by the relative hopelessness of guarding the whole northern frontier of North America against invasion by air. A fleet of bombers starting from Sakhalin, Irkutsk, and Moscow on a bombing attack against our great cities could fan out along a hundred different routes. To stop them in northern Canada or Alaska would require an enormously expensive series of military airfields at frequent intervals across the whole 4,000 miles from Labrador and Newfoundland to the Aleutian Islands. And even so, we should in no respect be protected from the far greater danger of quiet infiltration by peaceful-seeming agents who would place atom bombs in all our cities. Such a line of defence would be a mere Maginot Line, already far out-moded. The possibility of using helicopters to bring in enemy agents and their equipment may prove to be the greatest thing that aviation has done in respect to war. The only defence against such infiltration seems to be that there should be not only no atom bombs, but no plans for war against anybody. Such a condition means, in turn, that there must be a world federation of the nations and a degree of international friendship, compromise, and co-operation that will permit the United Nations to function properly.

Effect on the Culture Pattern

Let us turn, now, to the relation of aviation to one of the most basic but least recognized principles of anthropogeography: the progress of civilization increases the contrasts arising from diverse types of geographic environment. People who do not fully understand this law often question it. They have the mistaken idea that from decade to decade and century to century the backward parts of the earth are becoming more like the advanced parts. They suppose that new inventions, by bringing what we call civilization to remote and unprogressive regions, diminish the contrasts between one place and another. Nothing could be much farther from the truth.

New ideas and inventions almost invariably have more effect on the rich, progressive centres of civilization than upon the backward outposts. The sewing machine is now a century old. Where is it found? In Wisconsin only the rare home is without one. In Guatemala, only the rich have them. Many of the poorer people bring some of their sewing to men who sit with their machines in front of little shops and make a business of sewing for the public. In New Guinea sewing machines are unknown except in a few towns near the coast and on a few foreign plantations. This same kind of contrast prevails as to banks, art museums, scientific discoveries, and almost everything else. In the United States and England modern ideas of world unity and of a nation's responsibility to help less favoured nations have spread widely. In Bulgaria they are known only to the more thoughtful people, and have little effect. In Indo-China they are practically unknown. In each of the preceding instances, a new machine, institution, or idea has had three greatly diverse grades of influence. In the most advanced countries it has profoundly altered the habits, thoughts, or general conduct of the population as a whole. In countries where the status of civilization is intermediate the effect of the new machines, institutions, and ideas has been intermediate. In the most backward countries there has been practically no effect.

Even if a new invention is widely used in backward regions, its main influence is generally seen in the advanced regions which finance it and supervise its work. That is what has happened with oil-drilling machinery, mining equipment, coffee-drying apparatus, and facilities for gathering and transporting copra and rubber. The introduction of these new machines and processes affects the lives of only a small percentage of the people in backward regions. Advanced regions get the main profit from their use. They are the places where the manner of life is significantly affected by the manufacture and sale of the gasoline, lubricating oil, rare minerals, coffee, soap, and tyres produced from the raw materials turned out by the new machines and processes.

Aviation by means of aeroplanes, helicopters, or any other device is bound to follow this same basic geographic rule. It will inevitably be mainly employed in the advanced parts of the earth, and thus will increase the contrast between those parts and the more backward parts.

35

Consider the many factors which will concentrate aviation in the United States above all other regions and, to a lesser extent, in Canada, Australia, New Zealand, Great Britain, and western Europe. The first factor is sheer expense. The first cost of aircraft is always likely to be greater than that of motor vehicles. The cost of upkeep will be proportionately still higher because the danger to life in a badly functioning conveyance is bound to be far greater in the air than on the ground. Therefore, aircraft must be kept tuned-up to a much higher pitch than landcraft. Everyone knows how we groan over garage bills and curse incompetent repair men.

In speaking of tuning-up we have introduced another vital factor, one which favours the concentration of aircraft in regions where the population is not only wealthy, but dense. Motor vehicles are constantly being stalled on our roads. Sometimes tyres can be replaced or repairs made right where the vehicle stops. Often, however, the disabled vehicle must be towed away. When helicopters and private planes become common, we may be sure that forced landings will be frequent in spite of the great amount of money spent in keeping the aircraft tuned-up. What will happen if a plane does not function properly and has to land in the woods, or even in an open space far from a road? The great danger to life and limb in comparison with a similar failure of an automobile is obvious. But even if the aircraft and its passengers land safely, how about salvaging or repairing the machine? If the landing takes place on or near a road and not too far from a hangar, a salvaging operation is feasible, although costly. If it takes place where there are few roads, or where hangars and skilled mechanics are scarce, the plane or helicopter will often be a dead loss. Such conditions will not have much effect on regular aeroplane lines, but they will be of vital import for helicopters. They will not prevent the use of helicopters on a large scale, but they will have a strong tendency to concentrate such use in a few relatively small parts of the earth. The helicopter owner will fly freely in well-populated, rich sections of the world where a forced landing is almost sure to be near roads, hangars, and skilled mechanics. He will fly with hesitation where the population is scarce and he runs the risk of having to land far from facilities for transporting or repairing his craft.

It is often asserted that aircraft will be of supreme value to isolated mines, ranches, and plantations, especially in the tropics. This is true up to a certain point, but by no means generally. The mere matter of risks and costs imposes a rigid limitation on the use of either planes or helicopters in such remote places. Unless plantations are very large or very numerous, the expense involved in preparing and maintaining airports is bound to be excessive in comparison with the amount of traffic. If helicopters become safe and practical, no landing fields will have to be kept up, but the cost of maintaining the helicopter will be high, because the aircraft will need to be very perfectly serviced and often replaced in order to avoid the great dangers of forced landings in places where the passengers cannot readily be rescued. Then, too, even with the best of care, there are bound to be many forced landings. These will be attended by much expense and often by loss of the aircraft because there will be no means of getting them out. These considerations do not mean that aviation will fail to be of great benefit to isolated mines, plantations, and other outposts of civilization. What they do mean is that in such places the risks, the losses, and the costs of various kinds are bound to be so high that only the larger or more prosperous enterprises can stand them.

The advantage of size is also seen when cities are compared with one another. The big city tends to outstrip the little one in aviation even more than in transportation on the earth's surface. As time goes on, more and more airlines will run from New York to small, foreign cities as well as to the larger foreign ones. Regular service to cities such as Caracas in Venezuela, Bogota in Colombia, and San José in Costa Rica has far more prospect of being a paying proposition from New York than from any other American city. Size and the centralization of business both make the great metropolis a profitable centre for such traffic. Boston, Philadelphia, Buffalo, Cleveland, and even Chicago cannot support direct air lines to many cities to which lines can be run at a profit from New York. Hence, people from these other cities will tend to come to New York to get a plane, and that city will increasingly overshadow all others as a centre for aviation even more than for other kinds of transportation.

The net effect of aviation in *increasing the contrasts between different parts of the world* may be summed up thus: We are trying to create one world and to give the little man a better chance, but in some respects aviation blocks our efforts. Like practically all innovations it adds to the contrasts between two great types of regions—those that are rich, densely populated, highly industrialized, and full of big cities, and those that are poor, sparsely populated, primitive, and lacking in cities. It also adds to the contrast between big, prosperous enterprises and those that are small and poor, especially in the less accessible parts of the earth.

Redistribution of Population

Another geographic effect of aviation will be a redistribution of population, not great, perhaps, but well worthy of study. One phase of this will be an accentuation of the effect of motor vehicles on cities and their suburbs. The automobile has tended to spread out our cities and open them up. Many cities have had an experience more or less like that of New Haven, Connecticut, where I live. The automobile has made it feasible to reside in the country in places not served by any form of public transportation. Hence the population has actually declined in the city proper, although it has increased steadily in the metropolitan district. At the same time the congestion of the city streets and the need for arterial streets and open spaces for parking has been greatly increased by the pouring in of suburban automobiles. The use of helicopters is almost certain to increase all these tendencies. It will spread the suburban population more widely, increase the congestion in the centre of cities, make life there less agreeable, and co-operate with the automobile in forcing cities to open up their central areas with wide boulevards and parking spaces for aircraft as well as for motor vehicles. In this way, it will contribute to health.

Quite a different effect upon the distribution of population and industries may arise from the added strain which aviation is already placing on supplies of gasoline. Unless new sources of fuel are found, it seems certain that within a few decades we shall face a serious crisis in keeping our aircraft in operation. Alcohol is usually considered the most promising substitute. But how can we get enough? Corn stalks and similar farm products will scarcely suffice, and even if they would, such materials ought to be used largely for fodder or else returned to the soil as fertilizer. In the region known to geographers as the wet and dry tropics, however, hundreds of millions of acres of tropical grassland furnish a vast reservoir of quickly growing plants which can be readily harvested. There, at a distance of five to twelve hundred miles from the equator, the climate is especially favourable for big grasses, but not for trees.

Looking at the river bank from the upper deck of a Nile steamer, I once saw ten or fifteen white spots which appeared intermittently through the tops of the grasses. They seemed to be moving slowly parallel to our steamer. Then we came to a place where the grass was broken down, and I saw that the white spots were birds perched on the heads of elephants. The grass was so tall that it hid the largest of animals. Similar grasses form almost pure stands in vast areas of Africa and South America both north and south of the equator, and also in northern Australia, New Guinea, and elsewhere. They thrive in hot climates under the influence of three months or so of very heavy rain. Then they dry up and stand brown and sere through many months of scorching, blistering heat so dry that the parched earth often splits open in big cracks. Towards the end of the dry season I have seen the horizon broken on all sides by pillars of smoke. The widely scattered inhabitants burn the dead grass so that their cattle may feed more readily when the first rains cause fresh green sprouts almost to jump out of the ground. In many of these grasslands the dry season is so severe that for mile after mile no trees whatever break the monotony of what may some day become vast mowing fields, gigantic in both extent and height.

Today these grasslands are almost useless except to vast herds of antelope and far smaller herds of cattle. Most of the grass is burned, or rapidly decays during the season of warm rain. It might well be cut by great mowing and binding machines, and used to produce alcohol. Nowhere else, so far as I am aware, is any such abundance of vegetation so easily available and so constantly replenished. I surmise that in the relatively near future the demand for gasoline, stimulated greatly by aviation, may lead to a new industry and a new series of settlements here in one of the few great types of regions still remaining almost undeveloped.

In due time aircraft may also enable man to utilize the resources of unhealthful or unpleasant tropical regions without the physical discomfort and risk to health that now are almost inevitable. If power becomes cheap enough and helicopters sufficiently safe, fast, and inexpensive, hundreds of thousands—perhaps millions—of people may live among tropical mountains and work in the neighbouring lowlands. In low latitudes the disadvantages of mountains from the standpoint of aviation are far outbalanced by the great improvement in health, comfort, and efficiency which comes from living at an altitude of 3,000 to 6,000 feet instead of lower down. With efficient helicopters daily commutation flights to a distance of fifty or a hundred miles do not seem improbable. And weekend flights of several hundred miles may bring lowland workers back to their families in the mountains from Friday night to Monday morning.

Such a system would lead to a dense population in the most pleasant and healthful parts of the tropics where the spring-like climate is truly delightful. For hundreds of miles in the neighbouring lowlands the permanent population would be sparse, but daily or weekly commuters from the highlands would develop the resources of vast areas like the Amazon basin which are now of little use. Such a distribution of population and occupations will doubtless be slow in coming. It will be hampered by the fact that only the most successful plantations or other tropical enterprises can afford to support aircraft. The new system of commuting between mountain homes and lowland places of business will presumably begin with groups of northern executives who can afford expensive helicopters. They will set up mountain centres where their families can be comfortable and their children can have good schools. As the generations go on, however, we may perhaps expect that aircraft and power will become cheap, while appreciation of the value of the common man becomes great. Then it will be seen that large expenditures for the sake of health are worth while, and that every effort should be made so that all the children will have the greatest possible advantages from the standpoints of climate, diet, and training. In all of these respects compact groups of people in beautiful, cool mountain homes will have a great advantage over small, isolated groups widely scattered in hot, muggy, tropical lowlands.

Effect on Pests and Diseases

In studying the probable effects of aviation, other forms of life as well as man must be included. Aeroplanes and helicopters are already beginning to exert an influence on the health and geographical distribution of crops through their use in sprinkling insecticides. Soon they will doubtless be widely used to spray materials such as DDT for the purpose of exterminating flies, mosquitoes, ticks, Japanese beetles, gypsy moths, chinch bugs, and a host of other insects, fungi, or bacteria that bring disease to man and animals. In the summer of 1947 Iowa became the first large area to be almost completely freed from flies in this way. As a result the cattle put on weight as never before. Such treatment of insects is part of a vast and momentous geographic readjustment of living creatures. In getting rid of harmful insects we may also get rid of helpful ones. We may also prevent the fertilization of certain kinds of flowers, thus eradicating some species and leaving the way open for others. Birds of some species may be eliminated because the insects or seeds that they eat have become scarce. A similar fate may overtake small mammals such as field mice. The place of the displaced species is almost certain to be taken by some other form, for that is nature's method, and the new forms may be more noxious than the ones destroyed or driven out by spraying.

These alarming possibilities are by no means the whole story, for aircraft will almost inevitably bring many forms of life into new habitats. Regular airliners will doubtless be sprayed and inspected so that they will do little harm as carriers of insects, bacteria, and persons infected with disease. Private planes and helicopters, especially those that fly illegally as smugglers, will be the ones to be feared. Try as we will, it will be impossible to control them fully. Therefore, we face the ominous danger that new diseases, new insect pests, and probably new weeds will be spread all over the world. The speed and directness with which aircraft move will increase the risks of this sort many fold. Some of the newly introduced species will find environments that kill them off, but others will flourish better than in their old homes. Humorous Australians claim that Scotch settlers, rather than rabbits, are the worst of their introduced pests, but the rabbits have made it necessary to erect thousands of miles of wire fence. The shredded leaves left by the Japanese beetle and the bare trees left by the gypsy moth are examples of the exasperating devastation caused by insects imported from abroad.

In Brazil in the early 1930's the opening of an air route to Africa permitted one of the most deadly of all forms of malarial mosquitoes to establish itself and its disease. The Rockefeller Foundation was fortunately able to help the Brazilian government to get rid of the disease, but not till it had spread hundreds of miles and had caused a whole river valley to be depopulated. So many people died of malaria that the rest fled in a panic. The chances are that the spread of aviation will lead to many transfers of insects and diseases that will be as bad as the Japanese beetle and the malarial mosquito. Thus aviation may bring the world face to face with a geographic readjustment of living species and of diseases that will make previous similar experiences seem like child's play.

Many aspects of the geographic relationships of aviation have doubtless been omitted or not given the right emphasis in this article. Nevertheless, a few important conclusions stand out clearly. Aviation will not change a single basic principle of geography, but it will bring new applications of old principles. It will continue to intensify the fearfulness of war. Nevertheless, it will help to eliminate war by making the world so small that international contacts will vastly increase. It will break down international barriers and make free trade almost compulsory in the long run. It will add to the difficulty of solving problems such as those of migration and freedom of travel. Another powerful effect of aviation will presumably be to increase the relative importance of large cities, main trade routes, and large enterprises in remote regions.

Contrary to common opinion, it is not likely to cause any conspicuous development of Arctic routes. Nor will it be of so much benefit to mountain regions as to lowlands except in the tropics. It will increase rather than diminish the contrasts between the most advanced and the most backward regions. It will also change the distribution of population. The compact centres of cities will lose inhabitants and will become more open, while the suburbs will increase in size and area. Aviation may also help in originating new centres of population in low altitudes. One type may be found where the huge grasses of the wet and dry tropics are harvested for alcohol; another in healthful mountains from which people commute to their work in the lowlands. And, finally, in spite of all that we can do to prevent it, aircraft are practically certain to upset the present balance of nature by killing off some kinds of living creatures and carrying others to new regions. Mankind enters the so-called air age with the prospect that the great biological and cultural revolution, which began with the invention of the steam engine, will reach a might climax within a few generations.

CHAPTER XXIII

THE FIELD OF THE GEOGRAPHICAL SOCIETY

JOHN K. WRIGHT

John K. Wright, librarian, American Geographical Society, New York, 1920–37, Director since 1938. Author of Aids to Geographical Research *(1923; 2nd edition with the late E. T. Platt, 1947);* The Geographical Lore of the Time of the Crusades, *1925; &c.; editor of various books published by the American Geographical Society.*

Summary

ALTHOUGH facts in abundance are available concerning different individual geographical societies, little has been done to correlate these facts, and no studies of any consequence have been made of such institutions as viewed collectively or comparatively. Hence this paper is no more than a brief introduction to an almost wholly virgin field. After an outline of the development of geographical societies in modern times and an attempt to classify them, attention is directed to the nine leading geographical societies of the English-speaking world. The principal activities in which these nine engage and the broader educational and research functions which they perform are summarized, and their work as a whole is contrasted with comparable work done in the government, in the universities, and in business. The societies are shown to have especially valuable intangible assets, in that their motives are disinterested and they are free to shape their own policies.

Introduction

Because geography owes its foremost debt to great men—the Strabos, the Columbuses, the Von Humboldts, the Davises—its history has been written largely as the record of the successive contributions of individual explorers and scholars. Yet most of these individuals would have accomplished little had they not received the support of institutions—the state, the church, universities, industrial and commercial companies, societies[1] of various kinds. The institutional aspect of the advancement of geography deserves more study than it has yet received.

[1] See the detailed article, 'Societies, Learned', with bibliographical references, in *Encyclopaedia Britannica*, 11th edition, Vol. 25, 1911, pp. 309–19 (omitted in 14th edition); also 'Handbook of Scientific and Technical Societies and Institutions of the United States and Canada', 4th edition, Washington, 1942 (*Bull. of the National Research Council*, No. 106); Ralph S. Bates, *Scientific Societies in the United States*, New York, 1945 (an historical study).

The present paper deals with one phase of this subject: with a type of institution that has done much for geography during the past century and a half. A 'geographical society' is an association, club, or similar organization devoted specifically to the cultivation of geography as such. Many other societies, of course, are 'geographical' in a loose sense, being concerned in one way or another with areas or types of area or with the distribution of phenomena on the face of the earth. Mountaineering, travel, and other outdoor clubs; geological, zoological, and anthropological societies; associations engaged in the comprehensive investigation of regions (e.g. the African Association, the Institute of Pacific Relations) —all these have geographical interests, but since it would carry us far afield to consider such semi-geographical organizations, this discussion will be limited to geographical societies proper—societies which may usually be identified by the word 'geographical' or its equivalent in their titles; and which, unlike the governmental committees or commissions[1] or the sections of general scientific associations[2] that embrace geography, are independent corporate entities.

'The field of the geographical society' is mostly virgin, although much information is at hand for those who would cultivate it. Most of this information bears upon the history and current activities of particular societies, and is in the form of published transactions and similar records and of manuscripts in society archives. Histories of individual societies in goodly quantity have appeared on the occasion of fiftieth and hundredth anniversaries and at other milestones[3]—a few as books, the majority of

[1] e.g. National Research Council, Division of Geology and Geography.

[2] e.g. American Association for the Advancement of Science, Section E, Geology and Geography: and, especially, British Association for the Advancement of Science, Section E, Geography.

[3] There follows a partial list of references to historical studies of individual geographical societies as published in their periodicals or separately. Except where indicated by the title, the period covered by each study is shown in parentheses.

BELGIUM. *Bull. de la Société Royale Belge de Géographie*, Vol. 50, 1926, pp. 173–87 (1876–1926). *Bull. de la Soc. Roy. Belge de Géogr. d'Anvers*, Vol. 46, 1926, pp. 215–27 (1876–1926). BRAZIL. Max Fleiuss, *L'Institut Historique et Géographique de Brésil (Esquisse de son Histoire)*, Rio de Janeiro, 1928 (1838–1928) (see also *Bull. Pan-American Union*, Vol. 72, 1938, pp. 557–67). *Instituto Historico e Geografico de São Paulo, Jubileu Social, 1894–1944*, São Paulo, 1944. FRANCE. Société de Géographie de Paris: *La Géographie*, Vol. 36, 1921, pp. 137–208 (1821–1921). Société de Géographie Commerciale et d'Études Coloniales: *Revue économique française*, Vol. 57, 1935, pp. 5–37 (1873–1933). *Bull. de la Soc. de Géogr. de Lille*, Vol. 72, 1930, pp. 68–106 (1880–1930). *Bull. de la Soc. de Géogr. et d'Études Coloniales de Marseille*, Vol. 47, 1926, pp. 5–9 (1876–1926). GERMANY. *Zeitschrift der Gesellschaft für Erdkunde zu Berlin*, 1928, pp. 161–210; ibid., *Sonderband zur Hundertjahrfeier der Gesellschaft*, 1928, pp. 1–30 (1828–1928) (see also *Die Naturwissenschaften*, Vol. 16, 1928, pp. 369–74). *Festschrift*

less ambitious scope. Normally these consist of addresses delivered at ceremonies and tend to be more laudatory than critical. Studies of a synthetic type concerning 'the geographical society', as distinguished from accounts of 'the such-and-such geographical society', are almost completely lacking.[1] While brief mention is made of geographical societies in certain discussions of the development of geography in particular countries,[2] and a few works list the geographical societies of the

zur Hundertjahrfeier des Vereins für Geographie und Statistik zu Frankfurt am Main, Frankfurt am Main, 1936, pp. 1–35 (1836–1936). Mitteilungen Geogr. Gesellsch. in Hamburg, Vol. 36, 1924, pp. 1–27 (1898–1923: second 25 years). GREAT BRITAIN. H. R. Mill: The Record of the Royal Geographical Society, 1830–1930, London, 1930. 'The Royal Scottish Geographical Society: The First Fifty Years', Scottish Geogr. Mag., Vol. 50, 1934, pp. 257–80 (1884–1934). ITALY. Enrico de Agostini: La Reale Società Geografica Italiana e la sua opera della fondazione ad oggi (1867–1936), Rome, 1937. MEXICO. Primer centenario de la Sociedad Mexicana de Geografía y Estadística, 1833–1933, Mexico, 1933, 2 vols. NORWAY. Norske Geografiske Selskab: Norsk Geografisk Tidskrift, Vol. 7, 1938/9, Nos. 5–8 (English summary, pp. 25–33) (1889–1939). SPAIN. Boletín de la Real Sociedad Geográfica, Vol. 66, 1926, pp. 220–63 (1876–1926) (see also Quincuagésimo Aniversario de la R. S. G. . . . Madrid, 1926). SWITZERLAND. Jahresbericht der Geogr. Gesellsch. von Bern, Vol. 25, 1919–22, pp. 1–13 (1873–1923). Egmond Goegg: Coup d'œil sur la Société de Géographie de Genève de 1908 à 1933, Geneva, 1933. Mitteil. der Ostschweizerischen Geogr.—Commerciellen Gesellsch. in St. Gallen, 1928, pp. 5–55 (1878–1928). Mitteil. der Geogr.-Ethnographischen Gesellsch. Zürich, Vol. 39, 1838/9, pp. 5–29 (1888–1938). Egmond Goegg 'Historique de l'Association de Sociétés Suisses de Geographie . . .', Le Globe: Organe de la Soc. de Géogr. de Genève, Vol. 70, numéro spécial, pp. 12–36 (the association includes the Basel, Bern, Neuchâtel, Zürich, and St. Gall societies and the Société Suisse de Professeurs de Géographie). UNITED STATES. Annals of the Association of American Geographers, Vol. 14, 1924, pp. 109–16 (1903–23). 'The Geographical Society of Philadelphia: Fiftieth Anniversary, 1891–1941' (brochure). Gilbert Grosvenor, 'The National Geographic Society and its Magazine', in National Geographic Magazine, Cumulative Index, 1899–1946, Washington, 1948, pp. 1–115 (1899–1946). U.S.S.R. All-Union Geographical Society (formerly Imperial Russian Geographical Society): Izvestiia Vsesoiuznogo Geogr. Obshchestva, Vol. 73, 1941, pp. 335–52 (1845–1940); Vol. 78, 1946, pp. 25–90 (1845–1945). East Siberian Branch of same: Izvestiia Vostochno-Sibirskogo Otdela Gosudarstvennogo Russkogo G.O., Vol. 50, 1927, Part 2, pp. 3–53 (1851–1926). West Siberian Branch: Zapiski Zapadno-Sibirskogo Otdela Gosudarstvennogo R.G.O., Vol. 39, 1927, pp. 1–144 (English summary, pp. 141–4) (1877–1927).

[1] Little or nothing is said about geographical societies in the general histories of geography of Vivien de St. Martin, Peschel, Hettner, and Dickinson and Howarth. Siegmund Günther, Geschichte der Erdkunde, Leipzig and Vienna, 1904, gives some scattered facts on pp. 184–5, 232–3, and 296.

[2] See, for example, Roberto Almagià, La Geografia, 2nd edition, Rome, 1922, pp. 50–5 (on Italian institutions); Emmanuel de Martonne, 'Geography in France', New York, 1924 (American Geogr. Soc. Research Series No. 4a), pp. 6–17; W. M. Davis, 'The Progress of Geography in the United States', Annals Assoc. Amer.

world and present statistics and other facts about them,[1] no one has yet sought with any degree of scholarship and critical acumen to correlate the rise of geographical societies with larger historical events, to measure and appraise their influence, or to make a comparative analysis of their functions and problems.

Since no one has done this, no one is really competent to write authoritatively on the entire 'field of the geographical society'. This would demand extensive research, exceptional linguistic ability, and first-hand knowledge of the inner workings of representative societies, and would take years. The writer of this paper knows something at first hand of the inner workings of two American geographical societies, he has heard a good deal about certain others, and has dipped into the 'literature' here and there. Beyond that he makes no claim; what follows is not the 'last word' but merely some provisional 'first words'.

Historical Sketch

It has been said that geographical societies originated with the founding of the Société de Géographie de Paris in 1821;[2] but while that venerable institution was the first society of its kind destined to endure, it had pre-decessors nearly a century earlier.[3] In 1693 a proposal was made in Germany that an international association of scholars be formed to prepare accurate maps of all countries, and gather them in a *Corpus* 'upon the like of which

Geographers, Vol. 14, 1924, pp. 159–215 (ref. on pp. 177–8); C. C. Colby, 'Changing Currents of Geographic Thought in America', ibid., Vol. 26, 1936, pp. 1–37 (ref. on pp. 5–6, 17–19).

[1] Georg Kollm, 'Geographische Gesellschaften, Zeitschriften, Kongresse und Ausstellungen, I. Geographische Gesellschaften', *Geographisches Jahrbuch*, Vol. 32, 1909, pp. 409–19 (statistical table, arranged by countries, showing dates of foundation, number of members, and financial data pertaining to 125 societies and 36 branches in 24 countries and 160 cities). *Geographen-Kalender*, 12th year, 1914 (last published), pp. 69–350 (data, alphabetically arranged by cities throughout the world, concerning geographical and related societies, foundations, professorships, &c.); pp. 353–414 (list of geographical and related periodicals arranged alphabetically by titles). *Minerva*, 32nd year, 1937 (last published) (data, arranged alphabetically by cities), on a variety of different types of scientific and scholarly institutions, including geographical societies; no index locating the scattered pages on which geographical societies are listed). *Index Generalis*, 1939 (last published), pp. 2006–14 (data on some 50 geographical societies arranged alphabetically by cities).

[2] E. Behm, 'Einiges über die geographischen Reisen, Gesellschaften und Publikationen der Gegenwart', *Geographisches Jahrbuch*, Vol. 1, 1866, pp. 552–80 (ref. on p. 568).

[3] Günther, op. cit., p. 184.

the sun has not yet shone and on which posterity will be unable to bestow sufficient praise and glory'.[1] Nothing came of this, alas. There was, however, a fairly active Kosmographische Gesellschaft in Nuremberg in the 1740's, the word 'cosmography' then being used synonymously with 'geography'.[2] A geographical society also existed in Holland at about the same time,[3] and there may have been one at Leyden[4] at the beginning of the eighteenth century.

These early ventures were abortive. The times were not ripe, and during the eighteenth century the academies and kindred learned institutions sufficed well enough to meet the needs of geographically-minded scholars. The Royal Society of London frequently published papers on geographical subjects in its *Philosophical Transactions*.

The blossoming of geographical societies after 1820 came in response to broader social changes. As scientific discoveries, technological inventions, and educational progress have increased the number and variety of human occupations, new and ever more specialized institutions have been formed to serve new interests. This process was tremendously accelerated in the nineteenth century, when better means of transportation, communication, and publication made it easier for individuals to establish and maintain contact with one another. Furthermore, the nineteenth century was a time when special circumstances aroused fresh interest in geography itself.

Peace prevailed, if not uninterruptedly, for a hundred years after Waterloo and freed men to roam the world both in body and in mind. Energies that had previously been absorbed in wars and internal troubles could be expended in colonial ventures and settlement on remote frontiers, and geographical exploration was their accompaniment. Also, patriotic pride, due to the growth of national feeling both in the Old

---

[1] A. Heyer, 'Eberhard David Haubers Versuch, einer deutsche geographische Gesellschaft zu gründen (1727–30)', *Zeitschr. für wissenschaftliche Geographie*, Vol. 6, 1888, pp. 42–4, 53–7 (ref. on p. 42).

[2] Günther, loc. cit. This Nuremberg institution is mentioned as a 'geographical society' in such designations as 'Societatis geographicae sodalis', 'de la Soc. géogr.', &c., which follow the names of the compilers of certain maps in the great atlas published by the Homann heirs of Nuremberg. See Sophus Ruge, 'Aus der Sturm- und Drang-Periode der Geographie (Die älteste geographische Gesellschaft und ihre Mitglieder)', *Zeitschr. für wissensch. Geogr.*, Vol. 5, 1884, pp. 249–60, 355–64 (ref. on p. 249).

[3] See *Tijdschr. van het Aardrijkskundig Genootschap*, Amsterdam, Ser. 1, Vol. 3, 1879, p. 135.

[4] Günther, loc. cit., mentions this on the authority of a personal communication from Prof. [C. M.] Kan of Amsterdam. A cursory search in the library of the American Geographical Society has failed to disclose further details.

World and the New, stimulated citizens to take keen interest in the internal geography of their own countries.

The Société de Géographie de Paris, founded (in 1821) six years after the battle of Waterloo, provided a pattern and inspiration for similar institutions. It was followed by the Berlin Geographical Society in 1828 and the Royal Geographical Society in London in 1831. Mexico took fourth place with the establishment of a 'Geographical and Statistical Society' in 1833; Frankfurt am Main came fifth in 1836, and Brazil sixth in 1838 with the Instituto Historico e Geografico do Brasil; The Imperial Russian Geographical Society was seventh in 1845, and the American Geographical Society[1] eighth in 1852. By 1866, 18 genuine geographical societies had been organized, 11 in Europe, 3 in Asia, 3 in Latin America, and 1 in the United States.[2]

By 1930 the total had risen to 137, according to a statistical study of the chronology and distribution of geographical societies by Enrique Sparn,[3] who presents a table showing, for the geographical societies still in existence at the time of his investigation, the number that were founded in each decade. Fifteen had made their appearance between 1820 and 1870, 58 in the 1870's and 1880's, 10 in the 1890's, 11 in the 1900's, 10 between 1909 and 1920, and 31 in the 1920's. The increase in the 1870's and '80's may be attributed in part at least to the surge of national feeling following the unification of Germany and Italy, to the colonial activities of the Great Powers[4] and of Belgium (this was the period of the partition of Africa and of Oceania), and to the Polar explorations of these decades. The recrudescence of nationalism after the First World War doubtless accounts for the establishment during the 1920's of three new societies in Poland, one in Yugoslavia, one in Czechoslovakia, and one in Turkey.

Sparn's analysis does not take account of societies that have expired, but it is the writer's impression that geographical societies, when once established, often possess an almost feline vitality, coming to life again

[1] Known until 1871 as 'The American Geographical and Statistical Society'.

[2] Behm, op. cit., p. 568.

[3] Enrique Sparn, 'Cronologia, diferenciación, numero de socios y distribución de las sociedades de geografía', *Boletín de la Academia Nacional de Ciencias*, Córdoba, Argentina, Vol. 32, 1932–5, pp. 323–36 (statistical information largely from *Minerva*, Vol. 30, 1930; Vol. 31, 1933, and *Index Generalis*, 1933 (see above, p. 7); accompanied by three sketch maps showing the distribution of geographical societies).

[4] The important part played by the French geographical societies in colonial agitation in France in the 1870's is discussed by D. U. McKay, 'Colonialism in the French Geographical Movement 1871–1881', *Geographical Review*, Vol. 33, 1943, pp. 214–32.

after periods of torpor. Many of the files of their publications show gaps over long periods, notably the war years. The American Geographical Society nearly perished during the Civil War, and the First and Second World Wars were times when the vitality of most of the smaller societies was at a low ebb.

Of the 137 societies operating in 1930 according to Sparn, 92 were in Europe, 25 in the Americas, 13 in Asia, 5 in Africa, and 2 in Australasia. France and Germany with 25 and 22 respectively accounted for considerably more than half of the total number in Europe. The United States and the Soviet Union each had 8 apiece and no other country more than 6. The total membership was figured at 102,712;[1] 27 of the 137 societies had more than 1,000 members each, 29 between 500 and 1,000, and 81 less than 1,000.

Varieties of Geographical Society

Naturally, these societies have developed along divergent lines. Although the majority, nominally at least, accept the entire realm of geography as their field, a small minority, mostly in Europe, definitely limit themselves to specified regions or branches of geography. These specialized institutions are comparable to the more numerous historical societies that concentrate upon the history of particular periods, subjects, or regions. However, if not in avowed intent, in actual fact every geographical society lays disproportionate emphasis on the parts of the world with which its members or staff can best maintain contact: the home country, its neighbouring lands and overseas possessions, if any, and other areas within its spheres of interest. While this applies with particular force to the smaller societies, it is true to some extent even of the largest and most influential.

All of the older geographical societies are *laymen's* societies. Their memberships are not restricted to professional geographers or teachers, but are open to laymen in geography. These societies are also centralized, anchored permanently to the cities where they maintain headquarters. Although explorers, geographers, and teachers often played a part in their founding, fully as influential was the part played by other people of education and substance—in the professions, in business, and in government and military service—and persons of heterogeneous interests have always constituted the bulk of their members. Most of the laymen's societies have remained *local* or *regional* in character, with the majority of the members residing in one city or district, and most of these local and

[1] Obviously does not include members of the National Geographic Society.

regional societies, in fact, are little more than social clubs that afford the members pleasant opportunities for hearing popular lectures. A few, especially in Europe, engage in scientific work and issue periodicals and other publications of high grade.

In all but the most backward countries there are also *national* laymen's societies—national in that they are the leading institutions of their kind in their respective nations. Their memberships are usually widely scattered throughout the home country and may include individuals in foreign lands as well. Normally there is one outstanding national laymen's society in each country, with its headquarters in the capital (although the United States has two: the National Geographic Society in Washington and the American Geographical Society in New York). Such institutions, particularly those of the larger nations, are by far the most powerful and influential of all geographical societies, and their publications collectively constitute the most comprehensive and generally useful body of modern geographical literature.[1] Special advantages have enabled them to out-shadow the local and regional societies. Counting more members, they receive more revenue in annual dues, and their location in financial centres places them in a better position to gain support from wealthy patrons. Their financial strength, in turn, has made it possible for them to acquire substantial working facilities—buildings, collections, and, most important of all, staffs of full-time paid employees. They have also benefited from the contacts with the outer world that can be maintained more readily in national capitals than elsewhere.

Within the last fifty years new needs have arisen which the laymen's societies have been unable to satisfy. Partly owing to the influence of these societies themselves—in particular of the larger national societies—geography has been introduced into the universities and colleges and its teaching in the schools has been much improved, and as a consequence a new profession has come into being. Although there have long been geographers and teachers of the subject, not until recent decades have they developed a definite professional consciousness. At first the profession consisted almost wholly of university and school teachers, with a scattering of scientific explorers, but in the course of time it has grown to include others as well: government employees, research workers in scientific institutions, and even a few individuals in the employ of business firms.

While the geographer or geography teacher might profit in many

---

[1] For titles of the more important geographical-society and other geographical periodicals, with dates, references to indexes, &c., see J. K. Wright and the late E. T. Platt, 'Aids to Geographical Research', 2nd edition, Columbia University Press, 1947 (*Amer. Geogr. Soc. Research Series* No. 22).

ways from belonging to a laymen's society, he soon felt the need of an organization of his own that would bring him into contact with colleagues in other parts of his country. Hence, he took the initiative in founding *professional* societies of two types, *geographers'* and *school teachers'* societies. The professional society, unlike the laymen's, is decentralized: it meets from time to time in different places and normally maintains headquarters where the secretary or some other leading spirit happens to reside. Most of the professional societies are *national* in the distribution of their membership.[1]

Since the majority of geographers and school teachers are poor in worldly goods, the professional societies are correspondingly poor. They cannot maintain either collections of any consequence or paid staffs (except possibly a part-time stenographer). While the intellectual bonds that unite their members are stronger than in the laymen's societies, their facilities for producing publications are far less substantial. Whatever work they do must be done almost entirely by the members themselves as a labour of love.

Another important distinction must be drawn—namely between *research* societies and *educational* societies. The former, some of which are of the laymen's type and others professional, make the advancement of original investigations their primary concern; the latter are devoted chiefly to the dissemination of geographical knowledge, and may likewise be either of the laymen's or professional type. Naturally this distinction is merely one of emphasis: all research societies are educational in a broad sense and no educational society is wholly devoid of interest in the progress of geographical research.

The National Societies of the United States and Great Britain

It would be impossible in a paper of this length to do justice to geographical societies of all these various kinds in all parts of the world. Hence, from here on attention will be focused on nine institutions that are presumably of especial interest to readers of this book—the leading national societies of the English-speaking world. Four of these are laymen's societies and five professional: of the laymen's societies three are research societies and one is educational; two of the professional societies are devoted to research, two are educational (school teachers') societies, and

[1] The Association of Pacific Coast Geographers is an example of a regional professional group. The American Society for Professional Geographers maintains regional divisions. The latter amalgamated with the Assoc. of Amer. Geographers in Dec. 1949.

36

one, a promotional society, does not fall definitely in either the research or educational class.

The three *laymen's* research societies are the Royal Geographical Society (founded 1830),[1] the American Geographical Society (founded 1852),[2] and the Royal Scottish Geographical Society (founded 1884).[3] The National Geographic Society in Washington (founded 1888),[4] though it has carried forward certain research projects, is essentially a laymen's educational society. The two *professional* research societies are the Association of American Geographers (founded 1904)[5] and the Institute of British Geographers (founded 1933);[6] the two professional educational (school teachers') societies are the Geographical Association (British, founded 1893)[7] and the National Council of Geography Teachers (American, founded 1914).[8] The promotional society is the American Society for Professional Geographers (founded 1943),[9] which seeks to forward the progress of geographical research and geographical education alike by promoting and protecting the professional interests of geographers.

Specific Activities

Before dealing with the research and educational functions of these societies, let us pass briefly in review the principal specific activities which they carry on in order to perform these functions. (The actual conduct of research by certain of the laymen's societies will be discussed in the following section.)

These consist in the first place of activities designed to disseminate geographical information and ideas, notably the (1) *publication* of docu-

[1] In this and succeeding footnotes up to note 9 below, the titles and dates are given of the periodicals and other important series published by the several societies.
    The Geographical Journal (1893– ; succeeded *Journal of the R.G.S.*, 1830–80; *Proceedings*, 1855–78; *Proceedings*, New Series 1879–92), *Technical Series* (since 1920).
[2] *The Geographical Review* (1916– ; succeeded *Journal*, *Bulletin*, &c., 1852–1915). *Special Publications* (1915–). *Research Series* (1922–).
[3] *The Scottish Geographical Magazine* (1885–).
[4] *The National Geographic Magazine* (1889–).
[5] *Annals of the Association of American Geographers* (1911–).
[6] *Publications* (1935–).
[7] *Geography* (1901– ; title *The Geographical Teacher* to 1927). The New Zealand Geographical Society (founded in 1939), which originated as an overseas branch of the Geographical Association, is one of the most active of the professional societies in the British dominions. It publishes *The New Zealand Geographer* (1945–).
[8] *The Journal of Geography* (1897– ; title to 1901: *Journal of School Geography*). *Professional Papers* (1927–).
[9] *The Professional Geographer* (1943– ; title has varied).

ments and (2) *assembly*, or the holding of meetings. Publication is distinctive of the laymen's, and assembly of the professional society. The laymen's society renders its primary service to research and education by issuing one or more periodicals and in some cases books, maps, news letters, and other documents as well; its lecture courses and other meetings are of secondary moment. The professional society, on the contrary, accomplishes its more productive and influential results through the presentation and discussion of papers and projects at the time of its regular meetings and through the work of committees, and publication is of secondary importance, although the publications of the professional societies exert a considerably greater influence on the advancement of geography than do the meetings of the laymen's societies.

(3) *The collection and preservation* of geographical books, maps, photographs, instruments, &c., is an indispensable indirect aid to the advancement of geographical research and education, but, here again, only a few geographical societies are in a position to maintain libraries and map collections of any size—among the societies that we are here considering, the Royal Geographical Society and the American Geographical Society alone. Theirs are the pre-eminent geographical collections of the English-speaking world—if not in quantity of books and maps, certainly in adaptation to the special needs of geographers. Much of the strength of these two institutions is due to the use which their professional staffs make of their collections and to the assistance rendered research workers and teachers through the publication of bibliographical guides based upon their holdings and current accessions.

(4) The stimulation and recognition of research and educational achievement through the *award of honours*—grants-in-aid, prizes, medals, citations, and the like—is practised by the majority of geographical societies. The Royal Geographical Society, the American Geographical Society, the National Geographic Society, and the Association of American Geographers occasionally make grants-in-aid for the conduct of projects by others than their own staff members; and the Royal Geographical Society and Association of American Geographers have special funds earmarked for this purpose. The Royal Geographical Society awards monetary prizes, and the laymen's societies generally recognize outstanding contributions to geography and exploration by presenting medals and by elections to honorary memberships. Since membership in the Association of American Geographers is open only to those who have made fairly substantial original contributions to geography,[1] it is in itself a form of recognition. Contrary to a widespread

[2] This is no longer true, see footnote p. 551.

impression, this is not true of Fellowship (i.e. membership) in either the Royal Geographical Society or the American Geographical Society, where the only requirement (other than the payment of dues) is an interest in geography and a desire to support the institution in question.

(5) *Professional promotion* implies a variety of undertakings intended to advance or protect the interests of geographers and teachers collectively or individually, as, for example, placement services, efforts to secure the introduction or improvement of geographical teaching in schools and colleges or of geographical research in agencies of the government, and the facilitating of social contacts within the profession. The neglect of professional promotion by the established geographical societies of the United States led to the founding of the American Society for Professional Geographers.

These five types of activity may (or may not) be carried forward in such a way as to achieve a primary over-all function; the upholding of high standards of achievement in geographical scholarship and education. Standards are upheld only through the application and expression of criticism, and, to this end a geographical society must maintain constant critical vigilance in all of its varied activities. This vigilance is needed no less in the choice of documents for collections and of recipients for awards than in the selection and conduct of research projects and in the manner in which professional promotion is undertaken. The discussion of papers and projects at the sessions of the professional societies and the book reviews and notes in society periodicals provide opportunity for explicit criticism, the mere possibility of which can be a deterrent to careless preparation and presentation. The editors of geographical society publications hold a grave responsibility with respect to the whole development of geographical knowledge. The effective implicit criticism which they are in a position to exercise in rejecting, accepting, and revising manuscripts for publication gives them a special guardianship over standards. A similar responsibility rests on those who arrange programmes for the meetings of the professional societies, although for obvious human reasons standards cannot be maintained as rigorously here as in the case of publications.

Research Functions

Geographical research is systematic investigation designed to yield either new geographical knowledge, or new methods of applying, presenting, or disseminating geographical knowledge. It may be pursued either in the field or 'indoors', and it is not a monopoly of geographers; many others engage in it in one way or another.

There are substantial differences between geographical societies as regards the character of the research in which they are most interested. The teachers' societies are concerned with research bearing on new educational policies and new methods of teaching. The chief concern of the geographers' societies, of course, is with the kinds of research that geographers themselves pursue, especially geographers in the universities, who form the majority of the productive research workers in the profession. Such studies have been discussed elsewhere in this volume and need no elaboration here. While extremely varied in nature, they are, for the most part, short-range projects which individuals can carry out in time spared from teaching and administrative duties, and of immediate professional rather than of general interest. The geographers' research societies have also taken the lead in the development and discussion of the philosophical and methodological aspects of geography.

The laymen's research societies also encourage studies of this same sort. The American Geographical Society, the Royal Geographical Society, and the Royal Scottish Geographical Society have rendered invaluable services to geographers in the universities by publishing many of their papers and extensive commentary on their current work, and the American Geographical Society has issued a number of their books. But these societies have also been concerned no less with the geographical research of non-geographers, for all geographical knowledge is grist to their mills. Contributors to their publications include explorers, men of affairs, and scholars in fields related to geography, and their book reviews and notes deal with all manner of geographical publications and activities. If the laymen's societies thus tend to embrace a broader domain of research, the geographers' societies seek to develop the core of this domain with greater singleness of purpose.

Two fields of research in which the laymen's societies have been especially active, carrying on projects at their own cost, call for special comment. These are exploration and cartography.

Exploration

Public interest in contemporary exploring expeditions helped stimulate the founding of many of the older laymen's societies. The adventure and romance of exploration appealed to the imagination, and its political and commercial potentialities to the more worldly inclinations, of their heterogeneous memberships. Exploration offered possibilities of discovery of which the practical applications were clear. To determine the configuration of an unknown or little-known area was a problem in the solution of which well-defined techniques could be used and concrete, provable results achieved, at a time when other modes and purposes of geographical research were less clean cut.

Consequently, during the nineteenth century the laymen's societies made much of exploration and established a tradition that has persisted down to the present time. Situated in the world's greatest gathering place of explorers and travellers, the Royal Geographical Society of London has adhered to this tradition more consistently than have its American counterparts; but exploratory research, nevertheless, has always been a noteworthy interest of both the American Geographical Society[1] and the National Geographic Society.

Although geographical societies have often paid part of the costs of expeditions, only rarely have they organized, equipped, and conducted expeditions of their own. By endorsing the purposes of an expedition, a society has frequently made it easier for the leader to raise funds from other sources, and societies have loaned to expeditions instruments and scientific personnel from their staffs or memberships. Even more significant in the long run have been the services rendered by the professional and technical staffs of the laymen's national societies to the 'indoor' phases of explorations: the laborious work of planning and preparation that must precede, and the no less time-consuming and difficult process of compiling and editing the results that must follow after, every expedition.

The Royal Geographical Society and the American Geographical Society are conning towers from which the explorer or would-be explorer may survey the world, and choose areas to explore, scientific problems to solve, and suitable techniques to employ in solving them. Members of the professional staffs of these societies can usually give him direct advice on these matters, or place before him pertinent publications, or at least put him in touch with others able to do so. The American Geographical Society has often rendered such services to explorers of Latin America and the Polar Regions during the last quarter-century, and, by publishing two collaborative volumes in 1928 it correlated the experience and suggestions of geographers, explorers, and other authorities, in order to guide Polar research along scientific lines.[2] The American and the Royal Geographical Societies have also undertaken comprehensive studies of techniques applicable to exploration in general, intended to develop

---

[1] See editorial 'The Geographical Society and the Explorer', by Richard U. Light, President of the A.G.S., *Geographical Review*, Vol. 38, 1948, pp. 349–52.

[2] 'Problems of Polar Research', by 27 authors (*Amer. Geogr. Soc. Special Publ.* No. 7). Otto Nordenskjöld and Ludwig Mecking, 'The Geography of the Polar Regions' (ibid., No. 8).

methods and instruments of reconnaissance surveying both on the ground and from the air. Courses of instruction in these methods have long been offered at the Royal Geographical Society, and since the 1920's similar instruction has been available at the American Geographical Society. Both societies, but more particularly the Royal, have endeavoured to systematize and furnish to explorers and travellers practical information and advice regarding the leadership, organization, equipment, health, &c., of expeditions.[1]

Cartography

Since so much of geography would be utterly unintelligible without the aid of maps, cartography is, or certainly should be, a vital concern of every geographical society. Map making is costly and exacting, however, and only the more prosperous institutions have the resources for actually preparing and publishing good maps. The purpose of the majority of the maps issued by geographical societies is to clarify or supplement their textual publications, more especially articles in their journals.

Maps are needed in the reports of exploring expeditions. Frequently the making of a map is the chief scientific objective of an expedition, but even where this is not the case the report without a map is of little geographical value. Therefore, the staff cartographers of the Royal Geographical Society, the American Geographical Society, and the National Geographic Society have developed proficiency in the compiling of maps from notes and sketches furnished by explorers—a somewhat special art. These maps have usually been made under the supervision of the societies' experts in exploratory survey methods, who have also done much to develop the higher technical and mathematical aspects of cartography and its sister field of photogrammetry.

Within recent decades the Royal Geographical Society, the American Geographical Society, and the National Geographic Society have also undertaken large cartographical projects for which they employ teams of map compilers and draughtsmen. The American Geographical Society's *Map of Hispanic America*, 1 : 1,000,000, required a quarter of a century of work. In a very real sense it is an outgrowth of the Society's traditional interest in exploration, in that the map is a cartographic portrayal of the composite results of several thousand original exploratory surveys. During the First World War more than a hundred provisional sheets for Europe and south-eastern Asia of the International Map of the World,

[1] See *Hints to Travellers*, London, Royal Geographical Society, Vol. 1, 1935: Vol. 2, 1938.

1 : 1,000,000, were compiled at the Royal Geographical Society, and the National Geographic Society has issued many fine general reference maps of the world, the continents, and other large areas.

Educational Functions

The educational influence of a geographical society cannot be estimated in terms of the number of its members enrolled or of copies of its publications issued.[1] Quality here means more than quantity. The quantities are modest in the case of the research and the teachers' societies; and what counts is not how many persons read their publications or attend their meetings, but how influential individuals among those who do so make use of what they learn thereby. Unquestionably the level of geographical understanding among the American and the British public— low as it may be—would stand even lower did not these institutions indirectly affect schoolchildren and adults, who may be wholly unaware of their existence, by directly affecting teachers, the teachers of teachers, text-books and maps, and the work of popular writers and lecturers. An original article or book or map published by a geographical society or an original idea propounded at an annual meeting, though actually read or heard by only a few, may start a ferment of thinking in the minds of persons in positions of strategic importance, with far-reaching effects upon the development of geographical theory or education or in practical fields of human endeavour.

The geographical research societies are interested primarily in the dissemination of newly acquired geographical knowledge. There is, however, a large body of established facts and recognized principles in the field of geography that must be understood if the meaning of that which is new is to be grasped. Consequently, the educational societies must concern themselves, as well, with the dissemination of 'old' but nevertheless pertinent geographical information and ideas. Unfortunately, the old is easier to disseminate than the new. It has been more thoroughly digested and systematized, it is more familiar and less controversial. The temptation is great to make excessive use of it, though it constitutes only a small fraction of what ought to be taught in the schools and propagated through popular publications and lectures, if geographical education is to meet the needs of the times.

Research is constantly gnawing away at the foundations of old and well-established concepts; ceaselessly discovering new facts and developing

[1] See J. K. Wright, 'The Educational Functions of the Geographical Societies of the United States', *Journ. of Geogr.*, Vol. 47, 1948, pp. 165–73.

new principles to replace them. Furthermore, geographical research that bears on human life and the affairs of men, deals with phenomena that are rapidly changing in unpredictable ways, producing thereby a never-ending stream of new knowledge of new circumstances. Hence the teachers' and the popular societies cannot fulfil their functions without keeping abreast of current progress in geographical research and striving to adapt its results to the comprehension of children and of laymen. This means more than the mere purveying of attractive descriptive material in the form of pictures, maps, and texts. To portray the outer and more spectacular aspects of unfamiliar places does little to enlarge or deepen our understanding of important human conditions and serious human problems. Geographical popularization that will really accomplish this has long been and still is a crying need and a mighty challenge to geographical societies of all types.[1]

Essential Assets

Geographical societies and similar institutions possess in varying degrees three essential assets: *productive ability, freedom of choice*, and *disinterestedness of motive*. The first is the ability to do productive work. Financial resources and material equipment contribute to it, but fully as important are leadership, experience, continuity of effort, and other intangibles. The second asset is independence of outside control or interference in the selection of the work to be done and of the methods of doing it. The last is resistance to the influence of self-seeking motives, personal, political, social, or economic. Let us compare the national laymen's with the national professional geographical societies in terms of these assets.

The productive ability of the laymen's society when measured in man-hours devoted to research or in volume of publications issued greatly exceeds that of the professional society. Some reasons for this have already been given—the laymen's society's superior financial resources and equipment and its ability to employ a staff. The laymen's society can maintain greater continuity of effort on specific projects. Its management is more stable than that of the professional society, whose governing board completely changes every few years. In the professional society the

[1] That the scientific repute of geography had suffered from the superficial popularization of the subject promoted by certain geographical societies was argued by the late Professor Douglas Johnson in his Presidential Address before the Association of American Geographers in 1928 (*Annals Assoc. Amer. Geographers*, Vol. 19, 1929, pp. 167–231; ref. on pp. 201–4).

mortality of undertakings enthusiastically begun and assigned for execution to voluntary committees tends to be high. Yet it would not be fair to compare these two types of institution on such grounds alone. Only the professional society provides for a direct meeting of minds among geographers or teachers and for the breeding of dynamic ideas that such contact makes possible.

The geographical societies of Great Britain and the United States enjoy much freedom of choice and are impelled by notably disinterested motives, especially by comparison with the governmentally subsidized societies of other countries. The laymen's and the professional societies do not differ greatly from one another with respect to either of these assets, except that the former in times of war have temporarily relinquished some of their freedom of choice by placing their research facilities at the disposal of governmental agencies. One important distinction, however, must be pointed out.

In the professional society policy is determined ultimately by the membership itself. While the governing board actually frames specific programmes, the board itself is an organ of the membership, by which it is elected, of whom it is truly representative, and to whose will it is responsible and delicately responsive. This is not true in the laymen's society; here the board, self-perpetuating in fact, if not always on paper, and independent of any direct control by the members, determines policy. (The board, however, usually does so in consultation with and on the advice of the staff, which in many matters is the actual if not the constitutional guiding body.) It follows that the professional society *as a whole* is not strictly comparable with the laymen's society *as a whole*, but should be compared, rather, with the board and staff of the laymen's society.

Since the professional society is free to undertake whatever it sees fit, whereas the board and staff of the laymen's society are obliged to consider what the members will support, the former enjoys a somewhat greater measure of freedom of choice. In order to command the support of their heterogeneous memberships the programmes and projects of the laymen's societies have had to be of broader general interest than those of the professional societies. The National Geographic Society, having the largest and most heterogeneous membership of any geographical society, has gone the farthest in adapting its programme to the prevailing level of its members' tastes. The laymen's research societies have not gone so far, since their memberships are more selective and discriminating, and include a greater proportion of persons capable of perceiving the scientific or social value of undertakings which as individuals they may not wholly understand or for other reasons may not find personally 'interesting'.

This support, in the form of dues and donations, has enabled the research societies to make some of their most noteworthy and useful contributions to geography, by undertaking projects that are 'above the heads' of many of their members. Nevertheless, the necessity of considering what the members will support tends to keep the programmes of the laymen's research societies in touch with public needs and interests and is a guarantee against withdrawal into ivory towers.

Our attention has been focused exclusively upon the geographical societies themselves. The question arises: what can such societies do as well as or better than other institutions?

Obviously, no other institutions can perform the distinctive function of the professional society in assembling geographers and teachers, thus providing them means for concerted action and the direct cross-fertilization of ideas. On the other hand, many institutions perform functions that are much like those of the geographical societies in the fields of geographical research and education. These institutions are university departments, government agencies, publishing firms, and other business establishments. How do they compare with the geographical societies with respect to the three essential assets?

University Departments of Geography

The combined productive ability of the university departments of the country in terms of research accomplished and publications issued exceeds that of the combined geographical societies. The productive ability of the individual laymen's national society, however, is greater than that of any one university department. The professional geographers on the staff of the geographical society can normally devote more hours to consecutive research or editorial work than the professor can spare from teaching and administrative duties. Furthermore, the geographer in the geographical society commands for some of his work the assistance of one or more skilled, full-time technicians: research and editorial associates, map compilers, and draughtsmen—help that is a powerful tool in his hands. Many professors, of course, make use of their graduate students for similar assistance, but this work is less consecutive and usually less skilled. The university department, on the other hand, promotes the advancement of research in one way that does not lie open to geographical societies. This is by training new research workers. Unlike the professor, the geographer in the geographical society has no disciples.

If the freedom of choice of the management of the geographical research society is limited, as we have seen, by the need of considering what the members will support, that of the average university department may be even more restricted by the need of conforming to the larger educational and administrative policics of the university as a whole. The individual professor probably has greater freedom in determining his own research and editorial projects, if not in planning his teaching programme, than does the professional staff member of the research society. But if most of the work of the society's staff member must conform to the established programme of the institution, he has considerable influence upon decisions as to what this programme shall be and how it shall be conducted.

There is little to choose between the average university department and a geographical society in the matter of disinterestedness. Both stand on a high level. University departments, however, are in competition with one another. Standing aloof from such competition, the geographical societies of national scope are in a somewhat more advantageous position for undertaking or sponsoring co-ordinative or collaborative undertakings on a national or international scale.[1]

Government Departments

These probably do far more actual work than all other institutions combined in the amassing of new geographical data through surveys, census-taking, and other fact-gathering enterprises and in the dissemination of these data in the form of maps and other documents. Their productive ability for work of this sort, as well as for certain more refined modes of geographical research, vastly exceeds that of any geographical society. The geographical societies, nevertheless, enjoy advantages over the government departments. They are not affected by the shifts and changes of politics that make continuity of effort difficult in all but the most stable of the older government agencies, and they can exercise greater freedom of choice. In government agencies geographical research is always subsidiary or auxiliary to other purposes, administrative, military, political, social, or economic. The government, unlike the geographical societies, is not concerned with developing geography as a science or discipline or with disseminating geographical knowledge as such, but rather with applying geographical information to meet specific needs, and the geographical research conducted by government agencies

[1] As, for example, the American Geographical Society's programmes of Hispanic American, polar and pioneer-belt research.

must always be conceived and directed so as to bear directly on those needs. Hence, there is perhaps less scope in the government than in the geographical societies for free experiment in the development of new techniques, and certainly less scope for the study of geographical topics and regions that do not lie within the range of the government's requirements.

Since government departments are established to serve national interests, they cannot be strictly disinterested. While many national interests do not conflict with or contravene the larger interests of humanity others do, or are regarded as so doing by the government and inhabitants of other countries. Furthermore, government agencies in practice often serve special political or economic interests, such as pressure groups. The suspicion, whether or not well founded, that a government agency is not wholly disinterested may place it at a disadvantage in securing collaboration in geographical research, not only from foreign countries but at home. Many doors that remain closed to the representatives of government agencies are open to a geographical society whose disinterestedness of scientific motivation is above suspicion.

The two other types of organization most importantly engaged in geographical work are *business firms*, such as the oil companies, operating in the development of unexploited resources or areas, and *publishing houses*. The development companies do much geographical exploration and other research of the first importance and the commercial publishers are strong agencies for the dissemination of geographical knowledge. Since both must have an eye to profits, neither can exercise the degree of freedom of scientific choice or maintain the degree of disinterestedness of the geographical societies, which plough back their profits, if any, into further research or publication.

Conclusion

Much more might well be said about geographical societies did space permit. We might, for example, comment on the influential role of leaders in shaping the character and policies of specific institutions, notably Markham, Keltie, and Hinks of the Royal Geographical Society, Marion Newbigin of the Royal Scottish Geographical Society, Fleure of the Geographical Association, Daly and Bowman of the American Geographical Society, Grosvenor of the National Geographic Society. We might give attention not only to what different geographical societies do but to how well they do it, for there are variations in this respect. A critical appraisal, however, would be a difficult and an invidious task and one which the writer prefers to leave to others.

Another subject that can only be barely touched upon is the question of the future. Certainly there are many worthwhile things which the geographical societies might do that they are not now doing. In the field of research it is not difficult to conceive of large-scale projects of the first importance that a laymen's research society, if amply endowed, could carry forward to better advantage than other institutions. The cartographic facilities of such a society could be devoted to the production of scholarly atlases or comprehensive series of maps of types that governments or commercial publishers cannot undertake—for example, a national atlas of the United States, a general historical atlas, a compendium of statistical maps of the Americas. Another mode of research well suited to the laymen's research society is the collaborative investigation of problems that affect large parts of the world and in which geographical factors are of great importance—problems, for example, connected with land settlement and tenure, with public health and disease, with the destructive and constructive utilization of natural resources, with differential levels of living, with international relations.

Alluring avenues might also be followed in the field of geographical education. Despite the good work that the geographical societies have already done, a vast domain of black geographical illiteracy prevails among the general public and extends even into the ranks of college graduates. There are countless enterprises in which the geographical societies might take the lead towards remedying this deplorable and dangerous state of affairs: for example, the establishment of museums of regional and systematic geography, or the development of new equipment for geographical education, such as travelling exhibits, film strips, motion pictures (including animated maps and geographic diagrams), globes, dioramas, and demonstrations. Much could also be accomplished towards the improvement of books, maps, and other geographical publications designed for use in the schools and for popular and semi-popular reading. The proper function of the geographical societies in such enterprises would not be to compete with the commercial firms in the large-scale production of such materials, but rather to set standards and through pioneer experimental undertakings to open new fields.

The chief obstacles in the way of the expansion of the activities and influence of the geographical societies along such lines is not lack of ideas or of vision, but of funds and personnel. The future effectiveness of the geographical societies will depend partly on their ability to convince the public of their need for far more adequate financial support than they are now receiving, and partly on their ability to secure competent scholars to work for them. To do these things poses a serious but not insuperable problem. The future effectiveness of the geographical societies is also predicated on one more necessary assumption: that they continue to preserve their two priceless assets, freedom of scientific choice and disinterestedness of scientific motivation.

CHAPTER XXIV

GEOGRAPHY IN PRACTICE IN THE FEDERAL GOVERNMENT, WASHINGTON

JOHN KERR ROSE

John Kerr Rose, Ph.D. (Chicago), has been attached to a number of Federal services during the last dozen years. Among these are the Rural Electrical Administration, Natural Resources Planning Board, Board of Economic Warfare, and Foreign Economic Administration. In 1946 he was appointed Geographer of the Legislative Reference Service of the Library of Congress.

GEOGRAPHY is not a mere twentieth-century development in government service. Geography is old in official Washington, as old as the government itself. In those earlier years there were expeditions and explorations, surveys and reports, maps and charts, all an integral part of the discovery and advancing settlement of our great land. Such information was a practical necessity to the expanding functions of government. Hutchins, Lewis and Clarke, Schoolcraft, Emory, Wheeler, King, Hayden, Powell, Gilbert, and Gannett, were among the practising government geographers of the earlier period who loom large. Their interests, techniques, and accomplishments, in keeping with their day and age, can be observed best in their official work and publication. Those persons doing geographic work during the first century of the Republic were in most part classified officially under some other title; in fiscal year 1894, more than 100 years after our government was organized under the Constitution, of 11,471 positions paying annual salaries totalling more than $13,364,000 in the several Executive Departments and other government establishments of the nation's capital, only two geographers, specifically named as such, were provided.[1] The total number, including those geographers in disguise under some other title, was not large in comparison with total Federal employment.

More recently geography in Washington has come to what may be called a new era—a period of increased numbers and of somewhat new and different problems in keeping with the period and the work to be done. Apparently official Washington has learned to use geographers in more than token numbers; the total stands now at something like 200,

[1] *References to Laws Organizing Executive Departments and other Government Establishments at the National Capital*, Senate Report 41, 53rd Congress, 1st Session, p. 105.

a number that is of course still not large in relation to total Federal employment. In general they are used co-operatively with experts trained in other fields, amorphously as individuals or in small agglomerations and, even yet, not infrequently under other titles. The inclusion of geographers and geography in the vast work of the Federal Government is not academic nor sentimental, but functionally directed towards the solution of particular problems and the provision of expert technical services. Their retention in such relatively large numbers in government service, since World War II would seem to indicate a continuing major non-academic, employment outlet for the profession. The full significance of that development has not yet become apparent, but it may be presumed that a large and growing outlet will in the longer term be mutually catalytic on the academic. The present highly dynamic situation makes advisable a short review of the past, a survey of the present employment in some of its aspects and a brief exploration of some of the probable problems of the future use of geographers in the Federal service.

I. THE PAST[1]

(A) THE ANCIENT YEARS

The place of the geographer in the Federal Government during the period from its establishment until near the end of the 1800's was almost wholly in exploration, mapping, and surveying. The United States at its beginning became custodian of much land and later obtained still larger areas, mostly by purchase. Surveys were required and the officer in charge was, by the Ordinance of 20 May 1785, the 'Geographer of the United States'—a position to which Thomas Hutchins was appointed.[2] With the exception of special Presidential exploration missions (the Lewis and Clark expedition, for example), the Department of War carried on the early military and land surveys,[3] the Department of the Treasury participating in the latter.[4] A surveyor-general was provided for in 1796.[5] A General Land Office, under a Commissioner, was created in 1812[6] and it

---

[1] This does not pretend to be a full and documented history of the development of geography in the Federal Government, rather it is a brief survey of some old roots of the present period.

[2] Colby, Charles C., 'Changing Currents of Geographic Thought in America', *Annals of the Association of American Geographers*, Vol. XXVI, No. 1, March 1936, p. 2.

[3] 1 Stat. 49 (1789).   [4] 1 Stat. 65 (1789).

[5] Ibid., p. 467 (1796).   [6] 2 Stat. 716 (1812).

37

in turn became a part of the newly established Department of Interior in 1849.[1]

The Naval Observatory was authorized in 1842[2] and in 1846 'an observatory and chart depot was established, and was engaged in the multiple work of making astronomical observations, correcting chronometers, and of supplying charts to the Navy. . . .'[3] The Hydrographic Office became a separate establishment in 1866.[4] A Topographer was authorized in the Post Office Department in 1853.[5] A Signal Officer of the Army was authorized in 1860, the forerunner of the modern Weather Bureau.[6]

In 1834 a specific appropriation of $5,000 was made for 'geological and mineralogical surveys and researches' separate from *prior* and *later* surveys some of which were described as 'geographical' by the Army and General Land Office.[7]

The year 1853 is memorable for in that year $150,000 was appropriated for surveys to ascertain the most practicable and economical route for a railroad from the Mississippi River to the Pacific Ocean.[8] No ivory tower job, that; and it was an early adventure in co-operative field science—civil engineers, geologists, geographers, and others working in teams. Thirteen quarto volumes were published. Other western surveys by the Army and the General Land Office followed, between 1867 and 1879.[9] In 1878 the National Academy of Sciences was required to consider methods and expenses of such surveys and to report to Congress a practicable plan for surveying and mapping the territories of the United States. The United States Geological Survey in the Department of Interior resulted, to study the 'geological structure and the economical resources of the public domain'. Among the geographical aspects, public lands were to be classified; the mineral resources and products were to be examined as well as the geological structure.[10]

Appropriations for Scientific Assistants in the Geological Survey included one Chief Geographer for the fiscal years 1884 to 1894 inclusive, at a salary of $2,700. Three other geographers were provided for during

---

[1] 9 Stat. 395 and R.S. 75 (1849).   [2] 5 Stat. 576 (1842).

[3] Senate Rept. 1285 and H.R. 2740, 49th Cong. 1st Sess., p. 26.

[4] 14 Stat. 69 and R.S. 72 (1866).   [5] 10 Stat. 211 (1853).

[6] 12 Stat. 66 (1860).   [7] 4 Stat. 704 (1834).

[8] 10 Stat. 219 (1853).

[9] Senate Rept. 1285, pp. 29–34, i.e. *War Dept.*: King's Survey of 40th Parallel; Wheeler's Survey of the Territories West of the 100th Meridian. *Interior*: Hayden's Geological and Geographical Survey of the Territories; Powell, Survey of the Colorado of the West; Survey of the Rocky Mountain Region.

[10] 20 Stat. 394 and Supp. 251 (1879).

fiscal years 1884 to 1892 inclusive; then the economy efforts of the early 1890's resulted in this number being reduced to one for years 1893 and 1894, the salary continuing at $2,500. These are separate and distinct from the positions held by geologists, palaeontologists, chemists, and topographers (three in number 1884–92 inclusive, two 1893 and 1894) all of whom were provided for specifically during the years prior to 1894.[1] Nowhere else were geographers specifically provided for by name though the Weather Bureau appropriations for fiscal 1894 carried funds for six 'professors of meteorology' at salaries ranging from $2,500 to $4,000,[2] one topographer and hydrographer (combined) was provided in the Life Saving Service (Treasury Department) for the years 1883–94, plus as many as sixteen topographic and hydrographic draughtsmen in the Coast and Geodetic Survey (Treasury Department).[3] The Office of the Topographer in the Post Office Department in fiscal year 1849 carried appropriations for one topographer, twelve skilled draughtsmen and two map mounters.[4] The United States Board of Geographic Names came into existence by Executive Order in September 1893, thus formalizing previous co-operation of representatives of several interested Bureaux.[5]

(B) THE EARLY TWENTIETH CENTURY

In the early part of the present century, prior to World War I, it appears that geographers in Washington lost ground as compared to the situation in the period 1850–90. However, the emergency work of World War I, of the armed forces, of the Shipping Board, and of the War Trade Board brought to Washington some twenty or more of the outstanding geographers from the growing university departments. Their experiences and their accomplishments have not been adequately made a matter of printed record. In any case those war workers, for the most part, returned hurriedly to their university posts in the post-war period; only a few brave ones remained in government or went into the business world. The new generation of post-graduate students in geography heard much of the Washington experiences of their professors; and government work slowly began to be considered as a potential field of employment, though the orientation in training and in professional psychology was still definitely towards the academic.

Meanwhile, two developments occurred which were significant in

[1] 22 Stat. 624 (1883) and 27 Stat. 370 (1892).
[2] 27 Stat. 741 (1893).   [3] 27 Stat. 580 (1893).
[4] 27 Stat. 711 (1893).
[5] Sixth Rept. of United States Geographic Board, 1890–1932, Washington, 1933.

themselves and indirectly foreshadowed some of the developments of a later period. Geographers participated actively with the Commission which prepared in advance for peace negotiations and some later served as advisors at the Paris Conference. Geographers in the Department of Agriculture continued active and effective investigation of diverse aspects of land, agriculture, and population.

(c) THE 1930's

In line with the spirit of the times, this was a period of much geographic ferment and considerable expansion of geography in the Federal Service, particularly with respect to work on resources and planning. The Resettlement Administration, the Mississippi Valley Board, the National Resources Planning Board, the Reclamation Service, the Soil Conservation Service, and the Tennessee Valley Authority were the major agencies involved.

A modest number of geographers continued as full-time career employees, a large number served for shorter periods or as consultants and collaborators. Only two divisions or groups of geographers of considerable size developed, that in the T.V.A. and one in the Soil Conservation Service; for one reason or another those were already largely dispersed before the war began.

(d) WORLD WAR II

The government work of geographers during this period has been dealt with in publications elsewhere and need be only summarized and referred to here. As of December 1944, some 293 civilian geographers were employed by Federal Government agencies and an additional 265 were in uniform, in the field or in government offices.[1] George Deasy, at a later date, using a broad but nevertheless professional definition of the field, found the number of geographers in the United States to be about 2000.[2] The number in the armed forces increased from about 200 in 1942 to 300–350 by 1945.[3] In a sample of that group some 75 per cent

[1] *Bulletin of the American Society for Geographic Research*, Vol. 2, No. 2, May 1944, p. 2.

[2] Deasy, George F., 'Training, Professional Work and Military Experience of Geographers, 1942–1947', *The Professional Geographer—Bulletin of The American Society for Professional Geographers*, Vol. 6, December 1947, pp. 1–14.

[3] Deasy, George F., 'War-Time Changes in Occupation of Geographers', ibid., Vol. 7, April 1948, pp. 33–41.

reported having utilized officially their geographic skills in some degree. The number of geographers on the Federal payroll may have been as high as 500 in 1945, some of them consultants.

Thus, of the total something like two-fifths were government employees during the war as civilian or military personnel; another two-fifths, approximately, were engaged in military training programmes.[1] Thus, a full one-fifth apparently did not participate in the war effort in any way directly involving their professional training. This may be in part explained by the fact that women account for about one-third the total number of geographers but only two per cent of those in military service were women.

Some aspects of the war work of geographers in Washington have been covered in published material.[2] Ackerman in particular has discussed it realistically in terms of its relation to the training of geographic specialists and the philosophies of the subject:

Geography and geographers in this country were put to one of the severest practical tests that they have had by the many wartime demands placed on them in instruction programmes for the Services, and especially in the research of government intelligence agencies. As far as research is concerned, our success in meeting those demands can be measured in terms of two criteria: the extent to which we were able to provide properly trained personnel, and the usefulness of the body of facts accumulated by our previous basic research. Our score was not high in either, and our deficiencies can be explained by the pre-war emphasis on the regional method in training and research, no less than by the novelty of the tasks. . . . In most instances the information needed was of a sort which could have been gathered only by a group of systematic specialists.[3]

II. THE PRESENT PERIOD

Probably the most outstanding fact of professional interest about the present post-war period is that there are so many geographers still in Federal employment. True the number has declined from a wartime

[1] Miller, E. Willard, 'Geography in The Army Specialized Training Programme', ibid., Vol. 3, Nos. 3-4, May-June 1945.

[2] See especially Meredith F. Burrill, 'Reorganization of the United States Board of Geographic Names', Geographical Review, Vol. XXXV, No. 4, October 1945.

Also see The Professional Geographer—Bulletin of the American Society for Professional Geographers, Vol. 7, April 1948.

[3] Ackerman, Edward A., 'Geographic Training, Wartime Research, and Immediate Professional Objectives', Annals of the Association of American Geographers, Vol. XXXV, No. 4, December 1945, pp. 126-7.

maximum possibly as high as 500 to a number that may be as few as 200. But the lower figure appears to be present base level—some continue to leave Washington but as many or more come.

The reasons for departing or staying on in Washington differ in each case, but in most instances are complex. Many of those leaving are by training and long experience oriented towards the academic. Perhaps they have good jobs to go back to—jobs that compare very favourably with or exceed what they have had in Washington. Others have tenure on the campus, but were uneasy 'war service appointees' in the Federal régime. Some were galled by government regulations and restrictions on publication. The younger generation of geographers in particular appears to have developed a taste for the non-academic life of a civil servant—not often a bureaucrat. Most of the younger men had no particularly desirable post to return to; perhaps the government salary was comparatively attractive. Others received very favourable academic bids and responded. But this time there has been nothing comparable to the mad rush from Washington for the academic diggings which the historian reports at the end of World War I. And not infrequently, the spot vacated in Washington has been continued and filled with a geographer of lesser academic experience but with the more vicarious training and the rapid seasoning younger men received from heavy war-year responsibilities. Training received in that manner apparently makes a much less favourable impression on Deans than it does on Federal Administrators!

There has been a sharp decline in numbers but the exodus which some expected has not occurred. This may prove to be the outstanding development of our profession in the last decade. The successful establishment and retention of the first major non-academic outlet is not without possible significant implications to present geographers, would-be geographers, geography departments, geographic societies and the Federal Civil Service itself.

(A) NUMBER AND DISTRIBUTION

How many geographers are there in the Federal Service and where do they work? A survey made in December 1947 showed the number to be approximately 200. Since then there have been additions and subtractions. The Census Bureau for example, is building up in preparation for the 1950 census. Shifts within the Federal structure also occur—of individuals frequently, of groups sometimes. Some of those indicated as in the State Department have since shifted to the Central Intelligence Agency for example. As might be expected, the five executive departments dealing primarily with areas, resources and commodities utilize most of them:

Department or Agency	Approximate number of geographers employed
Defence	70
State	50
Interior	25
Commerce	18
Agriculture	15
Other	20
Total	200

Within the above distribution only five groups of considerable size exist. Three of the five groups are in the Department of The Army, another, the Board of Geographic Names, is in the Department of Interior and there is the already mentioned State-Central Intelligence group. It is a reasonable guess that not more than one-fourth of the total are officially called geographers—some are geologists, cartographers, climatologists, information specialists, or economic analysts.

(B) TYPES OF WORK DONE

What do these 200 people do? The wide variety of work performed is more than a little amazing. Something like half of those listed give their major attention to the oldest facet of the geographic profession: maps—map intelligence, map information, and map making. The other half is largely employed in research and report writing, though not a few are primarily co-ordinators, administrators, or consultants. It would not be far wrong to say that no two of the positions are the same.

The following description of the collections of the Map Division of the Library of Congress will serve to indicate the type of work involved in administering, supervising research on and helping official agencies and the public utilize one of the major map collections. Of the thirteen positions three are staffed by geographers, the others being librarians or secretaries.

The Division of Maps was organized in the summer of 1897 with a collection of about 48,600 maps and 1,600 atlases. Fifty years later, on June 30, 1947, its total holdings were more than 2,000,000 maps and 15,000 atlases, constituting the largest single collection of maps available to the people of the United States.

Especially rich in source maps relating to the American Colonial and Revolutionary war periods, it possesses the Faden, Howe, and Rochambeau Collections, which total more than 200 original manuscript maps. Some 2,300 additional manuscript maps supplement these. To aid the student of American history further, the Division has acquired photostats of original maps of America in British, French, German, Portuguese, and Spanish archives, as well as those in a number of American libraries, notably the William L. Clements Library and the New York Historical Society.

Other special collections that might be mentioned are the Lowery Collection of 750 maps of the Spanish possessions within the present limits of the United States, 1502–1820, the Kohl Collection of 474 manuscript tracings of rare maps relating to the discovery and early history of America, and the Marrisse Collection of a dozen rare manuscript maps, and approximately 600 tracings, relating to the discovery and early history of America.

The Division's treasures include the only surviving L'Enfant Plan of Washington, 1791, Samuel de Champlain's manuscript map on vellum of New England and Nova Scotia, 1607, Joan Vingboon's manuscript map of New Amsterdam, 1639, 9 manuscripts made or annotated by George Washington, 1 made by Thomas Jefferson, a number of others made by or owned by former Presidents of the United States, 13 manuscript maps attributed to Lewis and Clark, 11 portolan charts and 2 portolan atlases, an Eskimo map of the Crown Prince Islands in Disco Bay, Greenland, several maps engraved on powder horns, and many other unique items.

The collection also has originals, facsimiles, or photostats of 19 editions of John Mitchell's 'Map of the British and French Possessions in North America', 1755–1792, 24 editions of John Disturnell's 'Mapa de los Estados Unidos de Mejico', 1828–1858, 15 editions of John Melish's 'Map of the United States with the contiguous British and Spanish possessions', 1816–1823, 27 editions of Lewis Evan's 'General Map of the Middle British Colonies', 1749–1814, and 11 editions of John Filson's 'Map of Kentucke', 1784–1794. The Division's unique collection numbers some 420,000 map sheets issued by the Sanborn Map Company since 1866. More than 13,000 cities and towns in the United States that present fire hazards are represented on such large scales as to indicate every structure's height and construction, etc.

The atlas collection includes 92 volumes of Ptolemy's Geography, 68 editions of Ortelius, 37 editions of Mercator, 27 editions of Blaeu in 82 volumes, 19 copies of the Atlantic Neptune, 1775–1781, as well as several manuscript atlases, including one by Battista Agnese, ca. 1543, one by the Portuguese cartographer, Joao Teixeira, 1630, and one by William Hacke known as the Buccaneer's Atlas.

The globe collection includes a small manuscript globe inside an armillary sphere of 11 rings made by Caspar Vopel in 1543, a set of printed gores of Coronell's 43-inch globe, 1688, and two pairs of terrestrial and celestial globes by James Wilson, the first American globe maker.

The Division of Maps is the depository for atlases and maps copy-righted in the United States, as well as for all the official federal and state map publications, and the official maps of other governments received on international exchange.

Although the Division lacks a comprehensive catalog of all its holdings, its collections are so well arranged geographically, chronologically and by subject that readers are served expeditiously. Several useful catalogs are maintained, namely the catalog of all maps deposited for copyright since 1897, the catalog of geographical atlases, supplementing the printed *List of Geographical Atlases in the Library of Congress*, 4 Volumes, 1909–1920, and the catalog of manuscript maps. The Bibliography of Cartography containing references on cards to books and articles relating to maps, map making and map makers is a most useful reference tool.[1]

If anything, the work of the geographer in analysis, report writing, information, and administration is less standardized than work involving maps predominantly. In many instances, however, one or more of the natural resources will be involved—an evaluation of the resource itself, its exploitation or its conservation. In other instances the work may focus on a region, or some phase of the economy of a country or area. It is not too much to say that the breakdown, gross, might well be characterized as:

> Geographer—Cartographic
> Geographer—Physical
> Geographer—Economic

Within these categories some regional specialization does occur and administrative duties may be superimposed.

(c) TECHNIQUES USED

To attempt to describe research techniques utilized by geographers in the Federal Service is if anything more difficult than trying to characterize the work they do. Most of them make use of maps—that is they are more than a little concerned with the distribution of the phenomena of the problem on which they happen to be working—'How much of what is where, and what of it?'

This concern with the distributive aspects of the problem and coincidences or correlations in space seem to characterize the geographer more than other workers. In some instances, because of better foundation knowledge of spatial phenomena and relationships he appears to be able to think in spatial terms about new problems better than other workers.

Ability to write in the English language is fundamental. Some geographers have found their foreign languages very useful—some have emphasized the need for better foreign language training for work in Washington.

Field methods, particularly elementary techniques of survey, which do not adequately consider the problems of representativeness of sample, are

[1] From the Information Bulletin, Library of Congress, June 1948.

of no particular help—a good course in elementary statistical methods would be used many times more frequently. Bibliographic techniques are very useful.

(D) RECRUITMENT AND PLACEMENT

How does one find a position as a geographer with the Federal Government? The United States Civil Service Commission is the official recruiting and placement agency. At intervals, depending on the demand for geographers from the working bureaux and agencies of the Government and the situation as to depletion of the existing registers of eligibles i.e. those who have taken and passed the most recent geography examinations) new recruitment announcements are made and examinations offered. Such announcements are sent to the major departments of geography in the colleges and universities; they are also posted in Government departments and many post offices—places where they would most likely come to the attention of prospective examinees.

The examinations are roughly of two types. The basic one for beginners, that for Junior Professional Assistant, with a geography option, has been offered several times in the past ten years. Applicants must be citizens or owe allegiance to the United States and must have reached their eighteenth birthday but must not have passed their thirty-fifth birthday. All competitors must take an assembled three and one-half hour written general abilities examination which includes 'paragraph reading, vocabulary, English usage, graph and table interpretation, arithmetic reasoning, abstract reasoning and spatial perception'. Though the rating basis is 100 for this written examination the standards used in rating the various parts of the examination for each position depend on the abilities needed for job success therein. Non-military preference competitors must attain a rating of at least 70.

Though there is no technical subject-matter examination for the Junior Professional Assistant position, there is required education or experience which for the geographer is as follows:

Applicants must have successfully completed *one* of the following:
A. A full 4-year course, in a college or university of recognized standing, leading to a bachelor's degree. This study must have included or been supplemented by courses in geography consisting of lectures and recitations totaling at least 24 semester hours. Study in closely allied fields such as geology, archeology, cartography, etc., may be included in the 24 semester hours of geography provided the applicant shows at least 15 hours in purely geographic subjects; *or*
B. Courses in geography, in a college or university of recognized standing

consisting of lectures and recitations totaling at least 24 semester hours; plus additional appropriate experience or education which when combined with the 24 semester hours in geography will total 4 years of education and experience and give the applicant the substantial equivalent of the 4-year college course. Study in closely allied fields such as geology, archeology, cartography, etc., may be included in the 24 semester hours of geography, provided the applicant shows at least 15 hours in purely geographic subjects.

The following are types of experience which will be accepted in combination with education to complete the 4-year requirement:

Library or field research dealing with the collection and analysis of geographic or closely allied data.

Assisting in editing, abstracting, or translating documents, scientific literature, and preparing reports relating to geography, or closely allied fields such as geology or meteorology, etc.

Experience gained in such positions as geographic aide, scientific aide in geology, nautical science, air navigation, and other related fields.[1]

Those who are successful are placed upon the list of eligibles from which selections are to be made for P1—Junior Geographer positions—the beginning and lowest rung of the professional ladder. The work of that position is indicated as follows:

Geographers will perform or assist in performing professional work in the field of geography; perform related cartographic work including the compilation and the analyzing of geographic data; assist in studies and researches relating to industrial and commercial geography, soils, soil erosion and land utilization mapping, climatology, vegetation distribution, and allied fields; prepare reports on the geography (physical, economic, social, and political) of specified areas; and assist in the establishment and use of map collections.[2]

Except for field service, examination for geography positions P2 and higher has not been offered since 1942. The matter is at present under careful study with the prospect that an examination for positions P2 to P8 will be offered later this year. In view of the forthcoming announcement plus the fact that the requirements in 1942 were somewhat relaxed to meet the defence needs, the details of the 1942 recruiting circular will not be included here.

If a vacancy exists in an established position and its work and requirements are such that a geographer is required or desired to fill it, a request through channels to the Civil Service Commission procures certification of the three highest eligibles on the register having the necessary

[1] U.S. Civil Service Commission. *Junior Professional Assistant*, Announcement No. 75, Issued 14 October 1947, Washington, D.C., p. 11.
[2] Ibid., p. 10.

qualifications. Normally one of the three must be selected and if that person will accept the offer, he or she enters on a probational appointment of one year. At the end of the year, if all goes well it becomes a so-called permanent Civil Service appointment.

The above is the standard routine recruitment and placement. In reality probably half the geographers in Washington have come in by somewhat different routes—they were possibly employed in one of the agencies blanketed under Civil Service in the 1930's, or they may have been a war service appointee, or they were examined in position. In any case, in the past direct recruitment at least on a temporary basis by the agency and by geographers for their staff has been more prevalent.

(E) CLASSIFICATION AND SALARIES

Geographers now in Washington hold positions ranging from the P1 to the P8 level—the whole range of the classified professional ratings. Base salaries per year for these positions are:

	1939	July 1948	Increase (per cent)
P1	$2,000	$2,975	48·7
P2	2,600	3,727	43·4
P3	3,200	4,480	40·0
P4	3,800	5,232	37·7
P5	4,600	6,235	35·5
P6	5,600	7,432	32·7
P7	6,500	8,510	30·9
P8	8,000	10,305	28·8

Most geographers are concentrated in grades P3 through P6, though in the past few months P1 and P2 geographers have again become available from the graduate schools. The salaries are subject to a 6 per cent retirement reduction, but carry twenty-six working days of annual leave per year plus fourteen days of sick leave if needed. It would appear that on most if not all levels the salary is at least equivalent to those paid in the other major professional outlet, even allowing for the considerable upgrading that has gone on in the academic world since 1940. Even so, Government salary increases have failed to keep up with the increase in the cost of living which is estimated at something like 66 per cent for the same period.

(F) THE PRESENT WASHINGTON ENVIRONMENT—NON-GOVERNMENTAL
GEOGRAPHY

Geography in official Washington cannot be adequately envisioned in its many ramifications without some mention of two related but non-governmental aspects of Washington geography.

1. *Geography in the Educational Institutions*

The period between the two world wars was one of rapid development of geography in institutions of higher education in the United States. But Washington was not a part of that trend. The one city of the U.S.A. most concerned in its everyday work with the problems of other peoples and other lands gave such matters much less organized attention—educationally speaking—than the presumably more provincial universities. It is one of the remarkable short-sights and omissions of the University administrators, prior to a very recent date, that the several institutions of higher learning in the Washington area offered only a little geography, even to their numerous undergraduates. None of them had a Department except the Teachers College and it did not offer graduate work in geography. This neglect by the colleges and universities is all the more remarkable because within the Greater Washington area there was a concentration of professionally trained geographers probably unequalled in any other equivalent area in the world. Thus, in theory at least, the most extraordinary geography faculty to be found anywhere was already half assembled and potentially available. Most of them, to be sure, were employed by the Federal Government and hence available only on a part-time, evening or occasional basis. Even so, many of them, in terms of background and training, travel, and especially as to actual daily analytical or administrative experience with problems of national and international significance, were individually unparalleled in the regional institutions. Some of them indeed sometimes journeyed to distant universities to offer their wares as visiting professors. One distant school of geography seriously considered establishing a branch in Washington. One may wonder not only as to the reasons for the long neglect of organized training in geography in Washington, but also as to the indirect repercussions of that unfortunate situation on the use of geographers in government.

World War II, with its frantic official efforts to become quickly and adequately informed about foreign areas, seems to have provided the catalyst that awakened the local institutions to their long neglected opportunity. All of the general college or university educational institutions in the District of Columbia are now offering courses in geography. In addition there is a major department at the University of Maryland nearby. The comprehensive offerings of the Department at Johns Hopkins of Baltimore and the Virginia Geographical Institute at the University of Virginia, Charlottesville, are probably too far away to be considered.

In 1943 the University of Maryland set up a new Department headed by Dr. O. E. Baker, a long-time Agricultural and Social Geographer in the Department of Agriculture. W. Van Royen, then in Federal employment, was added almost immediately and several others of professorial rank have since been added. Graduate students on both the masters and Ph.D. level are in training and hundreds of undergraduates are taught. Somewhat later Kenneth Bertrand was invited to head a Department at The Catholic University of America and Robert Campbell at the George Washington University. Wilson Teachers College has expanded its offerings and Howard University has installed a full-time professor. Others are operating in geography with a part-time faculty. The offerings *in toto* are very extensive, comprising something over one hundred courses directly in the field of geography, ranging from introductory principles to advanced seminars conducted by international authorities in their fields. The opportunity to take closely related courses in the physical and social sciences and in methodology would appear to be unequalled elsewhere.

2. *The Professional Organizations*

Geography in Washington cannot be adequately considered without noting the mutual relations of the professional organizations. Until recently none of the several organizations were what might be called a professional service organization—they emphasized instead geographic publication in its many aspects.

Washington has long included a strong nucleus of the older organization of scientific geographers, the Association of American Geographers. That organization, with a present membership of something over 300, is still predominantly located in the major academic institutions of the country, but approximately one-fifth of its members are located in the greater Washington area, most of them in government work. Many others among its members have for shorter or longer periods been in Federal employ. The A.A.G., soon to celebrate its first half-century anniversary, has during that period held six of its annual meetings in Washington.

The much younger but very active American Society for Professional Geographers is in some degree of Washington origin, developing partly from the so-called 'Young Geographers' and partly, as a logical development, from a local and temporary Washington Geographers Association which held some meetings in Washington during the early part of the war. In any case, the wartime concentration in Washington of so many geographers, particularly younger geographers who had not yet been recognized by the older professional organization, the Association of American Geographers, gave the necessary impetus to the development of an organization having as its primary objective service to the profession. In addition to the usual annual meeting and publication media (*The Professional Geographer*), other major aspects have been regional organization, field trips, news letters, an active placement committee and active committee work on problems of the geographer in Government. The membership is approximately 1,000, of whom something like one-fifth are still in the Greater Washington area.

The National Geographic Society, born in Washington in 1888, now has a dues-paying membership of more than one and a half million. Its well-known monthly publication is on the popular side and is the most widely read of the world's magazines. Its objectives are scientific in special instances as well as educational. Various scientific expeditions and researches have been organized by it or participated in jointly. Though its primary purpose has not been that of service to geography as a profession nor co-operation with the official agencies of the government, relations have been cordial and some parts of the admirable facilities of the private organization have been available under special circumstances.

III. THE FUTURE—SOME PROBLEMS AND SOME QUESTIONS

The twentieth century is not quite half over. A consideration of twentieth-century geography and the Federal service therefore may well call for some speculative comment as to present or emerging problems and probable trends during the years ahead. It should be noted, with caution of course, that not much is certainty and imponderables are many.

For good or ill, the United States has arrived at a position of leadership among the nations. It is beside the point to argue here as to how we arrived at that position, whether that leadership was sought or unwanted and whether it found us unprepared for the task. We are on the spot; we cannot decline, we can only succeed or fail. Success can come only if we understand and can lead, or at least assist, in the solution of problems which lie largely outside our own domestic area.

This would seem to mean that in the future, unlike the past, it will be fundamental that United States citizens in general, and Washington and government employees in particular, be informed much more adequately about our own and other countries—their people, their customs and history, their economics, their natural resources, their relations to neighbours, their strengths and weaknesses, their problems, in short the co-variant factors of place, people, and period as how arranged in dynamic equilibrium. It is too much to anticipate that such understandings will be achieved overnight, but they must come if we are to have a civil service adequate to global problems and a democratic citizenry able to understand and sit in judgement on what the United States is doing in the world at large.

(A) WASHINGTON AND GEOGRAPHIC EDUCATION

One of the safer predictions is that in the years ahead much more educational attention will be devoted, both on the secondary and college levels, to comprehensive studies of foreign peoples, areas, and problems. In part this will represent an attempt by the educators and students to meet basic employment standards in the business world or in government. Additionally, it will represent an increasing awareness on the part of our leaders in education that global information and understanding are as basic to an educated citizenry under a representative government as the English language, American history, and mathematics. The part which professional geographers may play in such increased emphasis on global studies is of course uncertain; but in large part ultimately will depend on the geographers themselves, their aggressiveness, their numbers, their positions, their willingness to assume the privileges of and responsibilities for formulating and carrying out such comprehensive studies and of course their ability to co-operate with other educators.

The part which Washington and Washington geographers may serve in such educational advance can be very significant. The Commissioner of the Office of Education is aware of and has publicly pointed to the problem of our widespread geographic illiteracy. Professional geographers have been added to that office. Federal aid to education may involve indirect attention to the problem. Additional employment opportunities in government for geographers, both full time and as consultants, will help to focus attention on the problem of global understandings. Employment, particularly of young geographers for short periods in foreign areas will do much to vitalize and alert the graduate schools. Arrangement for frequent exchange of personnel between positions in Washington and major departments would be a very helpful step, as would more frequent exchange of personnel between Washington and foreign assignment. One of the emerging but yet unresolved problems of much concern to geographers is the degree to which specific graduate training on foreign areas (and perhaps college training as well) is to be conducted by institutes and specialized area divisions—and the part, if any, which geographers will play in such area organizations.

There are also other possible implications to professional aspects of geographic education which will be discussed elsewhere.

(B) WASHINGTON AND GEOGRAPHIC RESEARCH

There are those, both inside and outside of Washington, who are disappointed in the research output of Washington geographers as a group, perhaps as to quality, certainly as to quantity. Yet Washington is and will continue to be one of the better places in the world in which to attempt certain sorts of geographic research, an almost certain concomitant of available documentary, map and statistical facilities. It is true that most geographers in government find more than a little difficulty in getting research work done and published. This is due in part to the fact that a considerable number of them have been drawn into administrative work, without much time to push writing they might otherwise do. Others do research which they are officially prohibited from publishing. Some publish, at least occasionally, in media not often read by other geographers. Still others find their official work so technical or so marginal to the main interests of most geographers as to be hardly acceptable. A good share of government research is a joint product of several scientists from several fields, hence not to be published by any one of them. However many of these partial reasons may apply in a particular case, it is clear that a portion of those who spent the war years in Government service have returned to the universities partly in order to be in a position to have more time and freedom in which to pursue individual research—Washington was too frustrating in that respect.

In spite of the present difficulties which are in part a carry over from the war period, it would not be a bad guess that geographers in Federal Service will be as prolific of publication, official or unofficial, as his academic brother in research. Moreover, the problems studied will probably tend towards the immediate and the practical.

Two developments of much potential research importance are noted. One is Government contracting for research on specific problems, with particular university departments. Not only does such work escape some of the frustrations of Washington but it makes part-time use of high

38

grade personnel not otherwise available. Also it probably gives the younger faculty members and graduate students some additional orientation towards practical problems of the field.

Another probable development is that one or more of the Departments of Geography in the Washington area will make a real effort to aid and assist graduate students from other universities (and even the occasional professor) who wish to utilize Washington research facilities (office facilities, information on Washington availabilities and in the case of the graduate students, technical guidance and supervision as well as possible direction to problems of outstanding scientific or practical importance would be involved). From that should come in time one of the leading graduate schools of geography, differing significantly from others in that it would be specialized in fields and problems of primary interest to the Federal Government.

(c) WASHINGTON AND GEOGRAPHIC EMPLOYMENT

There are some, most of them geographers to be sure, who believe that geography on its record has established itself as the best basic training for hundreds if not thousands of jobs in Washington, not nearly all of which are now filled by geographers. These optimistic expansionists observe that the work is here to be done, the jobs are already set up though now filled by others; the positions have been filled with artists, engineers, economists, geologists, or whoever—partly because there have been too few geographers, at least too few wishing to work in Washington, particularly in peacetime.

Administrators, economists and even some Washington geographers take a more sober view of future Federal employment. The battle is not won. The geographers, even 200 of them, are a scant handful among two million nieces and nephews of Uncle Sam. The field is extremely broad and in most sectors not tightly held; and in Washington, as elsewhere, fields belong to the aggressive and those who cultivate them effectively. The profession presents some major problems in classification to the Civil Service Commission. Administrators, except in exceptional instances, are either unacquainted with the profession, or have found the geographer so broadly trained that he is not an authority in anything.

Somewhere is the happy medium. It would appear that the Washington opportunities for geographers will be reasonably abundant due to factors previously discussed of widespread governmental activities and more emphasis on foreign areas. Hence, it seems possible that employment of geographers in the Federal service might well grow faster, or meet with less serious retrenchment than would be true of the Government at large. Certainly there has been no difficulty in placing the well trained, well rounded individual in a good job. As is true of all fields, the occasional geographer may land in the wrong spot, or may be defective in special skills required, or lack an adaptable personality. That is no new story to the government administrator—there is some irreducible turnover no matter what precautions are taken.

It is perhaps idle for one who is still in Washington to speculate on what the situation means, or may mean to the academic departments. It would appear that never again will the Chairman or a professor be at a total loss for an answer when asked by a promising major what one can do with geography to earn a living, other than to teach. The old cycle of teaching to train geographers, who will teach to train other geographers to teach, would seem to be distorted in a major way if not broken. Though the placing of graduates is thereby diversified and the demand increased in relation to supply, there must in the long run be repercussions on and major changes in the teaching and training programme.

It appears that the student who anticipates Federal employment rather than teaching should give special concern to specialization. Though it would not be practical to attempt to prepare for a specific job in Washington, it is nevertheless probably true that the time has arrived when it will be highly desirable if not absolutely necessary for the student to decide whether he is to be an *economic* geographer, a *cartographer*, or a *physical* geographer. If he decides, for instance, to be an *economic* geographer, he must get as adequately acquainted as possible with economics—production, distribution, theory, and techniques. He must know what the problems of economics are, particularly the unsolved problems. This is fully as important as his training in geography. It is sad, of course, that more economists are not aware of and appreciative of geography, but the day is now past when we as a profession can afford to permit an 'economic geographer' to escape the training period innocent or nearly so of basic courses of economics and statistics—if he is to function in Washington as an *economic* geographer he has to work with the economists and statisticians and must know what they are talking about. The geographer who is adequate in economics and statistics can pull his oar nicely in the co-operative boat, captained probably by an economist, because he can add and defend an unorthodox point of view. But to play on the team he has to be a real *economic* geographer. With variations the same can be said about those who work with the political scientists, the agriculturists, the meteorologists, and several other groups.

There is another possible specialization for which the geographer would seem to be a natural—that of regional or area specialist. Ackerman has written knowingly of the problems of the regional geographer in Washington.[1] Certainly the lot of the systematic geographer would seem to be somewhat happier. But there *are* regional geographers and graduate students who wish to specialize in a region. More than that, there are positions in Washington, not a few of which call for regional experts.

In any case as an area specialist he must become a real expert on that area—not merely the academic geography of the area, but its history, its customs, its language as well as its cultural and natural landscape. It is most essential that he travel and live in the area. He must know *the area*, not just some small part of it, or some slightly important problem regarding it. He must be acutely aware of its present problems—economic, political, and social.

(d) A FEDERAL 'GEOGRAPHICAL SURVEY'?

During past years some have had the idea that a Geographical Survey is needed in the Federal Government, to be the focus of things geographic much as the Geological Survey is of things geologic. The idea, however, has not been adequately developed, even among professional geographers. The near future is one of possible or probable extensive reorganization of the Executive Branch. It is possible that part but not all of the present geographic activities might be concentrated to advantage and certain sorts of work pushed more actively than is presently the case. Recent governmental developments in Canada, Brazil, and the United Kingdom afford partial precedents.

[1] Ackerman, Edward A., op. cit.

CHAPTER XXV

GEOPOLITICS AND GEOPACIFICS

GRIFFITH TAYLOR

Mackinder and Mahan

ONE of the most recent branches on the geographical tree is that known as geopolitics. It was one of the chief features of the Nazi propaganda, and naturally was much discussed by other nations in the attempt to prove that the German arguments were in large part unsound. Many definitions of geopolitics have been published, of which the following is typical. 'Geopolitics is the science of the earth relationships of political processes, it is based on Political Geography, and views "space" from the standpoint of the "state".' In the extreme German form it considers the state as a necessarily expanding organism, in which the individual is entirely sub-ordinated to this organic state, which is to be aided in its growth by all the powers of the military and civilian population.

Geopolitics is clearly an extreme form of determinism, and its evolution goes far back into geographical history. Montesquieu about 1748 discussed the influences of topography upon the state in his *Esprit des Lois*. Herder (*ca.* 1790) and Hegel (*ca.* 1820) were German writers who discussed the paramount influence of soil and climate. Ratzel in a sense invented the term 'political geography' about the year 1880, and he had as a young disciple Karl Haushofer, who founded the *Zeitschrift für Geopolitik* in 1924. About 1900 Kjellen, a mystical Swedish writer, declared that 'Power is the most important attribute of the State.' He developed this concept at considerable length, and seems to have been the inventor of the term *Geopolitics*.

Of course many other lines of research were levied upon to support the new doctrines of geopolitics. A writer who was much quoted by the Germans was Halford Mackinder, one of the first geographers at an English university. There is little doubt that a paper which he wrote in the early years of this century has exercised more influence on world-thought than most memoirs produced since. I refer to his 'Geographical Pivot of History' (*Geog. Journ.*, London, 1904), which was followed by various articles and books on allied topics. I have discussed the importance of his concepts in several publications, and I quote from one of them.[1]

[1] *Our Evolving Civilization, an introduction to Geopacifics*, Toronto, 1947.

The thesis of Mackinder's contribution to military geography may be summarized in the following phrases which he used in 1919.

> Who rules East Europe commands the Heartland;
> Who rules the Heartland commands the World-Island;
> Who rules the World-Island commands the World.

The areas involved in these terms are charted in Fig. 52.

Mackinder commences his study by showing how the early empire-builders of Europe moved from island to promontory, from promontory to peninsula, and from peninsula to the whole littoral of the Mediterranean. Crete gave way to Macedon, and Greece to Rome. Rome first

FIG. 52.—Sketch showing Mackinder's Heartland

won the peninsula of Italy, then Spain, then Greece, and finally included all the Mediterranean lands in her Empire. In later centuries Charlemagne and Napoleon conquered vast areas in the centre and west of Europe.

After Trafalgar Britain controlled what Mackinder called the 'World Promontory', extending from Britain to Japan. The Indian Ocean became a closed sea comparable with the Mediterranean of the Roman Empire. In his opinion the next stage for a future 'Napoleon' was to control eastern Europe (Fig. 52), and so gain command of the Heartland of central Asia. The latter area is not to be reached from the sea, and is largely a land of nomads. The great populations of Eurasia live either to the north-west or to the south-east of the Heartland. They are so concentrated here that four-fifths of the total population live in two regions which together measure only one-fifth of the area.

Mackinder points out that the invasion of Siberia by the Russian

Cossacks in the sixteenth century brought in the man-power necessary to found a lasting empire in the Heartland. The German and Austrian 'Drang nach Osten' was another attempt to control the landways of Anatolia, Iraq, and Iran; probably with a view to dominating the Heartland from the south. In 1919 he wrote: 'A great military power in possession of the Heartland and of Arabia could take easy possession of the crossways of the world at Suez.' Britain has prevented any such design from maturing in the past; but as he goes on to say 'the facts of geography remain, and offer ever increasing strategical opportunities to land-power as against sea-power'.

It is but fair, however, to draw attention to two predecessors of Mackinder in this geopolitical field. In the period 1861–90 an American, William Gilpin—a strong booster for Denver as the vital centre of the United States—set forth many views on world strategy which foreshadow the deductions of Mackinder (*Harpers*, March 1944). His 'Isothermal Zodiac' extending from the west of U.S.A. across the world to eastern Asia, shows that he had a grasp of some of the implications of geopolitics. Brief mention must also be made of the views of the well-known naval author A. T. Mahan, who published, just before this century (in 1890), his *Influence of Sea Power upon History*. Summarizing Mahan's views we find that he warns a country with a large commerce not to trust to privateers, but to build up a strong and experienced fleet. He pointed out that such a fleet made it unnecessary for England to maintain a large standing army; and this thesis has been accepted for decades as a major principle of British defence.

The Haushofer School of Geopolitik

It is not generally realized that of the three Nazi nations Germany, Italy, and Japan, it was the latter which first put into practice many of the principles implicit in German *Geopolitik*. In the early years of the century Japan had waged a successful war against Russia, and had occupied Korea. In 1908 Major Karl Haushofer was sent to Japan to study the Japanese military techniques. He witnessed the annexation of Korea in 1910, and was greatly impressed by the 'rare national unity, where the Japanese was a faithful subject of his god-like emperor, and where the geopolitical instinct of the nation gave the government a free hand'.[1] The Japanese cabinet was practically unrestricted by parliament, which was a mere sounding-board of public opinion. It appeared to Haushofer that

[1] A. Dorpalen, *The World of General Haushofer*, New York, 1942.

the Japanese leaders had reached their objectives because they had seen the world political situation as the reflection of geographical, national, racial, religious, and many other factors. After this fashion Haushofer later patterned the German geopolitical school.

It is obviously impossible in this brief account to do more than give a few examples illustrating the ideology of the German geopoliticians. The *Zeitschrift für Geopolitik* had a flourishing existence from 1924 until the closing years of the war. It contains many maps and diagrams which endeavour to show that the German Nation constituted the *Herrenfolk*, that it was their destiny to dominate Europe, and later (they hoped) the world. The concept of *Lebensraum* was developed to the full, to the effect that the Germans were being crowded out of existence, and that they had every right to expand just so far as they had the power to do so. The older idea of a *Drang nach Osten* was revived, and the admitted German intention was to expand primarily to the east and south-east, without consideration for the desires of the unfortunate Poles and Ukrainians.

The reader will find many maps illustrating the Nazi views, reproduced and criticized, in such books as *German Strategy and World Conquest* (Whittlesey, New York, 1942) or *Generals and Geographers* (Weigert, New York, 1942). One of the most significant maps is shown in Dorpalen's *The World of General Haushofer* (p. 150, New York, 1942). This gives a map of Europe with the accepted boundaries of the Reich at that date, but with two significant additions. One includes the area where folk of German 'Race' have settled. As might be expected this is not a true (i.e. biological) race map, but merely shows where folk speaking languages akin to German are in the majority. It includes the Flemish, Dutch, Swiss, and Austrians; but these (as we have seen earlier) are classed by anthropologists as partly Nordic, partly Alpine; and in Coon's opinion, partly of 'palaeolithic Borreby race'. The map (reproduced by Dorpalen from the *Zeitschrift* of 1934) shows another marginal area which is bounded on the east by a line from Leningrad to Kharkov. This 'linguistic or cultural German territory' includes Poland, White Russia, and most of the Ukraine. (In a school atlas published by Justus Perthes, the same area is more justly described as that where the German language is widely used in commerce.) There is no doubt that the Nazi leaders took every occasion to suggest by such maps that Germany had political rights far beyond the boundaries of the Reich of 1919.

Other maps in the *Zeitschrift* show 'Mittel Europa' (including Germany) squeezed between inimical border nations both on the west and on the east (*Zeit.*, 1934). Much is made in a further example of the encircling of Germany by France on the western side and her Polish-

Balkan sympathizers on the east (*Zeit.*, 1931). What seems rather amusing to a non-German is a map of Germany showing the menace due to the air fleet of tiny Bohemia! (*Zeit.*, 1934). Many other maps justifying German expansion are reproduced from the *Zeitschrift*, &c., in the two books (by Dorpalen and Whittlesey) which have been cited above.

It need hardly be explained that it is not the data of political geography which are at fault, but it is the purpose behind the publications of the Haushofer School which is dangerous. The present writer published a small book in 1942 which he named *Canada's Role in Geopolitics*. There he points out a number of features in the political geography of the Dominion which seemed of interest to the student of world geography. His purpose was not, however, to inspire Canadians to expand across the 'unguarded frontier', conquer U.S.A., then Latin America, and finally the whole world! But one could imagine a Canadian 'Haushofer' having some such view, though no trace of such a person has so far come to light.

Haushofer considered geopolitics quite distinct from political geography. Geopolitics is essentially dynamic, and furnishes the implements for political action. In his words 'it becomes a technology capable of leading practical politics to a point where it can spring from a firm footing. It is only thus that the jump to action can be made from the solid ground of knowledge.' Further he states that geopolitik will and must become the geographical conscience of the state.[1]

Needless to state every branch of geography was utilized in the *Zeitschrift*, as well as the fields of anthropology, meteorology, and religion. War according to Kjellen is an experimental field for geopolitics; and the Haushofer School accepts war, in the best tradition of Von Clausewitz, as a continuation of diplomacy by different means (*Kiss*). All problems concerning population are of importance to the student of *geopolitik*. It is of interest that the *Zeitschrift* in 1940, when Britain had lost all her allies, declared that the age of the '*fragmentation of Europe*' had come to an end. Now at last the peoples of the continent could unite under the leadership of Germany without restraint from the maritime power of Britain, which (in Haushofer's opinion) had prevented the development of this happy condition ever since the Peace of Westphalia in 1648.

The pungent criticism by Isaiah Bowman in the same *Review* (1942) should be read by all students of geopolitics. Bowman points out that its arguments contain a poisonous self-destroying principle: when international interests conflict or overlap, *Might* alone shall decide the issue.

[1] See the useful article on this topic by George Kiss in the *Geographical Review*, October 1942. This article is followed by another by Isaiah Bowman in which he criticizes some of the fallacies of the German geopoliticians.

Against 'geopolitical needs' democracy opposes moral rights. German history seems to show by many illustrations a technique of *rationalizing* greed and violence.

The New World and Future Populations

While the Germans were producing innumerable articles in justification of their ideology, Isaiah Bowman published his most important volume, *The New World*. This is a major contribution to political geography; but is so well known to geographers that there is no need to do more than summarize its principles here in the author's own words. 'Its philosophy was one of gradualness of change by rational means. It interposed no ideological preconceived "system" between a problem and its solution in a practical world. It sought to analyse real situations rather than to justify any one of several conflicting nationalistic policies.'

As a second illustration of practical political geography Bowman proposed in 1935 a Pan-American Atlas on a co-operative basis. It was not a proposal to use science to conquer Latin America after the geopolitical fashion of the Germans; but showed how we could work together for common ends. One paragraph of his article (loc. cit.) well deserves quotation.

Let us consider for a moment the effect of such joint undertaking of more than continental magnitude upon the individual countries concerned. We are all aware of the uneven advances of the civilized countries of the world in the arts and sciences. Our material endowments are unevenly distributed, and to a varying degree different in kind. It results that one nation advances past its fellows in one line, only to be overtaken itself in another. In consequence we learn from each other, and in the end make a better and a richer civilization for us all.

It is to be expected that geographers with a less military outlook than Haushofer would react very differently to the disaster of World War. Accordingly from 1919 onwards a number of folk have been engaged in research with a view of promoting world peace rather than world domination. In this group were many who tried to ascertain the possibilities of various pioneer regions in regard to the spread of crowded populations.[1] They felt that the troubles of the twentieth century were to a considerable degree to be traced to the congestion of peoples in older established areas, chiefly in Europe and Asia, which had never before perhaps been so acute. At the same time it became obvious that the rich

---

[1] 'Limits of Land Settlement', by ten authors (with a preface by I. Bowman), is particularly helpful. (*Report to International Conference*, Paris, 1937.)

hitherto empty lands of the world had become occupied; first perhaps in south-east Europe, where the marginal wheat lands near the Caspian were occupied by wheat farmers throughout the nineteenth century; somewhat later in U.S.A. and the Argentine; about the middle of that century in Australia, since 1880 in the Canadian prairies; and since 1900 in Manchuria and the southern portion of Siberia.

It should be obvious that a geographer is as competent as most to discuss the limits of lands which are likely to support the population of the world in the future, and a number of estimates have been made in the early years of the twentieth century. Three of these may be mentioned here. In 1922 the writer published a lengthy paper on 'Future Settlement' (in the *Geographic Review*) in which the world was divided into seventy-four economic regions, including a number in Europe. The population of the latter was supposed to be 'saturated', and the remaining regions were investigated to find how many folk they would support according to European standards of living. O. E. Baker was primarily interested in the future wheat lands of the world. His paper (in the same *Review* for 1923) showed that of some 52 million square miles in the continents only about 4 million are arable at present, while about 6 million remain for croplands; and four-fifths of the land surface is of very little value for crops. Penck in the *Zeitschrift für Geopolitik* for 1925 forecast some extraordinary population figures, such as 49 per square mile in the future for Canada, whereas the writer thinks 16 too high a figure. Penck's figure of 2,800 millions for tropical lands seems also much too high. (See p. 604.)

World Leaders in Heavy Industry

In the present world crisis it is natural to be much interested in the power resources of the various nations—whether for peace or war. It should be unnecessary to point out in how many fields the teachings of geography are directly helpful. Military geography is a very practical side of our discipline. Strategy and tactics are inevitably linked with the distributions of land and sea, and of mountain and plain. But some of the broader aspects of environmental control, as affecting the distributions of the bases of heavy industry, may well be discussed at this point.

In Fig. 53 the graphs show by radii the relative values (as regards population, and steel, coal, oil and hydro outputs) for the chief military nations in 1938. The figures for U.S.A. are represented by radii in the dynograph which just reach the outer circle. In all other countries similar figures usually are less than half as great. In 1940–41 Britain faced four countries each of comparable military power. Hitler's challenge to U.S.A.

and U.S.S.R. inevitably turned his almost certain victory into certain defeat.

Almost all weapons of the belligerents depended on huge supplies of iron and steel, and these in turn can only economically be worked in the vicinity of large supplies of fuel. Of fuels coal is still by far the most important, for it supplies eight or ten times the power based on hydro-electric supplies, and four or five times the power based on oil. In my book *Our Evolving Civilization* (Toronto, 1947) I show that the distributions of coal, of petroleum, of hydro-electric power, and to a lesser degree of metallic ores, are to be linked with the broader features of the environment. Thus the oil of the world in almost every case is within those belts

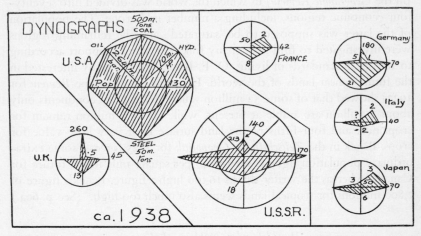

FIG. 53.—Dynographs showing the relative values of Heavy Industry in seven countries. Note the four 'Axis nations' opposed to the United Kingdom before U.S.S.R. and U.S.A. joined the Allies

of the earth which are characterized by the 'young mountains'. The 'domes' of an oilfield seem to be due to lesser folding forces on the flanks of the great line of Pacific mountains, or of the equally important chain running from the East Indies across to Gibraltar. No high young mountains are found in Australia or Africa (except in the Atlas), and there is little oil in these continents. (Fig. 54.)

So also with regard to coal, there are favourable and unlikely areas for deposits. Out of a total supply of some 7,000 million tons, only 4 per cent are found in southern lands. In the north we can cut out all geological formations older than the Carboniferous, for coal-forming plants were not evolved in earlier periods. The huge areas of late Tertiary deposits contain little coal better than peat, and they can be ignored. Moreover—though this relation is not absolute—not much coal has been discovered in arid lands. All the important coalfields except perhaps some in, or near Colorado (and the reported fields in Antarctica) occur in humid regions; which seems to suggest that the floras of the past developed in humid lands with climates not unlike those of today.

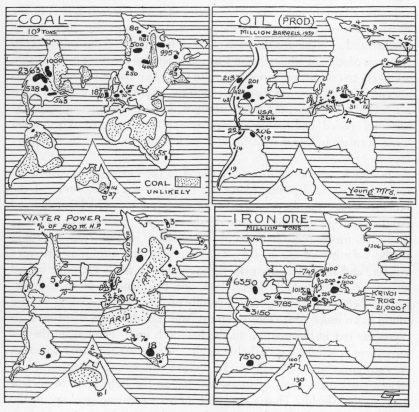

FIG. 54.—Outstanding 'World' supplies of Coal, Oil, Water Power and Iron Ore, which determine the 'Power Nations' of the World

It is curious that something the same distribution is true for the world's great iron deposits. In Fig. 54 are charted the twenty leading iron deposits of the world, and they too lie outside desert lands, though the reason is not obvious. Many iron deposits such as Mesabi and Lorraine are thought to be due to the secretions of iron-loving bacteria, such as form the bog iron ore of today. Possibly in the past these flourished best in the *wetter* parts of the world, which may have been in much the same latitudes as they are found today.

With regard to the metallic minerals such as gold, silver, copper, tin, &c. two types of environment are rather favourable for their occurrence. In general we believe that they originate as vapours or heated solutions which have risen from the metal-bearing central portions of the earth. Recent deposits have not had time to collect such precipitations from vapours or liquids, unless there has been extensive igneous action in the district. The older the rocks, the greater the chance for them to be cracked and available for the passage of such solutions from below. Thus the great *Shields*, of which that in Canada is perhaps the most noteworthy, are likely to contain such metals; and in Canada most of the metal mines are either in this type of formations or in the rival type. When mountains are folded into ridges, the ridges composed of the younger upper rocks are soon eroded, and the inner *cores* are exposed to the air. These older inner formations often contain ores which are absent in the younger layers.

In U.S.A. few metal mines are found in the Great Plains, which are formed of *young* deposits. Many are found in the older rocks of the Rockies where the deeper-seated formations are exposed by uplift and erosion. In some regions of considerable ancient igneous activity, as in Tasmania, metals occur in zones about a mass of igneous rock according to the volatility of the metals. Thus mercury and antimony are very volatile, and their deposits may be expected far from the once heated igneous mass (batholite). Silver, lead, and zinc tend to be in an intermediate belt. Gold and copper are readily precipitated on cooling and are found in an inner zone. Tin, wolfram, and molybdenum often seem to crystallize out in the margins of the batholith itself. Here again the environment is at least a partial clue to the distribution. In many countries we can ignore areas of widespread undisturbed young formations, and concentrate on the cores of mountains, or on the large areas of ancient rocks in the Shields. Thus a study of the structure and geology of the world shows a definite 'pattern' in the supply of those resources which determine 'heavy industry.'

Geography and Nation-Planning

If reference be made to the 'Geographical Tree' in Fig. 1 it will be seen that almost the youngest branch thereon is labelled 'Forecasting Settlement'. This aspect of the modern geographer's work seems to me to be of increasing importance in this age of Five Year Plans and world rivalries. It has been the good fortune of the writer to be directly concerned with the development of geography in the two largest sections of the Empire—Australia and Canada. So strongly have I felt the need for some plan to direct statesmen in their efforts to build up a strong nation, that I have made the frontispieces of both my lengthy studies of these two large areas take the form of 'Habitability Maps'. In other words they attempt to show what the population distribution will be like some generations later than the present time. (See Bibliography later.)

Let us for a moment consider some of the valuable pioneer work in Australia in this connexion. Apart from the usual collection of official data with regard to rainfall and temperature, not much geographic research of the planning type was carried out in the nineteenth century. Probably the research of Surveyor Goyder was the most informative. In 1865 he made a survey of the lands at the northern end of the Flinders Range in South Australia, with a view to determining the safe limits of the wheat-growing lands of the state. He traced on the map what is known as 'Goyder's Line', and it was found later to agree fairly well with the 12-inch isohyet, and to be a valuable indicator in future planning of agriculture.

In Canada much the same sort of forecasting in the early days was carried out by Captain Palliser in 1857 to 1860. He was sent out by the Colonial Office in London to the Prairie lands of Canada, and he divided them on an ecological basis into the northern 'fertile belt' and a southern 'semi-arid desert'. He enclosed a rather large region in a roughly triangular area, which has since become known as 'Palliser's Triangle'. (It is shown in Fig. 126 in the writer's recent text on Canada.) In 1880 the botanist John Macoun made a similar survey, in which he pointed out the northern belt of better rains, and the importance of studying the native flora as a clue to future progress. Around 1904 James Mavor charted his conclusions with regard to the future wheat-growing lands in the prairies, and he thought that 22 million acres might be devoted to this crop. Within a quarter of a century the actual acreage agreed very well with his reasoned forecast.

The forecast of the writer with regard to the population lines of Canada is given in Fig. 55. I think it likely that in about a hundred years we shall see 40 or 50 million folk in Canada, settled according to the isoiketes (lines of equal population) given in the map. However, I am much more certain of the position of the lines indicating the directions of future growth than I am of the totals that will be reached. The limit of agriculture on the map agrees fairly well with that suggested (in an official publication) for the northern edge of lands where the climate is warm enough for the growth of potatoes and other root crops. When this country is settled to the extent of similar lands in Sweden, Finland, and Russia, we may see a density of one to the square mile extending to this limit.

The next isoikete (5) shows where the growth of northern grains such as barley and oats and buckwheat may be expected. It agrees approximately with the line of 56° F. in July—which some experts adopt as the criterion limiting northern grain crops. The limit of dense wheat culture is much the same as that found on the northern edge of the wheat-belt today. A density of folk amounting to 16 per square mile seems to me to be reasonable. Judging by progress elsewhere, I feel sure that great strides forward will occur as the coal resources of Alberta are utilized. They are

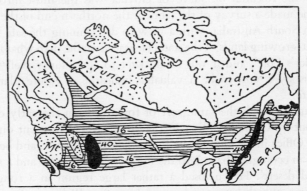

Fig. 55.—Future Settlement Zones in Canada

estimated as equal to those of Czechoslovakia or of the Ukraine, where population-densities of 40 to the square mile are to be found. Electric power can be produced from this coal, and carried three or four hundred miles all over the adjacent country-side; and we shall be sure to see an extension of this process as technology improves. I see no hope of noteworthy population in the vast tundra regions of the north.

One of my critics complains that I have given no place in my forecasts to the development of plastics and of atomic power. We can only argue from the *Known* to the Unknown, our data as to plastics and atomic power are still too nebulous to be of value. I would, however, like to drive home the fact that the pattern of world-population is not likely to be materially altered in the future—since those places where technological progress is most significant will in my opinion always be close to regions of power, and therefore of population. The present densely populated areas will tend to grow still more important, while the deserts and empty spaces will be relatively even less important than they are now, in the days to come.

Turning to my forecasts for Australia, they are shown in the similar map in Fig. 56. I drew up a map much like this as far back as 1919. and the progress in the last thirty years has but confirmed my forecast. There is no need to go into the technique at the basis of the map, for it is based on progress in other lands which—with similar environments— have advanced rather farther than the new lands in Australia. May I be allowed, in conclusion, to refer to an episode in my recent visit to Australia (April–July 1948).

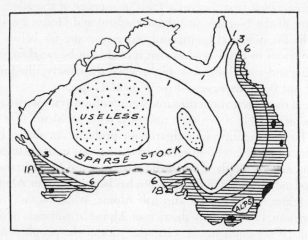

FIG. 56.—Future Settlement Zones in Australia

After making four traverses of the continent to observe the major changes which had occurred since I had left its shores in 1928, I was asked to meet over a score of scientific officers (stationed at Canberra) for a six-hour conference. I was somewhat perturbed to find that the agenda consisted largely of maps copied from my text on Australia, and that the main topic was 'Forecasting population in Australia'. I opened the conference by saying that I felt like an 'Aunt Sally', exposed to the shots of a score of folk, who had been working out these problems in the long years since I left Australia. One and all were kind enough to say that no objection had been found to any of my forecasts, but that they had built upon them in developing the more detailed research of today. Such an experience leaves me assured that the geographer can make forecasts which will be found of direct value by those most concerned with developing their native land.

Cultural Geography

Those of us who can remember the fields of geography before the First World War recall that not much interest was taken in a number of branches of geography which have become relatively popular in recent years. In the second decade of this century one of the chief topics on the borders of geography dealt with the so-called 'Yellow Peril'. The writings of Madison Grant and of Lothrop Stoddard were read widely, and they spread the belief that there was something unusually advantageous in belonging to the Nordic Race. For instance Stoddard in his book *The Revolt against Civilization* (1922) gives a table in support of the alleged mental superiority of the Nordics, in which England and Holland come at the top of the list, while Belgium and Norway come far below them. It seemed obvious to many readers that it could not be *racial* factors which placed England and Holland so high, while the closely allied nations of Norway and Belgium were so low in mental capacity.

Most of the writers about this time were confusing race with nationality, which is inexcusable if we are concerned with problems of a *biological* nature. To the scientific investigator no problem involving biological attributes can be discussed in terms of the nations quoted, since all four are hybrid nations. England is Nordic in the east and Mediterranean in the west; Holland is Nordic in the east, but has large groups of Alpines in the west; Belgium is half Nordic and half Alpine; while Norway is mainly Mediterranean, but has many districts of Alpine broadheads in the southwest. Only if we compare the characteristics of the people within areas which are *racially homogeneous*, can we derive any data as to the superiority of one race over the other. Ripley in his *Races of Europe* (p. 517 and p. 520) treated Divorce and Suicide data in France in such a fashion that one could deduce that the Alpines of central and eastern France were much less prone to divorce or suicide than were the Nordic and Mediterranean racial groups of France. In most cases the publicists who wrote on race perils at this period were ignorant of anthropology and of ecological principles, and their deductions were of little value. Sad to say the current opinions of the layman today are not much better, but in scientific circles there is a much greater knowledge of the essentials of population characteristics.

When the writer was one of the few scientists in the employ of the Commonwealth Government early in the second decade of this century, he had occasion to examine the scientific background of the arguments which supported the so-called 'White Australia' policy. He found the same confusion between cultural (i.e. national) traits and biological (i.e. anthropological). Since these problems are still facing us—though over-shadowed from 1932 to 1945 by the Nazi absurdities—it is well to investigate some of the racial problems as they affect world politics.

As discussed in Chapter XIX my study of the fundamental principles of anthropology led me to entirely different conclusions from those in current use. If we can show that almost all the leading nations of Europe are hybrid nations, a good deal of absurd propaganda with respect to the evils of 'Racial mixing' falls to the ground. Which are the nations of Europe which stand out in the march of civilization? Greece, in the early historic period, was a nation even then (as it is today) composed of Alpine tribes in the north and Mediterranean tribes in the south. Italy during her most renowned years (around the time of Christ) was of the same mixed origin. The north and east coasts were Alpine, while the west coast, Corsica and Sardinia were and are mainly Mediterranean. France is the sole European nation where there are three distinct races, as indeed Caesar pointed out before the time of Christ. Germany is Nordic (or Borreby) in the north and Alpine in the south. Our own England is hybrid as demonstrated earlier. What other five nations can equal the combined influence of those mentioned upon civilization? Do they not demonstrate the value of racial mixing, rather than the contrary?

Dispassionate analysis of racial groups (as shown in my maps published in 1919 in the *Geographical Review*) shows that these three racial types, Alpine, Nordic, and Mediterranean, are the components of the peoples of China and of the northern half of India. Hence I have never been able to see that there is any *racial* objection to the intermarriage of Europeans with Asiatics from the areas specified. The resulting hybrids are of the same type as those which have developed throughout the ages in Europe without question. (Of course due to prejudice and ignorance, there are all sorts of *social* objections to such mixed marriages, but as these are largely based on error, they will slowly vanish before the spread of accurate knowledge.)

Among the few writers who treat racial problems in a reasonable fashion is Ellsworth Huntington. His book *Character of Races* (New York, 1924) is one of the few which discussed world problems of this kind on a sound anthropological basis. Where he is dealing with biological traits he does not depend on national statistics, but tries to equate his data with real anthropological habitats.

Probably the most widespread prejudice of all is Anti-Semitism. It would seem well worth while to find out what were the main characteristics of the folk professing the Jewish religion. It has long seemed to me that discussion of this problem is something like the adage about the weather. 'Everyone talks about it, and no one does anything about it!' In the Nazi eyes, and to most laymen, this is essentially a question of race, and therefore biological.

I have read many memoirs in favour of the Jews or otherwise, but rarely do any of them examine the problem in terms of race and language, though from the point of view of religion and history the literature is immense. Here again Ripley's discussion (1900) is worth more than all the others, but has met with very little acceptance. As he taught 'the Jews are not a race, but only a people; in long-headed (North) Africa they are dolichocephalic . . . in brachycephalic Piedmont they are quite like the Italians of Turin; and all over Slavic Russia no distinction between Jew and Christian existed' (loc. cit., p. 317).

One peculiarly absurd dogma of the Nazis was involved in their use of 'Non-Aryan' as synonymous with Jew. Racially it is easy to show that the bulk of the Jews (before the late war) were of *Alpine* race, and belonged to that group which they themselves called 'Ashkenazim' (i.e. Scythian). This supports the theory that they are descended to a considerable extent from the (brakeph) Scythians or Khazars of the Ukraine, who became Jews in religion between the years A.D. 600 and 900. The other branch of the Jews centres about Spain, and they are known as 'Sephardim'. They are usually of pure *Mediterranean* (dokeph) stock, like their ancestors in Palestine before the days of dispersion.

Yiddish is the peculiar language of the Jews. When examined by philologists this is found to be essentially a medieval form of German, much as was spoken by the wealthy Jews living in the vicinity of Frank-furt-am-Main. This gradually became the literary language of most European Jews, even those living in or near Poland. To be sure it is written in Hebrew script, but that does not make Yiddish a Semitic or Non-Aryan language; any more than writing English in Pitman's short-hand alters the classification of English as an Aryan tongue. Further, just as English contains an immense number of words derived from Latin, yet it is still Teutonic; so also Yiddish contains many Hebrew words, but is still fundamentally 'Aryan'.

One of the most important books in this political field appeared in 1915 during the progress of the First World War. It is called *Nationality and the War*, by Arnold J. Toynbee, and discussed the various national problems in Europe and adjacent areas of the world. Of especial value were the maps, where linguistic boundaries were contrasted with political boundaries, and the areas which we call Irredenta (unredeemed) could readily be identified.

About this time the Department of Geography was organized at

Sydney, and the writer was appointed in 1920 as the first professor. He gave a course of lectures on Cultural Geography which departed to some extent from the usual programme (which stressed physical or economic geography), and made the study of the distributions of race, language, religion, &c. the basis of the lectures. This course was very well attended by many students, who were not so much interested in the economic as the historical and social aspects of man's development.

Considerable stress was laid on a graphic approach to these problems, and this led to a much greater appreciation of maps by students who did not realize that a map is not only a record of the past but a *valuable tool leading to the elucidation of new ideas*. In fact in studying the development of any region it is well to keep in mind the slogan 'Plan, Pattern, Principles, Parallels, Prospects'. We must draw a plan of the area in question, because it often offers us a pattern which suggests the major underlying principles. One of the main features which marks valuable research is to indicate *what may happen in the future*. This is often best learnt by studying the development of regions in parallel situations, some of which may be at a somewhat more advanced stage of evolution than the region originally investigated.

An example from the economic field will make this concept readily understood. If we *plan* the population of Canada, we see that the *pattern* is essentially a narrow zone usually less than 400 miles wide, along the southern edge of the Dominion. It is easy to equate this with the isotherms, which agree better with the population than do any other major isopleths, and so we discover that temperature is the determining factor in Canada's population. We thus learn the *principles* behind the distribution of population. We look further afield and notice *parallel* distributions in U.S.S.R.; and since the latter nation is much more powerful and wealthy than Canada, and has progressed much farther in her settlement of marginal areas, we can use her progress as a key to the *prospects* of the Dominion in the next century. Of course this technique is commonplace to the geographer, but it is by no means so familiar to students who have not had a geographic training. Yet it is of as much value to them in their problems as it is to the geographer. Further examples of geographic technique applied to other disciplines[1] will be found in a paper by the writer contributed to the 'Romer Volume' (*Geographic Society of Lwow*, 1934) and entitled 'The Block Diagram and its ecological uses'.

It will be gathered from what has been discussed in this chapter that there is no unanimity as to what constitutes geopolitics. Whittlesey has

[1] See also 'Correlations and Culture', the presidential address to Section E, Brit. Assoc., Cambridge, 1938.

used it as almost a synonym for Political Geography. The writer in his booklet of 1942 (op. cit.) has laid stress on the prefix 'geo', and used it to mean the broader *World-relations* of Canada. Neither of these uses agrees with the meaning given to it by the Germans, where the aim of the study is world-conquest by the Nazis. For this reason I have ventured to introduce the new term *Geopàcifics*, for geographical research in which the specific aim is to promote world peace.

Geopacifics—Geographic Aspects of the Path to World Peace

Since the writer of this chapter has devoted a good deal of his research since he first entered the field of geography to the furtherance of world peace, some notes on the evolution of the concept of geopacifics may not be out of place. Early in his lectures on these subjects he realized that there were three major agglomerations of folk at three different levels. The fundamental groups are those biological varieties which we call *race*. There are, as stated in an earlier chapter, three major races, Alpine, Mediterranean, and Negro; and two less important races, the Australoid and the Negrito. Approximate figures for these classes are:— Alpine 1,473 millions; Mediterranean 581 millions; Negroes 121 millions; Australoid 50 millions; and Negritoes about 70,000 (*Global Geography*, New York, 1944; p. 382).

The second type of agglomeration is what we call a *nation*, and these are in general much smaller units. In Europe the average nation has about 15 millions of inhabitants, though several nations have figures over 100 millions. The third agglomeration is the *city*, town, or village. In this group the units range downwards from eight million to a hundred or so. It is this latter grouping (as is explained in another chapter) which is most characteristic of our civilization. But the other categories of race and of nation are equally important in the development of civilization,[1] and cannot by any means be ignored.

War is the arch-enemy of civilization, hence it is obvious that a highly civilized world can only develop in a world at peace. Many years ago I projected a series of four volumes dealing with the varied aspects of Cultural Geography referred to above. Three of these have been published, and the fourth has just appeared. A quotation from the last page of the first volume (*Environment and Race*, 1927) is worth consideration.

The ideal towards which the most enlightened statesmen are working is surely a World at Peace. The chief obstacles in the way are Race Prejudice and National

---

[1] The best account of the Dawn of Civilization is found in the volumes of *Corridors of Time* by H. Peake and H. J. Fleure (Oxford and Yale Presses).

jealousy. The former in most cases is but another name for ethnological ignorance. The latter will tend to diminish as each nation realizes the place in the world's 'Order of preference' for which its racial, moral and economic status equips it. The foregoing study is an attempt to investigate some of these ethnological and economic problems. If it helps in however small a degree to promote the brotherhood of man, the writer's main object will have been accomplished.

Reference is made above to 'national jealousy', and to the need for a better knowledge of the resources and powers of various nations. Hence the second volume in the series appeared in 1936 with the title *Environment and Nation*. It dealt wholly (as the subtitle declares) with the geographical factors in the cultural and political history of Europe. After a discussion of topography and climate, the races and languages[1] of Europe were described. Using the 'Zones and Strata' technique discussed in Chapter XIX certain conclusions as to the development of the Indo-European languages were reached. For instance, it seems likely that the Keltic languages of Britain represent the survivors of the *earliest* Indo-European languages, and that the series of languages met with on a line from Ireland to Persia (or thereabouts) represents the stages in evolution of the great family of languages concerned.

A special method of charting historical data by Time-Space diagrams gave some interesting results as to the chief feature of European history. This might be described as the growth in importance of the Alpine broadheads of Europe, more especially that large group which speaks the Slav languages. Various phases of European development such as the spread of Christianity, or at a later date of the Renaissance movement, are more clearly shown by isopleth maps than by pages of non-graphic description. Throughout, the notable part played by topography in determining the bounds of stable cultural groups is demonstrated.

The third volume of the series (*Urban Geography*, London, 1949) is concerned with the evolution of villages, towns, and cities; but this has been fully discussed in Chapter XXI. The last volume is entitled *Our Evolving Civilization—an introduction to Geopacifics*; and this appeared early in 1947, though logically it should have been the last to be published. It links into a whole much that appears in greater detail in the three other volumes. Some topics are treated more fully, however, such as the effects of the World-Plan; the mechanism of an Ice Age; implications from the latest world-maps of blood groups; the superiority of the brakeph Alpine race; the distribution of racial intolerance; the probable cradleland of civilization; the rise of some nations, and the disappearance of others.

[1] Languages are the chief determinants of nations, and it is important to understand language differences in any attempt to produce a world at peace.

The last chapters dealt with various aspects of the late World War. The salient features are indicated in an isopleth map of the gradual invasion of Germany by the allies; world centres of power are indicated as dynographs, which clearly show the immense superiority of U.S.A. over all other nations (including U.S.S.R.); the character of the main breaks in the great wall across Europe (which resulted during the 'Alpine Storm' period of mountain-building) is illustrated. Territorial changes during and following the last World War are charted and explained. Suggestions as to the future re-alignments in Europe—based on the distribution of the resources of trade—are also depicted in maps. Finally the future populations of the world are foreshadowed on an isopleth map, much like that put forward in the *Geographical Review* of July 1922, which still seems a useful forecast some twenty-five years after it was first published.

To this wide picture of Cultural Geography, with a very definite aim in all four volumes, the writer has ventured to give the name of *Geopàcifics*. The word is admittedly hybrid, and is coined as the antithesis of Geopolitics. A summary of this latest department of geography is as follows:

Geopacifics is an attempt to base the teachings of freedom and humanity upon real geographical deductions; in a sense it is humanized geopolitics. It shows for instance, from a study of the World Plan, where the leading nations must arise; be it understood to lead not to conquer. It shows how the conflicts based on racial differences are usually absurd. There is no 'yellow race' and no 'white race', so that there cannot be biological conflict between them. It tries to understand the evolution of the Jewish folk, as the best answer to the poison of Anti-Semitism. It describes the widespread race mixing in Europe in the past, which is of much the same type as race mixing in India, South America, China, &c. today. It explains the realities of climatology with a view to aiding the world to improve the better portions of the world first; instead of encouraging wasted efforts whereby folk are urged to develop difficult terrains, when easier lands are available near at hand. It shows that we should study environmental control, so as to advance in harmony with our environment. It is a material philosophy, but not a complete one, because it does not pretend to discuss those basic principles which properly belong to distinct *ethical* disciplines.

Geopacifics and Education

I have now covered some of the main features involved in the study of Geopacifics. As in Haushofer's plan the details are not new. But I have hopes that defining our aim as World Peace would encourage many students to take much more interest in these later developments of geography than they had in the older economic geography. Some readers will say that historians, economists, &c. have been devoting much of their time to such problems for many decades. This is of course true— but they do not follow the objective (or one might say *visual*) plan which I have found very successful and popular in Toronto University.

Leading educators say we must 'soft pedal' physical science. We know all too much about atomic bombs, and all too little about human relations. 'Let us'—say they—'give far more attention to the humanities than we have done recently.' I do not agree with this proposal. The humanities have had a long innings of some 1,300 years in English lands, and do not seem capable of solving the novel world-problems of today. The orthodox plan is to study the classics as a necessary prelude to philosophy, to delve deeply into the latter to understand religions, to follow up with a study of the history of the last 2,000 years. This is admittedly an admirable plan if our students could spend thirty years on their education, but most students have only three years. They are not, as a whole, deeply interested in classics, philosophy, religion, or ancient history. They are, however, deeply interested in the causes of recent world wars, and especially in the prevention of future world wars.

Geopacifics has little in common with pacifist ideas. As long as we have thieves we must have police; and as long as Fascist and extreme national ideas persist, we need strong forces of an international type to check them.

Let us get down to brass tacks, and pose the urgent problems in a series of simple maps and diagrams. (Indeed psychologists tell us that we learn by 'visual patterns'.) Let us explain how the patterns depend on the environment; and study the relation of human groups in an objective way, rather than in the somewhat mystical fashion of Arnold Toynbee. This great writer pays little attention to the vast accumulation of *geographical* data of the last thirty years; which, in my opinion, alters our whole concept of the growth of nations, and of civilization itself. It is my opinion that in the liaison subject of geography—which carries across the teaching of sciences (like geology and physics) to the realm of man; and which emphasizes world-patterns—we have the answer to this extremely urgent problem. We have not much time. Rome is burning. My panacea for the world's unrest is to implement the Atlantic Charter on the international front; and to ensure—on the educational front—that *all* university students are exposed to a course of lectures on civilization, preferably of an objective, graphic type such as I have tried to offer in my studies of geopacifics. If this type of scientifically-derived data is grafted on to the age-long teachings of religion we shall perhaps make real progress towards a World at Peace.

BIBLIOGRAPHY

Banse, E., *Germany prepares for War*, New York, 1941. A frank discussion of German aims published in Germany before the war.

Bowman, I., *The New World*, New York, 1928. The best discussion of the major political problems of the world, with many maps.

Darby, H. C. (*et al.*), *Historical Geography of England*, Oxford, 1936. An excellent geographic account of the growth of a nation.

Dorpalen, A., *The World of General Haushofer*, New York, 1942.

Gregory and Shave, *The U.S.S.R.*, London, 1944. Contains many useful economic maps.

Johnson, D. W., *Topography and Strategy in the War*, New York, 1917. Fine topographic maps dealing with the First World War.

Mackinder, H. J., *Democratic Ideals and Reality*, New York, 1942. A new edition of the famous book of 1917.

Seversky, A. P., *Victory through Air Power*, New York, 1942.

Taylor, Griffith. The four volumes on Cultural Geography (*Race*, 1917; *Nation*, 1936; *Cities*, 1949; *Civilization*, 1947) quoted in the text.

Australia, London, 1948; and *Canada*, London, 1950.

Toynbee, A., *Nationality and the War*, London, 1915.

Weigert, H. W., *Generals and Geographers*, New York, 1942. (Geopolitics.)

Whittlesey, D., *The Earth and State*, New York, 1939. A general study of political geography.

CHAPTER XXVI

A CONCISE GLOSSARY OF GEOGRAPHICAL TERMS

GRIFFITH TAYLOR

The terms in the following list are taken from texts by Finch and Trewartha, E. Hills (Melbourne), W. H. Hobbs, P. James, Tarr and Von Engeln, Griffith Taylor, and others. The dozen books chosen for consultation were concerned with varying geographical fields, but if a term did not appear in them it was perforce omitted in this tentative glossary. The definitions are *concise rather than detailed*, since complete definitions would take more space than is available. For the same reason only the 700 words which most appeal to the editor have been included. Such a list shows that geography has a nomenclature whose scope is similar to that of other natural sciences. The glossary will be found to be of use, for instance, when one has to point out to freshmen that they cannot tackle senior lectures without preliminary work, since they have no knowledge of the considerable vocabulary. It would be interesting to know when the later terms were invented, and by whom. An asterisk denotes those introduced by the editor, many of which are described in his book *Geographic Laboratory* (Toronto, 1942). He will welcome additions to this glossary for later editions. The editor has received considerable help in this compilation from his son, David P. Taylor.

A

AA LAVA: Jagged, blocky, surface.

ABKASIAN: A tribe in the Caucasus (speech akin to Amerind).

ABRASION: River beds attacked by boulders, &c.

ACCORDANCE OF HILLTOPS: Indicates a former uniform surface.

ACID ROCKS: Rocks rich in silica.

ADIABATIC: Heat due to compression of air, &c.

ADOLESCENT TOPOGRAPHY: When original flat divides still survive.

ADRET: The sunny side of a valley.

AETA: Negrito tribe in Philippines.

AGAVE: A semi-desert plant in Mexico.

AGGRADED VALLEY: Floor built up by river deposits.

AGGRADING: Where rivers are building up their beds.

AINU: Nordic(?) tribe in Japan.

AIR MASSES: Large units of polar (or tropic) air.

ALFALFA: A legume (lucerne) used for fodder.

ALFOLD: Plain in Hungary.

ALKALI FLATS: Marshy areas in arid regions rich in salts.

ALLUVIAL: Deposits of silt and gravel.

ALPIDES: Crustal folds in Europe.

ALPINES: Broad-headed races.

ALPINIZATION: Influx of Alpine race.

ALTIPLANO: High plateau of the Andes.

AMERIND: Aborigines in America.

ANABRANCH: A secondary channel to a river.

ANCHOR-ICE: Forms on the floor of shallow seas.

ANCYLUS: Former immense lake east of Sweden.

ANEMOMETERS: Instruments to measure wind velocity.

ANEROID: An instrument to measure heights.

ANIMISM: Primitive religion.

ANSCHLUSS: Political absorption.

ANTHRACITE: Type of hard coal.

ANTICLINE: Ridge-fold in rocks.

ANTITRADES: High-level westerly winds.

APATITE: A mineral source of phosphorus.

APHELION: Furthest distance between earth and sun.

APPALACHIA: Ancient continent to NE. of U.S.A.

APPALACHIAN STORM: A period of Permian mountain-building.

APPOSED GLACIERS: Glaciers joined like Siamese twins.

ARAMAIC: Early Semitic language.

ARC: A curved earth-fold.

AREG (see ERG).

AREIC: A surface lacking streams.

ARETE: A narrow rock ridge.

ARMORICAN STORM (see APPALACHIAN).

ARROYO: A gully.

ARTESIAN: Water rising above surface through pressure.

ARUNTA: Desert in E. central Australia.*

ARYAN: Major language class in Europe.

ASBESTOS: A fibrous mineral.

ASHKENAZIM: Polish Jews.

ASPECT (climate): Relation to dominant winds.*

ASTHENOSPHERE: Zone in the crust where rocks flow.

ASTROLABE: Instrument which measures vertical angles.

ATOLL: A ring-shaped coral island.

ATRIPLEX: A semi-desert plant.

AUGITE: A common rock mineral.

AUSGLEICH: Political Union.

AUSTRALOID: Aboriginal folk in Australia.*

AUSTRALOPITHECUS: A fossil ape.

AVALANCHE: A mass of snow slipping from a mountain.

AVARS: Early tribes in Hungary.

AZIMUTH: Angles measured in a horizontal plane.

AZONAL SOILS: Very youthful soils.

B

BACK SLOPE: Surface of a tilt-block.

BAD LANDS: Deeply gullied soils in arid lands.

BALLON SONDE: Upper-air instrument.

BANKS: Lands drowned by shallow seas.

BARCHAN: A crescentic sand dune.

BAROGRAPHS: Measure changes in air pressure.

BARREN GROUNDS: Treeless areas in N. Canada.

BARRIER REEF: Zone of coral along a coast.

BARS: Ridges of sand piled by waves.

BASALT: A fine-grained igneous rock.

BASE-LEVEL: Lowest to which a stream can cut its bed.

BASQUE: Linguistic group in N. Spain (akin to Amerind).

BASTIDE: A medieval (military) town.

BATHOLITH: Deep-seated igneous mass.

BATHYMETRY: Measuring ocean depths.

BAUXITE: Earthy ore of aluminium.

BAYOUS: Abandoned channels of a river.

BEAKER FOLK: Primitive group in Britain.

BEAUFORT SCALE: Indicates wind strength.

BERBER: Tribes in NW. Africa.

BERGSCHRUND: A marginal crevasse.

BETEL: Nut chewed in Pacific Isles.

BETRUNKED RIVERS: Lower portions drowned by sea.

BILLABONG: Abandoned river channel.

BITUMINOUS: A type of coal.

BLACK EARTH (see CHERNOZEM).

BLIZZARDS: Cold winds usually filled with snow.

BLOCK DIAGRAM: Shows topography in three dimensions.

BLOCK-DRAUGHTER: An instrument for drawing block diagrams.*

BLOCK MOUNTAINS: Are elevated along fault planes.

BOLSON: A shallow depression in deserts.

BONANZA: A rich vein of gold.

BOTTLE-NECK VALLEY: Wide at head with narrow outlet, in eastern Australia.

BOULDER CLAY: Debris laid down by a glacier, &c.

BOULEVARD: An avenue on the site of a town-wall.

BRAIDED STREAM: Many small streams on a wide flat bed.

BRAKEPH: Broad-headed.*

BRECCIA: Rock formed of angular fragments.

BRUSH TIMBER: A forest akin to selva in E. Australia.

BRYTHONIC: Tribes speaking Welsh.

BUCKWHEAT: A grain grown in cold climates.

BURAN: The cold blizzard of Russia.

BUSHMEN: Pygmy tribe in S. Africa.

BUTTES: Small conical level-bedded hills.

BYSMALITH: A faulted type of laccolite.

C

CAATINGA: Arid scrub-lands in Brazil.

CACAO: Tree whose pods produce chocolate.

CACTI: Thorny plants common in arid lands.

CALCITE: Carbonate of lime crystals.

CALDERAS: Unusually wide volcanic craters.

CALEDONIAN STORM: Mountain-building about 300 million years ago.

CALLITRIS: A common tree in arid Australia.

CAMPOS: Warm grasslands in Brazil.

CANYONS: Deep narrow river gorges.

CAPILLARY WATER: Water films around soil particles.

CARBONIFEROUS: A period about 200 million years ago.

CARDO: A Roman main street.

CARIBOU: Wild reindeer.

CARTOGRAMS: Dot diagrams.

CASCADIA: Ancient continent NW. of U.S.A.

CATALAN: A group in NE. Spain.

CATASTROPHIC: Periods of great change in the geological record.

CAUCASIAN: Outmoded racial term for Europeans.

CELESTIAL SPHERE: On which stars, &c. are marked.

CEMENTATION: The binding of deposits by lime, &c.

CENOTES: Sink-holes in Yucatan.

CENTRAL COOLING: A technique used in hot climates.

CENTRES OF ACTION: Control wide circular air movements.

CENTRUM: The centre of earthquake activity.

CEPHALIC INDEX: Measures width of skull.

CHAMPLAIN SEA: Former sea reaching west to Toronto.

CHAPARAL: Scrub-lands in Mexico, &c.

CHELLEAN: Early period in human history.

CHEQUERBOARD: Grid pattern in towns.

CHERNOZEM: Soil rich in humus.

CHESTNUT EARTH: A rich soil

CHICLE: A gum from Mexico.

CHINE: Gully in a cliff.

CHINOOK: A warm wind in Western America.

CHOROGRAPHY: Geography of regions.

CHRONOGRAPH: The rotating drum in recording instruments.

CIMMERIAN: An early culture in E. Europe.

CINCHONA: Tree from which quinine is derived.

CIRQUE: An 'armchair' valley.

CIRRUS: High 'horsetail' clouds.

CLAY BELT: A region of glacial clays in E. Canada.

CLIMOGRAPH: A twelve-sided graph of climate.*

CLOUDBURST: Exceptionally heavy rains.

CLUSES: Notch-like gorges in the Juras.

CO-ALTMETER: Instrument measuring co-altitude and time.*

COCA: Drug from S. American shrub.

COIGN (see SHIELD).

COL: A low portion on a mountain ridge.

COLD LOOP: Indicates cold climate in isotherms.

COLLUVIAL SOIL: Collects at the foot of slopes.

COMB RIDGE (see ARETE).

COMFORT FRAME: A graph to show where conditions are pleasant.*

COMPANY TOWN: Built by owners near a factory.

CONCESSION: A small subdivision of land (Can.).

CONFLUENCE: Junction of two rivers.

CONGLOMERATE: Rock built of pebbles.

CONSEQUENT RIVERS: Flow directly down major slopes.

CONTINENTAL CLIMATE: Is one with large extremes.

CONTINENTAL SHELF: The slightly submerged margin of a continent.

CONURBATION: Cluster of cities.

CONVECTION: Upward movement of warm air.

COPRA: Dried kernel of coconut.

CORDILLERAS: A group of mountain systems.

CORE: The inner, older part of a mountain.

CORN: Wheat or other grain in England, maize in America.

CORRASION: Mechanical attack producing river channels.

CORRIE (see CIRQUE).

CORRELATION COEFFICIENT: Measures dependence of one thing on another.

CORRIDOR: A route used in tribal movements.

CORROBOREE: An aboriginal assembly.

COUVADE: A custom associated with birth.

CRANNOG: An islet built of piles.

CRATER: The cup-like hollow of a volcano.

CREEP: Slow movement of earth.

CREVASSES: Tension cracks on a glacier.

CROMAGNON: Primitive tribe in France.

CRYPTOREIC: Drainage by underground channels.

CUESTA: Outcrop of edge of hard stratum.

CUMULUS CLOUD: Heaped cloud with flat base.

CUSPATE FORELAND: Due to meeting of two sand-bars.

CUSPS: Projections from a sand-bar, &c.

CUT-OFF: Deviation across a river bend.

CWM (see CIRQUE).

CYCLE OF EROSION: Topographic changes affecting a landscape.

CYCLONE: A low-pressure system.

D

DECIDUOUS FOREST: Trees drop leaves in winter.

DECLINATION: Angle between true north and magnetic north. Angular distance of star from celestial equator.

DECUMANUS: A Roman road in a town.

DEEP LEADS: Gravels buried under lava.

DEEPS: Deep furrows in the ocean floor.

DEFLATION: Lowering of land surface by wind.

DENDRITIC PATTERN: Streams like twigs of a tree.

DENUDATION: The wearing away of a land surface.

DESICCATION: Deterioration due to drought.

DETERMINIST: (In geography) One who believes in dominant environmental control.

DEW: Vapour condensed by cooling ground.

DEW-POINT: Temperature where vapour condenses.

DIABASE: A form of basalt.

DIASTROPHISM: Crustal movements.

DIATOM: Microscopic marine plants.

DIKE: A narrow crack filled with lava.

DINARIDES: A line of crustal folds across Europe.

DIORITE: A form of igneous rock.

DIP: The angle of slope of a formation.

DISTRIBUTARIES: River channels in deltas.

DIVIDES: Water partings between river basins.

DIVISION TOWN: Where trains are 'serviced' on long railways.

DOKEPH: A narrow-headed race.*

DOLDRUMS: Calm areas in tropical latitudes.

DOLINE: Hollow due to collapse of cave.

DOLMEN: Ancient table-stone.

DOLOMITE: A form of limestone.

DOMES: Gentle bulges in strata which may contain oil.

DONGA: A gully in S. Australia.

DOWNFOLD: Depression due to crustal folding.

DRAVIDIANS: Early migrants into India.

DRIFT ICE: Floating ice (pack).

DRUMLINS: Oval heaps of glacial debris.

DRY FARMING: Where rainfall is uncertain.

DRYOPITHECUS: A fossil ape.

DUMMYING: False ownership of land in Australia.

DUNES: Ridges of windblown sand.

DURICRUST: Hard layer below soil (Aus.).

DUST-BOWL: Region ruined by drought.

DYNE: A measure of force.

DYNOGRAPH: A chart which shows relative status in military power.*

E

ECLIPTIC: The plane in which the earth moves round the sun.

ECOLOGY: Study of distributions of living organisms.

ECONOGRAPH: Diagram of resources of a region.*

EDAPHIC FACTOR: Affects vegetation through soils.

ELBASIN: An elevated basin, often wrongly called a plateau (e.g. upper Yukon R.).*

ELBOW OF CAPTURE: Gives a marked angle in a river.

ELUVIAL: Lower layer of soil.

ENANTIMORPH: Image—as in a mirror.

ENDOREIC DRAINAGE: Has no outlet to sea.

ENGLACIAL DRIFT: Debris enclosed in glaciers.

ENGRAFTED RIVERS: Joining of formerly independent streams.

EOCENE: Period about 40 million years ago.

EOLITH: Earliest known stone tools.

EOTECHNIC: Towns are medieval in pattern.

EPEIROGENIC: The uplift of lands without folding.

EPICENTRUM: The surface above the centre of an earthquake.

EPICONTINENTAL SEAS: Shallow waters over the continental shelf.

EPIGENE FORCES: Act on the surface of the earth.

EPIPHYTES: Plants growing on trees.

EQUINOX: The period when the sun crosses the equator.

ERG: Areas of shifting sand.

ERODED DOME: A dissected crustal 'blister'.

ERRATICS: Blocks carried far away by ice.

ESCARPMENT: The steep face (outcrop) of a sloping hard formation.

ESKIMO: An aboriginal people in the far north of America.

ESPARTO: Grass from Spain.

ETHNOGRAPH: Diagram charting racial data.*

ETRUSCAN: Primitive folk in Italy.

EUCALYPTUS: Commonest tree in Australia.

EUSTATIC MOVEMENTS: World-wide changes of sea-level.

EVERGLADES: Swamps in Florida.

EXFOLIATION: The peeling-off of thin layers of rock.

F

FALL LINE: Where streams drop from a hard rock to a softer one.

FAUBOURG: A suburb.

FAULT: Rupture across a series of rocks.

FELDSPAR: A common rock mineral.

FELL: A bleak plateau in Norway.

FERREL EFFECT: Earth rotation determines direction of winds.

FERTILE CRESCENT: The corridor from Mesopotamia to Egypt.

FERTILITY RATE: Measures survival chances of a group.

FESTOON ISLANDS: Summits of crustal folds above sea-level.

FETCH OF WAVES: Distance travelled by the water.

FIARD: Irregular bay somewhat modified by ice.

FINGER LAKE: Elongated lake deepened by ice erosion.

FIORD: A deep valley occupied by the sea.

FIRN: Loose snow in snow-field.

FIXED DUNES: Sand-ridges held by vegetation.

FLOCCULATION: The collection of suspended clay particles into lumps.

FLOE-ICE: Floating pieces of pack ice.

FLOOD PLAINS: Alluvial plains laid down by rivers.

FLUVIO-GLACIAL DEPOSITS: Silts, &c. deposited by streams from ice-front.

FLYSCH: An Eocene formation.

FOEHN WIND: A warm wind occurring in the lee of mountains.

FOLK-WANDERING: Of tribes in early medieval times.

FOLSOM CULTURE: Is the earliest in U.S.A.

FORE-DEEP: Trough alongside crustal fold.

FORESHORE: Zone washed by tides.

FRAZIL: Submerged river-ice.

FUMAROLES: Steam vents in volcanic areas.

FUNDAMENT: The original natural features of a region.

G

GABBRO: Coarse basic, igneous rock.

GARDEN CITY: Type of town-planning.

GATE: A broad low gap between highlands.

GAULISH: Pre-Latin speech in France.

GEOCOL (see GATE).

GEOCRATIC: Control of man by Nature.*

GEOPACIFICS: Study of geography to promote peace.*

GEOPOLITICS: Study of geography to promote conquest (Nazi).

GEOSYNCLINE: A very extensive syncline.

GEYSERS: Fountains of heated water.

GHETTO: Jewish quarter in a town.

GIBBER PLAINS: Are covered with desert pebbles.

GLACIERETS: Small glaciers, may develop from snow-drifts.*

GLINT: A cliff-like front (Sweden).

GLOBIGERINA OOZE: A deposit on the floor of oceans.

GNEISS: A banded form of igneous rock.

GNOMONIC PROJECTION: Eye supposed at centre of sphere.

GONDWANA: A former land west of India.

GORE: A triangular subdivision of land.

GRABEN: A depression bounded by faults.

GRADIENT OF WIND: Slope of isobaric surface.

GRASSLANDS: Develop where rains are seasonal.

GREAT CIRCLE: Lies on surface of globe with centre at centre of globe.

GREEN BELT: Trees around a city.

GREY EARTH: Type of infertile soil.

GROUND MORAINE: Debris which lay under ice.

GROUNDWATER: The water found in permeable formations.

GUAYULE: Rubber-producing plant.

GUM CREEKS: Streams with narrow fringe of trees (Australia).

GUNZ ICE AGE: Occurred about 800,000 years ago.

H

HABITABILITY: Suitability of lands for future settlement.

HALOS: Rings &c. due to refraction by ice crystals.

HAMADA: Large areas of level rock in deserts.

HAMITIC: Language group in N. Africa.

HANGING VALLEYS: With beds high above main valley.

HARDPAN: Mineralized B level in a soil.

HARMATTAN: Hot dusty east wind in Sahara.

HEAD INDEX: Denotes the breadth of crania.

HEADWARD EROSION: Streams cut back towards their heads.

HEARTLAND: Central part of the Old World.

HEAVY INDUSTRY: Steel &c. which determine military power.

HEIGHT OF LAND (see DIVIDE).

HERCYNIAN PERIOD: An age of mountain-building.

HIGH: Anticyclone or high-pressure area.

HINTERLAND: Region behind the coast.

HITTITE: Early tribes in Anatolia.

HOGBACK: Narrow ridge of resistant rock.

HOMO SAPIENS: Biological group following Neandertal man.

HOMOCLIMES: Places having similar climates.*

HORN: Sharp rocky peak.

HORNBLENDE: A common rock mineral.

HORSE LATITUDES: Belt of variable winds near latitude 27°.

HORST: An elevated crustal block.

HUERTA: A fertile area in E. Spain.

HUMUS: Soil rich in vegetable matter.

HUNDRED (see TOWNSHIP).

HURON LOBE: A tongue of former Ice Cap.

HURRICANE: Huge and violent storm system.

HYDROSPHERE: The water envelope covering most of the globe.

HYGROMETER: Measures humidity.

HYTHERGRAPH: Twelve-sided graph of temperature and rainfall.*

I

IBERIAN: Early tribes in SW. Europe.

ICE-BLINK: Sky-glare above ice.

ICECAP: A huge area of ice, as in Greenland.

ICE-FOOT: Ice attached to the shore.

ICE-THAW CHANNELS: Due to flow along front of former icecap.

INDELTA: Inland area where a river subdivides (e.g. mid-Murray).*

INDIAN SUMMER: Warm spell in the Fall.

INDO-EUROPEAN: Major language-group in Europe (Aryan).

INFANTILE TOWNS: Have barely developed a street plan.*

INLIER: Old rocks projecting through younger rocks.

INSELBERG: Isolated rocky hill in deserts.

INSEQUENT STREAMS: Are not directed by structure.

INSOLATION: Heat received from the sun.

INSULA: A 'block' of streets in a Roman town.

INTERFLUVE: Flattish area between parallel rivers.

INTERGLACIAL: A warm period between ice ages.

INTRAZONAL SOILS: Are affected by salt or extra water.

INTRENCHED MEANDER: Due to uplift of an 'old' meander.

ISANOMALOUS LINES: Indicate variations of climate from normal.

ISARITHM (see ISOPLETH).

ISOBAR: Line of equal air pressure.

ISOGONIC MAP: Shows lines of equal magnetic declination.

ISOHYET: Line of equal rainfall.

ISOIKETE: A line graphing equal habitability.*

ISOKEPH: Lines charting cranial variation.*

ISOMETRIC: Projection used in drawing block-diagrams.

ISOPLETH: A line of equal abundance (*1910).

ISOPOTENTIAL: Surface to which artesian water can rise.

ISOPRACT: A special chart to demonstrate populations, &c.

ISOSEISMAL: Lines joining places affected equally by earthquake.

ISOSTATIC THEORY: Lighter portions of crust float on heavier.

ISOTERPS: Lines indicating equal comfort.*

ISOTHERM: Line of equal air temperature.

J

JETTIES: Silt built out by rivers in lakes, &c.

JOINT PLANES: Vertical cracks in rocks.

JOKUL: A small icecap.

JURASSIC: A period 50 million years ago.

JUVENILE TOPOGRAPHY: Where all valleys are narrow.

K

KAME: Irregular heap of glacial debris.

KAOLIANG: A millet grown in China.

KARLING: A cluster of cirques.

KARST: Landscape due to limestone erosion.

KASBA: Fort in an Arab town.

KAVA CULTURE: Drinking customs in Pacific islands.

KENTUM AND SATEM: Two major divisions of Aryan languages.

KETTLE HOLES: Hollows in till due to melting of ice.

KHAZARS: A Turkish group who became Jews.

KLIPPEN: Hill where old rocks overlie young.

KURGAN FOLK: Built grave mounds in Russia.

L

LACCOLITE: Deep-seated mass of igneous rock.

LADIN: A language in SE. Switzerland.

LAG OF SEASONS: Time interval after solstice, &c.

LAGOONS: Shallow lakes on shores.

LAND-BREEZE: Moves off the land at night.

LAND VALVE: Which partly blocks early human migrations.*

LAPSE RATE: Change in temperature with elevation.

LARAMIDE REVOLUTION: Crustal folding about 40 million years ago.

LATENT HEAT: Set free when a vapour becomes liquid.

LATERAL MORAINE: Debris piled at side of a glacier.

LATERITE: An iron-bearing surface deposit.

LATIFUNDIA: Settlement near huge plantations.

LEACHING: Dissolving salts from soil.

LEBENSRAUM: A German concept concerning wider territory.

LEVEES: Walls of alluvial bordering rivers.

LIANAS: Tropical creeper plants.

LIDO: A sand-bar (Ital.).

LIGNITE: Early stage of coal.

LIMAN: A type of lagoon.

LIMES: Walls of defence across a district.

LINEAMENT: A well-marked linear feature (in structure).

LITHOSPHERE: Solid rock crust.

LITTORAL: Coastal area.

LITTORINA SEA: Formerly occurred off Sweden.

LLANOS: Grasslands of Argentine, &c.

LOESS: Deposit of wind-blown loam.

LOGAN'S LINE: Geological boundary in SE. Canada.

LONGITUDINAL RIVERS: Flow along major fold valleys.

LOW-PRESSURE AREAS (see CYCLONES).

LOWS (see CYCLONES).

M

MAGDALENIAN AGE: A stage in Palaeolithic times.

MAGNETIC POLE: Where magnetic lines converge.

MAIZE: A grain first grown in America.

MALLEE: A small eucalypt species (Aus.).

MANGROVE: Tree growing in salt water.

MANIOC: A tuber used for food.

MANTLE-MAP: A chart depicting structure.*

MANTLE ROCK: Surface layer of loose rock.

MAQUIS: Scrublands in south Europe.

MARAE MONUMENTS: Ancient stone walls in Pacific isles.

MARCH (MARK): A borderland.

MARJELEN LAKE: Held between glacier and cliff.

MASSIM: Tribes in eastern Papua.

MATÉ: Shrub giving tea in S. America.

MATURE RIVERS: When valleys are wide and fairly deep.

MATURE TOPOGRAPHY: Shows wide valleys and rolling hills.

MATURE TOWNS: In which functional pattern is complete.*

MEANDER: A twisting river-course.

MEDIAN MASS: A resistant block amidst earth folds.

MEDITERRANEAN RACE: Narrow-headed, dark, slender folk.

MEGALITH: A large stone monument.

MEGALOPOLIS: The overgrown city.

MERIDIANS: Circles joining pole to pole.

MERINO: Chief type of sheep in Australia.

MESA: An isolated hill of level-bedded rock.

MESETA: Central Spanish tableland.

MESOZOIC AGE: Between 50 and 120 million years ago.

MESQUITE: A common desert shrub.

MESTIZOES: Half-castes.

METAMORPHIC ROCKS: Have been greatly altered by pressure and heat.

METEOROGRAPH: Measures upper-air data.

MIGRATION ZONES: Result from races moving out from central Asia.*

MILLET: A grain grown in warm lands.

MILLIBAR: A unit of air pressure.

MILLSTONE GRIT: Carboniferous Sandstone.

MIOCENE AGE: Occurred about 8 million years ago.

MIR: Village pattern in Russia.

MIRAGE: Image due to heated air.

MISFIT VALLEY: A small stream in a wide bed.

MISTRAL: A cold north wind in south of France.

MOLASSE: Middle Tertiary Sandstones.

MONGOLIAN RACE: An outmoded term for eastern broad-heads.

MONOCLINAL FOLD: Gentle fold in crust leading up to a plateau.

MONSOON: A wind changing with the seasons.

MONTANA: A region in Peru.

MORAINE: A ridge of glacial debris.

MOULINS: Wide vertical holes in glacier.

MOUND SPRINGS: Deposits of lime, &c. around springs.

MOUSTERIAN: An early stage of Palaeolithic culture.

MULGA: Common acacia in Australia.

MUSKEG: Swamp-lands with small conifers in Canada.

MUSK-OX: A large herb-eating polar animal.

N

NAPPES: Overfolds in Swiss Alps.

NATURAL REGION: Exhibits a useful degree of homogeneity.

NEANDERTAL: A heavily-built primitive form of man.

NEAP TIDE: Low tides when sun and moon opposed.

NEBULA: Enormous rotating mass of hot gas in the heavens.

NEGRITOES: The pygmy races.

NEOTECHNIC: Cities developed according to plan.

NESIOT: Tribes in East Indies.

NEVÉ: A snow-field.

NEVER-NEVER LAND: Semi-desert areas in Australia.

NILOTIC: Tribes in Sudan.

NIMBUS: Heavy cloud producing rain.

NIVATION: Thaw and freeze erosion.

NON-ARYAN: Strictly refers to language only, but wrongly used for race.

NORDIC: Tall fair race in Europe.

NORMAL FAULT: Displacement along a crack in the crust due to tension.

NOTONECTIAN CURRENT: An important warm current off E. Australia.

NUNAKOL: A rounded rock 'island' in a glacier.*

NUNATAK: A peaked rock 'island' in a glacier.

O

OASIS: Isolated area in deserts with some water.

OBSEQUENT STREAMS: Flow down a scarp.

OBSIDIAN: A glassy lava.

OCCIDENTAL CITIES: Developed on Western plan (not oriental).

OCCLUSION: When warm air-mass lifted above surface.

OCCUPANCE: Direct or indirect activities of man.

OLDER-MASS: The older formations in a large region.

OPISOMETER: Measures distances on a map.

OPTIMUM CLIMATE: That best suited for man or crops.

ORDOVICIAN: A period about 400 million years ago.

ORIENTAL CITIES: Have crowded, primitive, patterns.

OUTLIER: Isolated mass of young strata.

OUTWASH PLAIN: Debris washed out from ice front.

OVERFOLDS: Occur in complex crustal folds.

OXBOW LAKE: Due to a winding river.

P

PAHOEHOE LAVA: Ropy, smooth, surface.

PALAEO-ALPINE: A racial group named by Dixon.

PALAEOTECHNIC: A type of industrial city.

PALAEOZOIC AGE: Between 150 and 500 million years ago

PALIMPSEST THEORY: Glaciers overriding cirques.*

PAMPAS: Grasslands in Argentina.

PANTAGRAPH: Enlarges or reduces plans.

PARALLELS OF LATITUDE: Circles parallel to the equator.

PARAMO: High-level grasslands.

PAREOEAN: Tribes in East Indies.

PARKLAND: Grasslands with scattered trees.

PAX ROMANA: The peace due to the Roman control.

PEDALFER: A major division of soils.

PEDIMENT: Gravelly plains about desert mountains.

PEDOLOGY: Soil science.

PENEPLAIN: An undulating rocky plain.

PERMAFROST: Frozen ground.

PERMIAN: About 150 million years ago.

PETRIFACTION: Organic matter changed to stone.

PIEDMONT GLACIER: Coalescing glaciers as they reach lowland.

PINDAN: Semi-desert scrub in NW. Australia.

PINGOES: Mound-springs in Arctic.

PIRACY: Capture of one stream by another.

PITHECANTHROPUS: The earliest ape-man.

PLACER: Alluvial with gold.

PLAIURI: The plateaux in Roumania.

PLANE TABLE: A simple survey instrument.

PLANIMETER: Measures areas.

PLAYA: A salt lake.

PLEISTOCENE: The last million years.

PLIOCENE: A period about 2 or 3 million years ago.

PLUCKING BY GLACIERS: Shown on lee side of rock knobs.

PLUTONIC ROCKS: Rocks solidified far below the surface.

PODSOL: Ash-coloured infertile soil.

POLAR FRONT: Advancing edge of a mass of cold air.

POLDER: Lowlands diked against the sea.

POLYE: Valley dissolved out of limestone.

POLYPS: Animals which secrete coral.

PORPHYRY: Igneous rock with large crystals.

PORTAGE: A carrying-place between rivers or lakes.

POSSIBILIST: A geographer who stresses human control.

PRE-CAMBRIAN: Geological time earlier than 500 million years ago.

PRE-DRAVIDIAN: The earliest migration into India.

PRESSURE RIDGE: Develops in bay ice.

PRIMATE CITY: The dominant city in a country.

PROFILE: Vertical section through soil.

PROJECTION: Representation (on plane) of spherical surface.

PROTO-GOTHIC: An early form of Teutonic speech.

PROTRACTOR: Instrument to measure angles.

PUEBLO: Primitive house of tribes in America.

PUMICE: Vesicular lava.

PUNA: Bleak plateau in Peru.

PUSZTA: Grasslands of Hungary.

PUYS: Small volcanic cones.

REVERSED FAULT: Displacement along a crustal crack due to thrust.

RIA: A shallow inlet with fern-leaf plan.

RIFT VALLEY: Broad valley bounded by faults.

RINGSTRASSE (see BOULEVARD).

RISS ICE AGE: About 200,000 years ago.

ROADSTEAD: A type of open harbour.

ROARING FORTIES: Strong west winds.

ROCHES MOUTONÉES: Rocks rounded by glacial erosion.

ROCK FLOUR: From rocks ground by ice.

ROMANSH (see LADIN).

ROUND BARROWS: Ancient grave mounds found in Britain.

Q

QUOGRAPH: A graph giving same results as a slide-rule.*

R

RACE: Denotes breed, not culture.

RADIO-SONDE: Transmitter of upper-air data.

RAIN SHADOW: Dry slopes in lee of mountains.

RAISED BEACHES: Are elevated above sea-level.

RAISED REEFS: Coral terraces now above sea-level.

RAVINE: A large gully.

REGELATION: Union of ice fragments under pressure.

REGOLITH: Mantle of loose rock.

REJUVENATED RIVER: Narrow valley in base of a broader valley.

RELATIVE HUMIDITY: Percentage of possible moisture in air.

RELIC-STUMPS: Relics of former young mountains.

RENDZINA: Dark soil derived from limestone.

RESECTION: A method used in surveying.

S

SAETERS: High pastures of Norway.

SAGE-BRUSH: A common desert plant.

SAHUL LAND: A drowned area north of Australia.

SANDY HOOK: Built by longshore currents.

SANSKRIT: The ancestor of many Indian languages.

SAPPING: Undercutting a river bank.

SASTRUGI: Small ridges on icecap.

SAXATILE FLORA: Flourishes on rocks.

SCALLOP SHORES: Are found along Lake Erie.*

SCARP (see ESCARPMENT).

SCHIST: Somewhat layered igneous rock.

SCLEROPHYLL: Leaves with hard leathery surfaces.

SCORIA: Ashes thrown from a volcano.

SEDIMENTATION: Process of depositing silts, sands, &c.

SEICHE: Water-level affected by air pressure.

SEIGNEURIE: An early subdivision in Canada.

SELVA: Tropical Jungle.

SENILE VALLEYS: Are very wide and flat.

SERACS: Jagged ice ridges between crevasses.

SERIR: Pebbly surface in deserts.

SEXTANT: A nautical instrument for measuring angles.

SHALE: Layer of hardened clay.

SHATTER BELT: Rocks shattered along a zone of movement.

SHEAR-CRACKS: Develop in bay ice.

SHEET FLOOD: Flows over talus core.

SHIELD: A resistant area of the crust.

SHOTTS (see PLAYA).

SILL: A level sheet of lava between strata.

SILURIAN: A period 350 million years ago.

SINANTHROPUS: Primitive human fossils in China.

SINITIC: Referring to China.

SINK HOLE: Due to solution of limestone.

SINTER: Deposits from hot springs.

SIROCCO: Hot winds drawn towards a cyclone.

SISAL (see AGAVE).

SKAUK: An extensive field of crevasses.*

SKERRIES: Rocky islets off Norway.

SKEW-BASE: A stage in drawing a block diagram.*

SKYSCRAPER: A building of many storeys.

SLUMPING: Occurs when wet soil slides down slopes.

SNOW-LINE: The lowest level where snow lies all the year.

SOLAR-CONTROL MODEL: Shows how sun's motion affects seasons.*

SOLIFLUCTION: Flow of thawed soils.

SOLSTICE: Is when the sun seems to 'stand still'.

SORGHUM: A food millet.

SOY BEAN: Valuable food plant.

SPARSELANDS: Semi-desert pastoral regions.*

SPHAGNUM: Moss common in swamps.

SPINIFEX: A tall grass in Australia.

SPIT. A tongue of sand.

SPRING TIDE: Maximum tide when sun and moon pull together.

STACK: Isolated column of rock.

STAGE DIAGRAM: Shows successive maps of a place in position.*

STALACTITE: An 'icicle' formed of limestone.

STATION: A ranch in Australia.

STEATOPYGIC: Having big buttocks.

STEPPES: Cool grasslands.

STILL-STAND: A region which has not shared in local uplifts.

STOP-AND-GO DETERMINISM: A concept suggesting relative controls exercised by Nature and Man.*

STORM TRACKS: Paths of cyclones.

STRASSENDORF: A village along one street.

STRATOSPHERE: The outer layers of the atmosphere.

STRATUS CLOUDS: Occur in low, level, layers.

STRIAE: Are scratches made by rocks held in ice.

SUB-ARTESIAN: Water which does not rise to the surface in a bore.

SUB-INFANTILE: The smallest type of settlement.*

SUBSEQUENT STREAMS: Develop along a scarp.

SUPERIMPOSED STREAM: Is affected by rock structures exposed during erosion.

SURVIVAL RATE: A method of determining future populations.

SYNCLINE: A downfold in a series of rocks.

T

TAIGA: Coniferous Forest.

TALUS: Debris at foot of a hill.

TALUS CONES: Deposited at foot of steep gully.

TANK: An artificial pool (Aus.).

TASMANITE: Shale with much oil (Aus.).

TECTONIC: Due to earth-folding.

TELEMETER: A range-finder.

TERRAMARA: A prehistoric 'grid' settlement.

TERTIARY: The last 40 million years.

TETHYS SEA: The enormous ancestor of the Mediterranean Sea.

TETRAHEDRAL THEORY: Suggests the earth approximates to a pyramid.

THEOCRATIC: Divine control of human affairs.

THEODOLITE: A surveying instrument.

THERMAL EQUATOR: Line joining hottest places on earth.

TIERRA CALIENTE: Hot lands on Mexican coasts.

TILL: Glacial debris.

TOMBOLO: Sand-bar linking island to coast.

TOPSOIL: Upper layer of valuable soil.

TORNADO: Fierce local whirlwind.

TOWNSHIP: A subdivision of a county (a village; Aus.).

TRADE WIND: Blows from the east in warm latitudes.

TRANSHUMANCE: Seasonal migration of stock.

TRAVERTINE: Surface deposits of limestone.

TRELLIS DRAINAGE: Rectangular pattern in streams.

TRI-PENINSULAR WORLD: A concept of three land-masses projecting from central Asia.★

TROPOPAUSE: Upper limit of troposphere.

TROPOSPHERE: The lower turbulent layer of the atmosphere.

TROUGH: A type of weather map (Aus.).

TRUCK FARMING: Horticulture some distance from markets.

TSUNAMI: A tidal wave.

TUFA: Soft form of surface limestone.

TUFF: Ashy beds of volcanic origin.

TYPHOON: Fierce storm system (hurricane).

U

UBACH: The shaded side of a valley.

ULOTRICHI: Folk with frizzy hair.

UMLAND: Area affected by a city's trade.

URBANIZATION: Shift of people from country to city.

V

VALES AND CUESTAS: Topography based on alternating hard and soft formations.

VALLEY DIVIDE: Usually in the floor of a vast glacial valley.

VARVE CLAYS: Thin parallel layers of glacial clay.

VEINS: Cracks filled with mineral matter.

VELDT: Grassland (S. Africa).

W

WALLOON: Belgians of French culture.

WARM LOOPS: Loops in isotherms projecting from equator.

WARPS: Broad gentle folds in the crust.

WATERSPOUT: A column due to rotating air.

WEND: Slavs living south of Berlin.

WE-OCRATIC: Human control as opposed to environmental control.★

WET BULB: A form of thermometer.

WHITE AUSTRALIA: A ruling which prevents coolie immigration.

WILLY-WILLY: A hurricane in W. Australia.

WIND GAP: A gap formerly used by a stream.

WINDOW: A wide gap in Alpine strata exposing older folds.

WIRO: The first folk who spoke Aryan.

WOMERAH: A lever to propel spears.

WURLIES: Leaf-huts in Australia.

WURM ICE AGE: A period about 30,000 years ago.

WYND: A narrow lane in a Scottish town.

X

XEROPHYTE: Plant adapted to dry conditions.

Y

YELLOW PERIL: The danger of invasion by Mongolian hordes.

YELLOW RACE: Outmoded racial term.

YIDDISH: The German dialect used by Jews.

YOUNG MOUNTAINS: Have risen during Tertiary times.

Z

ZENITH: The spot on celestial sphere vertically above the observer.

ZONE OF FLOWAGE: A deep-seated part of the crust.

ZONES AND STRATA THEORY: A technique deducing order of Evolution.*

INDEX

Printed in Great Britain by Butler & Tanner Ltd., Frome and London